Presented t[illegible]

the Library of Eastern College,
with the best wishes of

Harold J. Abrahams

THE EXTINCT MEDICAL SCHOOLS OF BALTIMORE, MARYLAND

by

HAROLD J. ABRAHAMS

FOREWORD by GEORGE W. CORNER

MARYLAND HISTORICAL SOCIETY
Baltimore, Maryland
1969

Library of Congress Catalogue Card Number: 68-58323

In Memoriam

CHARLES ABRAHAMS

TABLE OF CONTENTS

INDEX

The names of the individual professors, graduates, matriculates, lecture-courses, and text-books are not indexed as such. For names of professors see sections 3A and 3B of each of the chapters on the particular schools, where biographical sketches of some of these persons are also given. For graduates and matriculates see section 5 of each school. For lecture-courses see section 2; for textbooks, section 4; for buildings and equipment, section 1.

For individual names of professors, graduates, matriculates,etc., see the particular chapter involved.

For individual names of professors, graduates, matriculates, etc., see the particular chapter involved.

For individual names of professors, graduates, matriculates, etc., see the particular chapter involved.

For individual names of professors, graduates, matriculates, etc., see the particular chapter involved.

The Reverend Thomas E. Bond, M.D., of the Washington Medical College, *(from Historical Sketch of the University Of Maryland School of Medicine, 1807-1890)* **by Eugene F. Cordell, (1891).**

A.J. Foard, M.D., of the Washington University School of Medicine, *(Copyright CIBA SYMPOSIA, formerly published by CIBA Pharmaceutical Company).*

PREFACE

The study of extinct schools of medicine which were located in other cities of the East near Philadelphia seems to be a natural sequel to the study of the schools of that city which was compiled many months earlier. The present work might just as correctly bear the title: "Extinct Medical Schools of Maryland", since all of the schools of that group were located in Baltimore. Two other schools may be mentioned in this study, but they have virtually no history which can be considered: "The Medico-Chirurgical and Theological College of Christ's Institution", (see Appendix A for a variant form of this name), chartered in 1910, issued one poorly gotten-up Announcement, but nothing further about it has come to hand, and it may be presumed to have held few, if any, sessions; the second phantom school was the "Maryland College of Eclectic Medicine and Surgery", which was organized in 1912, and bore three different names in as many years, (see footnote 2, Chapter One.) The American Medical Directory, twentieth edition, 1958, says that "its Dean was reported as not licensed in Maryland, having failed to pass the license examination. This college was reported as not recognized by the Maryland State Board of Examiners. Corporation dissolved in 1915. Several of its diplomas were reported sold in subsequent years." For purposes of a study having the nature of the present one, examination of the few available artifacts of two such schools seems hardly likely to result in anything significant.

Everything claimed for the schools which comprise this study is based upon statements made by the institutions themselves, in their annual Announcements, and the assumption is made, for purposes of the study, that the claims were, for the most part, (and allowing for the quirks of human pride), made in good faith. Yet we know that this is far from being correct, as the reader can judge from the excerpts of the Flexner report, which are given in the chapters on Maryland Medical College and Atlantic Medical College. I trust that I have done justice to all concerned, by merely reporting what I have found in the publications of the colleges, with a kind of disharmonious counterpoint supplied through the instrumentality of Dr. Flexner.

It is a pleasure to record my deep gratitude to the American Philosophical Society, for a generous grant from its Penrose Fund, which made this study possible, by underwriting a good part of the costs involved.

The tedium involved in putting together certain parts of such a study is relieved in large measure by thoughts of the kind friends of the project, who willingly lent helping hands. Their names are set forth in the section on acknowledgments which follows each chapter.

St. Davids, Pa.
June 1, 1969

Harold J. Abrahams

FOREWORD

To study the extinct medical schools of Baltimore, as Dr. Harold J. Abrahams has done with assiduous care following a similar study of Philadelphia schools,[1] is to throw new light into a dark corner of American educational history. In the tangled course of human undertakings we tend to forget those that do not survive, though oftentimes "the meaning shows in the defeated thing." The medical schools, now defunct, which Dr. Abrahams describes, did not all die because they were inadequate or downright bad (although some were); nor were all of them created for improper reasons or operated by self-seeking, ill-qualified men.

Their story, as this book shows, is in fact not a simple one. Each school poses its own problem for the historian. The Medical School of Washington University, for example, was founded by competent physicians with enlightened ideas and high aims. It was well equipped for its day, and through its intimate association, from the start, with a good hospital, it was ahead of its time. It competed vigorously for repute and enrollment with its older rival, the University of Maryland. Its history strikingly parallels that of the best of the now extinct Philadelphia schools, the Medical Department of Pennsylvania College. Such institutions came into being for worthy reasons. A prosperous young nation, rapidly populating its hinterland across the Alleghenies, needed more doctors than the older schools could turn out. Many physicians were available in the eastern cities who craved the opportunity to teach their art, but found no place in the older faculties. Professorships in successful schools provided not only prestige but also honorable and often considerable income from student fees.

Some of the schools aimed to fill special needs. The Woman's Medical College of Baltimore, like its more durable predecessor in Philadelphia, was organized when women were still largely excluded from the study of medicine. The early history of these schools is closely related to that of the nation-wide movement for women's rights. The Atlantic Medical College met a demand for physicians of the homeopathic school of medical practice. The "Medico-Chirurgical College of Christ's Institution."[2] so short-lived and undocumented that Dr. Abrahams can do no more than mention it, was a Negro enterprise; behind its ludicrous title we can dimly perceive the yearning of half-educated men to create professional opportunities for their own people.

Thus the now extinct schools were founded for diverse reasons. Their demise, also, resulted from various causes. The Washington University school, hard hit by the loss of Southern students at the beginning of the War of the Rebellion, was temporarily reorganized thereafter but lacked financial resources to meet the needs of the 1870's for laboratory facilities and teachers of preclinical sciences. Dr. Abrahams has shrewdly observed that the chance of survival through periods of national stringency and of educational reform, was greatly strengthened by a genuine university connection, as in the case of the University of Pennsylvania, or at the least by the support of a lay board of trustees, as those of Jefferson Medical College of Philadelphia and the University of Maryland Medical School in Baltimore. Such control, which the Washington University school lacked, was also a valuable stabilizing influence in the internal disputes of ambitious and individualistic professors, unhappily frequent in the first half and more of the 19th century.

The Woman's Medical College of Baltimore, losing its chief claim upon the community when women were generally admitted to other schools, was too weak financially for independent existence. Those proprietary and pseudo-university medical faculties which (to put it charitably) never reached creditable levels of faculty strength and of equipment, were forced to close by public and professional reaction to Abraham Flexner's devastating report of 1910, *Medical Education in the United States and Canada*, and by the American Medical Association's effective demand for improvements beyond their intellectual and financial capacity.

The detailed account of curricula, schedules, and text-books presented in this volume illustrates the intellectual progress of American medical teaching from the time when instruction consisted almost solely of lectures with some practical work in anatomy, to the period of reform and curricular expansion in which these struggling schools, emulating sounder institutions, tried to acquire or at least claimed to possess laboratory facilities in all the premedical sciences. With regard to the weaker of the Baltimore schools that were still surviving in 1910, Dr. Abrahams has done well to set the factual observations of Dr. Abraham Flexner in contrast with the unfounded and even dishonest claims made in their catalogues as quoted here.

The personnel records of the extinct schools will be found interesting by many others than medical historians. Numerous well-known Baltimore families are represented by ancestors who served the community, according to their lights, as professors or trustees of the medical schools. Anyone familiar with the city's nineteenth-century personalties could now fairly accurately rate the relative quality of these defunct schools by the standing in public, professional and social life of those whose names appear in the catalogues. The ladies and gentlemen on the board of the Woman's Medical College, for example, were mostly listed also in the Blue Book of Baltimore society. Among its teachers, who served on nominal salaries or none at all, for the sake of the cause, were physicians and surgeons of national standing. The role of the lesser schools as training grounds for rising young teachers and incidentally for men of influence in civic life is illustrated by the participation in the better schools in the 1870's and 1880's, of men who later joined the clinical faculties of Johns Hopkins and the University of Maryland. Among the trustees also we find a number who afterward put their administrative experience at the service of more enduring institutions.

The evil done by the worst of the extinct medical schools has long since been ended; the good done by the best of them should not be forgotten.

George W. Corner

1. Harold J. Abrahams, *The Extinct Medical Schools of Nineteenth Century Philadelphia,* Philadelphia, The University of Pennsylvania Press, 1966.
2. The writer of this Foreword recalls that the full name of this institution, on a sign across the front of a converted dwelling in which it was housed, anticlimactically ended " . . . of Christ's Institution, *Ltd.*"

The Washington Medical College building, on Broadway, ***(taken from the Circular for 1837).*** **The building plan was not carried out in entirety – the only portions which ever rose were the central section, (without the"obelisk roofs"), and the right wing.**

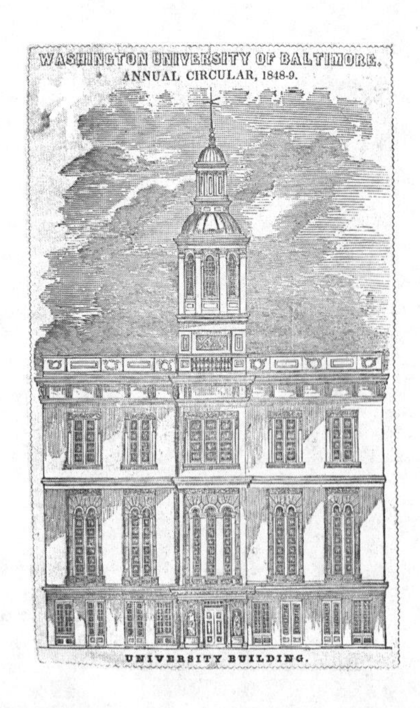

The University building, (the third and last), as shown in the ***Circular*** **for 1848.**

THE WASHINGTON MEDICAL COLLEGE
WASHINGTON UNIVERSITY SCHOOL OF MEDICINE
OF BALTIMORE

In the years which spanned the period from 1807 to 1912 there arose, in the city of Baltimore, eleven medical schools. One school[1] never functioned, and one[2] was dissolved in 1915, very shortly after it was organized. Of the remaining schools, three were absorbed by the University of Maryland School of Medicine, either directly, or following earlier absorption by one of this group, and four became extinct[3]. One of these eleven schools, the Washington University School of Medicine, could be placed in either the absorbed or extinct category, as it became extinct, and remained so for sixteen years, was revived, and lasted for a period of ten years, then was absorbed by the College of Physicians and Surgeons of Baltimore, which was, itself, in turn absorbed by the University of Maryland. The history of the Washington University School of Medicine is of both interest and importance, and having really passed into oblivion for a time, it rightfully finds a place in the foregoing study of a total of five medical schools of the City of Baltimore.

The ink on Dr. George McClellan's charter for Philadelphia's Jefferson Medical College, (1825), was scarcely dry, when Dr. Horatio Gates Jameson, a graduate, (1813) of the University of Maryland School of Medicine, widely known and esteemed surgeon, physician and author, aware of the prosperity and growth-potential of the city of Baltimore, and conscious that his efforts to be appointed to the Faculty of his alma mater had been rudely frustrated, conceived the idea of organizing a new medical school. (For the names of those who took part in organizing the school see section III (A) below, the list of the Faculty for the session of 1827-28). Dr. Jameson also had other considerations in mind – the growing success of the already-existing school, and the intramural struggle which was going on there, thus weakening it, and creating an opportunity for the rise of a second school. (It is hoped that the reader will pardon a momentary digression: In 1825 the right of two members of the Faculty of the University of Maryland School of Medicine to conduct private classes was questioned by their colleagues. As a result the Maryland Legislature was asked to make a change in the 1812 charter. Despite objection by the rest of the Faculty, supported by the Board of Regents, and the opinion of eminent legal counsel, including Daniel Webster, the Legislature, by act, abolished the Board of Regents, and transferred entire control of the University to a Board of Trustees, consisting largely of non-medical men, with no representation of the Faculty, nor of the previous Board of Regents. The new Board could appoint and dismiss provost and professors at will, create new professorships, and abolish old ones, and the Governor of the State could fill vacancies on this Board of Trustees. The reasons given for this "usurpation on the part of the State" were that the State had authorized the lotteries from which revenues had been derived, that it had also made a loan of $30,000 to the school in 1821, and that the corporation had a public character, since it had been created for the public good, i.e., the preservation of life and health. In 1838 the Court of Appeals, the opinion being rendered by Chief Justice Buchanan, reversed the Lower Court, and pronounced the Act of 1825 null and void). Horatio Jameson probably felt that the situation at the College which has just been described, created an advantageous opportunity for a rival school, as has already been noted, and that, in addition, his great gifts as a surgeon (bold and original) and consulting physician deserved to be put to use in as wide a field as possible. He therefore, in the company of a group of physicians, applied for a State charter, but, by reason of resistance from the University, was denied his request. Most probably aware of George McClellan's recent strategem in a similar situation, he turned to Washington College, a small liberal arts college of Washington, Pennsylvania, and during the winter of 1825-26, won authorization to establish his medical school in Baltimore[4] under Washington's charter. The association between the two institutions was only nominal, none of the Arts and Sciences graduates entering the Medical Department of Washington College to win his medical degree there. (As has so frequently been pointed out, such a tenuous hold on a mother institution could bring little benefit to a medical college). A second attempt to obtain a charter from the State was successful, the Maryland Legislature passing the act of incorporation in 1832. (The Charter itself bears the date March 4, 1833. Some of the interesting provisions of this charter were: a professor could be removed by a vote of 5/6 of the Faculty – there was to be a board of visitors consisting of twenty-four members which would cooperate with the Faculty in granting and countersigning diplomas, attend lectures and examinations if they wished to do so – the lectures on botany "might be given in the season best fitted for it". The act stipulated that the College should be "for the benefit of students of every country and every religious denomination, who shall be freely admitted to equal advantages and privileges of education . . . without any religious or civil test, or urging their attendance upon any particular religious worship or service: nor shall any preference be given, in the choice of a President, Professor, Lecturer . . . on account of his particular religious profession; but regard shall be solely paid to his moral character, and other necessary qualifications . . . "[5].) The school was now free of its former ties.

In 1839, the bright future which its growing prosperity seemed to hold out for it caused the College to request and obtain a new charter permitting it to change its name from the Washington Medical College to the Washington University of Baltimore, and to add departments of Arts and Sciences, Law, Divinity, and essential academies or preparatory schools. However, none of these departments was ever set up. In December, 1812, the Maryland Legislature had passed an act, by which the College of Medicine of Maryland became the University of Maryland, the process involving creation of new departments of Arts and Sciences, Law, and Divinity. Eugene F. Cordell[6] relates this development to the later struggle between the Legislature and the Faculty of the University of Maryland, to which reference has been made above. A parallel might be found between the experiences of both schools on the subject of the consequences of their efforts to expand, for the enlargement resulting from the conversion of Washington College to Washington University, far from producing anything good, was followed by the subsequent feeling that the school was too distant from the city proper, for which reason a central-city location was determined upon. Instruction began in a new building in 1849. By 1851 a lack of funds and the sheer magnitude of the undertaking caused the entire enterprise to collapse, and the school was obliged, by the circumstances, to close down, after having enjoyed many successful years as a formidable rival of the University of Maryland. (One of the professors alleged that the college building was found to be "plastered over with liens", the result of the misuse of the building funds, with the consequence that it was attached and sold under the Lien Law, and the former home of the school "soon shared a similar fate". See Eugene F. Cordell, p. 345.) Thus, after having graduated considerably more than 200 doctors did the mechanism of the Washington University of Baltimore grind to a halt. Washington had thus, on the basis of known graduates, as of this writing, averaged less than ten per year, while the University of Maryland had averaged about 39 per year, from 1810 to 1839, (Lockard, p. 136).

There is extant the commencement address delivered on March 17, 1834 by Samuel Annan, M.D., professor of anatomy and physiology at Washington Medical College. On that occasion Dr. Annan pointed out to the newly trained doctors the necessity of avoiding undue veneration for great names and of repudiating fondness for hypothesis, the "besetting sin of so large a number of our profession."

> "... It is facts and legitimate induction, which constitute true science; and the great object of all preliminary education should be to discipline the mind to the patient exercise of the cold-blooded deductions of an unsophisticated logic; to accustom it to repress the vagaries of a prurient imagination; and to distinguish the sober livery of truth, from the gaudy ... ornament of error.
>
> The medical philosopher should flee poetry and all its vanities. The fine arts should be an abomination unto him.
>
> Look over the history of medicine, and see who have been its greatest benefactors. Is it Akenside and Darwin? Men of resplendent genius, whose thoughts glitter like the sunbeam ... but to apply them to the wear and tear of the ordinary business of life, would be desecration. Is it not rather Hunter and Bell, Bichat and Magendie? Faithful and laborious cultivators of the wilderness of undiscovered facts; whose imaginations were kept in due subjection ... The former are now but faintly remembered ... while the latter have created for themselves a reputation as advancers of science and friends of humanity ... "

Dr. Annan told his audience that "habits of accurate observation and critical analysis" were of "paramount importance to the medical inquirer". "Disease is so much modified and altered by vicissitudes of climate, changes in the manner of living ... that remedies" are not necessarily applicable to all similar cases. Besides, epidemics of new diseases visit us from time to time, as do new forms of old diseases, "which baffle our utmost skill, until we become familiar with their mode of attack". Even as the Romans, from time to time, would encounter new and unusual fighting methods of various nations, (the most intrepid Roman legions falling victim to dismay, and their ablest tacticians temporarily held in the grip of their puzzlement, until they could understand the true nature of the tactics and strategy of the enemy), so the physician must be prepared to meet disease in all its manifestations, and, if he does not have the capacity to learn from his defeats and errors, in dealing with the skillful maneuvering of the enemy, disease, he will never attain eminence as a physician. Some persons have not, in early youth, formed habits of close and accurate observation. They see no merit in anything unless the dust of ages has made it venerable. They fight everything new, which, they think, must be false, because new.

Dr. Annan thus cautioned against visionary speculation, on the one hand, and against permitting false prejudice to become inveterate, on the other. For the advancement of true science, let the motto be: "In medio tutissimus ibis".

He warned the graduates against developing the hobby of simplifying the practice of medicine. If only the doctor's limbs were at stake when he mounted his hobbyhorse it would not so much matter, but so frequently doctor and patient are thrown by the animal, injuring both, and giving a "melancholy example of wretched horsemanship". Therefore, even though the doctor may have made certain of his facts and principles, the latter should not be thought applicable to every situation, for there are times when more suitable remedies are available.

He urged his hearers to try to contribute to the general stock of medical knowledge:

> "... He who discovers a mode of curing a disease previously immedicable; or a more safe, certain, pleasant, and speedy method, of arresting any malady, than was before known, is unquestionably better entitled to the laurel crown, and the poet's lays, than he who subjugates empires at the expense of human suffering and human life."

He concluded with a thanatopsis:

> "... Now the thought of living unknown, unnoticed, unrenowned; of dying unpraised, and unepitaphed, chills the current of your spirits, and comes like a nipping frost ... Then, when the tottering frame gives too sure tokens of decay; and the spirit-stirring movements of ambition are hushed to slumber; ... it will not be the remembrance of the honors you shall have acquired ... that will cheer your downward progress to life's close. Then, when the noisy tongue of fame can no longer rouse the sleepy feelings, and calm philosophy ... appears like the minister of death, bearing the dreaded summons, your anxious minds will instinctively turn to the recollection of the tears of the widow, which shall have been dried; to the cries of the orphan, which shall have been hushed; to the ragged and hungry children of poverty, who shall have been clothed and fed, by the soothing ministrations of your benevolence.
>
> The review of a well spent life ... will ... enable you to submit with resignation, to the final blow, of the universal conqueror of our race."

Thomas E. Bond, Jr., A.M., M.D., Professor of Therapeutics, Materia Medica and Hygiene, delivered an interesting "Introductory Lecture", on November 11, 1848. On the previous evening a most able and eloquent colleague had addressed the class and made a remarkable speech, and now Dr. Bond found himself under the necessity of giving a talk which would, inevitably, be compared with that of his predecessor, and probably suffer thereby. Dr. Bond told of his having once met a lady and gentleman, who, while visiting a magnificent church building in New York, stood in awe and admiration of the noble dome, the seemingly endless colonnade of chiseled shafts and polished capitals, bathed in soft light streaming through the multi-colored windows, and the many other wonders of the structure. Overcome by the sheer beauty of the structure, the stranger was at first speechless, then, recovering from the trance, he turned to his wife, and exclaimed: "Polly, Polly, when we go home, we must whitewash the meeting-house!" Dr. Bond told his audience that only the recollection of the fable which warns of the result of "inflating one's-self beyond the natural dimensions" kept him from going home, after hearing of his colleague's great introductory lecture, and putting a better appearance upon the lecture which he had prepared for this evening. Then he remarked that there was room in the world for the humble meeting-house, as well as for the gorgeous temple, for the former's homely accommodations are often greatly appreciated, and, whitewashed or not, its evident lack of pretentiousness "will secure it from criticism."

Turning to the serious side, he gave voice to the principles which he thought should guide students at the College:

Long ago there was a country called Cockgaine, where it rained hot custards three times a week, and where all that one had to do to obtain other good things was to sleep for them. Unfortunately, the location of the country never became known, so "the recollection of its walls of sausage, roofs of lard and laths of barley sugar" are only memories of the past, sweet and mournful to the soul. That men long for the land of Cockgaine, where life is passed as "one long summer's day of indolence and ease" is not surprising, but to seek for it in the realms of Esculapius is the height of folly – the hot custards and barley sugar do not exist along any path which we have yet discovered. No one who has any longings for such ease should enter upon the study of medicine.

The study of this science puts every faculty of mind, (and morals) to full use. Only the noble and intelligent are worthy of its honors and pleasures – the delights of learning about the curiosities of the natural world, as well as the beauties of the realm of mind and soul. The medical student is privileged to learn and discover truth, i.e., not only to learn the dogmas, but also to examine centuries-old observations, in order both to deduce laws of action and to add whatever he may himself discover, and in order both to observe the "putrid relics of decayed mortality", and to strip away the disguises of Nature, that he may seek and find truth beneath plausibility and deceit. The truth he seeks is not for himself alone, but for everyone. His predecessors in the profession are honored men, devoted to the welfare of mankind, men who represent what is best in the intellectual world, and with whom he may enter into partnership by strivings of his own.

The practical duties of the profession, to "stand between the living and the dead and stay the plague", requires a degree of benevolence to match its nobility. To dispense health to the sick, beauty to the deformed, cause wandering reason to return "to her deserted throne", gives the doctor a power truly magnificent.

Having elected to enter the profession, the student may attain his objective by keeping in mind the following requisites: the first is a reasonable measure of good health, for he must have an active mind in a quiescent body, as an active physician often faces duties too severe for even the strongest person. There is perhaps no profession from which so many are compelled to retire because of physical inability. Our medical classes are, with few exceptions, composed of robust men, chiefly drawn from the country, and free of the physical weaknesses of city persons. Yet it is not uncommon for some of them to break down so utterly that commencement day finds them unable to enter the promised land of their dreams, or, if they are well enough to do so, they can practice for but a few years, after which they either die, or are obliged, by illness, to forsake the profession, for a less-taxing pursuit. Yet there is nothing in the study of medicine which is prejudicial to health. One cause of poor health is dissipation, varying from irregular health habits to excessive profligacy, the evil pleasures offered by a great city to an inexperienced young man, which plunge him into vicious indulgence. Another strain upon good health is excessive study, resulting in overworking the mind and body, and leading to infirmity, or even untimely death. This is all the more sad, since the victim is likely to be the talented and industrious person, who gives the most promise of eminence in medicine, and usefulness to mankind. In many a grave there lies a young man whose epitaph might be the beautiful lines of Byron:

> "Oh! what a noble heart was here undone!
> When Science's self destroyed her favorite son!
> Yes, she too much indulged thy fond pursuit:
> She sowed the seeds, but death has reaped the fruit.
> 'Twas thine own genius gave the fatal blow,
> And help'd to plant the wound that laid thee low.
> So the struck eagle, stretched upon the plain,
> No more through rolling clouds to soar again,
> Viewed his own feather on the fatal dart,
> And winged the shaft that quiver'd in his heart.
> Keen were his pangs; but keener far to feel
> He nursed the pinion which impell'd the steel,
> While the same plumage that had warmed his nest,
> Drank the last life-drop of his bleeding breast."

Estimate your powers of attention and endurance. Budget your time wisely. "The excessive feeder is always badly fed." The nourishment of the mind depends less upon quantity than upon completeness of digestion. It is not profitable to read when it is painful to fix attention, and requires repeated efforts to do so. At such times it is better to relax. This does not mean that one should not read, except when vehemently inclined. Some students have so little inclination to study, that, were they to wait for the urge to come upon them, a whole session might not be long enough for "the accomplishment of a course of study more extensive than that comprised in Patrick Henry's library, which is said to have consisted of Blackstone's Commentaries, Shakespeare's Plays, a bottle of brandy, and a "fiddle", and at commencement time their total medical knowledge would be "second in extent and accuracy only to that of Dame Quickly, who described Falstaff's fatal illness as a 'burning quotidian tertian'". The student should allow himself an hour or two for agreeable conversation each evening. This is far better than theatrical shows or than going out, at bed-time, to those preposterous parties, and standing on your reluctant legs till morning, devouring oysters and ices, pound-cake and poultry. The social company of ladies is necessary for remaining civilized, but it is better to chat for an hour with a sensible woman of sixty, than to dance for two hours with a lively gypsy of sixteen. The society of an older, if not pretty, lady will prevent the danger of falling in love during the college-session, the most dreadful of dangers – "utter calamity – the very verge of catastrophe itself."

Many students desecrate the Sabbath by continuous study. This is not hygienically sound. One should rest on the Sabbath, and not recklessly overwork or exhaust himself. Whatever else one may say about the benefits of the Parisian system of education it has strengthened the tendency to be forgetful of Sabbath observance, and made it fashionable to feel a certain superiority over public opinion upon the subject. "Sunday has been made the operation day in hospitals", encouraging the student to look upon science as the chief good, and leading him to have a feeling of exemption from all moral restraint.

Another dangerous error against which to guard is a lack of the correct comprehension of the nature and end of medical science. Everyone has suddenly conceived a passion for the word philosophy. The term strikes you in the face when you open a child's school book; breeches are made upon philosophical principles, the bench philosophizes upon law, the pulpit upon religion, the physician upon medicine, the farmer ploughs a philosophical furrow, the barber's razor is sharpened on philosophical principles and the dancer cuts a pigeon-wing on laws of the philosophy of motion. The word serves only to confound things essentially different, and "what is ostentatiously paraded as philosophy, is often, of all things, the most unphilosophical." Medicine has nothing to do with metaphysics, with abstractions or violent assumptions, with essences or first causes. Whereas metaphysics has been well described as the art of methodically bewildering one's-self[7] medicine deals with phenomena or facts, with observations and a knowledge of the laws based upon these. Your medical philosopher or metaphysician speculates upon the essential nature of life, in order to deduce rules for medical practice. This is bound to fail. Life cannot be paralyzed, separated from its sensible phenomena. To practice medicine upon our ideas or notions about it is to "presume to instinctive knowledge and intuitive comprehension of what cannot be comprehended."

"Optics good it needs, I ween,
To see what is not to be seen."

Many persons think that philosophy is identical with truth, yet abstract philosophy has always been false. From Plato, to Samuel Thomson, the steam doctor, all have based their doctrines on false assumptions. It may seem humorous to mention the two names above in the same breath, yet the latter's system was purely philosophical in nature. It was based upon a presumed knowledge of essences, heat being life, and cold death, for which reason he stewed his miserable patients, in happy disregard of the results. Dr. Rush used to say that science was an eel, and forming theories was taking it by the tail.

Homoeopathy is another example of the absurdity of flying in the face of experience and common sense "for the sake of a baseless theory: a system which, as the sailors say of a rickety ship, is only kept together by its paint." Homoeopathy "is unreality set to practice nothingness". This farrago of absurdities defies all efforts to detect the mental process by which they were conceived, or how they got into any "unfurnished head". (Perhaps it has been ordained that every community should have some way of distinguishing between persons who think and those who do not). Hahnemann's great leading principle is that "to the entire human organization is superadded an immaterial principle – a dynamical or moving force – active in itself, by which the organization is ruled and controlled. It is this . . . principle upon which all morbific causes . . . act." The disturbance thus produced ". . . operates . . . upon the organization, deranging its healthy actions . . . " Here we have medicine being turned into metaphysics. Disease is said to be beyond the "organization", i.e., beyond the body of man. How can anything which has no materiality be either added or subtracted? We have no evidence – only the ipse dixit of Hahnemann. Upon this unverifiable proposition, with its assumed modification in the immaterial principle being beyond the reach of investigation, Hahnemann declares laws of medicine. Man's immateriality is the injured party, not his exposed nerve, when acid is brought into contact with it, and changed, not chemically, but homoeopathically, causing it to ache, (until the Homoeopath slyly applies a good dose of morphine). It might shock a truly sick man, who has placed reliance upon Hahnemann's system, to learn that the little pill which he swallows so hopefully is "composed of exactly as much brimstone as would balance a moonbeam in the scales". It is true that wild speculation has resulted in various benefits to mankind, but this was only accidental, as witness the auguries based upon the bowels of slaughtered beasts in ancient times, which laid the foundations of physiology, and the horoscopes of the astrologers, which led the way to great discoveries in astronomy, but there were also evil consequences of the work of augur and astrologer.

Even though we know how to cure many diseases, the ultimate cause of not one of them is known, nor is it of the least consequence that we should, for it would not make any positive contribution to medical science if we did. Medicine has resulted from the long-continued and wise observation of the living body and its relations, to some small degree explained by microscopic examination and collateral inquiry. The study of medicine consists of learning the facts discovered from those observations of phenomena, and the acquisition of the skill to use this knowledge, in order to preserve health and cure disease. Theories are all right in their way, but to base practice upon them is to build a pyramid upon its apex. Medicine is not responsible for theories, and their overthrow has no effect upon medical experience. Day and night came with the same regularity when the Earth was thought to be a plane, as it does now, when we know it to be a sphere, and the physician relies upon the established truths of experience as safely under the reign of one hypothesis as under another.

Nor is medicine a mathematical science. Ipecac is an emetic, opium a narcotic. If medicine were a mathematical discipline it would be necessary to take these agents to pieces, find out why each acts as it does, and demonstrate the necessity of each action. This would require us to begin with a perfect knowledge of elementary tissues. However, only the Creator can have a perfect knowledge of His works. It is sufficient that we can find out by experience that beefsteak is nutritious. No a priori reasoning upon abstract principles could have taught us this fact. All our medical knowledge consists of separate, isolated facts, having no necessary connection with each other. Opium does not narcotize because ipecac is an emetic. It is to experience that we must look for improvement of medicine. The student is told that he must seek fundamental principles of practice in necroscopic examination of the dead, instead of observation of the sick, that pathology is the foundation of medical science, that he should devote a very undue proportion of his time to it. This is absurd. Daily we cure disease of whose pathology we know nothing, nor probably ever shall – for example, intermittent fever. Where pathology has won greenest laurels, pointing to lung tissues, and demonstrating the cause of consumption, it but exhibits the secondary consequences, without bringing to light the primary essential. An even-more powerful microscope, trained upon "some globules or atoms of morbid origin", might reveal these to be the consequences of still earlier changes, but "the primary point of attachment upon which all depend, will be as far off as ever." Pathology can never be perfect, and, although useful, it can never be more than an important accessory to medical science. Has the use of the most powerful microscope, in the hands of so many able and industrious doctors, teachers, writers, etc., used in pursuing the minutest inspection of the human body, made us any better able to cure disease, or added one single medicine to our materia medica? It is claimed that to know what is the matter is the first step in curative treatment. The fallacy here is that necrotic pathology does not expose the actual disorder, but merely traces its progress. It confounds the facts in the history of the disease with the disease itself. This must sound like heresy, and the speaker must expect to be misunderstood, misrepresented, or even defamed. It is still true. The study of pathology is useful, but not worthy of the position assigned to it, in comparison with other medical studies.

It is time that our country had its own "school" of medicine. Dr. W. Holmes says that, of studying medicine, the Frenchman asks "what is there to see about it?", the German "what is there to think about it?", and the American "what is there to do about it?". It is time that America founded a "do about it" school, to which doctors of other nations could contribute but which it could not control. It will be difficult to establish this, for the teaching of medicine is in the hands of persons of great influence, who have little experience as practitioners, and overcoming this influence, which is enjoyed because of their talents and position, will be far from easy. But an American school will rise, despite them. The Washington University wishes its competitors, in this and other cities, happy and prosperous careers, and hopes that they will co-operate in this work. Even a sense of respect will not prevent Dr. Bond and his colleagues from attacking error wherever it is found. Great sacrifice has gone into the setting up of the Washington University School of Medicine, and the Faculty will do all that it can to deserve success.

Dr. Bond's stricture against Homoeopathy found a ready opponent in a person by the name of J. Schmidt, who published a pamphlet having the title: *A Letter to Thomas E. Bond, A.M., M.D., on Homoeopathy, Baltimore, 1851.* Schmidt says that Bond's desire to propagate the teachings of his own school among his students is natural, and, had he done so in the privacy of his class-room, no matter how emphatically, it would have made little difference. But Dr. Bond has ridiculed, in public, a method of practice whose aims are as philanthropic as his own, and whose pharmacy is more in accord with modern developments in that field than is that of Allopathy. Without ridiculing the different kinds of practitioners or schools, down through the ages, or giving time to a discussion of the arrogance and acrimony which the practitioners of Allopathy exhibit toward their patients or to each other, so amusingly dramatized by Moliere from life in his day, Schmidt says that he wishes to emphasize two points: 1) there always is opposition, or worse, to new discoveries, many of which eventually become sanctified by the Faculty, and, 2) the theory of medicine is still uncertain, despite the many contributions, from the days of Hippocrates, to those of our own time. Schmidt would only try to demonstrate that in place of an understanding of Homoeopathy, Bond has erected a shadow creature of straw, and has taken pleasure in trying to overthrow that imaginary shadow, not the shadow which Bond says is the essence of Homoeopathy.

Allopathy seems to like to lunge at other schools. That may be as harmless and picturesque as summer lightning. But Bond's denunciation may stem from fear that Homoeopathy may eventually triumph over Allopathy – else why should he feel disturbed about this "non-entity", as he implies that Homoeopathy is? He hasn't really studied this system, and should, therefore, not discuss it in public. He has been both uncharitable and untrue. Had he given his version of the principles of Allopathy, (which he *has* studied), it is probable that three-fifths of his Allopathic colleagues would criticize and denounce him as being incapable of explaining the principles of his own school. How much more, then is he incapable of giving a correct discussion of a system which he *has not* studied?

Bond has dealt only in vague generalities: He says that Homoeopathy is but a name. Are not Allopathy, Medicine and Science but names? A name is a sign. Words are signs. Bond says that Homoeopathy is a word which is not a sign. (Schmidt then continues, briefly, in this vein).

He next attacks Bond for speaking of the pillicules peddled by Homoeopaths. Are little pills worse than the big pills of the Allopaths? If Bond were a country practitioner wouldn't he be grateful that someone had done something to reduce the size of the portable pharmacy which such doctors must carry about with them, and have everything ready for immediate relief from pain, instead of having to lose many hours, while a messenger makes a trip to the city pharmacist and back, to bring the medicine which could have been administered immediately, if the doctor could carry with him all the medicines which he might need in his practice? Is it a disgrace to peddle such pillicules? Many Allopathic graduates know so little practical pharmacy that they could not be trusted to compound the medicines which they prescribe! They are only too glad to be relieved of the burdens assumed by a good apothecary. The Homoeopath takes full responsibility for his medicines, so there is no apprentice apothecary to make the terrible error of dispensing oxalic acid, instead of Epsom salt, or arsenic, instead of powdered chalk. Pillicules, indeed! Are the massive boluses, pulverulent aggregates and copious solutions, often having scents clearly unlike those of the fragrances of Araby, any more desirable?

Bond says that Homoeopathy contends against diseases which are beyond materiality. He seems to imply that the Homoeopaths claim success where the ponderous medicines of Allopathy have failed, (i.e., epilepsy, derangement of the optic nerve, some phases of hemiplegia, etc.) and that these diseases are thus immaterial. He must, at this point, have been facetious. He laughs at the medicines which defy analysis and measurement. Does he know of any competent chemist who has failed to analyze them, and does he need a microscope to measure pillicules which range in size from 1/75 to 1/15 of an inch? Once more, he must be joking. He laughs at those Allopaths who have turned to Homoeopathy. It is obvious that they made this change because they found Allopathy to be inadequate, or even wrong.

A good guide is the quality of the minds and hearts of the devotees of a system. Dr. John Forbes celebrates Hahnemann's great learning, genius, and achievements as an exclusive founder of an original system of medicine, destined to bring about more fundamental changes in medicine than any since the days of Galen. Hahnemann was sincere. That there are charlatans in Homoeopathy need not surprise us. There are charlatans among the Allopaths, too. Other prominent men have given favorable testimony on Hahnemann – Henderson, professor at Edinburgh, and Tessier, of the Hotel-Dieu of Paris. Bond's analogies are not accurate, and his generalizations are precisely the reverse of homoeopathic principles. For example, he says that Homoeopaths claim that "experience is a fallacious guide". The usual charge against them is that Homoeopaths rely too much upon experience, rather than not enough. Hahnemann, (and perhaps Hippocrates, long before him), said: "there are patients, but no diseases". That does not show a rejection of experience. Bond ridicules Homoeopaths for denying the applicability of physical science to medicine, while he, himself, defends physical science. Yet the Pharmacopoeia obstinately retains the nomenclature which was in use before the rise of modern chemistry, a singular fact, for, of all physiologists and pathologists, Hahnemann was the most of a chemist, and of all chemists the most of a physician. Furthermore, it is odd that Bond's criticism should be directed against the system whose pharmacy is based upon the most brilliant discovery of the present century, ("the atomic proportions of matter"), and whose practice is in harmony with the most advanced ideas of atomic behavior. Bond seems to confound physics with physic. He really lacks a knowledge of what Homoeopathy professes to be. He does not take an optimistic view of what is possible. Who would have believed in the marvels of photography, the wonders of galvanoplasty or the seeming miracles of telegraphy? Yes, the real man of science doubts nothing, ridicules nothing, except the claim that matter can exist without God.

Why not proceed as follows: Let a ward in some public hospital be devoted to persons who wish to go there for Homoeopathic treatment. After a year the statistics will show (more convincingly than essays or hundreds of unqualified claims), which system of medicine is better. Refusal to co-operate in such a test will not argue well for Allopathy.

There is also extant a four page broadside: *Circular to Medical Students and to the Friends of Medical Education*, (March 1, 1851), by "A Lover of Science", the intent of which was to arouse sufficient public feeling to protect the school against the necessity of having to close its doors. The pamphlet may be summarized as follows:

Medicine, as a field of learning, has made as much progress in our country as have literature and the arts. Our area and population have so far increased as to heighten the demand for professionally trained doctors, while our interest in the science of medicine, and its benefits to man, are reflected in the growing number of physicians annually graduated, our many able medical teachers, and the existence of an active medical press.

At one time it was necessary to go abroad to study medicine. Now this is no longer true, for the American mind has shown its usual ability and independence, the result being the rise of medical schools in almost all of our large cities. In these schools there are Faculties of able physicians, whose intellectual attainments are very high, and who enjoy the unqualified confidence and approval "of the World".

Until now the North has led in training doctors. The schools of Philadelphia, New York and Boston have drawn students so heavily from all the States of the Union for so many years that it has become customary to assume that facilities for medical education in those cities are superior to those at the younger schools of the South. But the public is gradually learning that this assumption is unfounded, and that now it is Baltimore that seems destined to become the seat of "popular and successful medical instruction". Each year this city graduates able and thoroughly trained doctors, and the time will soon come when it will be thought of as far superior to any in our nation, for convenience and efficiency, as a place to obtain a medical education, despite the excellent schools of the North.

The special advantages of studying medicine in Baltimore are:
a). The central geographical position of this city, and the ease of reaching it – Southern students can go speedily to and from Baltimore by train, making it possible to visit home and friends, without such loss of time as would interrupt their studies, if carried on at more distant places.
b). The climate is much milder than that of the North.
c). Board is moderate in price.
d). The existence of fewer temptations toward immorality than in Philadelphia and New York. Baltimore, other things being equal, therefore has a decided advantage over Northern cities.
e). A special advantage is the ease with which subjects for anatomical investigation and preparation may be obtained here. Some students graduate from Northern schools with "little or no opportunity of personal examinations with the dissecting knife". The large size of classes, and the scarcity, and consequent difficulty of securing dissecting material result in the fact that some students have never "stood over a subject they could call their own". Some of the shortage has been made up by shipment from Baltimore, which has a special advantage in facilities for procuring "subjects".

In addition Washington University now has a building unsurpassed in "comfort and convenience" by any school in the United States. The location of the building is central-city yet far enough away from the noise of congestion and commerce. It has a large and well-designed chemical hall, completely and extensively equipped with apparatus. The anatomical and general lecture room is convenient, "and the dissecting room is probably unequalled in arrangement and general conformity to its purpose". The school has superior anatomical and obstetrical models, made in France, and other teaching devices, whose costliness is justified by the efficient way that they are used by the professors, and by the profit resulting to the students.

The professors are eminent men and competent teachers, known to residents of Baltimore as having long been associated with what is best in medical practice. They have shown remarkable zeal and diligence in their professional relation to their school, and their lofty moral character, as a group, enhances their influence upon their students, who, in later life, will always remember them for their "word of affectionate counsel, of moral as well as scientific import, so repeatedly given and so impressively enforced".

The writer of this broadside had attended a number of lectures, in the session of 1850-51, as an auditor, and had mingled, to some extent, with students "for the purpose of enlarging his acquaintence with general science". He was deeply impressed by the "uniformity of attendance", the attentiveness of the students, the mutual respect and kind feeling between students and teachers, and the high quality of the several departments of the school. ". . . "As a duty,

> then, which he owes to the community, and particularly to those who may have determined for themselves or for others the choice of the Medical profession, he respectfully invites the attention of his countrymen to the strong claims presented (to) [for] public encouragement by the Washington University at Baltimore.
> March 1, 1851 *A Lover of Science."*

I. BUILDINGS and EQUIPMENT

The first session of the Washington Medical College of Baltimore was held in the Fall-Winter of 1827-28, in a building on North Holliday Street, between Lexington and Saratoga, and, although it had been especially erected for the College, its completeness did not compare with that of the University of Maryland School of Medicine. The College having early enjoyed popularity, and been aware of the need for a hospital, it had a large building, its second home, built on the outskirts of the city, on the S.E. corner of Market and Hampstead Hill Streets, (North Broadway). This structure was both hospital and college and came into use in 1838.(8) (The Maryland Historical Society Library possesses a note about a lease of land to the Washington Medical College, valid for 99 years, renewable forever. "The rent was $229.75, payable half yearly . . . extinguishable at any time on the payment of $3829.17". See Genevieve Miller: *A Nineteenth Century Medical School: Washington University of Baltimore*, – Bulletin of the History of Medicine, Volume 14, 1943, p. 17, footnote 12). The pleasant site was on elevated ground, with a splendid view of the Patapsco River and surroundings and away from the noise and bustle of the city. It is described as having been planned to have a length of 195 feet on Hampstead Hill Street, with a central building, circular in shape, of about a forty foot diameter, with four stories of unequal height to house lecture halls, laboratory, library, museum and dissecting rooms. (The theaters were of the most approved design, and conveniently connected with the practical anatomy laboratories, which had plenty of space, light and security, and all possible conveniences for profiting from carrying on work in this field.) There were grand plans to adorn this part of the building by flanking it "at four corresponding equidistant points by turrets, six stories high, castellated with obelisk roofs, and decorated with Gothic windows and doors". There were also to be two wings, five stories high, sixty feet long and forty wide, spacious and lofty, "affording ample room for the classification of the patients", and containing between three and four hundred beds. There were comfortable accommodations for about fifty "house students", who wished to reside in the College building. The Faculty felt that the housing of students on the campus had great and unusual advantages: no daily loss of time in travelling from and to distant residences, no distractions of mind resulting from the company of the families with whom the students boarded while in the city, and therefore no interference with their concentrating upon their medical studies, which deserved, (as widely admitted), terms longer than the current fashion of four months, instead of periods of study made even less adequate by reason of factors just cited. (However, boarding at the College was not obligatory). Another advantage of residence at the College was that it favored prosecution of the study of anatomy, a thorough knowledge of which was so fundamental for the mastery of other subjects. It took strength of character to overcome a natural resistance to: labor and privation; odors inhaled in the dissecting room, or absorbed by the clothing, resulting in embarrassment when mingling with society; making the trip to the College, especially in inclement or cold weather. But, later in life, the doctor who had not made the most of his opportunity to work in the dissecting room would regret it sorely. On the other hand, a resident student at Washington would find every inducement for the acquisition of a good knowledge of anatomy – he could go, early or late, to a "convenient, well-ventilated and warm dissecting room, where, undisturbed, he . . . could . . . pursue investigations . . . " There was plenty of material – so much that "anatomical schools in adjacent cities make up their deficiencies . . . by importing . . . from Baltimore . . . " Further, ". . . such advantages are afforded to the student in obtaining, at a moderate price more than he can possibly use during the term of lectures." Another advantage which resident students had was the opportunity to study disease at the bedside, at all hours of the day and night – all the phenomena of disease as they arose, the effects of remedies, and the final test of truth afforded by post-mortem examination. (The hospital "connected" with lecture rooms and students' quarters, so that students could pass readily from one to another.) Only thorough, clinical study, not reliance upon merely visiting patients at a fixed hour every few days, could give a student a true understanding of the relation between diseases and their symptoms, and a knowledge of the value of therapeutic agents. (The Circular for 1838 claimed that "the number of medical and surgical patients admitted . . . is between three and four hundred, principally since August last".) Washington Medical College claimed to be the only school where so large a number of students could find such training easily available, without increased costs, a fact not true of other medical schools, where appointment to the post of resident student resulted from favoritism.[9] For many years the Circulars emphasized this feature of the school.

There were accommodations for strangers who had fallen ill while in the city, and who wished to avoid the noise and confusion of life in a hotel, and have the advantage of good nursing and medical services. (The charge was much more reasonable than at any public house.) These patients could be attended by physicians of their choice, and have as many visitors as desired. They could have, free of charge, the benefit of consultation with the professors. No infectious diseases were admitted to the wards of the hospital.

In truth, however, only the central section, (without obelisk roofs), and the right wing[10] were ever built, the remainder proving to be just a dream, not an actuality. (Although earlier pictures of the building show these obelisks ending in pyramidal tops, the illustration in the Circular for 1846-7 shows four obelisks terminating in battlements, not pyramids.) After using this building, (at present a part of the Church Home and Infirmary), for a short time, the Faculty felt that it was located too far from the city, and therefore had another building, (later known as the "New Assembly Rooms") erected at Lombard and Hanover Streets, each professor contributing $1,000 to the building fund. (Reference to the misuse of this fund has been made above.) This was the third, and last, home of the Washington University of Baltimore. Only the lecture and anatomy rooms were abandoned, permitting the use of this space for hospital purposes. The hospital and general infirmary, as well as the students' quarters, remained in use as usual, and an obstetrical department was opened, thus providing an opportunity for students to obtain practical instruction in mid-wifery. Transportation between College and Hospital was effected by omnibuses, "running frequently". Classes were held in the new building from 1849[11] until 1851, when the school was compelled to close, despite the noteworthy zeal, enterprise and courage of its Faculty.

Instructional facilities at the College were comprehensive. There were anatomical models by Auzoux, (one that of a perfect human figure, which could be separated into its parts, and examined very minutely), models for pathological anatomy by Thibert, and for obstetrics by Guy, "the largest and best series of Obstetrical Models ever imported into this country," all from Paris. (See below, on the course in obstetrics in 1848.) There were complete sets of surgical instruments, (showing "late valuable inventions and improvements") for performing "new and delicate" operations by students of the practical surgery class, which was "about to be formed," (1841), and a magnificent collection of 1100 dried medicinal plants, accompanied by a great number of "elegantly colored" drawings, to illustrate every item mentioned in the lectures on materia medica. There was a cabinet of the important preparations of morbid anatomy, and large cabinets of minerals, shells and "other subjects in Natural History . . . open to the inspection of the student and visitor; and if anyone wished to investigate chemical subjects experimentally, the apparatus from the laboratory was always at command", (1839). The chemical apparatus, sufficient "for present purposes", would be augmented, as soon as possible, and had been selected "for the purpose of illustrating the great doctrines of the science under its new and modernized form". New pieces, dealing with late discoveries, had been added and there were no old and obsolete ones in the collection, such as are present in the larger collections, made long ago by other colleges. (Such old apparatus serves no useful purpose, as it only encumbers the collection and reduces its efficiency). The class in practical chemistry had been found to be so beneficial, that it would be continued, (1841), "the members of the class themselves conducting the processes." The library, a good medical and miscellaneous collection, was, however, admitted to be deficient. The wonder, says the Report for 1839, was that despite the brief life of the school, and the numerous and formidable difficulties with which it had been faced, "it had succeeded so well in furnishing such valuable and varied advantages to its students."

II. CURRICULUM

In the earliest years of the College the curriculum was that taught by the usual six medical school departments (See Faculty arranged by Session, III-a). The four-months-session ran from the last Monday in October until the first day of March, "which experience has shown here to be a period over which the powers of the most assiduous student cannot be strained with advantage." (Circular, 1841). However, conscious of the need for longer training, the Faculty "earnestly exhorted [ed] all who [could] do so, to extend their collegiate studies over a term of three years instead of two." (The College claimed that many students remained for a third session.) In 1848 the session was lengthened to four and half months (end of October until March 15th). The College emphasized the advantages which it afforded for clinical study, and claimed to be the only one in this country which provided such an opportunity, thus making it a pioneer in this phase of medical instruction. It certainly was a practical way to learn how to become a doctor. The large number of sailor-patients, and those of the lying-in hospital, later established, provided a great opportunity to learn from a rich clinical experience, under the instruction of the attending physicians-professors. Six months of study in a hospital, it was stated, could teach a student more than six years "passed in an occasional and superficial examination of disease." It was necessary to co-ordinate study from books and attendance upon lectures with systematized observation, experience and reflection. An estimated more than two-thirds of the medical students who graduated from our best medical schools annually, had not had "opportunities afforded them, to witness profitably the daily progress and treatment of medical and surgical cases, so that they might be enabled immediately on their entrance into practice, to pursue it with confidence . . . " By locating the hospital within the walls of the College buildings, the student was able to have close contact with patient and physician or surgeon,[12] professors at the College. Students learned from seeing patients prescribed for, detailed case-histories developed, and patients entrusted to their care, under direction of the professors. In cases which terminated fatally, students could observe the pathological changes which had taken place, by attending the post-mortem examination. Thus the students had the great advantage of learning from practical illustrations of the precepts taught in the lecture room.[12a] (The College also exploited its nearness to the city of Washington, by inviting Members of Congress, whose sons might wish to study medicine, to have the latter enroll there, making it possible for daily reports regarding health, general welfare and educational progress, to pass between parent and College).

The Circular for July, 1837, in discussing the methods used by this school for training its students to become practitioners, approaches the matter by a circuitous route: the quality of medical eduction, both at home and abroad, is thought to be declining below the standard "at which it may be esteemed useful, efficient and honorable", due, in part, to the inequality of time, labor and expense required for the medical degree at different schools. The cause of this is the improper rivalry of our medical colleges, and the outcome is that every graduate, no matter how inferior his training, claims the same rights and privileges. The value of the medical degree therefore declines in the public's esteem. The situation in England is even worse. Medical schools there are exceedingly numerous, and rivalry between schools is great, with the result that they are rapidly levelling themselves and their pupils down to the position of the practitioners who never had a regular education, but whose pretensions are greater even than that "which high graduated merit would blush to use." To an extent this sad state of affairs is true in our own country. Are we, then, prepared to reform? We could improve our present educational practices so as to produce the best doctors in our history, and thus win the public's confident reliance upon the whole profession. If we established such a healthy state of the public mind, then also added a "wider diffusion of medical information," we would set the world free from its slavery to charlatans and quacks. The profession would then be assured of the respect which it is now rapidly losing. Another reason for making medical education more thorough is that the general diffusion of every kind of knowledge among all classes of people is growing, making it necessary for a doctor, himself, to grow in knowledge to an extent at least equal to that of his patients, if he is to hold their respect. A medical school must, therefore, not only give good medical training, but also train for "habitual precision of thought and observation", not only in medical subjects, but also in problems with which graduates may have to deal, as citizens of the world.

Washington University makes its contribution to this worthy cause by careful teaching, rigid weekly examinations, practical instruction at the patient's bedside in its hospital, and making certain of the full qualification of its graduates, before "ushering them into public life." True teaching does not load the memory with facts alone, but fills the mind with principles, of which the facts are the basis and illustrations. Pupils are taught to be careful observers of the classroom exhibits, anatomy demonstrations, and diseases of patients in the hospital. (The Circular then repeats its oft-stated and enthusiastic discussion on the value of the clinical training at Washington University – the closeness of the students' rooms to the class room or sick-ward, under tutelage of attending physician-Faculty member, the history of each patient traced and recorded, the mode of combatting symptoms planned, the indicated remedies prepared and administered, and all stages in the progress of the case observed, i.e., the striking and the less-marked changes, and the warning signs put out by Nature.) The housing of all facilities under one roof is something new in this country. Summer may be spent as a resident student, gaining clinical experience, and there is an annual course of lectures, free of charge, beginning on the first day of June. "A permanent list of cases of diseases, averaging constantly sixty in number", (U.S. seamen of the port of Baltimore), assured the student plenty of learning experiences, and there was a "great accession of private patients . . . " to add variety to the clinical experience of the student. The professors drew upon these cases to illustrate their lectures. Students were also permitted to visit the Baltimore Alms House (where 500 persons were housed), for further experience in observation. The ease and speed of learning how to become a physician at this school, it was claimed, made it unnecessary to cram for examinations, a process which, because of the great mass of undigested facts, only impeded and confused a student. This university wished to make medical education "extensive, sound and easy of attainment, by practical and experimental teaching."

The thread which ran through the philosophy of medical education of the Washington University, as stated in the Circulars, remained the same from year to year, i.e.: the excellence of its system of teaching the art, by giving the student a great deal of hospital instruction in medicine and surgery, by use of superior clinical facilities. An example is afforded by the Circular for 1840. The world seemed to wish for more and more from less and less – despite the fact that the science of medicine was daily expanding, there was prevalent the absurd desire to shorten the term of study. Washington University was opposed to such curtailment. Perhaps genius could perform the Egyptian task of making bricks without straw but medical students were, generally, not geniuses, and the desirable plan, therefore, would be to allow sufficient time for even the dullest to acquire a knowledge of all that is important, and at the same time not allow the genius to be bored, but, instead, to keep him on his mettle throughout. A too-short medical education produces graduates whose views are narrow and judgments hasty, the resulting "malpractice" being prejudicial to the profession, and injurious to society. The University therefore placed itself on record as opposing the "very prevalent fashion of shortening the term of medical education". The old teaching system should be abandoned. Formal enunciation of principles without illustrative cases, and the lecture book, with yellowed pages, were no longer tolerable. An art which relies so much upon practical skill for success in curing disease must be taught by example, as well as by precept, for a doctor who is lacking in the confidence born of practical knowledge is like a mariner who never goes to sea without suffering the most disastrous consequences. No graduate should be so lacking in practical knowledge as to be utterly confounded upon being faced for the first time by an emergent case of disease – to the practical eye the case may present nothing unusual, but the person who has learned only from books and lectures may recall no such case, and "his mind becomes confused, hands palsied, theories useless, learning defied. His remedies produce results he did not wish and the symptoms remain unsubdued." The well-educated practitioner has the wisdom to size up conditions, and act accordingly. Nothing which might endanger the patient's future escapes him. His curative means are speedy, and "compatible with a sure continuance of health after convalescence". In a dangerous situation he remains calm, because of experience, knowledge and reflection. "To him the most daring course is the simplest, and most easily executed as soon as it is proved to be expedient".

The practical experience gained during the summer months was strengthened by the biweekly lectures and frequent examinations during those months, thus producing indelible and accurate impressions, instead of "floating images", so that there would be "no disappointment in the hour of trial" which required prompt and efficient action. (The fee for the summer course of lectures was $10 to each professor, the student being permitted to elect the courses desired. The joint fee for a complete set of tickets was $50.) One great distinction between the scientific physician and the ignorant empiric is the ability to detect the true nature of disease, no branch of medicine being now more successfully cultivated than Diagnosis, which makes of medicine an exact science. In private practice skill in Diagnosis can be acquired only after many harrowing years, during which patients are subjected to hazardous blunders. In a hospital a great deal of knowledge can be acquired in a brief time, as a consequence of which a student who has had the benefit of residency shows, in later life, the great advantage which he earlier enjoyed. He comes before the public fully prepared to treat any case.

In 1845 the University announced the creation of an additional professorship, (without increased expense to the student). To relieve the overburdened chair of the theory and practice of medicine, and to "provide for a full, and most necessary, although much neglected instruction in the science of morbid condition," the new department of General Pathology, Special Pathology, Physical Diagnosis and Treatment of Diseases of the Chest was added, and Dr. Samuel Annan appointed professor. The claim was made that this school now gave a medical education equal to that at any fully organized medical institution, and that its courses were more numerous than those given at most of them. (Constant emphasis was laid, in the Circular, from year to year, on the pre-eminent opportunities for learning both anatomy and operative surgery in Baltimore, because of abundance of material, and the special advantages existing at this school.)

The Circular for 1845 gave a detailed discussion of the curriculum, from which the data below are taken:

THEORY AND PRACTICE OF MEDICINE

The course began with a brief view of the history of medicine, in order that the student might understand fully the various theories of the past, and the changes which they have undergone. The art of carrying on medical observation was then explained, followed by an introduction to the principles of medicine and pathology, needed for an understanding of the morbid changes in the body which result in disease. Subsequent lectures were devoted to the following six divisions:

1. Diseases Involving Various Organs.
2. Diseases of Nutrition and Evacuation.
3. Diseases of the Circulatory Apparatus.
4. Diseases of the Respiratory System.
5. Diseases of the Brain and Nervous System.
6. Diseases of the Generative or Reproductive System.

The professor adhered to a systematic order – the diseases of each system were listed, then the most important and frequent were selected for individual and detailed discussion – the location, general history, causes, varieties, symptoms, distinctive features, tendencies, results, treatment. Illustrative helps included engravings, morbid specimens and hospital cases.

CHEMISTRY AND PHARMACY

The course began with a treatment of the general principles of physics, (to which less than half of the term was devoted), and was followed by a description of the chemical elements and their compounds, their application to medicine, special reference to poisons and their antidotes, the preparation of medicinal substances, and explanation of the phenomena of animal physiology, ("based upon modern doctrines"). There were abundant supplies of apparatus and specimens for profusely illustrating the lectures by experiments and exhibiting the chemicals discussed in each lecture.

ANATOMY AND OPERATIVE SURGERY

The lectures in this department dealt with the "special" structure of the human body, its minute texture, and its surgical and operative details, and were illustrated. Special attention was given to the grouping of organs, (after their separate description), their relationship to each other was emphasized, and such deductions drawn as would be of the greatest value to the future practitioner. The practical anatomy rooms afforded an opportunity to verify that which was taught in the anatomy theatre, and to practice the various operations of surgery, under the constant attention of the able demonstrator. There were dried and wet specimens, both healthy and morbid, models, and drawings, but the professor was careful not to let these replace his more important illustrative, (i.e. actual anatomical), material, for too great a reliance upon accessory means, as practiced in schools where anatomical material was not abundant, could result in inaccuracy of knowledge and erroneous impressions, instead of correct and reliable conclusions.

GENERAL AND SPECIAL PATHOLOGY, PHYSICAL DIAGNOSIS, AND TREATMENT OF THE DISEASES OF THE CHEST

After giving a complete explanation of the principles of physical diagnosis, illustrated and applied, using hospital cases, (necessary for an understanding of the diseases of the chest) the various acute and chronic diseases of the heart and lungs were studied, and their pathology and treatment "minutely detailed". Recent specimens showing the changes due to disease were shown. The latter part of the course was devoted to discussions on important questions in pathology, a knowledge of which is so important to scientist and practitioner.

INSTITUTES AND PRACTICE OF SURGERY

The professor endeavored to make his course as practical as possible, basing his method of teaching upon the best teaching which he had observed both at home and abroad. He made abundant use of models, magnified drawings, "imitations of disease", and cases of disease or injury in the hospital wards, to illustrate and demonstrate his lessons. He gave faithful attention to surgical pathology, and exhibited and explained the recent morbid specimens which he had gathered in public and private practice. He likewise demonstrated every instrument useful in the practice of surgery, and the apparatus approved by surgeons the world over. The various operations in surgery were performed on the dead subject, and, as far as possible, also shown upon patients in the surgical wards of the hospital.

MATERIA MEDICA, THERAPEUTICS AND HYGIENE

The professor presented the various articles of the materia medica, so classified as to be useful and practical to his students. The properties of each class were discussed and the modus operandi explained. The physiological, toxicological and therapeutic effects of each particular agent were described, the comparative value in the treatment of individual cases demonstrated, and the different forms of preparation and administration enumerated. Reliable, new preparations were taken notice of, and the entire range of materia medica examined with reference "to the renewed facilities which modern researches in chemistry, physiology and pathology have afforded us". The lectures on therapeutics dealt with the different applications of the materials for the cure of disease, and the theories of their operation. Hygiene, covering the elementary principles which sustain and invigorate life in a state of health, a knowledge of which is so important for the prevention of disease, was taught as fully as the time needed for the other parts of this course allowed.

OBSTETRICS, DISEASES OF WOMEN AND CHILDREN AND MEDICAL JURISPRUDENCE

There were four divisions in this course:
1. "The anatomy and physiology of the series of organs, which, in women, are subservient to procreation, gestation, parturition, and lactation.
2. Hygiene, pathology and therapeutics, as applicable to the sexual peculiarities of women.
3. Hygiene, pathology, and therapeutics, as applicable to children.
4. Medical jurisprudence."

The aim was to give a clear and comprehensive understanding of this branch of medical science, and to develop the ability to discriminate between true and false, valuable principles and doubtful ones. The professor used the usual illustrative devices – plates, instruments, etc., to illustrate the lectures in obstetrics. Parturition in all its ordinary and its difficult forms was taught, and the nature and management of the latter were given thorough and special emphasis, based upon the sanction of the widest experience of practitioners at home and abroad, in the use of intervention by means of discreet and skillful aid.

Among the changes in the 1846 course – contents were the following:

MATERIAL MEDICA, THERAPEUTICS AND HYGIENE

Therapeutics:
- a.) the proper method of studying it
- b.) history
- c.) general principles

Hygiene:
- a.) nature of the subject
- b.) aims

Materia Medica:
the sources and character of medicines, various forms, effects, mode in which the effects are

produced, modifications due to accidental circumstances, physiological classification of medicines and a detailed discussion of the separate articles of the classes – description, history, composition of each agent, effect upon the body in health, therapeutic application in disease, diseases in which agent has been found most beneficial, best rules and methods for use in these diseases, toxicological properties fully considered, and these as well as their curative effects illustrated by the general principles of organic and inorganic chemistry, animal and plant physiology and, in particular, pathology.

ANATOMY AND PHYSIOLOGY

(Both professor and grouping of subjects were different from that of 1845.)
a.) a description of the general organization of the human body, an examination of its minute texture, its various forms and adaptation to function.
b.) special anatomy, comprising a minute description of the various organs, their relations, dependencies and functions. The professor used, as collateral aids, the usual drawings, models, preparations and specimens, and gave full and constant demonstrations on the recent subject.
c.) practical anatomy as usual.

OBSTETRICS, DISEASES OF WOMEN AND CHILDREN AND MEDICAL JURISPRUDENCE

a.) theory and practice of midwifery: the principal changes and improvements, in doctrine and treatment, brought about in scientific midwifery in recent years, lengthy discussion of embryology and the physiology of generation, comprehensive exposition of the best established principles of practice in natural, morbid and instrumental midwifery, correct views on the mechanism of parturition, (taught with great care); the constant use of the manikin, plates, instruments, to impress forcibly, upon the mind, general truths, and illustrate their practical relations.
b.) maladies of women, many of which are most intricate, rapidly-progressing and dangerous – a true, simple and practical exposition of these, so as to form a safe and efficient guide to diagnosis and treatment.
c.) the general peculiarities of infant structure and constitution, the management and physical education of children, the pathology of the diseases peculiar to infancy and childhood and the therapeutics applicable to them; throughout the course the professor's aim was to present, as clearly as possible, the important general truths and practical precepts taught at the Dublin School of Midwifery.
d.) medical jurisprudence as usual.

In 1848 a marked change in the curriculum took place, with the addition of two weeks to the length of the session and the addition of lectures on mental diseases. The lectures in this subject were added because of a growing interest in it, and because of a wish expressed by the National Convention. The professor, Dr. William H. Stokes, physician to a large insane asylum, had had experience in the field. It was hoped that, as a result of "remodeling the Faculty, and extending and enlarging the course of study in obedience to the . . . wish of the late National Convention", the students would not only obtain a better professional training, but that an impetus would also be given to the elevation of the standards of medical education.

INSTITUTES OF MEDICINE, MEDICAL JURISPRUDENCE AND MENTAL DISEASES

a.) Dr. Stokes lectured, as follows, on institutes:

1. physiology – (the healthy state; laws of the several functions of the body) – introduced by first giving a general and comprehensive view of the connection between physiology and the other branches of medicine, and the relations of the science of life to medicine in general, the distinction between animals and plants, the general subdivisions of the animal kingdom, the character of its "four primary groups", the place of man in the scale, and his characteristics in particular; simple and elementary exposition of the functions of the normal human frame, (the first-year students being given a "clear and comprehensive idea of these important subjects", whilst at the same time an epitome of Physiology . . . was offered to those who are more advanced in their studies";
2. pathology – (causes which change the structure and derange the functions of the different organs, the nature of these changes and derangements, and the accompanying phenomena) – lectures on the elements of this subject, and discussions on the fundamentals, with explanations of the general principles which guide the physician.
3. therapeutics – (principles and rules in the treatment of disease) – guided by the knowledge of the first and second divisions above, (physiology and pathology) – the student was taught how to determine "the various indications to be fulfilled . . . and to determine the

methods necessary for restoring the system to its healthy state."

On medical jurisprudence, (forensic medicine and medical police), he lectured as follows: application of all medicine to the purposes of the law, the relations between human nature and social institutions, the application of the principles of medical science to the administration of justice, and to the preservation of the public health; (deserving the utmost attention, because of its importance, the professor took particular pains to explain the real nature and aims of medical jurisprudence); a discussion of the medical jurisprudence of insanity, and the nature of, and special arrangements required for, the successful management of mental cases.

The entire course was abundantly illustrated by the use of diagrams and preparations from the museum. Each lecture began with a brief recapitulation of the previous lecture, and there was a weekly examination.

Other changes in 1848 involved the following.

ANATOMY AND PHYSIOLOGY

The professor gave special attention to surgical anatomy, emphasizing the relations and dependencies of the organs which become more particularly the subjects of surgical treatment.

INSTITUTES AND PRACTICE OF SURGERY

The course began with a thorough consideration of inflammation – the results on the different tissues, and those modifying influences which generally determine its consequences. The principles of surgery were then presented, not as by a lecturer, but rather as by a teacher, anticipating the difficulties which cross the path of the young practitioner, and aiming at a full understanding of the principles of surgery, avoiding theoretical discussion as much as possible, and striving to be practical. The course was closely geared to that in anatomy, the professor hoping, thereby, to impress more fully and readily the principles and practice of his subject. There were daily examinations.

OBSTETRICS AND THE DISEASES OF WOMEN AND CHILDREN

This consisted of:

a.) anatomy of the pelvis; external and internal organs of generation, departures from the normal.

b.) menstruation in normal and abnormal states; conception, including ovology and fetal pathology; utero-gestation, including departures from the normal state, such as sterility, superfetation, etc.

c.) parturition, in different stages and varieties.

d.) rules for the comfort and safety of the mother, during utero-gestation and accouchment, and the management of the infant after birth.

e.) diseases of women and children, with directions for their treatment. The teaching aids included the use of numerous models, (a papier mache obstetric model, life size; models of the uterus, in the different stages of utero-gestation, from the twelfth day to the ninth month; models of the different classes of extra-uterine pregnancy; models illustrating diseases of the uterus, etc.) some made in France, and some specially prepared for the course under the supervision of the professor, who also drew upon the cases in the hospital. The school later (1850), claimed to have particular strength in the department of obstetrics.

THERAPEUTICS, MATERIA MEDICA AND HYGIENE

The professor's philosophy held that if a student's knowledge of therapeutics were defective, all other knowledge was insufficient to prepare him for the duties of a physician. The course consisted of:

Therapeutics

a.) elements of therapeutics – an explanation of fundamental principles.

b.) philosophy of medicine.

c.) special therapeutics – the use of particular medicines to relieve specific morbid conditions. (The professor drew upon his own experience, imparting such important knowledge as was "most difficult to obtain from books". He dwelled at length on the subject of blood-letting, laying down simple and practical rules for its use, thus enabling the young doctor "to avail himself fearlessly and safely of this most efficient of therapeutical means").

Materia Medica

a.) the natural and medical history, qualities, doses, method of preparation of the most important members of the various classes of medicines, ignoring unimportant matter, and emphasizing that which the professor himself had found most useful, and therefore regarded as most important.

b.) the art of prescribing, and as much of pharmacy as was thought necessary. (Illustrative material included the specimens in the large and excellent herbarium, colored plates, etc.) –

Hygiene

a discussion of the effects of various agents (both good and bad) upon the healthy body – climate, atmosphere, (vitiated or pure), food, exercise, clothing, employment, etc. There were frequent examinations in the course.

PRACTICAL ANATOMY

Regular demonstrations during the whole course, and emphasis upon surgical anatomy, all important surgical operations being performed on the dead subject, first by the demonstrator, then by the class. There was an advantage in doing his dissecting during the month of October, for then a student need not interrupt his work in order to attend lectures.

To the very end of its existence the College emphasized that it was equipped to teach obstetrics more adequately than most medical schools, as these did not produce physicians capable of practicing this art with safety to their patients or themselves. The Circular for 1849-50 stated that new and extensive teaching facilities at the school, (including the largest and best series of costly obstetrical models ever imported into this country, so excellent that they could not help imparting a correct knowledge of the things which they were designed to teach), could enable a diligent student, upon graduation from Washington, to practice the art, under the most difficult circumstances. The College also continued to emphasize the great advantages of studying practical anatomy in Baltimore, conceded by everyone to be the best place to pursue this science.

In 1849-50 Dr. Monkur's lectures on theory and practice followed the same pattern as those of 1845, his lectures on institutes followed the pattern of those of 1848, and the lectures on medical jurisprudence and on mental diseases followed the structure of those given by Dr. Stokes in the previous year. Other course contents remained the same as in recent years. Teaching assignments were, however, different. Practical anatomy was made the responsibility of the chair of anatomy, as was, (temporarily), the department of materia medica and therapeutics. The last named department boasted a "hortus siccus", (herbarium), specimens of items in the U.S.P., and many figures, (drawings). The "chemical relations" of medicines, (incompatibilities), were taught by actual experiment, (demonstration), in order that the student might learn to avoid blunders, due to ignorance of this science. There were frequent examinations on the lectures.

In 1850 surgery was grouped with physiology. The aim was to trace the history of the gradual change from the state of health to that of disease, marking the different steps in the change. From this, it was claimed, the transition to the principles of surgery was easy and natural. There were lectures on the pathology and therapeutics of surgical diseases, illustrated by plates, drawings, models and specimens of morbid anatomy.

Plans called for the opening of a dispensary (first announced in 1849) in connection with the chair, where any second-year student could have frequent opportunity to perform minor surgical operations, as well as observing.

In that year, in anatomy and operative surgery, the professor began with a study of the elementary tissues of the organs of the body, then turned to an examination of the various organs, "as far as possible, in their physiological order", hoping by this plan to give as complete and thorough a knowledge as possible of the organs, their relations, actions and history of their development: The fresh subject, wet and dry preparations, models and a fine set of recently acquired anatomical drawings were used in regular daily demonstrations. After each region was described, the various operations pertaining to that region were shown, this plan seeming most advisable, because the structure was familiar to the student. Attention was given to general anatomy and physiology, particularly in their relation to the other practical branches of medicine. Surgical anatomy, to meet the exigencies of the practice of surgery, was taught. Every student was required to submit to the daily examinations on the lectures.

Requirements for Graduation

To obtain the degree of doctor of medicine the requirements were:

a.) attendance upon two sessions of lectures[13]

b.) passing of a rigid examination on all the subjects taught by the Faculty, (a gold medal going to the person who achieved the highest grade.)

c.) presentation of an acceptable thesis.[14]

Late Circulars state that a candidate for the degree must be 21 years of age, and have passed a period of three years as an apprentice, in addition to the three requirements listed above.

(Preparatory to obtaining the tickets from the professors a student was obliged to have his name registered on the College books. Professor William F. Norwood, in *Medical Education before the Civil War*, p. 245, suggests that the purpose of this may have been "to insure a check on preliminary education, but the Circular made no mention of Latin or natural philosophy".)

The Maryland Medical Recorder, Volume 1, (1829), p. 158, carried a list of names of twelve persons who had graduated in 1828, after attending but one session "and passing the usual private and public examinations," the explanation being given that they had previously attended other medical schools. On p. 770 of the same volume of the *Recorder* the statement is made that two courses were required, but on p. 356 of Volume 2, (1831), announcement is made that the Faculty now resolved to adopt regulations similar to those of the school of medicine of the University of Maryland, that is, a student would have to "attend lectures two winters, and during that time take all the tickets once. A course in any other respectable college will be considered equal to one in this." (Harvard did not require attendance upon two courses until 1834, when it also increased the length of the session to thirteen weeks.)

FEES AT WASHINGTON MEDICAL COLLEGE
UNIVERSITY SCHOOL OF MEDICINE

	LECTURE TICKETS	MATRICULATION	(DISSECTION OPTIONAL) DEMON-STRATOR'S FEE	GRADU-ATION (DIPLOMA)
1828	$15.00	$5.00	$ 5.00	$10.00
1837	$15.00	$5.00	$10.00	$20.00
1841*	$15.00	$5.00	$10.00	$20.00
1845**	$10.00 (seven courses, total of $70.)	$5.00	$10.00	$20.00
1846	Entire course $90.00	$5.00	$10.00	$20.00
1850	$15.00 (entire course, $90.)	$5.00	$10.00	$20.00

*"Boarding in the College buildings, with the privileges of Resident Students, $4.50 per week".

**Reduction in fee may have been due to competition.

Clinical attendance was free. "Comfortable boarding" could "be had for $2.50 to $3.50 per week", presumably off-campus, (1848-1850).

When the graduates of Washington Medical College appeared for licensing, the question was raised as to whether they should be granted a license solely upon the strength of the diploma, as was done for graduates of the school of medicine of the University of Maryland. It was decided by the Medical and Chirurgical Faculty of the State of Maryland that in the future the Board of Examiners should require all applicants except graduates of the University of Maryland prior to June, 1828 to pass an examination. (However, Dr. Robley Dunglison, in Cordell's "Annals" (1836), makes reference to the fact that the Court of Appeals later decided that a diploma from the University of Maryland was a license, and holders were exempt from the examination requirement.)

The Maryland Medical Recorder

Horatio Jameson was not only the prime mover in the founding of the Washington Medical College, but also, as a voluminous writer, was a person with a natural interest in medical journals, one of which, the quarterly *Maryland Medical Recorder,* he founded in 1829, and which he served, with distinction, as editor until 1832, when the journal ceased to appear. He contributed much of its contents, other members of the Faculty joining him in publishing articles in the *Recorder.*

Volume I of the *Recorder*, for example, contained a seventy page article on the subject of typhus fever, by Dr. Jameson, a ten page contribution on retention of urine, written by Dr. Annan, ten pages on the relation of chemistry to medicine, by Dr. James B. Rogers, twelve pages on tumors of the superior jaw also by Dr. Jameson, and an article on therapeutics by Dr. Jennings. The plan of Jameson's first-named paper is as follows:

Reproduced below is a statement which appeared, under "Miscellany", in Volume 2, (1831), on p. 733. Also reproduced is a table of contents, (1832).

WASHINGTON MEDICAL COLLEGE

We trust the completion of our second volume, will obtain the approbation of our friends to the assurance which we have given, and now repeat, that this Journal was not gotten up for party purposes, for the dissemination of particular doctrines, nor for collegiate purposes, except so far as an impartial diffusion of medical knowledge, may indirectly subserve all colleges, and all individuals.

While we express our thanks to our patrons, we must acknowledge that we have been put poorly sustained, by a large portion of the profession at home, who look with something more than distrust, upon every thing coming from a competitor in business, while they willingly contribute to that which comes from abroad – we have only to say on this point, that we have faithfully, and we trust, not profitably, (to those whose eyes are not prejudiced,) labored to collect in this city, and distribute without affection or favor, or prejudice, every thing which came before us.

No one can charge us with any undue effort in giving publicity to the proceedings of Washington College, over any other – our work has always been open to all – but in closing the present volume, we have pleasure in assuring our several friends, who inquire after the prospects of this college, that it is in a favorable state of progression – The names of twenty-one candidates are now on the list, for the approaching examination, many of whom complete their third course of lectures with us, this term.

TABLE OF CONTENTS FOR NO. IX
1832

Page

III. (A). FACULTY

Session of 1827-28

Horatio Gates Jameson, M.D., Professor of Surgery and Surgical Anatomy
Samuel K. Jennings, M.D., Professor of Therapeutics and Materia Medica
William W. Handy, M.D., Professor of Obstetrics and Diseases of Women and Children
James H. Miller, M.D., Professor of Theory and Practice of Medicine
Samuel Annan, M.D., Professor of Anatomy and Physiology
John W. Vethake, M.D., Professor of Chemistry and Medical Jurisprudence

Session of 1828-29 until Session of 1834-35, inclusive

James B. Rogers, M.D., distinguished chemist, later on the Faculty of the University of Pennsylvania, replaced Dr. Vethake in 1828.
Thomas Emerson Bond, M.D., taught Theory and Practice of Medicine, replacing James H. Miller in 1832.

Session of 1835-36

John P. Mettauer, M.D., Professor of Surgery
Samuel K. Jennings, M.D., Professor of Therapeutics and Materia Medica
William W. Handy, M.D., Professor of Obstetrics and Diseases of Women and Children
John C. S. Monkur, M.D., Professor of Institutes and Practice of Medicine

Edward Foreman, M.D., Professor of Chemistry
. . . . ? Professor of Anatomy and Physiology
James H. Miller, M.D. ???

Session of 1837-38 until Session of 1841-42, inclusive

James H. Miller, M.D., Professor of Anatomy and Physiology
Samuel K. Jennings, M.D., Professor of Materia Medica, Therapeutics and Legal Medicine
William W. Handy, M.D., Professor of Obstetrics and Diseases of Women and Children
John C.S. Monkur, M.D., Professor of Institutes and Practice of Medicine
Edward Foreman, M.D., Professor of Chemistry
John R.W. Dunbar, M.D., Professor of Surgery and Surgical Anatomy
Washington R. Handy, M.D., Demonstrator of Anatomy

Session of 1842-43 until Session 1844-45, inclusive

Henry W. Baxley, M.D., became Professor of Anatomy and Operative Surgery
Charles Bell Gibson, M.D., became Professor of Institutes and Practice of Surgery

Session of 1845-46

John C.S. Monkur, M.D., Professor of Theory and Practice of Medicine
Edward Foreman, M.D., Professor of Chemistry and Pharmacy
H. Willis Baxley, M.D., Professor of Anatomy and Operative Surgery
Samuel Annan, M.D., Professor of General Pathology, and the Special Pathology, Physical Diagnosis, and Treatment of Diseases of the Chest
Charles Bell Gibson, M.D., Professor of Institutes and Practice of Surgery
William Thomas Wilson, M.D., Professor of Materia Medica, Therapeutics and Hygiene
John Fonerden, M.D., Professor of Obstetrics, Diseases of Women and Children and Medical Jurisprudence

------

Marshall P. Howard, M.D., Demonstrator of Anatomy, and Adjunct Professor of Obstetrics

Session of 1846-47

John C.S. Monkur, M.D., Professor of Theory and Practice of Medicine
Edward Foreman, M.D., Professor of Chemistry and Pharmacy
Charles Bell Gibson, M.D., Professor of Institutes and Practice of Surgery
William Thomas Wilson, M.D., Professor of Materia Medica, Therapeutics, and Hygiene
William T. Leonard, M.D., Professor of Anatomy and Physiology
William H. Stokes, M.D., Professor of Obstetrics, Diseases of Women and Children, and Medical

Jurisprudence

Wakeman Bryarly, M.D., Demonstrator of Anatomy
(John R. Quinan, in Medical Annals of Baltimore, P. 38, gives the Faculty for 1848 i.e., 1847-48, (?), as Monkur, Leonard, Stokes, McCook, Roberts, Bond, Wright).

Session of 1848-49

John C.S. Monkur, M.D., Professor of Theory and Practice of Medicine
Edward Foreman, M.D., Professor of Chemistry and Pharmacy
William T. Leonard, M.D., Professor of Anatomy and Physiology
William H. Stokes, M.D., Professor of Institutes of Medicine, Medical Jurisprudence and Mental Diseases
George McCook, M.D., Professor of Institutes and Practice of Surgery
George C. M. Roberts, M.D., Professor of Obstetrics and Diseases of Women and Children
Thomas E. Bond, A.M., M.D., Professor of Therapeutics, Materia Medica and Hygiene

------

Wakeman Bryarly, M.D., Demonstrator of Anatomy

Session of 1849-50

John C.S. Monkur, M.D., Institutes and Practice of Medicine; Medical Jurisprudence and Mental Diseases
George C.M. Roberts, M.D., Obstetrics and Diseases of Women and Children
Reginald N. Wright, A.M., M.D., Chemistry
A. Snowden Piggot, A.M., M.D., Anatomy and Physiology
Reginald N. Wright, A.M., M.D., Surgery
A. Snowden Piggot, A.M., M.D., Therapeutics, Materia Medica and Hygiene
The duties of the Demonstrator were performed by the Professor of Anatomy. "The Faculty intend, as soon as possible, to fill the vacant chairs with gentlemen thoroughly qualified to meet the responsible duties thereof." (Circular for 1849-50).

Session of 1850-51

John C.S. Monkur, M.D., Institutes and Practice of Medicine; Medical Jurisprudence and Mental Diseases
George C.M. Roberts, M.D., Obstetrics and Diseases of Women and Children
Thomas E. Bond, Jr., A.M., M.D., Therapeutics, Materia Medica and Hygiene
Reginald N. Wright, A.M., M.D., Chemistry
A. Snowden Piggot, A.M., M.D., Principles of Surgery and Physiology
Washington R. Handy, M.D., Anatomy and Operative Surgery
John W. Bond, M.D., Demonstrator

Session of 1851-52[15]

Drs. Monkur, Roberts, Bond and Wright as in 1850, Dr. Piggot holding the chair: Anatomy and Physiology, and Valentine Mott, Jr., M.D. the chair: Principles and Practice of Surgery and Pathological Anatomy.

III. (B) ALPHABETIZED LIST OF MEMBERS OF THE FACULTY[16]

(For Faculty grouped by year, see above)

(A question mark means that the year which precedes it is not certain)
Annan,[17] Samuel, M.D., 1827-28, 43(?)-46
Baxley,[18] Henry W., M.D., 1842-47
Bond, John W., M.D., 1850-51
Bond,[19] Thomas Emerson, A.M., M.D., 1832-35(?), 42-43(?)
Bond,[20] Thomas E., Jr., A.M., M.D., 1850-51
Bryarly, Wakeman, M.D., 1846-49
Dunbar*, John R.W., M.D., 1837-42
Fonerden,[21] John, M.D., 1845-46
Foreman, Edward, M.D., 1835-49
Gibson,[22] Charles Bell, M.D., 1842-48
Handy, Washington R., M.D., 1837-(?), 1850-51
Handy, William W., M.D., 1827-42

Howard, Marshall P., M.D., 1845-46
Jameson,[23] Horatio Gates, M.D., 1827-35
Jennings,[24] Samuel K., M.D., 1827-45
Leonard, William T., M.D., 1846-49
McCook, George, M.D., 1848-49
Mettauer,[25] John P., 1835-37
Miller, James H., M.D., 1827-32, 35(?)-42(?)
Monkur*, John C.S., M.C., 1835(?)-51
Mott,[26] Valentine, Jr., M.D., 1851
Piggot, A. Snowden, A.M., M.D., 1849-51
Roberts, George C.M., M.D., 1848-51
Rogers,[27] James B., M.D., 1828-35
Stokes, William H., M.D., 1846-49
Vethake, John W., M.D., 1827-28
Wilson, William T., M.D., 1845-48(?)
Wright, Reginald N., A.M., M.D., 1849-51

III. (C) INCORPORATORS, CHARTER OF 1833

Horatio G. Jameson
Samuel K. Jennings
William U. Handy
Thomas E. Bond
Samuel Annan
James B. Rogers

Board of Visitors

Rev. John M. Duncan
Dr. William Donaldson
Charles F. Mayer
Reverdy Johnson
John S. Tyson
Rev. John Finley
Dr. John Buckler
William R. Stewart
Rev. John Gibson
Dr. Amos A. Evans
Dr. Peregrine Wroth
Dr. Henry Howard
Dr. John Martin
E. L. Finley
John V. L. McMahon
Dr. Joseph Nichols
Dr. Richard M. Allen
Dr. Robert Goldsborough
Dr. Samuel B. Martin
Col. William Stewart
Dr. Robert Archer
Dr. John P. Mackenzie
Dr. Francis P. Phelps
James Campbell

III. (D) TRUSTEES OF THE BUILDING 1837-1847

Hon. Charles F. Mayer
James Corner, Esq.
Capt. James Frazier
Capt. William H. Conkling

OFFICERS OF THE COLLEGE, 1837, 1838

James H. Miller, *President*
John C. S. Monkur, *Treasurer*
Edward Foreman, *Secretary*
Samuel K. Jennings, *Dean*

OFFICERS OF THE COLLEGE, 1840

Rev. John M. Duncan, *President*
John S. Tyson, *Secretary, Board of Visitors*

IV. TEXTBOOKS USED

1845
Anatomy and Operative Surgery
Special Anatomy – Cloquet, Quain, Wilson, Horner, Wistar
Surgical Anatomy – Velpeau, Blandin, Burns
Operative Anatomy – Velpeau, Hargrave, Fergusson, Pancoast, Liston
Chemistry and Pharmacy
Turner, Graham, Chemical articles in Pereira's Materia Medica
Materia Medica, Therapeutics and Hygiene
Pereira's Materia Medica, Dunglison's Thereapeutics, Bell's Materia Medica, the Medical portions of the United States Dispensatory
Obstetrics, Diseases of Women and Children and Medical Jurisprudence
Obstetric Medicine and Surgery – Ramsbotham

Diseases of Women — Colombat
Diseases of Children — Condie
Medical Jurisprudence — Beck
General Pathology, Special Pathology, Physical Diagnosis and Treatment of the Diseases of the Chest
Walshe on the Lungs
Hope on the Heart
Stokes on the Chest
Watson's Practice of Medicine; Andral's Clinique Medicale
Theory and Practice of Medicine
McIntosh; Eberle; Dunglison's Practice
Institutes and Practice of Surgery
Gibson's Surgery; Liston's Surgery;
Cooper's Surgical Dictionary

1846
Anatomy and Physiology
Anatomy — Cloquet, Horner, Pancoast's Wistar
Physiology — Carpenter, Dunglison
Chemistry and Pharmacy — see 1845
Materia Medica, Therapeutics and Hygiene
Pereira's Materia Medica and Therapeutics; the medical portions of the United States Dispensatory; Edwards: On the Influence of Physical Agents on Life
Obstetrics, Diseases of Women and Children and Medical Jurisprudence
Obstetric Medicine and Surgery: —
Davis' Elements of Obstetric Medicine; Ramsbotham; Churchill
Diseases of Women: — Ashwell; Churchill
Diseases of Children: — Evanson and Maunsell; Condie
Medical Jurisprudence: — Taylor, Beck
Theory and Practice of Medicine — see 1845
Institutes and Practice of Surgery — see 1845

1848
Anatomy and Physiology
Cruveilhier's Anatomy; Wilson's Anatomy; Carpenter and Dunglison's Physiology
Chemistry and Pharmacy — see 1845
Theory and Practice of Medicine — see 1845

DATA for COMPARISON and EVALUATION

Certain comparative data are of interest. The Washington University School of Medicine is praiseworthy for having pioneered in emphasizing bedside instruction of medical students, and helping to make widespread this feature of medical education. As to statistics, one must point out that the hospital claimed an originally-planned capacity of from three to four hundred beds, (when completed), and that, in the little over two years of its initial existence, (late 1836, until the end of the year 1838), it had received 530 patients, and 359 in the next year. (Its predecessor, the hospital of the University of Maryland, had opened thirteen years earlier, with four wards, which, by 1833 had doubled in number, with ninety beds, and a daily average of sixty to seventy patients.) In Philadelphia, the hospital of the University of Pennsylvania had not opened until 1874, with 642 patients. (The Philadelphia University of Medicine and Surgery claimed a charter for a hospital in 1865, with a surgical hospital already in-being for twenty to thirty patients.)

Washington University also claimed living quarters for fifty students, a feature shown by none of the Philadelphia schools. Its college structure was elegant and modern, (a statement which, in the case of Philadelphia, could be made only of the building which had been erected for the Medical Department of Pennsylvania College, in 1853, occupied first by that school, and subsequently by other now-extinct medical schools of Philadelphia.) Equipment seems to have been adequate, for the times, but not quite so elaborate as that at the Allopathic schools of Philadelphia. The Faculties of the schools of both cities numbered among them many distinguished and illustrious men, but they were more numerous in the larger metropolis.

Matriculation and graduation numbers were much smaller at Washington than at the now-extinct Philadelphia schools. For example, while graduating classes at the Medical Department of Pennsylvania College ranged about thirty-five, Washington averaged about nine per session. However, in the period 1828 to 1838, of 181 matriculates, 101 earned the M.D. degree. Thus the ratio of matriculates to graduates was high, (56%), a fact not true at most of the contemporary schools.

At first Washington, as far as can be ascertained from its early Circulars, required but one session of attendance, but it soon expanded that to two sessions, as required by the Philadelphia schools. The curriculum was closely similar in both cities, and the length of sessions at Washington was comparable to that at Philadelphia. When, in 1848, two weeks were added, the sessions at Washington were as long as at virtually any medical school.

The Philadelphia College of Medicine, as late as 1858, spoke of an obstetrical clinic as a "new idea in medical schools", but the Washington University had obstetrical cases in its hospital many years earlier, and had been giving its students much training in this field, making it strong in that department. The medical schools of neither city made a course in practical anatomy a requirement, but Washington University was located in a city where there was access to a great deal of anatomical material, and it could therefore have taken the lead in making dissection obligatory for winning the medical degree, thus setting an example for the rest of our medical schools, (as it had done with its program of bedside instruction). Yet the Philadelphia schools may not be held too far from reproach on the same grounds. (On the other hand, the University of Maryland does have the distinction of having required practical anatomy in 1833, but the requirement was abandoned after a short time – in 1839.) It is also to be noted that the lectures, at Washington, on mental diseases, had no counterpart in the Philadelphia schools, at the time. As forward-looking as this was, we cannot ignore the fact that the Eclectic schools of Philadelphia in the early 1850's could not find adequately scathing words with which to denounce resort to blood-letting as a curative method, but at Washington the professor of therapeutics, materia medica and hygiene, in 1848, laid down "simple and practical rules" for its use by doctors, enabling them to use "this most efficient" therapy without fear or danger. The lectures in chemistry at Washington University seem limited in comparison with the treatment given this subject in Philadelphia. The textbooks in use at Washington University were adequate, but lacked the wide range at the Allopathic schools of Philadelphia, and at the University of Maryland School of Medicine, (in which school there were in use the works of such authors as Haller, Magendie, Blumenback and Bichat in anatomy and physiology, Lavoisier and Black in chemistry, Dessault, Abernethy, and Cooper in surgery, and Cullen, Rush, Sydenham, Erasmus Darwin, etc., in institutes and practice). Thus we may conclude that the Washington University School of Medicine was in some matters further advanced, and in some less so, than the Philadelphia schools.

One thing which this school had in common with its counterparts, the extinct medical schools of Philadelphia, was the weakness which operated toward the untimely end of all of them: as a proprietary school it had no neutral governing body to stabilize it, and lend it financial and other forms of organizational aid, counsel and support. In other words, it had all the weaknesses of any small, independent commercial undertaking, especially sensitive to the violent tremors resulting from erroneous policies, from which the larger organization is more likely to recover, given sufficient time and resources.

V. LIST OF MATRICULATES AND GRADUATES OF THE WASHINGTON MEDICAL COLLEGE-WASHINGTON UNIVERSITY SCHOOL OF MEDICINE, OF BALTIMORE

(First Period)

The letters M.D. indicate that the degree of Doctor of Medicine was conferred by this school in the year stated immediately following the degree.

The absence of M.D. after a name means that the available records show only that the person named was a matriculate in the year or years given.

The letter (a) after a name means that the person graduated in one of the years 1831 to 1838, inclusive.

The letter (d) after a name means that the matriculate attended in one or more of the years 1827 to 1837, inclusive.

Any years stated after the first date mean that the person spent that time, after receiving the degree, as a post-graduate, or as a second year student.

Parentheses around M.D., i.e., (M.D.), mean that neither the date nor the school which conferred the degree is evident from the available records alone.

Parentheses around a letter, name or State indicate that the existing records show variations, and the possibility that two different persons might be involved cannot be ruled out with certainty.

An asterisk before a name means that the person was a "resident student".

A question mark indicates that there is some doubt about the year in which the degree was conferred.

Title of thesis and name of preceptor are given, when available. If the thesis was written in

Latin, that fact is also noted, (James Bunting and Daniel Hoffman, both in 1840).

Honorary and ad eundem degrees are so noted.

The names of graduates for the years 1843, '44, '46, '47 and '50, (a total of fourteen names, on the basis of statements of other authors that there were 183 graduates in all), are missing, as are those of matriculates for the years 1840 to 1847, inclusive, and 1849 to 1851, inclusive. College "Circulars" for the years 1827 to 1836, inclusive, 1842, '43, '44, '47, '51 and '52(?), have not come to hand. However, names of graduates for 1828, '29, and '30 were located in the *Maryland Medical Recorder*, those for 1840, '41, and '42 in the *Maryland Medical and Surgical Journal*, and those for 1845, '48 and '51 in the *Baltimore Sun*. Five names of graduates – Adam Carl, Edward A. Cromwell, John Pierce, William Hayes and William Marshall, appear in the *Maryland Medical Recorder*, Volume 1, p. 158, and p. 581, but do not appear in the cumulative list for 1828-'39, published by the College, in the "Circular" dated July, 1839.

Most of the "Circulars" from which the data for this study have been drawn are among the holdings of The Library of the College of Physicians of Philadelphia, The Welch Medical Library of Johns Hopkins University, The National Library of Medicine, and The Library of the New York Academy of Medicine. The Historical Library of the School of Medicine of Yale University, The Boston Medical Library, and The Enoch Pratt Free Library, of Baltimore, also have holdings on this school.

Ahl, John, M.D., '45
Pennsylvania
Airey, George W., M.D., '49
Maryland
Albaugh, William H., '48
Maryland
Alexander, J.C., M.D., '51
Virginia
Anderson, John, M.D., (a)
Maryland
Andrews, G.W., Honorary M.D., '39
Maryland
Angel, Arthur, M.D., (a)
Maryland
Applewhite, Arthur, M.D., '29
North Carolina
Archer, John G., M.D., '42
Maryland
Dr. Dunbar
Arnold, Abraham B., M.D., '48
Pennsylvania
*Bagwell, Thomas H., M.D., '42
Virginia
Dr. T. P. Bagwell
Bailey, D.H., M.D., '42
Georgia
*Bailey, George W., M.D., '39, '39
Maryland
Absorbent System
Baker, Edward, M.D., (a)
Maryland
Baker, William H., '48
Maryland
Baldwin, Edwin C., '39
Connecticut
Dr. Kinnemon
Balfour, Eleazer (M.D.),
Honorary M.D., '41
Virginia
Ballard, Charles M. (W), M.D., '49
New York
Barlucky, Charles N., (M.D.),
Honorary M.D., '41
Pennsylvania
Barnes, Charles A., M.D., '51
Maryland

Bartholow, Wesley, M.D., '41
Maryland
Scarlatina
Dr. I. S. Warfield
Basset, John Y., M.D., '30
Alabama
Baxter, John N., M.D., '40
Maryland
Anatomy and Physiology
of the Skin
Beall, Burgess L., M.D., '28
Georgia
Beall, John (H.T.G.), M.D., '41
Maryland
Variola
Dr. L.H.T. Cockey
Bealmear, Thomas (d)
Ohio
Bealmere, Thomas, M.D., '30
Maryland
Scrofula
*Bell, Daniel, '38
Virginia
*Beltz, Henry E., M.D., (a)
Maryland
*Benedict, Daniel T., M.D., '39
Pennsylvania
Materia Medica and
Therapeutics
*Benedict, Jacob (d)
Pennsylvania
Berry, George H., M.D., '48
Maryland
Bingham, N., (M.D.)
Honorary M.D., '42
London
Biser, C.C., M.D., '49
Maryland
Blake, Richard, M.D., (a)
Maryland
Bland, Lane (Zane), M.D., '49
Maryland
Blandy, A.A., M.D. '49
Ohio
Bond, Augustus (A.M.), M.D., (a)
Maryland

Bond, Thomas H., M.D., '30
Maryland
Fever
Brashears, Robert J., '48
Maryland
Breerwood, George W., M.D., '49
Maryland
Brien, Jean B. H., (M.D.), '39
Lower Canada
Brisbine, Albert G., '48
Ohio
Brooks, Joseph D., M.D., '48
Maryland
Broom, John, M.D., '28
Maryland
Brown, Samuel P., M.D., '45
Pennsylvania
Bryan, James L., M.D., '49
Maryland, (Virginia)
Bryarly, Wakeman, M.D., '40
Maryland
Acupuncturation
Dr. Dunbar
Bunting, James, M.D., '40
Maryland
De Signis Morborum
(Latin thesis)
Dr. J. S. Warfield
Bunton, Sylvanus, M.D., '45
New Hampshire
Burkhart, Francis M. (d)
Maryland
Burridge, Lewis S., M.D., '51
New York
Busbee, William L. '48
North Carolina
Busk, T.M., M.D., '40
Maryland
Stethoscope, Its Use and Abuse
Dr. Monkur
*Butts, John R., '38
Pennsylvania
Byers, Henry K., M.D., '45
Pennsylvania
Cadden, Charles W., M.D., '51
Maryland
Carl, Adam, M.D., '28
Pennsylvania
Cass, David M., M.D., '28
Maryland
Cass, Edward, (d)
Maryland
Castle, Noah, M.D., '45
Maryland
Chalmers, George W., M.D., '28
Maryland
*Chaplin, Noah Zane (d)
Virginia
Chappell, Philip S., M.D., '29
Maryland
Cherbonier, A.V., M.D., '49
Louisiana, (Maryland)
Chesley, Nathan D., (d)
Maryland
Church, Samuel T., '48
Maryland
Clark, Ashur, (d)
Maryland
Clarkson, James (S), M.D., (a)
Maryland, Pennsylvania
Conrad, A.M.H., M.D., '42
Virginia
*Cole, George W., '38, '39
Maryland
Dr. J. H. Miller
Cole, J. H., '39
Pennsylvania
Dr. Monkur
Comegys, John, '38, '39
Maryland
Dr. Dunbar
Cook, Septimus T., M.D., '29
District of Columbia, Virginia
*Cornthwaite, D. Wilson, M.D., '39
Illinois, Maryland
Digestive Absorption
Cox, Christopher C., M.D., (a)
Maryland
Craggs, J. H., M.D., '42
Maryland
Dr. G. McElhiney
*Crawford, George W., M.D., (a)
Delaware
Crawford, James, (d)
Indiana
Cromwell, Edward, M.D., '30
Maryland
Hepatitis
Cromwell, Joseph, M.D., '30
Maryland
Uterine Hemorrhage
Crook(s), Joseph, '39
Pennsylvania
Dr. J. P. Scots
Cullen, William M., M.D., '51
Ireland
Cullum, J. W., '48
Maryland
Curren, Robert, (N.,W.), M.D., (a)
Virginia
Cushing, Joseph J., (d)
Maryland
Davies, Daniel, (M.D.), '39
Maryland
Davies, David W., M.D., '41
Maryland
Yellow Fever
Dr. Monkur
Davis, David, '38
Maryland
Davis, Francis T., M.D., '45
Maryland
Day, Everett H., (d)
District of Columbia
Day, R.H., M.D., (a)
Bladensburg
Day, Richard H., (d)
District of Columbia
Day, William B., M.D., (a)
Bladensburg
Day, William D., (d)
District of Columbia

Dellenbaugh, Christopher W., '48
Ohio
Diffenderffer, William L., M.D., '45
Pennsylvania
Dill, Edward W., M.D., (a)
Maryland
Dinsmore, Andrew, M.D., (a)
Pennsylvania
Dixon, G. C., M.D., '42
Maryland
Dorsey, Dennis B., M.D., (a)
Maryland
*Dorsey, George W., M.D., '39
Maryland
Hemorrhage
Dorsey, John, (d)
Maryland
*Dorsey, Septimus, M.D., '39
Maryland
Round Ligament of the Uterus
Dougherty, John, (d)
Maryland
Douglass, A.B., M.D., '39
Maryland
Eclampsia
Douglass, Richardson, M.D., '49
(Dinglass)
Maryland
*Downes, Dion, M.D., '39
Maryland
Tetanus
Dunahue, James H., '48
Maryland
Duncan, Alexander J., M.D., '48
Maryland
Duncan, James B., (d)
Pennsylvania
*Dunn, Thomas W., M.D., '39
Pennsylvania
Anatomy, Physiology and
Pathology of the Teeth
Durkee, Robert A., (M.D.), '40
Honorary M.D.
Maryland
*Duty, Samuel, '39
Maryland, North Carolina
Duvall, M. (Marcan, Mareen), M.D., (a)
Maryland
Ebert, Philip, M.D., (a)
Pennsylvania, Maryland
Eichelberger, G. F., M.D., (a)
Pennsylvania
Elbert, William H., M.D., (a)
Maryland
Eldridge, Henry B., M.D., '45
Virginia
Ellery, William, '39
Maryland
Dr. C. S. Harris
Eoff, John (D), (Q), M.D., (a)
Virginia
Essender, James, M.D., (a)
Maryland
*Evans, John, M.D., '40
Maryland
Innervation
Dr. Dunbar
Finley, Elliott, (d)
Pennsylvania
Fisher, Levi, '48
Ohio
Ford, Joseph T., M.D., '51
Virginia
Foreman, Edward, M.D., '30
Maryland
Physiology of the Brain
Forney, Daniel S., M.D., '28
Maryland
*Forrest, John W., M.D., '40
Maryland
Modus Operandi of Medicine
Dr. L. D. Lutton
Foulks, Charles T., M.D., '45
Maryland
Garber, Abraham, M.D., '40
Pennsylvania
Indigestion
Dr. Dunbar
Garlic, Theodosius, (d)
Ohio
Garrison, H. G., (d)
Maryland
Gatchell, Eli M., M.D., '40
Maryland, Pennsylvania
Yellow Fever
Dr. George W. Bailey
*Gibbons, Giles C., '38
Virginia
Gibbons, John L., M.D., '41
Virginia
Intermittent Fever
Dr. Dunbar
Gibson, Rezin, (T., B.S.), M.D., '39, '39
Maryland
Anatomy and Physiology of the Liver
Gibson, William, '39
Maryland
Dr. Dunbar
*Glascock, Richard, (d)
Virginia
*Godwin, John W., '38
Virginia
*Goodwyn, Edward O., (M.D.), '39
Virginia
Gove, H., M.D., '42
New York
Grafton, Samuel, M.D., (a)
Virginia
Gray, (Grey), R.H., M.D., (a)
Maryland
Grier, W., (d)
U.S.N., Virginia
Grier, William, M.D., (a)
Maryland
Gross, Henry, '39
Maryland
Dr. R. A. Durkee
Guyer, John W., M.D., (a)
Maryland
Hackett, Urie, '48
Pennsylvania
Hales, ----

Honorary M.D., (a)
Virginia
Hamilton, James, (d)
Maryland
Hammond, Allen C., M.D., '28
Maryland
Hammond, George, M.D., '51
Maryland
*Hammond, R. (P., T.), M.D., (a)
Maryland
Hance, Benjamin O., M.D., '48
Maryland
Handy, Jesse T., M.D., (a)
Maryland
Handy, Marmaduke, M.D., (a)
Delaware
Handy, Thomas,
Honorary M.D., '30, (?)
Delaware
Handy, Wash. R., M.D., (a)
Delaware
Harlan, David, M.D., (a)
U.S. N., Maryland
Harris, C.A., (M.D.), (d)
Maryland
Harrell, J.A., M.D., '42
North Carolina
Harrison, B.B., M.D., '42
Virginia
*Harrison, Richard E., M.D., (a)
Virginia
*Harrison, William D., '40
Virginia
Tetanus
Dr. C. C. Marsteller
*Hartman, Andrew, M.D., '39
Pennsylvania
Digestion
Hayes, William, M.D., '30
Maryland
Convulsions
*Heiner, Jesse T., M.D., '39
Maryland, Pennsylvania
Menstruation
Helman, Orlando, '48
Ohio
Henderson, James T., (d)
Pennsylvania
Henderson, John, (d)
Pennsylvania
Hills, David, (d)
Maryland
*Hoffman, Daniel P., M.D., '40
Maryland
Phthisis Pulmonalis, (Latin thesis)
Dr. J. H. Miller
Hood, Benjamin, M.D., (a)
Maryland
Hoop, Israel G. F., M.D., '51
Pennsylvania
*Hooper, J. Edwin, (John E.O.), M.D., '41
Maryland
Acute Dysentery
Dr. Z. H. Rosse
Horner, David, (M.D.)
Honorary M.D., '41
Pennsylvania
Hubbell, E., M.D., '42
Maryland
*Hughes, Benjamin, (E., G.), M.D., '41
Maryland
Effects of Iodine upon the Human Organism, and Its Use as a Medicine
Dr. W. Waters
*Hull, Tideman, M.D., '40
Maryland
Purpura Hemorrhagica
Dr. R. C. Cumming
Irons, James, (d)
Pennsylvania
Jackson, Samuel K., M.D., '39
Virginia
Mortification
Jameson, Alex, C., M.D., (a)
Maryland
Jameson, David, (G., D.), M.D., (a)
Maryland
Jameson, Horatio G., M.D., (a)
Maryland
Jameson, L., (d)
Maryland
Jennings, Robert C., (d)
Virginia
Jennings, Samuel K., M.D., '48
Maryland
Johns, John A., M.D., '51
Virginia
Johnson, William, M.D., (a)
Pennsylvania
Johnson, William M., M.D., '41
Maryland
Iodine
Dr. Dunbar
Johnston B., M.D., (a)
Pennsylvania
Johns(t)on, Benjamin, M.D., '28
Pennsylvania
Jolliffe, S. G., (d)
North Carolina
Jones, Samuel A., M.D., (a)
Maryland
*Kean, Louis, M.D., '40
Maryland
Local Inflammation Connected with Various Grades of Fever
Dr. John Sappington
Kendall, Thomas E., M.D., '48
Maryland
Kenney, Maxwell, M.D., (a)
Maryland
Kinnemon, P.S., (M.D.), '39
Maryland
Klein, Madison C., M.D., (year?)
Virginia
Knapp, Frederick H., '39
Maryland
Dr. Dunbar
Knight, James, M.D., (a)
Maryland
Knight, Samuel H., M.D., '42
Maryland
Dr. J. H. Miller

Knox, M. M., M.D., '42
Ohio
Kolb, Wilson (N.W.), M.D., '28
Maryland
Kramer, John W., '48
Maryland
Lacout, P.J.F.F.
Honorary M.D., (a)
Cognac, France
Langsdale, P.W., M.D., (a)
Maryland
*Laphen, James G. (C.), M.D., '41
District of Columbia
Apoplexy
Dr. W. Washington
Large, Nathan L., '48
Pennsylvania
*Lauck, J. S., '38
District of Columbia
Laveille, Robert D., M.D., '30
District of Columbia
Intemperance
Lee, Richard D., M.D., '48
Maryland
L(e)(i)ggett, John E.H., M.D., '40
Maryland
Nature, Efficient Cause and
Ultimate Purposes of the
Menstrual Fluid
Dr. James Liggett
Long, B.C., M.D., '30 (?)
Maryland
*Long, John S., M.D., '40
Virginia
Evil Effects of Tight Lacing
on the Female Constitution
Dr. R. M. Sherry
*Loomis, Isaiah C., M.D., '40
Pennsylvania
Colic
Dr. Ira Day
Love, William S., M.D., (a)
Maryland
Lynch, Samuel D., M.D., (a)
Maryland
Lyons, Michael, M.D., (a)
Virginia, Maryland
Macgill, Lloyd T., M.D., '51
Maryland
Magrath, John T., '48
Maryland
Marshall, William, (M.D.), '30
Honorary M.D.
Maryland
Marston, F., '48
Maryland
Martin, James S., M.D., '45
Maryland
Martin, J. James T., '38, '39
Maryland
Dr. S. B. Martin
Martin, Samuel B.
Honorary M.D., (a)
Maryland
Martin, Samuel H., M.D., '45
Maryland
Massey, Aquilla, M.D., (a)
Maryland
Maulsby, D.J., M.D., (a)
Maryland
*McCaine, A.M., M.D., '39
South Carolina
Asclepias Tuberosa
McCann, David (d)
Ohio
McClellan, H.M., M.D., (a)
Maryland, Pennsylvania
McCulloch, H.D., M.D., (a)
Maryland
McCurdy, John K., M.D., (a)
Pennsylvania
McDowell, Hamilton, M.D., '49
Maryland
McDuel, John A., (d)
District of Columbia
McGill, Thomas, M.D., '49
Maryland
McGowan, D.S., (d)
Pennsylvania
McHenry, James
Honorary M.D., (a)
Pennsylvania
McIntyre, James, M.D., (a)
Maryland
McKean, Alexander M., (d)
Maryland
McKeehan, B.F. (T.), M.D., '49
Maryland
McKeehan, Samuel, M.D., '29
Maryland
McKenney, Alexander F., (d)
Tennessee
McKenny, James, M.D., (a)
Pennsylvania
McLaine, A.M., M.D., '39
South Carolina
McPherson, W. C., (d)
Pennsylvania
McVoy, Diego, M.D., '51
Alabama
Michael, Charles, M.D., (a)
Pennsylvania
Miller, Samuel, (d)
Pennsylvania
Miller, Theodore K., (d)
Maryland
Miller, W., '39
Pennsylvania
Monroe, William R., M.D., '49
Maryland
Moore, Reuben, M.D., (a)
Virginia
Morgan, Gerard E., M.D., '51
Maryland
Morgan, N.J.B., '38
Virginia
Mosely, Robert B., M.D., '48
Virginia
Murray, John J., '48
Maryland
Myers, Louis S., M.D., '49
Maryland

Myers, John J., M.D., '28
Maryland, Pennsylvania
Musgrave, William, (O., C.), M.D., (a)
North Carolina
Newman, R., Honorary M.D., (a)
Virginia
Norris, Richard, (d)
Maryland
Norris, William W., M.D., '48
Maryland
O'Brien, John M., M.D., '48
Virginia
O'Donnell, Louis, M.D., '45
Maryland
Oellig, John, (d)
Pennsylvania
Offat, T. B.
Honorary M.D., '39
Vincennes
O'Keefe, David, M.D., '48
Maryland
Owings, John H., M.D., '28
Maryland
Parker, John C., M.D., (a)
Maryland
*Parker, Joseph M., '38
Virginia
Peale, John W., (d)
Alabama
Pennington, J., (M.D.)
Honorary M.D., '42
Virginia
*Perderain, Hyp. C., (d)
Paris, France
Perine, John, (d)
Maryland
Perry, John, M.D., (a)
District of Columbia
Pierce, John, M.D., '30
Baltimore
Duties of the Physician
Pool, W.W.S., M.D., '42
Virginia
Poole, James M., (d)
Virginia
*Poole, Samuel T., (d)
North Carolina
*Poole, William H., M.D., '40
Maryland
Intermittent Fever
Dr. Zollicoffer
Porter, J. B., M.D., '42
Pennsylvania
Price, William, M.D., (a)
Maryland
Pumphrey, W. (S., T.), (William), '39
Maryland
Dr. H. Howard
Ramsey, R. H., M.D., (a)
Honorary M.D., (a)
Virginia
Ranck, N., (M.D.)
Honorary M.D., '42
Pennsylvania
Redgreaves, T.J., M.D., '42
Maryland
Reese, John, (J.), (T.), M.D., '29
Maryland
Reynolds, Peter S., '48
Ohio
Richardson, E. Hall, M.D., '48
Maryland
*Riggs, Amos, (Artemas), '39
Maryland
Dr. Augustus Riggs
Riggs, Artemas, M.D., '41
Maryland
Apoplexy
Ringrose, William D., M.D., (a)
Maryland
Robinson, William T., M.D., '48
Maryland
Rowles, William T., M.D., '29 (?)
Virginia
Ryan, William M.D., Rev., M.D., '51
Virginia
*Sanborn, S. (J.) G., M.D., '39
New Hampshire
Phthisis Pulmonalis
Savage, J.G., M.D., '42
Virginia
Scaniker, George W., '48
Missouri
Schwartze, Agustus J., M.D., '29
Maryland
Schwartze, Edward, M.D., '28
Maryland
Scott, Oliver G., (d)
Pennsylvania
Secord, Vancourtland, M.D., '49
Canada
S(e)(i)ebold, William (F), M.D., '42
Pennsylvania
Dr. J. R. Lotz
Shepherd, Samuel, '38
Maryland
Shorb, Basil, (d)
Pennsylvania
Shriver, William E., M.D., '48
Maryland
Sie(ei)ker, Edward A., M.D., '49
Prussia
*Skillman, Charles, M.D., (a)
Maryland
Smith, A., (M.D.), (d)
Pennsylvania
Smith, Adolphus C., (d)
Virginia
*Smith, Alvah C., M.D., '39
New Hampshire
Indigestion
Smith, J.P., (M.D.)
ad eundem M.D., '42
Virginia
Smith, Samuel R., M.D., (a)
Virginia
Smith, William H., '38
Maryland
Smith, William L., (d)
Maryland
Smithson, George W., M.D., (a)
Maryland

Smyser, Henry, M.D., '29
Pennsylvania
Speake, Rufus (K.) (H.), M.D., '29
District of Columbia
Stanbury, James, (d)
Maryland
Stansbury, W.M., (d)
Maryland
Stevens, Elias, M.D., '29
Virginia
Stevenson, J.S., '39
Kentucky
Stewart, Alexander, M.D., (a)
Maryland
Sugg, E. C., Honorary M.D., (a)
Indiana
Taylor, Milton N., M.D., '48
Maryland
Thompson, Robert, M.D., '45
Maryland
Thomson, Thomas, M.D., (a)
Maryland
*Tilden, W. Perry, M.D., '40
Maryland
Structure and Functions of the Absorbents
Dr. J. H. Miller
Tracy, James C., '38
Maryland
*Treadwell, Samuel E., M.D., '39
Maryland
Respiratory Organs
Tudor, Samuel (M), M.D., (a)
Pennsylvania, Maryland
Turner, Charles, M.D., '29
Delaware
*Turner, Lewis T., M.D., '40
Georgia
Delirium Tremens
Dr. Richardson
Tyler, Elijah, M.D., '45
Maryland
*Tyler, George Colbert, M.D., '40
Virginia
Generative System
Dr. T. P. Bagwell
Tyson, Samuel E., M.D., (a)
Maryland
Umberger, David, (M.D.)
Honorary M.D., '41
Pennsylvania
*Vogelson, William (G.), M.D., '41
Pennsylvania
Fracture Cervix Femoris
Dr. H. M. McClellan
Wachter, Leander, '48
Maryland
Wallace, Jesse, M.D., (a)
Pennsylvania
Wallace, Wesley (M.), (W.), M.D., (a)
New Jersey
Walter, L. P., '38
Pennsylvania
Walters, James W., (d)
Maryland
Ward, R.A., M.D., (a)
Maryland
Ward, Richard, (d)
Mississippi
Webber, Robert, M.D., (a)
Virginia
Weems, Levin C., M.D., '48
Maryland
Weir, Robert (W.) (P.), M.D., '28
Virginia
Wells, Robert, (d)
Maryland
West, Jesse D., (d)
Maryland
Wickersham, W.P., M.D., '42
Maryland
Dr. Monkur
Williams, Benjamin, M.D., '45
Virginia
Williams, James C., M.D., '48
Virginia
Williams, James R., (d)
Maryland
Wilkins, John M., (d)
Maryland
*Wilson, James (J.), (S.), (Q.), M.D., '41
Maryland
Irritability
Dr. John Broome
Winnell, William, (d)
Pennsylvania
*Woodbridge, Grafton, M.D., '39
Georgia
Intermittent Fever
*Worrall, George W., M.D., (a)
Pennsylvania
*Worrall, Isaac (A.) (S.), M.D., (a)
Pennsylvania
*Worrall, Thomas A., M.D., (a)
Pennsylvania
Worman, Andrew D., M.D., '45
Maryland
Wrol, J.A., M.D., '42
District of Columbia
Young, John M., (d)
Pennsylvania
Zimmerman, W., M.D., '42
Maryland
*Zollickoffer, William
Honorary M.D., (a)
Maryland

BIBLIOGRAPHY

FIRST PERIOD

1. Circulars of the Washington Medical College — University School of Medicine for the years referred to above. Also the *First Annual Report to the General Assembly of Maryland . . . of the Washington Medical College of Baltimore*, January, 1839.
2. Eugene F. Cordell: The Medical Schools of Baltimore, *Transactions of the Medical and Chirurgical Faculty of the State of Maryland*, 1881, pp. 342-351.
3. Genevieve Miller: A Nineteenth Century Medical School: Washington University of Baltimore, *Bulletin of the History of Medicine*, Volume 14, (1943), pp. 14-29.
4. William F. Norwood: *Medical Education in the United States before the Civil War*, Philadelphia, University of Pennsylvania Press, 1944, pp. 242-246.
5. The Maryland Medical Recorder, Volumes 1, 2 and 3.
6. The Maryland Medical and Surgical Journal, Volumes 1 and 2.
7. G. Carroll Lockard: Early Medical Education in Baltimore, *Bulletin of the School of Medicine, University of Maryland*, Volume 23, (1938), pp. 128-137.
8. Bernard C. Steiner: *History of Education in Maryland, Washington*, D. C., 1894, pp. 286-291.
9. Allen Johnson, editor: *Dictionary of American Biography*, Charles Scribner's Sons, New York, 1928.
10. Howard A. Kelly and Walter L. Burrage: *Dictionary of American Medical Biography*, D. Appleton Co., New York, 1928.
11. Samuel Annan: *An Address Delivered to the Graduates of Washington Medical College . . .* etc. March 17, 1834, Baltimore, John D. Toy.
12. Thomas E. Bond, Jr.: *An Introductory Lecture . . . Medical Department of The Washington University*, November 11, 1848.
13. J. Schmidt: *A Letter to Thomas E. Bond, A.M., M.D., on Homoeopathy*, Baltimore, 1851.
14. *Baltimore Sun*: Files for March, 1843-1851, inclusive.
15. *Circular to Medical Students and to the Friends of Medical Education*, by A Lover of Science, March 1, 1851, (in the Toner Collection, Rare Books Division, Library of Congress).
16. Eugene F. Cordell: *Medical Annals of Maryland*, Baltimore, 1903.
17. *Western Lancet*, Volume 4, (1845-46), pp. 474-5.
18. John R. Quinan: *Medical Annals of Baltimore . . .* Baltimore, 1884.
19. N. S. Davis: *History of Medical Education and Institutions in the United States from the First Settlement, etc.*, Chicago, 1851.
20. William F. Norwood: Medical Education and the Rise of Hospitals, *Journal of the American Medical Association*, Volume 186, (December 14, 1963), pp. 1010-1011.

FOOTNOTES TO CHAPTER ONE

First Period

(1) The Medico-Chirurgical and Theological College of Christ's Institution, (See Appendix A).

(2) The Maryland College of Eclectic Medicine and Surgery, originally the Eclectic School of Medicine of Milton University, (1912), called itself the Eastern University School of Medicine, (1913), then by the first of the three names in 1914. Unrecognized by the Maryland State Board of Medical Examiners, it was dissolved in 1915. (See Appendix B.)

(3) a. Woman's Medical College of Baltimore. b. Baltimore University School of Medicine. c. Atlantic Medical College, (originally known as the Southern Homoeopathic Medical College). d. Maryland Medical College, (not to be confounded with the College of Medicine of Maryland, which later became the University of Maryland School of Medicine). The reason for including a fifth school in this study is given above.

(4) McClellan had obtained for his Jefferson Medical College authorization from the Jefferson College of Canonsburg, Pennsylvania. Eventually the Pennsylvania Legislature, (1840), made it unlawful for any "college incorporated by the laws of the State, to establish any Faculty for . . . conferring degrees . . . in any City or County . . . other than that in which said college is or may be located". See William Frederick Norwood: *Medical Education in the United States before the Civil War*, page 94.

(5) The Circular of the College, dated September, 1837, gives extracts from the charter, on pp. 7 and 8. The charter itself is to be found in Laws of Maryland, Volume 12, chapter 189. A manuscript copy of the several charters of the Washington Medical College may be seen at the University of Maryland Medical School.

(6) Eugene F. Cordell: The Medical Schools of Baltimore, in *Transactions of the Medical and Chirurgical Faculty of Maryland, 1878, p. 331.*

(7) In view of the steadily diminishing size of the particles with which the physicists of our century have contended, someone has quipped that scientists are always learning more and more about less and less, and will eventually know everything about practically nothing. This witticism might be a collateral descendant of Dr. Bond's bon mot.

(8) "The college edifice contains the following apartments: On the ground floor of the college is the refectory, circular, 40 ft. in diameter. On the second floor is the saloon, [sic!], circular, 40 ft. in diameter. On the third floor is the chemical lecture hall, circular, 40 ft. in diameter. On the fourth floor is the dissecting room, circular, 40 ft. in diameter. On the fifth floor is the anatomical and surgical theater, circular, 40 ft. in diameter.

Each of the turrets contains five rooms for students, to lodge two persons. In the hospital department, the ground floor is used as a kitchen and servants' rooms. Second story, four apartments for private patients, and two for steward's family. Third story, four apartments for private patients, and one for nurses. (In the Circular for 1840, p. 7, the third story had five apartments for private patients; the sixth floor was for surgical cases only.)

Fourth story, six apartments for colored patients, and kitchen for seamen's ward. Fifth story, large ward for United States' seamen, ninety feet long. Sixth story, convalescents' room, 90 feet long." First Annual Report to the General Assembly of Maryland . . . of the Washington Medical College, January 1839, p. 5. (The Report emphasized the fact that private patients were entitled to the services of the professors, as consulting physicians, free of charge, and that the building was light, airy, neatly kept by the steward, and of comfortable design. Until now "carried on by private enterprise and means entirely," it could, "by reasonable legislative aid . . . take rank with the first medical schools in the Union.").

The Circular for 1841 claims that the plan of this building "has been copied by a celebrated Medical School in the English metropolis." (Guy's Hospital, of London, which announced that it would erect chambers for resident students upon their premises, "no medical school there having made this all-important arrangement, which has been in operation at Washington for four successive sessions".) Furthermore, the city of Baltimore had erected, within a few minutes walk of this structure, a hospital for contagious diseases and "by lease placed it under control of this Faculty." This provided students with a unique opportunity.

(9) "This hospital will afford a most agreeable residence to students of Medicine, who may desire hospital advantages during the summer months, where they will have charge of the cases under the direction of the Professors. The hospital was opened in the latter part of 1836, and the number of patients to January 1, 1839, was 530." (*First Annual Report to the General Assembly of Maryland . . . of the Washington Medical College, January 1839*, P. 5). From January 1, 1839 to January 1, 1840 the number was 359.

(10) Edgar Allen Poe, found unconscious on a Baltimore street, was removed to this hospital, where he expired on October 7, 1849. (See Genevieve Miller: *A Nineteenth Century Medical School*, in Bulletin of the History of Medicine, Volume 14, (1943), p. 19).

Two upper stories of this hospital were devoted to men of our Navy who fell ill, while in service. (See section on Curriculum of this study.)

(11) "Circumstances beyond the control of the Faculty for the present preventing the use of the . . . building in the course of construction on Lombard Street," the daily lectures of at least part of the session of 1849-50 were delivered in rooms on Liberty Street, one door north of Baltimore.

(12) The First Annual Report (1839) claimed that "no surgical operation has as yet failed". (p. 5)

(12a) Of thirty-three medical schools which replied to an inquiry, sent to fifty, by the American Medical Association, in 1849, only eight stated that they required hospital attendance by their students. Twelve replied that they did not require it. Many of the others either had no hospitals, or were relying upon college clinics instead. William F. Norwood: Medical Education and the Rise of Hospitals, *Journal of the American Medical Association*, Volume 186 (December 14, 1963), pp. 1010-1011.

(13) It was claimed that many students took a third course. (Recorder, Volume 2, (1831), p. 733.

(14) Genevieve Miller, p. 16. The only requirements mentioned in references to the College, in the Maryland Medical Recorder of early date, are attendance upon two sessions and passing the examinations. Part of the 1832 charter is reprinted in the Circular for 1837.

Section 12 of this charter likewise stipulates only attendance upon two terms of lectures, one term of which may be satisfied by study at any other medical school of established reputation, and the passing of an examination.

(15) Eugene F. Cordell, p. 346. The school apparently closed before this session could be held.

(16) Eugene F. Cordell states that Thomas E. Bond was a lecturer in 1832, that Edward Foreman was a lecturer in 1835-36, and that Dr. Peregrine Wroth may have been Professor of Chemistry for a time.

(17) Dr. Annan was well known as a teacher and medical scholar. He won his M.D. at Edinburgh. After graduating he was an assistant at Guy's and St. Thomas's Hospitals, London. Upon his return to the United States, in addition to his activities at Washington Medical College, he lectured at the clinic of the Baltimore Alms House. He invented a highly useful instrument for relieving prolapsus uteri. The device was tested out thoroughly at hospitals in Paris, after which it was commended by many distinguished accoucheurs and surgeons. He was the first superintendent of the Western Lunatic Asylum, Hopkinsville, Kentucky, was a professor at Transylvania University, Lexington, Kentucky, a surgeon in the Confederate Army, 1861-64, and a contributor to the literature, especially the American Journal of the Medical Sciences. He published the first recorded cases of bronchotomy in Maryland.

(18) Henry Willis Baxley was a founder of the first dental collefe in the world. Among the posts which he held were: demonstrator of anatomy, then professor of anatomy and physiology at the University of Maryland, as well as at the Baltimore College of Dental Surgery, professor of surgery at Washington University, physician to the Baltimore Alms House, the chairs in anatomy and in surgery of the Medical College of Ohio, inspector of hospitals. He was a "thorough anatomist, able teacher and surgeon." He was author of two great works, written while abroad: *What I Saw on the West Coast of North and South America . . .* (1865, New York, 632 pp., illustrated) and: *Spain, Art Remains, Art Realities, Painters, Priests and Princes, Being Notes of Things Seen and Opinions Formed . . .* (London, 1875, two volumes). Dr. Baxley was thought to have sided with the Trustees in the disagreement of 1825 and, when that group elected him to the chair of anatomy in 1837, the school was disrupted, two Faculties being formed, a two-year legal suit followed, and eventually the old order restored by the Court of Appeals, in 1838.

(19) Thomas Emerson Bond was "a founder of the College of Medicine of Maryland, and its first professor of materia medica". He held one of the only three M.D. degrees ever bestowed by act of assembly of the Maryland Legislature, and held an honorary M.D. from the University of Maryland, (1819), as well as the degree of D.D. He was a local preacher in the Methodist Episcopal church, president of the Board of Health, Baltimore, professor at Washington College, surgeon of cavalry, a Trustee of Baltimore College of Dental Surgery, editor of *The Itinerant*, and of *The Christian Advocate and Journal*.

(20) Thomas Emerson Bond, Jr., won his M.D. at the University of Maryland. He was one of the founders of the Baltimore College of Dental Surgery, and professor there of special pathology and therapeutics until 1872, as well as dean, (1842-49). He was professor of materia medica at Washington. He wrote: *Treatise on Dental Science*, and was joint editor of *Guardian of Health*. He was also a minister in the Methodist Episcopal church, editor of the *Baltimore Christian Advocate* and author of: *Life of John Knox*.

(21) John Fonerden was a Baltimore alienist, philanthropist, and friend of Johns Hopkins. He was president of the Medico-Chirurgical Society, professor at Washington University, visiting physician to the Bay View Asylum, city physician during the cholera epidemic, and co-editor of the Baltimore *Colonization Journal*. He was superintendent of the Maryland Hospital for the Insane, from 1846 until his death.

(22) Charles Bell Gibson was a Virginia surgeon and professor of surgery in the Medical Department of Hampden-Sidney College. In 1861 he was appointed Surgeon General of Virginia. He was one of the first persons in the state to use anesthetics. He contributed to: *American Journal of the Medical Sciences* and to the *Virginia Medical and Surgical Journal*.

*According to Bernard Steiner, (op. cit.) Dr. Dunbar was "a man of genius", a "brilliant writer and speaker" with "unbounded enthusiasm in his profession", and an excellent surgeon. Ungifted with business acumen, he fell into great debt. The result was a seizure, by creditor and landlord, of his valuable library, which has been assembled at great expense and by years of effort. The shock killed him.

(23) Horatio Gates Jameson is credited with having made a tremendous contribution toward winning fame throughout the civilized world for the city of Baltimore as a center of medical and surgical research. He was born in York, Pennsylvania, the son of David Jameson, a graduate in medicine at Edinburgh, who emigrated to Charleston, South Carolina, in 1740. Horatio Jameson studied medicine under his father, and was a practitioner at the age of seventeen, (1795). He journied down the Ohio, and practiced in the backwoods from 1799 to 1801, later writing an interesting account of his voyage and professional experiences. Many years later he attended lectures at the University of Maryland, taking his M.D. there, in 1813. He carried on a business as a druggist and manufacturing chemist, at the same time practicing medicine. Dr. Jameson was surgeon to U. S. troops in the War of 1812, at Baltimore. In 1817 he published two lectures on *Fevers in General*, and his *American Domestick Medicine . . . Designed for the Use of Families*.

We have seen above that he was the prime mover in the founding of the Washington Medical College. It has been said that his natural gifts, resulting in wide fame and success, won him the jealous enmity of the leaders of his own alma mater, leaving him no hope of winning a professorship there, and that one of his motives in founding another school was to find an outlet for his creativity. We have also referred to his *Maryland Medical Recorder*, above, as well as to his contributions to this journal.

In 1830, on special invitation, he read a paper on *Non-Contagiousness of Yellow Fever*, before the Society of German Naturalists and Physicians of Hamburg, being the first American to attend these meetings.

His great essay: *Observations upon Traumatic Hemorrhage, Illustrated by Experiments upon Living Animals*, published in the *Medical Recorder*, is an exhaustive study, using sheep and dogs, and showing the value of animal ligatures, introduced by Physick, in 1814, and used by Astley Cooper, in 1817. Jameson, having used them for about seven years, preferred buckskin. In the many amputations which he had performed, not one ligature had ever slipped, nor was there ever a secondary hemorrhage.

Dr. Jameson was prominent as a surgeon in Baltimore, Washington and Philadelphia. He was surgeon to the Baltimore Hospital, physician to the city jail, and consulting physician to the Board of Health. In 1832 he was superintendent of vaccination, and improved the virus being used by repassing it through the cow. During the great epidemic of cholera he was in charge of hospitals, and later wrote his book: *A Treatise on Epidemic Cholera*, (Philadelphia 1854).

He was noted for his mechanical ingenuity, his bold and successful, original operations, his tirelessness as a scholar and investigator, and his numerous and graceful writings.

He believed in bleeding and in antiphlogistic methods.

His attempt to establish a medical school in Baltimore resulted in such animosity against him, that Dr. Jameson was forced to bring a defamation-of-character suit against Dr. Frederick E. B. Hintze, in the Spring of 1828, in Baltimore City Criminal Court, as a result of which Hintze was fined. (See the American Medical Recorder, January, 1829.)

(24) Samuel Kennedy Jennings studied medicine with his father, Dr. Jacobs Jennings. In 1812 he received an honorary M.D., from the University of Maryland. He was a Baltimore preacher, president of Asbury College, (1817-18), and president of the Medical Society of Baltimore, (1823-24). Dr. Jennings, in addition to his roles as one of the founders of Washington Medical College, and professor of materia medica and therapeutics, also taught anatomy at the Maryland Academy of Fine Arts, (1838-43). He was the author of:

A Plain, Elementary Explanation of the Natural Cure of Diseases, (Richmond, 1814).

Letters and Certificates Recommending the Patent Portable Warm and Hot Bath, (Norfolk, 1816).

The Married Lady's Companion, (Richmond).

A Compendium of Medical Science; or Fifty Years Experience in the Art of Healing, (1847).

(25) John P. Mettauer, the son of a regimental surgeon under Lafayette, was a gifted surgeon, teacher and author. He was educated at Hampden-Sidney College, and won his M.D. at the University of Pennsylvania, (1809), where he was taught by Rush. He was one of the first surgeons in the United States to operate successfully for cleft palate, (1827). He made contributions to nearly every medical journal in our country. As a result of the wish of so many young men to become his private pupils, and the need for assistants and nurses in his enormous work, he organized a medical school in 1837. This school was at first known as Mettauer's Medical Institute, (1837-38), and from 1848 to about 1860 as the Medical Department of Randolph-Macon College, where he was professor of medicine and surgery, clinical medicine, therapeutics, materia medica, midwifery and medical jurisprudence.

Dr. Mettauer was a very busy and highly successful surgeon for a great many years. He was also a gifted mechanic, designing and inspiring his students to design surgical instruments, some made of silver and gold.

(26) Valentine Mott, Jr., was an eminent surgeon, of New York. After graduating in medicine he made a trip to Europe, and while in London observed the best men at their work. He was a pupil of Sir Astley Cooper, and associated with Hope, Playfair and Gregory. On his return to New York he lectured and demonstrated on operative surgery, being the first in his city to give private lectures. At the age of twenty-six he was professor of surgery at Columbia College, and, upon union of that school with the College of Physicians and Surgeons he became professor of surgery at the united schools. He was a founder of Rutgers Medical College. Dr. Mott was one of the first to give clinical instruction. His work showed originality, and it has been said of him that "No surgeon, living or dead, ever tied so many vessels, or so successfully, for the cure of aneurysm, the relief of injury, or the arrest of morbid growths." (Gross). He is believed to have ligated the great arteries of the body one hundred and thirty-five times. His 4,000 volume library, and his plates and instruments are now at the New York Academy of Medicine.

Steiner tells us that Dr. Monkur was a "mainstay" of the College during most of the period from 1835 to 1851. One of the most eminent physicians of his time in Baltimore, he was a man of "acute perception, indefatigable industry", an "admirable logician, skillful diagnostician, a bold and varied therapeutist and a clear and profound lecturer".

(27) James Blythe Rogers was a physician with strong leanings toward chemistry and geology. Some years after leaving his post as professor of Chemistry at Washington, he took up a similar one at the Franklin Medical College, of Philadelphia, for one year, after which he held the chair at the University of Pennsylvania. He assisted in the geological surveys of Virginia and Pennsylvania. Dr. Rogers was the author of a number of valuable scientific articles, and, with his brother Robert edited the last American edition of Turner's *Elements of Chemistry*, and Gregory's *Outlines of Organic Chemistry*. With his brother he also wrote and published: *A Text-book on Chemistry*. He was famed for his clarity as a lecturer on scientific subjects. Dr. Rogers was a member of the American Philosophical Society.

WASHINGTON UNIVERSITY SCHOOL OF MEDICINE

Second Period (1867-1877)

Dr. Edward Warren, professor materia medica and therapeutics at the University of Maryland, had left his post there, at the outbreak of the Civil War, and become surgeon-general of North Carolina. Upon his return to Baltimore after the war, he found his position on the University Faculty no longer available to him, (the school having waited for his return for two years, then having notified him that the chair could not possibly go unfilled any longer). Refused his request for restoration to the Faculty, he gathered together a group of able physicians and surgeons, among them Drs. A. J. Foard and Harvey L. Byrd, who, like himself, had served the Confederacy, and, learning that the charter of Washington University was available, obtained from Drs. Roberts, Bond and Monkur, survivors of the Washington Faculty, transfer of that charter and all the rights and privileges thereof. Thus the school once more became a going concern.

The first session of the revived school was that of 1867-68.

The Announcement for 1868 tells us that the City of Baltimore and the State of Maryland had each made its own contribution to the establishment of the College Hospital, and the school regarded this liberality as an endorsement, placing it on "a far different basis from that which it had previously occupied". No longer was there any need to feel "humble and uncertain", the words for impoverishment, for it was now a great and permanent state institution, under special patronage of the Board of Visitors, chosen by the Legislature for their ability and high standing. The College was very hopeful of a great future, one omen of which was the fact that, despite the "pecuniary embarrassment of that section upon which it is especially dependent for patronage" there were about one hundred and fifty matriculates in the first session of the newly organized school, and the income was more than adequate to cover all the expenses of re-establishing the school. No other medical school had had such success so early in its career. The location of the school in the City of Baltimore was a favorable factor. The city was not only a place of many interests but in addition, had a great abundance of clinical material. The townspeople were neither exposed to the vicissitudes of a northern climate nor the fatal epidemics of the South. The people of Baltimore were persons of patriotism, social virtue and devoted to the principles of Constitutional liberty and the traditions of their fathers. Among them "no noxious political dogmas" could germinate, and no white man, regardless of his opinions or antecedents would be denied the right to think, speak and act as his conscience directed, fearless of "bayonets or bastiles", said the Announcement. Numerous factors conspired to make Baltimore a good place in which to study medicine, the city having all the essentials for a thorough medical education, "in an atmosphere of freedom among a fraternal, sympathizing and independent people".

Because the young men of the South had suffered from the misfortunes of the Civil War, the College, prompted by the desire to do something helpful for them, had determined to accept one student from each Congressional District of the former slave-holding States, as a "beneficiary" of Washington University, precedence going to wounded and disabled soldiers. (In 1870, the Announcement read "sons of physicians and clergymen, and to wounded and disabled soldiers".) This, said the University, was being done out of sympathy for those who were struggling against "the poverty and mutilation" which militated against obtaining a medical education. The school was glad to take the opportunity of helping these victims of the War, regretting only that it could not fling open its doors to all "who have thus served and suffered". Such students paid a fee of $35.00, (until 1871, when the fee was raised to $55.00). In addition to these scholarships, the Maryland Legislature, in return for its assistance to the school hospital, required the institution to educate, annually, one student from each Senatorial District of the State, free of charge, except for payment of matriculation, ($5.00), dissection, ($10.00), and graduation ($20.00), fees. (In 1875, this was reduced to $20.00.) The University stated that the identity of such students would remain undisclosed, in deference to their sensibilities. (Since these students paid $35.00 for each session, in effect they paid the graduation fee twice.)

The strongly sectionalist spirit is clearly discernible in the Announcement for the next year, (1869). This publication proudly presents all of its talented and well-known professors as Southern born (except Dr. Reuling) and active participants "in the late contest for truth and Southern liberty", in which they ministered to the sufferings of thousands of their compatriots who now gratefully acknowledge "indebtedness for their tender and skillful care". Despite the lack of affluence of the South, three hundred students, representing nearly all of the Southern States (see Recapitulation below), "were in actual attendance upon its lectures the past two sessions", with indications that the next session would be even better patronized. The same sectionalist spirit is shown as late as 1872, when the school refers to itself as a Southern Medical School, (in italics).

STATES FROM WHICH STUDENTS WERE DRAWN (SESSION OF 1868-69)
RECAPITULATION BY STATES

Virginia	45
North Carolina	38
Maryland	27
Alabama	12
South Carolina	9
Tennessee	5
Georgia	4
Mississippi	4
Missouri	3
Arkansas	2
Florida	1
Kentucky	1
Delaware	1
Nebraska	1
District of Columbia	1
England	1
	155 1869

The Announcement for 1873 claimed that the total matriculation from 1867 to date was about 900, of whom 320 had won the M.D. degree. Among these were some of the most promising young doctors of the country. Many of the Southern students who had journeyed to Baltimore in order to obtain an education in medicine, had chosen Washington University, and now could testify to its superiority.(1)

For about six years the enrollment was high; the school seemed to be competing well with the University of Maryland, and its prosperity augured well for a long and successful life. However, in 1872, disagreement among the members of the Faculty resulted in the resignation of Dr. Warren, who joined with other recently-arrived physicians in the city to found another medical School – the College of Physicians and Surgeons of Baltimore. Many members of the Faculty resigned in a short period of time, and satisfactory replacements were difficult to find. The school lost prestige, and with it, the prosperity resulting from the large enrollment which it had earlier enjoyed. The fees were revised downward in order the better to compete with the other two Baltimore schools. This measure proved unavailing. In the Spring of 1877 the school decided that it had had enough, and entered into an agreement with the College of Physicians and Surgeons to transfer to that school all of its franchises and property. The merger was confirmed by Act of Legislature in due time. J. Thomas Scharf, in *History of Baltimore City and County*, states (p. 738) that the total number of graduates of both periods in the life of Washington University was about seven hundred. The figures resulting from the present study add to a total of 648, with data for five classes of the first period missing.

A sad phase of the history of Washington University School of Medicine relates to its quarrel with the Medical Department of the University of Louisiana. In July, 1871, the latter school disseminated among the medical schools of our country, a circular condemning the diploma of Washington University, as based upon inadequate instruction, and stating that this diploma should not be recognized.

Washington University, on July 25, 1871, replied to this attack by publishing: *"A Statement of Facts in Reference to an Assault upon Washington University . . . "*, (Baltimore, 1871, 7 pp.) In this publication, the University stated that Dean Chancellor had received a letter on March 7, 1871, from a student at the University of Louisiana, asking for information about the regular summer course at Washington. The student said that he had attended the lectures on anatomy, materia medica, physiology and chemistry, and had had a full course in practical anatomy, all at the University of Louisiana. He had also read "a little on Surgery, Practice of Medicine, etc." He asked whether the combination of the summer course at Washington, plus the work which he had already done at Louisiana, would count as one course, and would he not be entitled to graduate at the end of the next winter session by attending Washington for that session. On March 11, 1871, Dean Chancellor wrote the student that the partial course at Louisiana, plus the summer course at Washington, would count as one full winter session, and that he could therefore present himself for graduation after attending the summer course and the following winter course.

Thereupon Dean Richardson of the Medical Department of the University of Louisiana, wrote Dr. Chancellor (April 15, 1871), inquiring whether the report was true that one of its students had been informed that, although only a partial student, "who had commenced the study of Medicine less than a year ago" he could, by attending the lectures that summer and the following winter at Washington, have "the privilege of appearing next Spring for the degree of

Doctor of Medicine, before the Faculty of the Medical Department of Washington University".

Dr. Chancellor, on April 22nd, replied that since Washington's summer course was in every respect a full course, there was no reason to deny the Louisiana student the same privilege which "we would grant to students from other accredited Colleges", a procedure conforming with the ethics and general usages of all Medical schools.

The result was the circular of July, 1871, alluded to above, in which the correspondence between the two schools was made public, the announcement made that the Louisiana school would not recognize the diploma and tickets of Washington University as long as it pursued its present policy, and the request made that all medical schools join in similarly denying recognition.

In the *Statement of Facts* etc., Dean Chancellor pointed out that there could be no objection that the two year period of medical instruction had been curtailed, for the student would be required to pass the full courses of lectures in two successive years, one at Louisiana and one at Washington, a procedure "strictly in accordance with the rule established by the American Medical Association. (See Vol. 13, 1860, page 33, of the transactions of that body.)" The Dean pointed out that there was here no lowering of standards, as the student would have had his two full required courses at Washington, plus the work at Louisiana, i.e., actually he would have had not *less*, but *more*, work than required, and he expressed his mystification as to the grounds for the action of the Louisiana school, and left it to sister schools to reach their own judgments.

The Commencement Address on February 22, 1872, delivered by H. Clay Dallam, Esq., Secretary of the Board of Visitors, is of some interest.

Mr. Dallam tells us that the effort to reopen the medical school in 1867 "was liberally encouraged by aid from the State and City", and the motive was neither hostility toward nor rivalry of the University of Maryland, but rather the commendable one of helping "advance and promote the cause of sound scientific medical education". Indeed, there were graduates of the University of Maryland on the Board of Visitors of Washington. All true scientists recognize the fact that there is no room for petty jelousies and animosities, and that sister institutions must always live in harmony, any rivalry being limited to efforts to excel each other in the quality of teaching. The time for reoganizing the school was regarded as highly propitious. In common with their brothers of the South, Marylanders believed that the reopening of the school could "arrest the tide that tended Northward, and offer to the young men of the South congenial homes, hospitable welcomes, and all the advantages for professional study that can be found in the most favored institutions in the land". The steady growth of the school had shown how wise the State and City had been in lending a helping hand. This aid imposed an obligation in discharge of which a hospital, in which patients from every district of the State and City would be treated, free of charge, had been organized, and placed under control of the Faculty. Cases of contagious disease could be removed from the crowded areas, and placed in the hospital, thus preventing the spread of these disorders, at the same time providing facilities for clinical instruction, by experienced teachers.(2) A double blessing resulted – the great boon to the suffering poor, and an opportunity for students of medicine to acquire the knowledge and experience which only hospital practice can give.

In the ancient world little was done by society to help the mentally afflicted. Hospitals for lunatics were unknown, the first such institution in Europe coming into existence in the fifteenth Century. Prior to that time the poor demented person was made an outcast, or excommunicated by the Church, as a witch or one possessed by demons (and sometimes put to death). But the distinguished feature of modern civilization is the care which society takes of the afflicted and suffering, for which more credit is due to the medical profession than to any other agency. "The cruelties of theological narrow-mindedness and superstition, after inflicting untold horrors on the poor unfortunates" gave way before medical progress. Morgagni in Italy, Cullen in Scotland, and Pinel in France, revolutionized the treatment of the insane, and two great benefits resulted: First, by segregating such cases and studying them, professors were able to relieve or cure some of the cases hitherto considered incurable; Second, the critical examination and comparison resulting from this close study of the demented, caused many obscure points among the problems of lunacy to be cleared up and brought about permanent advance in the treatment of nervous functional derangement.

Mr. Dallam told the graduates that they might hear the old cry: Fuge medicos et medicamenta, si vis esse salvus. Yet the man who in good health laughs the most at doctors is, when ill, generally the first to send for one, and many persons, writhing in pain and having to decide between priest and physician, would rather "take his chances with the latter".

Where medical education has most flourished, there the average life span has most lengthened, and infant mortality most diminished. In London, where eighty years ago annual mortality was five per cent, it is now a fraction above two. In France, at the close of the eighteenth century, the average life lasted less than twenty-nine years, but in 1853 it had risen to thirty-three years. Infant mortality before the age of five, one hundred years ago, was seventy-five percent. Now it is twenty-five percent. Much of this progress is due to growth of medical science.

Despite the great progress, no field is more inviting for those who feel any ambition to make discoveries. William Lecky, in *The History of European Morals*, has said that medicine is the field in which accomplished results are most obviously imperfect and in which unrealized possibilities are most extensive, but in which the most wonderful results might be expected if the human mind gave itself to the problems of medicine, as it has during the past century, to industrial invention, "and especially to overcoming space". We are almost entirely ignorant of the causes of some of the most fatal diseases. Inhalation causes most diseases and effects most cures, yet the medicine of inhalation is in its infancy. The medical powers of electricity are still unexplored. The proved possibility of controlling the emotions and feelings by external suggestion may yet teach us how to alleviate pain and perhaps contribute to "that euthanasia which Bacon proposed to physicians as an end of their art". But the greatest advance in medicine, or in any other field, would be the raising of moral pathology to a science, and the unification of the many fragmentary observations which have already been made. Mind and body react upon each other. Every passion or characteristic tendency probably has a physical predisposing cause, and if we were acquainted with these, we might be able to treat, by medicine, the many varieties of moral disease, as we treat physical disease, at present. Such knowledge would have other great scientific value, for it would enable us to deal with the moral influence of climate, and place the great question of the influence of race on the firm basis of experiment, complementing the labors of the historian.

Mr. Dallam pleaded with the graduates to be undismayed by the magnitude and profundity of these unsolved problems in medicine, but, instead, to try to make their own contribution to the art.

He reminded his audience of the discovery by three chemists, forty years earlier, of chloroform. Doctors later discovered what a valuable medical ally it was. This story should teach the importance of scientific experimentation. For he that seeketh, assuredly findeth. He counseled the graduates against losing their tempers if:

"after a most skillful and successful treatment you sometimes find a patient who utterly fails to recognize what you have done for him, or attributes what is directly due to your skill to the fashionable quack of the neighborhood who is called in when the crisis has passed and the patient is convalescent, only to pluck the laurels that are rightly yours. And even when this is not the case, the recovery due to your treatment is often credited to the recuperative powers of the patient, and with his restoration you are forgotten, and probably your bill disputed. For it is true:

'God and the doctor we like adore,
Just on the brink of danger – not before;
The danger past, both are alike requited –
God is forgotten, and the doctor slighted.'"

As Sir Astley Cooper made only five guineas in the first year of his practice, twenty-six pounds in the second year, and thirty-four in the third, "but in these weary waiting days . . . acquired that knowledge which, in after years, brought him boundless fame and fortune", so the young doctor should not become discouraged while he awaits "calls".

I. BUILDINGS AND EQUIPMENT

The first four sessions (1867-68 to 1870-71, inclusive), were held in a large building, recently renovated to make it as suitable as possible (after having originally served as a warehouse), located at the northeast corner of Calvert and Saratoga Streets. There was a free college dispensary for the treatment of the poor, where from ten to twenty patients came each day. Facilities for the study of practical anatomy, which received particular attention, were claimed to be as good as at any medical school in the country. There were models, paintings and diagrams "executed by a skillful artist, under the direction and supervision of the Professor of Anatomy", many preparations of organs and tissues, and an abundant supply of dissecting material. (The dissecting rooms were open every day but Sunday, during the session, until 10 pm.) There were many plates, diagrams and models for teaching obstetrics, and adequate supplies for teaching chemistry.

Eugene F. Cordell tells us that a State appropriation in 1868 enabled the College to *purchase*, not erect, the building, and ground on the opposite corner, (northwest corner of the same intersection, i.e., Calvert and Saratoga Streets), from the Mayor and City Council of Baltimore, at so low a figure, that it practically amounted to a donation. The building was fitted up as a hospital, (under exclusive control of the Faculty), with lecture rooms and "other conveniences" for instruction, and came into use in 1871. (However, the Announcement for 1872 says that the Faculty had *"erected a new and commodious . . . building in connection with their hospital . . . the Student may now pass directly from the Lecture room into the Hospital wards, where he can observe at the bedside the characteristic symptoms of disease, and witness the result of treatment in each case.").* [3]

The Announcement for 1875 states that a new building, especially adapted for dissection, well lighted and ventilated, and equipped with all modern improvements, was in process of construction, and would be ready for that session. From the Announcement for the next year, we learn that the hospital had been enlarged by the addition of five wards, and was under the charge of the Sisters of Mercy. The free dispensary had likewise been enlarged and "suitable appliances provided for the treatment of diseases of women, of eye and ear, of throat and chest, and of the nervous system". The additional building promised in the previous year, housing a dissecting room, (as well as a laboratory and a museum), had indeed been erected.

It is to be regretted that nothing else concerning apparatus and equipment can be ascertained from a study of the Announcements.

II. CURRICULUM

The regular session of the Washington University ran for about five months, (from the first day of October until a date late in February). Also a four months' summer course, "as complete as the winter course, and so recognized in the requirements for graduation", was given by the Adjunct Faculty, from early April until late July, (or early March until late June), but no mention of such a session is made after the year 1873.

Emphasis was laid upon clinical instruction and facilities for providing it. Lectures were illustrated by cases of disease and injury presented and thoroughly explained to the class. Thus didactic and practical knowledge were blended. Part of each lecture period was devoted to a quiz on the previous lecture. Students had access to Bay-view Asylum and numerous hospitals of the city (Baltimore Special Dispensary, Southern, Eastern and General Dispensary, St. Agnes Hospital, the Home of the Friendless, Union Protestant Infirmary, etc.), as well as the great advantages of the daily public clinic of the College Dispensary, where the abundance of opportunities to learn equalled that at "the oldest and best endowed schools", claimed the University.

Students were encouraged to observe, examine, study and record facts from personal observation, thus acquiring ability to investigate, and experience in treating disease in its various manifestations. The class was divided into two sections, each half receiving special instruction in diagnosis and treatment of disease, at the bedside. An effort was made to force students to think out for themselves the relation between phenomena and treatment.

As we have already noted above, another feature which the University felt to be a cause for reasonable pride was the particular attention given to practical anatomy, and it repeatedly stressed the fact that a student could, under the guidance of the University's Demonstrator, acquire a practical knowledge of the body in all its parts.

Of some interest is the fact that in 1868 there was a professor of microscopic anatomy and practical physiology, but no permanent chair was established, and no further mention is made of the course, after that date.

From the Announcement for 1869 we learn the following details about the lectures:

SURGERY

The great object of the professor was to "embalm theory with fact", i.e., to demonstrate his lectures by teaching at bedside and clinical amphitheatre. His text-book was mainly the skeleton, the cadaver and the patient, and upon these he depended for principles and illustrations. There were great numbers and varieties of cases treated, and operations performed in the presence of the class.

OBSTETRICS

This was a full and practical course, illustrated by plates and diagrams. The signs of pregnancy, its diseases and their relief, the period of utero-gestation and signs of approaching labor, natural labor, management of placenta, tedious, preternatural, complex or anomalous labor, were all considered. Obstetrical instruments were explained, and their use demonstrated on the manikin.

PHYSIOLOGY

The structure and functions of the various organs of the body, in health and disease, latest discoveries in this field, and emphasis upon "the physiology of the brain and nervous system, secretory system, vascular system, etc., etc." were taught and demonstrated.

MATERIA MEDICA AND THERAPEUTICS

The principles of classification, arrangement and nomenclature of sources of food, medicines and poisons. The professor selected what was most interesting, reduced it to order and method, built up a system of therapeutics in which was stated and explained the particular operation of each class and individual species upon the living body. Particular attention was "paid to the neat and classical method of writing prescriptions, etc."

DISEASES OF WOMEN AND CHILDREN

An explanation of the sexual characteristics of the female constitution, its numerous derangements and their treatment, the various displacements of the uterus and many of its diseases were taught from accurate plates and models, and the different theories of generation and menstruation, causes of female sterility and its relief, management of infants and children and their diseases, were all taught.

MEDICAL JURISPRUDENCE AND HYGIENE

The College claimed as thorough a course as any given elsewhere in America. All of the leading and most recent doctrines of Judicial Medicine were dealt with, because of the importance of this area of learning to the interests of Society. Particular attention was paid to the subject of hygiene – the influence of climate, soil, food, sleep, clothing, exercise upon body and mind, the passions of the mind, and the various trades and occupations as direct or indirect sources of disease. Attention was given to the "sensible and adventitious qualities of the atmosphere . . . in the production of Endemic and Epidemic disorders."

CHEMISTRY

All of "the facts and doctrines of the science, which tend to the preservation and recovery of health" were taught and illustrated. The best mode of preparing medicines, "how they are altered by mixture", and detection of adulteration and fraud were also taught.

ANATOMY

Beginning with a brief consideration of the history of anatomy, the lecturer went on to a consideration of the principal parts of the body, the use of each and the manner of their connection, thus giving a general idea of the animal economy. Particular attention was given in the demonstrations, to the relative anatomy of parts, and how this knowledge can be applied to practical purposes. The lectures were illustrated by use of models, plates, anatomical preparations and ample dissections.

THEORY AND PRACTICE OF MEDICINE

A description of the various diseases, so arranged as to enable the student to acquire a knowledge of the character, cause, means for prevention and cure of each. The wards of the college hospital were drawn upon for observing the application of the principles taught in the lectures, and obtaining a practical knowledge of the symptoms, causes and treatment of the commonest maladies of our climate and country.

OPHTHALMIC AND AURAL SURGERY

In order to enhance the instructional facilities at Washington University, and render them at least equal to any school, a chair in this subject was created, without raising the costs paid by students. Dr. George Reuling, a specialist who had had a great deal of experience in European hospitals, was appointed to the new professorship for the session 1869-70, (after which the chair ceased to exist).

There were special lectures, dealing with such subjects as: genito-urinary organs, ophthalmic and oral surgery, physical diagnosis, etc.

Advanced students who wished to give particular attention to special branches of medicine or surgery could have ample opportunity to work with competent teachers in those fields.

CLINIC AND HOSPITALS

The first announcement of the University, upon its resumption in 1867, promised a daily public clinic (where a student could receive thorough instruction in every variety of disease and injury, and become acquainted with the practical applications of remedial agents) and an infirmary, to serve as the nucleus of an extensive hospital. In addition, arrangements had been made to permit students of Washington University to profit from the educational opportunities of the public hospitals of the city. In 1868 a special clinic for eye and ear, held every Saturday during the session, was announced. The diseases, anatomy and physiology of these organs would be investigated, in the presence of the class, "the most modern and improved instruments for diagnosis being employed and explained at the same time". Ample opportunity was to be afforded to those interested, to give particular attention to Endoscopy, Laryngoscopy, Rhinoscopy, Percussion and Auscultation, Diseases of the genito-urinary organs, skin, etc.

The Announcement for 1869 speaks of the advantages which the University hospital has for treating private patients, where there were attentive nurses and every convenience for the care of the sick. The building was located with an eye for convenience of transportation from all parts of the city, had "large and well ventilated wards, and comfortably furnished private rooms", and was "surrounded by ample ornamental grounds to which patients have free access". There were Medical, Surgical, Lying-in and Eye and Ear Wards. All cases, medical and surgical, were admitted, except those of contagious diseases. There were experienced nurses for women during confinement. The Medical and Surgical Staff consisted of the professors of the University, but members of the profession in good standing could attend their patients in the hospital. There was an experienced physician in residence in the hospital, and he was ready to give "impartial attention to all patients". The charges were:

General Wards, per week ("invariably in advance") $4.00
Private Rooms, per week . . . . $7.00 to $15.00

In that year the Announcement reported that in the previous year the free dispensary had furnished three thousand prescriptions, to patients suffering from "every variety of disease". The City of Baltimore made general annual contributions to sustain this work.

In 1873 the dispensary and wards of the hospital had 9,368 patients, of which 838 were casualties. Advanced students, under the supervision of the professors, ministered to a number of obstetrical cases. There were from forty to fifty dispensary patients daily, (among which there were "cutaneous, infantile, syphilitic and other diseases", and cases some of which afforded the students the opportunity of performing many minor surgical operations.

In 1874, there were 6,364 patients in the hospital and dispensaries. Among these, there were 495 "indoor" patients, 927 surgical cases, (comprising fractures, dislocations, every variety of wounds, strangulated hernia), burns, scalds, frost bites, poisonings, 200 eye and ear cases, 355 throat cases, 205 cases of diseases of the chest, and 302 cases of women's diseases. The hospital had practically become the casualty hospital of Baltimore, and so far as possible, all accident cases were treated in the presence of the class in order to familiarize students with methods of managing recent injuries, effects of shock, hemorrhage, indications for primary and secondary amputation, etc. In 1875, there were 1,020 patients in the hospital, and 7,257 persons were treated in the dispensary, the cases being almost endless in variety. Seven clinics were held:

Monday		1 PM	Medical	Prof. Arnold
Tuesday		1 PM	Cutaneous and Syphilitic	Prof. Page
Wednesday		1 PM	Surgical	Prof. Monmonier
Thursday		1 PM	Throat and Laryngoscopic Cases	Dr. Hartman
Friday		1 PM	Eye and Ear Diseases	Prof. White
Saturday	a)	12 M	Nervous System	Dr. Van Bibber
	b)	1 PM	Diseases of Women and Children	Prof. Scott

In 1876, the changes in the schedule above were as follows:

Tuesday:	Clinic in the hands of Dr. Green
Wednesday:	Profs. Monmonier and Walker
Saturday:	Clinic in the hands of Prof. Monmonier

(Clinical instruction was given free to all students of medicine during vacations, daily from 12 M to 2 PM.)

FROM THE ANNOUNCEMENT FOR 1868

THE FOLLOWING DISEASES
Have received proper Medical Treatment at the College Clinic since October 1st, 1867.

Amenorrhoea
Anasarca
Anaemia
Angina Pectoris
Ascarides
Ascites
Asthma
Bronchitis, Acute
Bronchitis, Chronic
Catarrh
Cardiac Dropsy
Cephalalgia
Colic
Constipation
Coryza
Crustea lactea
Cystitis
Debility
Diarrhoea
Dysentery
Dysmenorrhoea

Dyspepsia
Endocarditis
Enteritis
Erysipelas
Fever, continued
Fever, Intermittent
Fever, Remittent
Functional Dis. of Heart
Gastritis
Gastrodynia
General Debility
Gout
Haemoptysis
Hemiplegia
Hepatitis
Hypertrophy of Heart
Hypertrophy of Spleen
Hysteria
Incontinence of Urine
Indigestion
Influenza
Intestinal Worms
Jaundice
Laryngitis
Lead Palsy
Leucorrhoea
Lumbago
Menorrhagia
Metritis
Nephritis
Neuralgia
Odontalgia
Otitis
Otorrhoea
Oedema
Paralysis
Paraplegia
Parotitis
Pertussis
Pharyngitis
Phthisis, Incip't.
Phthisis, Confirmed
Phthisis, Catarrhal
Phthisis, Laryngeal
Phthisis, Tubercular
Phosphatic Diath
Pluritis, Acute
Pluritis, Chronic
Plurodynia
Pneumonia
Portal Congestion
Rheumatism, Acute
Rheumatism, Chronic
Rheumatism, Gonorrhoeal
Salivation of Pregnancy
Sciatica
Scurvy
Scrofula
Splenitis
Spinal Irritation
Syncope
Stomatitis
Tonsilitis, Imf.
Tonsilitis, Follicular
Tubercle
Vertigo

THE FOLLOWING DISEASES AND INJURIES
Have received proper Surgical Treatment at the College
Clinic since October 1st, 1867.

Abscess of Axillary Glands
Abscess of Cervical Glands
Abscess of Lachrymal Glands
Abscess of Mammary Glands
Adenitis
Amaurosis
Amblyopy
Anchylosis of Elbow Joint
Anchylosis of Knee Joint
Atrophy, Muscular
Atrophy, of Testicle
Balanitis
Bronchocele
Bubonocele
Burns
Bubo
Caries
Cataract, all varieties
Concussion of Brain
Concussion of Spinal Cord
Contusions, all varieties
Conjunctivitis, all varieties
Chancre, Hard
Chancre, Soft
Chancre, Urethral
Choroiditis
Coxalgia, all varieties
Dislocations of Elbow
Dislocations of Hip
Dislocations of Phalanges
Dislocation of Shoulder
Dislocations of Wrist
Dysuria
Ecthyma
Eczema
Enlarged Prostate
Epididimitis
Erysipelas
Erythema
Fistula, Anal
Fistula, Lachrymal
Fractures of Clavicle
Fractures of Exp. Cond. Hum.
Fractures of Int. Cond. Hum.
Fractures of Femur
Fractures of Phalanges
Fractures of Radius
Fractures of Ribs
Fractures of Tibia
Fractures of Ununited
Gangrene
Gleet
Gonorrhoea
Granular lids
Hemorrhoids
Hernia
Herpes
Iritis, Rheumatic
Iritis, Scrofulous
Iritis, Syphilitic
Keratitis, all varieties
Lipoma
Mentagra
Mydriasis
Myosis
Necrosis of Femur
Necrosis of Maxillary Bone
Necrosis of Nasal Bone
Necrosis of Oscalcis
Necrosis of Radius
Necrosis of Ulnar
Neuromata
Onychia
Ophthalmia, all varieties
Orchitis
Osteo Sarcoma
Ozena, Catarrhal
Ozena, Scrofulous

Ozena, Syphilitic
Paraphymosis
Phymosis
Palypus Nasal
Pott's Disease
Rupia
Sclerotitis
Scorbutus
Scrofula, all forms
Spermatorrhoea
Sprains
Stricture of Urethra
Stump, Ulceration of
Sublaxations
Synovitis
Syphilis, Primary
Syphilis, Secondary
Syphilis, Tertiary
Talipes
Tonsilitis
Tumours, all varieties
Ulcers, Irritable
Ulcers, Indolent
Ulcers, varicose
Ulcers, syphilitic
Ulceration of Cornea
Urinary Infiltration
Urethritis
Varicose Veins of Leg
Varicocele
Whitlow
Wounds of various parts
Wounds, Gunshot
Wounds, Contused
Wounds, Incised
Wounds, Lacerated
Wounds, Poisoned
Wounds, Punctured

REQUIREMENTS FOR GRADUATION

> 1867 – a student must "prove to the satisfaction of the Faculty that he is of good moral character, has studied the usual time, and has attended two regular courses of lectures, one of which must have been in this University," before he was allowed to take the examination. A thesis on some medical subject, in either English, German, French, or Latin, (accompanied by the graduation fee), was also required.

The Announcements from 1868 until 1870, inclusive, state that "public examinations are regularly held by the different professors, and it is expected that candidates for graduation will attend them." After that date, and until 1875, nothing is specified about moral character (nor had anything been stated earlier about years of apprenticeship to another physician), the stated requirements being two courses, a thesis and "a satisfactory examination before the Faculty".

In 1871, a University statute read:

> "Students who have attended one full course of Medical Lectures in an accredited College may present themselves for examination after attendance on the Summer Course in this College, and should their examinations prove satisfactory, a *Certificate of Honor* will be awarded, which will admit them to the ensuing Winter Course *free of charge*, and will entitle them, at the expiration of this term, to a Diploma from the Institution.
>
> Candidates who have attended two full sessions of an accredited Medical School may graduate after attendance on the Summer Course alone."

In 1873, the summer session, (of four months duration), was regarded, in every respect, as "thorough and complete as the winter course, and is so recognized in the requirements for graduation". Attendance upon two regular courses was still a prerequisite to graduation, "but the diploma of a respectable dental college, or four years continuous study and practice of medicine, is received as the equivalent of one full term of lectures, and students presenting satisfactory evidence of such preparation will be permitted to offer for graduation in this school after attendance upon one of its sessions."

In 1874, the requirements remained the same, but the degree would "not be conferred upon any candidate who absents himself from the public commencement without special permission of the Faculty".

In 1875, the requirements included that the age of twenty-one be attained, that the candidate be of good moral character, have had two courses, written a thesis, passed an examination, and *taken a course in practical anatomy, under the guidance of a Demonstrator of Anatomy*. He must also be present at the commencement exercises.

The Announcement for 1868 reported that a number of persons who bore the University good will, and who wished to "encourage a legitimate spirit of emulation among its students", had placed one hundred dollars in the hands of the Faculty, to be awarded as a prize for the best thesis by a candidate for graduation, the decision to be announced and the award made at the next Commencement.

FEES (1867-1871, inclusive)

Matriculation	$ 5.00
Dissection	10.00
Professors	120.00

Graduation 20.00
Beneficiary (scholarship) 35.00
(fluctuating slightly for some years)

Graduates of other respectable medical schools paid matriculation, dissection and graduation fees only.

The fee for the full course of summer lectures was $75.00.

FEES (1872 and 1873)

Full Course of Lectures, including
Dissection and Hospital Tickets $65.00
Matriculation Fee, (paid but once) 5.00
Graduation Fee 20.00

(The decline in cost of tickets was probably due to vanishing popularity and the rise of competition. A student was permitted to take only such tickets in the departments of instruction as were desired, upon payment of the matriculation fee and $10.00 for each ticket.)

FEES (1874 to 1876, inclusive)

Full Course of Lectures, including Hospital Tickets,
First Year $60.00
Second Year 50.00
For each succeeding year of attendance 20.00
Dissection, including a sufficient quantity of material 15.00
Matriculation Fee, (paid but once) 5.00
Graduation Fee 20.00

The payment of $100 entitled a student to a perpetual ticket, exclusive of graduation and dissection fees. If he so desired, a person could be a resident student of the hospital, upon payment of $25. per month, which entitled him to "board and commons." Graduates of the University were permitted to attend lectures free of charge, and graduates of other schools, after three years of practice, were required to pay matriculation fee only, but prior to three years of practice such graduates paid a fee for a general ticket, at $25.00, and a matriculation fee.

Board could be had, from $4.50 to $7.00 per week, (1867). In 1868 "excellent board" cost $5.00 to $6.00 per week, (and patients who wished to have the medical services of the professors of the Faculty could "be supplied with private rooms, nursing and medicines, at from $5.00 to $10.00 per week, according to the accommodations furnished". This rose, in 1869, to $7.00 to $15.00). Later Announcements, (1872 and on), stated that board could be had at from $3.00 or $4.00, to $6.00 per week.

III. (A) FACULTY

Session of 1867-68(4)

Rev. THOMAS E. BOND, M.D., President
GEORGE C. M. ROBERTS, M.D., L.L.D., Emeritus Professor of
Obstetrics and Diseases of Women & Children.
A. J. FOARD, M.D., Professor of Descriptive and
Surgical Anatomy, and Dean.
JOSEPH P. LOGAN, M.D., Professor of the
Principles and Practice of Medicine.
HARVEY L. BYRD, M.D., Professor of Obstetrics.
MARTIN P. SCOTT, M.D., Professor of Diseases of Women and Children.
EDWARD WARREN, M.D., Professor of the Principles and Practice of Surgery.
JOHN F. MONMONIER, M.D., Professor of Physiology and General Pathology.
JAMES J. MOORMAN, M.D., Professor of Medical Jurisprudence and Hygiene.
JOSEPH E. CLAGETT, M.D., Professor of Materia Medica and Therapeutics.
CLARENCE MORFIT, M.D., Professor of Medical Chemistry and Pharmacy.
JOHN N. MONMONIER, M.D., Demonstrator of Anatomy.

The members of the Adjunct Faculty gave the lectures of the summer course. For the summer session, supplementary to the regular 1867 session (i.e., held in the Spring of 1868), the following persons made up the Adjunct Faculty:

THURMER H. WINGFIELD, M.D., Adjunct to the Chair
of the Institutes of Medicine.
ALFRED H. POWELL, M.D., Adjunct to the Chair of Surgery.
JOHN N. MONMONIER, M.D., Adjunct to the Chair of Anatomy.
CHARLES M. MORFIT, M.D., Adjunct to the Chair of Practice.
C. SHIRLEY CARTER, M.D., Adjunct to the Chair of Obstetrics.
WM. LEE, M.D., Adjunct to the Chair of Materia Medica and Therapeutics.

JAMES E. LINDSAY, M.D., Adjunct to the Chair of Chemistry.
R. WYSONG, M.D., Adjunct to the Chair of Diseases of Women and Children.

BOARD OF VISITORS

ELI J. HENKLE, M.D., President
JAMES MONTGOMERY, M.D., Vice President
H. CLAY DALLAM, Esq., Secretary
Col. JAMES R. HERBERT, Treasurer

Hon. Oden Bowie
Hon. James T. Earle
Hon. Reverdy Johnson
Rev. Thomas E. Bond, M.D.
Rev. Richard Fuller, D.D.
Rev. Henry A. Wise, Jr.
Edward J. Chaisty, M.D.
E. Hall Richardson, M.D.
Peter W. Hairston, Esq.
Charles Marshall, Esq.
Sam'l W. Smith, Esq.
Hon. Thomas Swann
Hon. James M. Buchanan
Hon. Edwin H. Webster
Rev. James J. Bullock, M.D.
Rev. John B. Ross, M.D.
Rev. C. M. Callaway
Thos. W. Hammond, M.D.
John C. Parker, M.D.
Robert J. Brent, Esq.
Alexander H. Hobbs, Esq.
Alexander Hagner, Esq.
David T. McLaughlin, M.D.

SESSION OF 1868-69

The Faculty was the same as that of 1867 except for the following: Dr. Foard was replaced by Charles W. Chancellor, M.D., and Frances T. Miles, M.D. held the new chair of Microscopic Anatomy and Practical Physiology. Joseph P. Logan was Dean.

ADJUNCT FACULTY

THURMER H. WINGFIELD, M.D.
Adjunct to the Chair of Physiology
ALFRED H. POWELL, M.D.
Adjunct to the Chair of Surgery
CHARLES M. MORFIT, M.D.
Adjunct to the Chair of Practice
R. WYSONG, M.D.
Adjunct to the Chair of Diseases of Women and Children
C. SHIRLEY CARTER, M.D.
Adjunct to the Chair of Obstetrics
JAMES E. LINDSAY, M.D.
Adjunct to the Chair of Chemistry
WILLIAM LEE, M.D.
Adjunct to the Chair of Materia Medica
JOHN N. MONMONIER, M.D.
Adjunct to the Chair of Anatomy
JACQUELIN A. MARSHALL, M.D.
Adjunct to the Chair of Medical Jurisprudence

SESSION OF 1869-70

FACULTY

Rev. THOMAS E. BOND, M.D., President
GEO. C. M. ROBERTS, M.D., L.L.D.
Emeritus Professor of Obstetrics and Diseases of Women and Children
EDWARD WARREN, M.D.
Professor of the Principles and Practice of Surgery
HARVEY L. BYRD, M.D.
Professor of Obstetrics
JNO. F. MONMONIER, M.D.
Professor of Physiology and General Pathology
JOSEPH E. CLAGETT, M.D.
Professor of Materia Medica and Therapeutics
MARTIN P. SCOTT, M.D.
Professor of the Diseases of Women and Children
JNO. J. MOORMAN, M.D.
Professor of Medical Jurisprudence and Hygiene
CLARENCE MORFIT, M.D.
Professor of Medical Chemistry and Pharmacy

CHARLES W. CHANCELLOR, M.D.
Professor of Descriptive and Surgical Anatomy
D. A. LANGHORNE, M.D.
Professor of the Principles and Practice of Medicine
GEORGE REULING, M.D.
Professor of Ophthalmic and Aural Surgery
ALFRED H. POWELL, M.D.
Demonstrator of Anatomy
C. W. CHANCELLOR, M.D.
Dean of the Faculty

ADJUNCT FACULTY

JAMES E. LINDSAY, M.D.
Adjunct to the Chair of Chemistry
THOMAS OPIE, M.D.
Adjunct to the Chair of Surgery
ALFRED H. POWELL, M.D.
Adjunct to the Chair of Anatomy
THURMER H. WINGFIELD, M.D.
Adjunct to the Chair of Physiology
R. WYSONG, M.D.
Adjunct to the Chair of Diseases of Women and Children
CHAS. M. MORFIT, M.D.
Adjunct to the Chair of Practice
H. L. SPICER, M.D.
Adjunct to the Chair of Obstetrics
P. GOOLRICK, M.D.
Adjunct to the Chair of Materia Medica
JOHN C. WISE, M.D.
Adjunct to the Chair of Medical Jurisprudence and Hygiene

OFFICERS OF THE HOSPITAL

Resident Physicians
JNO. C. WISE, M.D., Va.
W. P. CALDWELL, M.D., W. Va.
Apothecaries
W. W. WHITE, Md.
H. L. LEWIS, Ky.
Resident Students
CHARLES G. HILL, N. C.
S. K. COLEMAN, Miss.
H. P. WOMERSLEY, England
Mrs. RUTH A. PENTZ, Matron

SESSION OF 1870-71

REV. THOMAS E. BOND, M.D., Praeses
EDWARD WARREN, M.D.
Professor of the Principles and Practice of Surgery
HARVEY L. BYRD, M.D.
Professor of Obstetrics
JOHN F. MONMONIER, M.D.
Professor of Physiology and General Pathology
JOSEPH E. CLAGETT, M.D.
Professor of Materia Medica and Therapeutics
MARTIN P. SCOTT, M.D.
Professor of the Diseases of Women and Children
JOHN J. MOORMAN, M.D.
Professor of Medical Jurisprudence and Hygiene
CHARLES W. CHANCELLOR, M.D.
Professor of Descriptive and Surgical Anatomy
JAMES E. LINDSAY, M.D.
Professor of Medical Chemistry and Pharmacy
JOHN RANDOLPH PAGE, M.D.
Professor of the Principles and Practice of Medicine
N. W. LITTELL, M.D.
Clinical Lecturer on Ophthalmology and Aural Surgery

ADJUNCT FACULTY

ALFRED H. POWELL, M.D.
Demonstrator of Anatomy
THOMAS OPIE, M.D.
Adjunct to the Chair of Surgery
THOS. P. TEMPLE, M.D.
Adjunct to the Chair of Practice
H. P. WOMERSLEY, M.D.
Assistant Demonstrator of Anatomy
H. L. SPICER, M.D.
Adjunct to the Chair of Obstetrics
P. GOOLRICK, M.D.
Adjunct to the Chair of Materia Medica
W. G. REGESTER, M.D.
Adjunct to the Chair of Chemistry
CHAS. W. CHANCELLOR, M.D., Dean

SESSION OF 1871-72

The Faculty was the same as that of 1870-71, except that Dr. Warren was replaced as Professor of Principles and Practice of Surgery by George G. Farnandis, M.D., and Dr. Powell of the Adjunct Faculty of 1870-71, became Demonstrator of Anatomy in the regular session. Adjunct Faculty was no longer listed.

SESSION OF 1872-73

REV. THOMAS E. BOND, M.D., Praeses
JOSEPH E. CLAGETT, M.D.
Professor of Obstetrics
JOHN F. MONMONIER, M.D.
Professor of Physiology
MARTIN P. SCOTT, M.D.
Professor of the Diseases of Women and Children
CHARLES W. CHANCELLOR, M.D.
Professor of Descriptive and Surgical Anatomy
JAMES E. LINDSAY, M.D.
Professor of Medical Chemistry and Pharmacy
JOHN RANDOLPH PAGE, M.D.
Professor of the Principles and Practice of Medicine
GEORGE G. FARNANDIS, M.D.
Professor of Surgery
*Professor of Materia Medica and Therapeutics
A. H. POWELL, M.D.
Demonstrator of Anatomy
CHAS. W. CHANCELLOR, M.D., Dean

**The Chair of Materia Medica and Therapeutics will be filled by the beginning of the Session.*

SESSION OF 1873-74

JOSEPH E. CLAGETT, M.D.
Professor of Obstetrics
JOHN F. MONMONIER, M.D.
Professor of Physiology
MARTIN P. SCOTT, M.D.
Professor of the Diseases of Women and Children
CHARLES W. CHANCELLOR, M.D.
Professor of Surgery, and Dean of the Faculty
JAMES E. LINDSAY, M.D.
Professor of Medical Chemistry and Pharmacy
ABRAM B. ARNOLD, M.D.
Professor of the Principles and Practice of Medicine
JOHN S. CONRAD, M.D.
Professor of Materia Medica and Therapeutics
H. B. TRIST, M.D.
Professor of Anatomy
GEO. B. REYNOLDS, M.D.
Demonstrator of Anatomy

SESSION OF 1874-75

The Faculty was the same as that of 1873-74 with the following exceptions: Dr. Chancellor became Emeritus Professor of Surgery, and President of the Faculty; Joseph A. White, M.D., became Professor of Eye and Ear Diseases; William Green, M.D., became Professor of Materia Medica and Therapeutics, Dr. Conrad giving up this chair to become Professor of Surgery in Dr. Chancellor's stead. Dr. Lindsay became Dean. (No Professor of Medical Jurisprudence had been announced, beginning with the Session of 1872-73, until that of 1875.)

SESSION OF 1875-76

CHAS. W. CHANCELLOR, M.D.
Emeritus Professor of Surgery and
President of the Faculty
JOSEPH E. CLAGETT, M.D.
Professor of Obstetrics
MARTIN P. SCOTT, M.D.
Professor of the Diseases of
Women and Children
JOHN F. MONMONIER, M.D.
Professor of Physiology
JAMES E. LINDSAY, M.D.
Professor of Chemistry
ABRAM B. ARNOLD, M.D.
Professor of the Principles and
Practice of Medicine
H. B. TRIST, M.D.
Professor of Anatomy
JOSEPH A. WHITE, M.D.
Professor of Eye and Ear Diseases
WILLIAM GREEN, M.D.
Professor of Materia Medica
and Therapeutics
JOHN N. MONMONIER, M.D.
Professor of Operative and Clinical Surgery
ISHAM R. PAGE, M.D.
Professor of Principles and
Practice of Surgery
GEORGE E. NELSON, A.M.
Lecturer on Medical Jurisprudence
J. H. HARTMAN, M.D.
Lecturer on Diseases of Throat and Chest
JOHN P. VAN BIBBER, M.D.
Clinical Lecturer on Neurology
GEORGE B. REYNOLDS, M.D.
Demonstrator of Anatomy
J. E. LINDSAY, M.D.
Dean of the Faculty

SESSION OF 1876-77

CHAS. W. CHANCELLOR, M.D.
Emeritus Professor of Surgery and
President of the Faculty
JOSEPH E. CLAGETT, M.D.
Professor of Obstetrics
JOHN F. MONMONIER, M.D.
Professor of Diseases of
Women and Children
JAMES E. LINDSAY, M.D.
Professor of Physiology
ABRAM B. ARNOLD, M.D.
Professor of the Principles and
Practice of Medicine
JOSEPH A. WHITE, M.D.
Professor of Eye and Ear Diseases
WILLIAM GREEN, M.D.
Professor of Materia Medica
and Therapeutics
J. N. MONMONIER, M.D.
Professor of Anatomy and
Operative Surgery
P. B. WILSON, M.D.
Professor of Chemistry
EDMUND R. WALKER, M.D.
Professor of the Principles and
Practice of Surgery
GEORGE E. NELSON, A.M.
Lecturer on Medical Jurisprudence
J. H. HARTMAN, M.D.
Lecturer on Diseases of the Throat and Chest
JOHN P. VAN BIBBER, M.D.
Clinical Lecturer on Neurology
WM. F. LOCKWOOD, M.D.
Demonstrator of Anatomy
J. E. LINDSAY, M.D.
Dean of the Faculty

III (B) ALPHABETIZED LIST OF MEMBERS OF THE FACULTY

(For Faculty grouped by year, see previous pages)

ARNOLD, Abram B., M.D.[5] 1873-77
BOND, Thomas E., M.D., President 1867-73
BYRD, Harvy L., M.D.[6] 1867-72
CARTER, C. Shirley, M.D., ... 1867-69
CHANCELLOR, Charles W., M.D. 1868-77
CLAGETT, Joseph E., M.D. 1867-77
CONRAD, John Summerfield, M.D. 1873-75
FARNANDIS, George, M.D. 1871-73
FOARD, A. J., M.D.[7] 1867-68
GOOLRICK, P., M.D. 1869-71
GREEN, William, M.D. 1874-77
HARTMAN, Jacob H., M.D. 1875-77
LANGHORNE, Daniel A., M.D. 1869-70
LEE, William, M.D. 1867-69
LINDSAY, James E., M.D. 1867-77
LITTELL, N. W., M.D. 1870-73
LOCKWOOD, William F., M.D. 1876-77
LOGAN, Joseph P., M.D. 1867-69
MARSHALL, Jacquelin A., M.D. 1868-69
MILES, Francis T., M.D.[8] 1868-69
MONMONIER, John F., M.D. 1867-77
MONMONIER, John N., M.D. 1867-69
1875-77

MOORMAN, John J., M.D. 1867-72
MORFIT, Clarence, M.D. 1867-70
NELSON, George E., M.D. 1875-77
OPIE, Thomas, M.D. 1869-71
PAGE, Isham R., M.D. 1875-76
PAGE, John R., M.D. 1870-73
POWELL, Alfred H., M.D. 1867-73
QUINAN, Pascal A. 1867-67
REGESTER, W. G., M.D. 1870-71
REULING, George, M.D.[9] 1869-70
REYNOLDS, George B., M.D. 1873-76
ROBERTS, George C. M., M.D. 1867-70
SCOTT, Martin P., M.D. 1867-76
SPICER, H. L., M.D. 1869-71
TEMPLE, Thomas P., M.D. 1870-71
TRIST, H. B., M.D. 1873-76
VAN BIBBER, John P., M.D. 1875-77
WALKER, Edmund R., M.D. 1876-77
WARREN, Edward, M.D. 1867-71
WHITE, Joseph A., M.D. 1874-77
WILSON, P. B., M.D. 1876-77
WINGFIELD, Thurmer H., M.D. 1867-70
WISE, John C., M.D. 1869-70
WOMERSLEY, H., M.D. 1870-71
WYSONG, R., M.D. 1867-70

(Eugene F. Cordell, (*op. cit.* pp. 350-1) states that the following were members of the Faculty, but their names do not appear in the Announcements of the University:

GROESBECK, H. J.
HOPKINS, Henry St. George
KLOMAN, W. C.
QUINAN, Pascal A.
WALLS, J. William

IV. TEXT BOOKS

1867

Anatomy – Wilson's or Gray's Anatomy.
Practice of Medicine – Watson's, Aitken's, Flint's, or Dickson's Practice of Medicine.
Surgery – Erichsen's, Druitt's, and Warren's Surgery, and Paget's Surgical Pathology.
Obstetrics – Hodge's, or Meigs' Obstetrics.
Diseases of Women and Children – West on Diseases of Women and Children, and Tanner on Children.
Institutes – Carpenter's or Dalton's Physiology.
Chemistry – Graham's, Turner's or Fownes' Chemistry.
Materia Medica – Wood's, Stillé's or Pereira's Materia Medica.
Medical Jurisprudence – Wharton & Stillé's, or Beck's Medical Jurisprudence.

1868

Practice of Medicine – Watson's, Aitken's or Flint's Practice.
Surgery – Erichsen's, Druitt's or Warren's Surgery.
Anatomy – Wilson's or Gray's Anatomy.
Obstetrics – Hodge's or Meig's Obstetrics.
Diseases of Women and Children – West on Diseases of Women and Children, Tanner on Diseases of Children.
Physiology and Pathology – Kirke's, Carpenter's or Dalton's Physiology.
Materia Medica and Therapeutics – Wood's, Stillé's, Biddle's or Waring's Therapeutics, and U. S. Dispensatory.
Medical Jurisprudence and Hygiene – Wharton and Stillé's or Beck's Jurisprudence.
Chemistry – Fownes' Chemistry.

1869 and 1870

Same as for 1868, except that Marshall's *Outlines of Physiology* replaced Kirke.

1871

Same as for 1868, except that:

In surgery Warren was no longer used; in physiology Kirke had been replaced by Marshall (in 1869), and in chemistry Odling was added.

1872

Practice of Medicine – Watson, Aitken or Flint.
Surgery – Erichsen or Druitt.
Anatomy – Wilson or Gray.
Obstetrics – Hodge, Meigs or Cazeaux.
Diseases of Women or Children – West or Hewett; Tanner on Diseases of Children.
Physiology – Carpenter or Marshall.
Materia Medica and Therapeutics – Wood, Stillé, Biddle or Waring, and U. S. Dispensatory.
Chemistry – Fownes or Attfield.

1874

Practice of Medicine – Watson, Aitken, or Flint.
Surgery – Erichsen, Druitt, or Hamilton.
Anatomy – Wilson, or Gray.
Obstetrics – Hodge, Meigs, Cazeaux, or Smith.
Diseases of Women or Children – West, or Hewett; Tanner on Diseases of Children.
Physiology – Carpenter, Marshall, or Dalton.
Materia Medica and Therapeutics – Wood, Stillé, Biddle, or Waring, and U. S. Dispensatory.
Chemistry – Fownes, or Attfield.
Diseases of the Eye – McNamara, or Wells.
Diseases of the Ear – Roosa.
Medical Jurisprudence – Wharton and Stillé, or Taylor.

1875

Same as for 1874, except that in chemistry Barker was added.

1876

Same as for 1874, except that in chemistry Barker, and in surgery Bryant, were added.

V. LIST OF MATRICULATES AND GRADUATES OF THE WASHINGTON UNIVERSITY SCHOOL OF MEDICINE, OF BALTIMORE

Second Period

The letters M. D. indicate that the degree of Doctor of Medicine was conferred by this school in the year stated immediately following the degree. The absence of M. D. after a name means that available records show only that the person named was a matriculate in the year or years given. If the M. D. is enclosed in parentheses, i.e., (M. D.), neither the date nor the school which conferred the degree is evident from the available records alone. Any years stated after the first date following the "M. D." mean that the holder of the degree spent that time, subsequent to receiving the degree, as a post-graduate. Parentheses around a letter or a name indicate that the existing records show variations in spelling, and the possibility that two different persons might be involved cannot be ruled out with certainty.

The names of all of the graduates of the University's second period have been found (all but the last class, that of 1877, in publications of the University, and those of the class of 1877, in the Baltimore Sun for February 23, 1877). The names of matriculates of all entering classes, except those for the years 1873, 1875, and 1876 have also been found. Many of these names will, however, be found among the names of the graduates of the years subsequent to the entering years.

Adams, Francis Bennett, M.D., '77
  Maryland
Adams, Frank B., '74
  Maryland
Adams, Nelson, '71
  Virginia
Albaugh, W. A., (M.D.), '69, '70
  Pennsylvania
  Washington Uni.
Alford, Henery M., M.D., '71
  North Carolina
  New York University
Allen, John T., '71
  Alabama
Allison, T. H., '69
  Missouri
  Dr. Atkinson
Allison, Wm. R., '72
  North Carolina
Amoss, Chas. F., '70
  Maryland
  Washington Uni.
Anderson, B. P., M.D., '69
  Virginia
  Uni. of Virginia
Anderson, W. S., M.D., '68
  North Carolina
  Uni. of Pennsylvania
Anderson, W. T., (M.D.), '70
  Virginia
Antrim, W. W., M.D., '69
  Virginia
  Uni. of Virginia
Appelby, David Jeffries, M.D., '77
  Pennsylvania
Arnold, Jacob Dennis, M.D., '76

Maryland
Arthur, Henry A., '70
Virginia
Dr. Coleman
Ashley, William, '71
Georgia
Ashton, Philip C., (M.D.), '72
Virginia
Ashton, Thomas W., '71
Virginia
Ashton, R. B., M.D., '68
Virginia
Uni. of Maryland
Atkins, George R. (B.), M.D., '71
Virginia
Dr. H. C. Stevens
Attmore, George S., M.D., '70
North Carolina
Dr. R. S. Primrose
Augspath, L., '69
Russia
Baltimore Dental College
Aylor, J. W., (M.D.), '68
Virginia
Uni. of Virginia
Ayres, John E., '70, '71
Virginia
University of Virginia
Baggett, John B., M.D., '69
Arkansas
Dr. G. W. Lawrence
Bagley, Charles, M.D., '72
Maryland
Dr. Bagley
Bagley, Paul, '67, '68, '70
Maryland
Uni. of Maryland
Baird, Elisha, '71
North Carolina
Baker, Blair P., '71
Virginia
Baker, T. H., M.D., '68
Georgia
Dr. A. J. Foard
Ballance, William P., M.D., '73
North Carolina
Banes, Robert T., '71
Missouri
Banks, Arthur E., '72
Virginia
Barbour, C. C., (M.D.), '70
Virginia
Medical Department, Georgetown College
Bard, G. S., '67
Maryland
Dr. A. J. Foard
Barnes, W. H., (M.D.), '68
Maryland
New York University
Barnes, W. T., '70
Maryland
Dr. Bristoe
Barnett, Joseph A., '71
Maryland
Barr, Thomas, '71
West Virginia
Bartlett, Joseph T., M.D., '72
Maryland
Bass, Eugene W., '71
Virginia
Bass, John B., M.D., '70
Alabama
Uni. of Virginia
Baxter, Percival, (M.D.), '71
Georgia
Baylor, W. C., M.D., '69
Virginia
Uni. of Virginia
Bealor, John Weibly, M.D., '76
Pennsylvania
Bean, J. B., (D.D.S.), M.D., '69
Maryland
Baltimore Dental College
Bear, A. W., '69
Missouri
Dr. J. H. Wolf
Beasley, James A., '70
Georgia
Dr. Beasley
Beatty, Henry M., M.D., '70
Tennessee
Uni. of Louisville
Bell, J. B., (M.D.), '70
Virginia
Berry, Joseph G., '71
Tennessee
Best, William L., M.D., '72
North Carolina
Dr. W. P. Uxun
Bevans, H. S. (L.), M.D., '69
Maryland
Uni. of Louisville
Black, J. S., '69
Alabama
Dr. J. W. Garrison
Blue, John H., M.D., '70
Alabama
Dr. W. J. Hunter
Bond, James L., M.D., '69
Maryland
Dr. Zollicoffer
Books, Alfred T., '71
Tennessee
Boteler, R. L., M.D., '69
Maryland (Missouri)
Dr. J. E. Clagett
Bowen, G. F., '69
Tennessee
Bowen, William E., '72
Virginia
Boykin, T. J., (M.D.), '67
North Carolina
Uni. of Pennsylvania
Brasher, T. H., M.D., '69
Alabama
Drs. Patterson and Dixon
Bristow, John P., M.D., '72
Virginia
Dr. G. L. Nicholson
Bristow, Lewis S. (T.), M.D., '73
Virginia
Brock, C. W. P., (M.D.), '71

Virginia
Brockett, C. T., (D.D.S.), M.D., '75
Maryland
Brooks, George W., '72
Maryland
Broome, R. G. B., M.D., '74
Maryland
Brown, A. T., '70
Virginia
Dr. G. Brown
Brown, Isaiah M., '71
North Carolina
Brown, John D., '70
Georgia
Dr. J. N. Vanmeter
Brown, Nicholos C., M.D., '74 (?)
Virginia
Dr. Samuel Gleave
Brown, Robert C., M.D., '72
Virginia
Brown, Robert M., M.D., '73
Tennessee
Brown, W. E., M.D., '69
Arkansas
Dr. J. D. Harris
Brown, W. T., '69
Virginia
Dr. J. Taylor
Brown, Wm. W., M.D., '73
West Virginia
Brubaker, John L., M.D., '75
Maryland (Virginia)
Bruce, Walter, M.D., '69
Virginia
Medical College of Virginia
Bryan, John D., '68
North Carolina
Dr. D. McCallum
Buchen, Albert Z., '74
Maryland
Buck, John L., '70
Virginia
Drs. Hunt and Tuttle
Buddenbohne, Charles Lewis, M.D., '74
Maryland (Prussia)
Burgwyn, Wm. H. S., M.D., '76
Maryland
Burnes, C. W. H., '71
Maryland
Burns, H. R., '70
North Carolina
Dr. King
Burns, Robert K., M.D., '72
Maryland
Dr. J. S. Martin
Burton, John W., M.D., '72
North Carolina
Dr. William H. Parks
Burwell, Philip, M. D., '72
Virginia
Dr. Archie C. Randolph
Byrd, S. D. M., (M.D.), M.D., '69
South Carolina
Byrd, William E., '68
Virginia
Dr. H. Gilmore
Byrne, Walter, '74
Kentucky
Caldwell, E. B., '70
North Carolina
Dr. Caldwell
Caldwell, G. J. W., M.D., '68
Kentucky
Uni. of Virginia
Caldwell, James Polk, '71
Tennessee
Caldwell, W. P. (B.), M.D., '69
Virginia
Dr. J. J. Moorman
Cameron, Robert A., '69, '70
Georgia
Drs. C. H. Montgomery and J. W. Cameron
Campbell, Jas. R., M.D., '70
North Carolina
Dr. O. Campbell
Campbell, R. Bruce, '72
Virginia
Campbell, Thomas B., '71
Alabama
Campbell, William, '72
West Virginia
Canter, J. W., '70
Virginia
Prof. Byrd
Carlton, Edward Carey, '71
Georgia
Carpenter, Sampson B., '74
North Carolina
Carson, W. R., M.D., '69
North Carolina
Dr. L. C. Coke
Carter, Henry Lee, '71
Virginia
Cassiday, Jas. S., (D.D.S.), M.D., '71
Kentucky
Ohio Dental College
Cauwthorn, G. T., M.D., '68
Virginia
Atlanta Medical College
Chamblin, , (M.D.), '68
Virginia
Medical College of Virginia
Chancellor, J. J., '69
Virginia
Chancellor, Rush W., M.D., '74
Virginia
Chapman, E., M.D., '71
Maryland
Jefferson Medical College
Chapman, William H., '71
Alabama
Charter, W. A., M.D., '69
Virginia
Uni. of Virginia
Cheek, Marion A., M.D., '73
North Carolina
Chester, Samuel H., M.D., '71
Tennessee
Dr. J. Chester and Prof. Chancellor
Christian, John, '72
North Carolina
Clapham, E., M.D., '74

West Virginia
Clark, A. T., '69
North Carolina
Dr. Campbell
Clark, John E., '72
North Carolina
Clark, T. H., '67
Tennessee
Dr. S. M. McElroy
Clarke, Henry, '67
Maryland
Dr. Edward Warren
Clarkson, David, M.D., '72
Missouri
Clarkson, Joseph A., (Ph. D.), M.D., '75
Maryland
Clements, R. H., '69
Virginia
Dr. Benson
Clendinin, W. H., (M.D.), '69
Maryland
Uni. of Maryland
Cline, Philip L., M.D., '69
Tennessee
Baltimore Dental College
Cline, W. S. (I.), M.D., '68
Virginia
Uni. of Maryland
Clyment, J. R., '72
Maryland
Coats, C. R., '71
Texas
Cockreill, Walter S., M.D., '70
Missouri
Dr. G. W. Martin
Coleman, Silas K., M.D., '70
Mississippi
Dr. K. C. Divine
Collier, William M., '72
Tennessee
Collins, John J., '72
Georgia
Collins, Lemnel H., '70
Maryland
Dr. E. N. Tingle
Collins, Sam H., '72
Maryland
Conn, W. A., '67
Virginia
Dr. J. L. Campbell
Conn, William A., M.D., '72
Virginia
Connoly, F. G., M.D., '72
Maryland
Prof. Dunbar
Conway, C. C., M.D., '69
Virginia
Dr. A. J. Grinnan
Conway, W. B., M.D., '69
Virginia
Dr. S. R. Rixey
Cook, George S., '72
North Carolina
Cook, J. C., Jr., M.D., '69
Georgia
Drs. Stanford and Foard
Cook, John P., M.D., '75
Texas
Cooke, Walter J., '70
North Carolina
Dr. B. T. Green
Cooley, Charles Oliver, M.D., '71
Dacotah (?) (Virginia)
Coonan, Joseph Vincent, M.D., '75
Maryland
Copeland, James Joseph Edward, M.D., '76
Virginia
Corbell, John T., M.D., '71
Virginia
Drs. J. T. Phillips – Albaugh
Corry, A. A., '70
Tennessee
Dr. Magee
Cosby, John B., M.D., '73
Tennessee
Cosper, W. T. (Y.), M.D., '69
Alabama
Drs. Powell and Morgan
Covington, K. McR., '68
North Carolina
Dr. D. N. Patterson
Cowan, R. V., M.D., '68
North Carolina
Richmond Medical College
Coy, Byron F., (D.D.S.), '72
Maryland
Coyle, J. H., '69
Georgia
Baltimore Dental College
Coyner, Lewis P., '71
Virginia
Coyner, S. F., (M.D.), M.D., '70
Virginia
Uni. of Virginia and Washington Uni.
Crandall, Charles E., M.D., '70
Maryland
Dr. E. Hall
Craven, James L., '71
North Carolina
Crawford, S. (J.) M., M.D., '71
Alabama
Uni. of Louisiana
Credle, Onslow Stalen, M.D., '76
North Carolina
Crittenden, H. H. W., M.D., '68
Virginia
Uni. of Virginia
Crockett, Henry S., M.D., '72
Virginia
Dr. T. H. Mayo
Crothers, Ransom B., '71
Maryland
Crouse, William L., M.D., '73
North Carolina
Dr. M. L. Brown
Crow, A. J., '67
Alabama
Dr. J. R. Scurry
Crowder, Charles M., '71
Virginia
Crowther, Rodney, '71, '72
England

Washington Uni.
Croyeau, A., '71
France
Crute, H. P., (M.D.), '67
Pennsylvania
Uni. of Louisville
Dabney, John Davis, M.D., '72
Mississippi
Dabney, W. C., (M.D.), '68
Virginia
University of Virginia
Daniel, D. Rush, M.D., '76
Nebraska
Darling, Henry, (M.D.), '71
Maryland
Dashiell, Rufus W., M.D., '72
Maryland
Professor N. R. Smith
Davidson, Daniel S., '71
Alabama
Davie, W. S., (M.D.), '70
Alabama
Davis, E. Campbell, '72
Georgia
Davis, William Asbury, M.D., '75
Georgia
Day, William R., '70
Virginia
Dr. C. T. Davis
Dean, James Henry, '71
Arkansas
Develbiss, James E., '68
Maryland
University of Maryland
Devoe, J. Russell, M.D., '77
Maryland
Dick, F. N., (M.D.), M.D., '69
North Carolina, (Nebraska)
University of Virginia
Dickey, James A., '68
Virginia
Dr. W. N. Dickinson
Dicks, William Penn, M.D., '75
North Carolina
Dickson, John F., '70
North Carolina
Dr. R. B. Hill
Dillard, Edmund Pendleton, '71
Virginia
Dixon, Henry P., '72
North Carolina
Dodd, Gaston H., M.D., '70
North Carolina
Dr. C. H. Harris
Dorsey, Michael A., '74
Maryland
Douglas, J. D., (M.D.), '74
Georgia
Douglas, John Webb, M.D., '74
Texas
Drennen, Charles, '71
Alabama
Drew, Columbus, Jr., M.D., '69
Florida
Dr. E. T. Sabal
Drewry, John W., '70
Virginia
Dr. E. A. Drewry
Du Bose, F. D., '69
Alabama
Dr. J. H. Phillips
Du Bose, Hampton C., '71
South Carolina
Duck, Joseph J., M.D., '71
Virginia
University of Virginia
DuLaney, William H., '71, '72
Louisiana
Duncan, John T., '72
North Carolina
Dutton, Benjamin B., M.D., '72
Virginia
Drs. White and Sears
Ean(m)(n)es, R. W., M.D., '70
Virginia
Ebberts, Joseph A., M.D., '76
Maryland
Edmonson, Charles G., '72
Virginia
Edwards, E. N. (W.), '69
Virginia
Dr. Edwards
Edwards, James Barbour, '71
Virginia
Edwards, R. H., (M.D.), '70
Virginia
Eggleston, William May, M.D., '75
Virginia (Maryland)
Elderdice, Irvin H., M.D., '72
Maryland
Dr. E. J. Henkle
Ellington, James H., M.D., '72
North Carolina
Dr. J. Scales
Ellington, Samuel, M.D., '72
North Carolina
Dr. J. Scales
Elliot, J. C., '70
South Carolina
Dr. Harris
Ellis, J. R., M.D., '68
South Carolina
Charleston Medical College
Ellis, James, (M.D.), '71
Missouri
Emory, George A., '70
Virginia
Dr. Hunter
Evans, James A., (M.D.), '70
Tennessee
Evans, R. S., '69
North Carolina
Dr. J. T. Wilson
Evans, Robert Edward, '71
Alabama
Evans, S. T., M.D., '69
Virginia
University of Virginia
Ewell, Jesse, Jr., M.D., '76
Virginia
Ewell, Oscar B. B., M.D., '77
Maryland
Ewing, W. S., (M.D.), '71

Tennessee
Farrar, Edward W., '71
Georgia
Faulds, William Henry, '74
Pennsylvania
Ferguson, Samuel T., '71
West Virginia
Fewell, J. T. (W.), M.D., '68
South Carolina
Charleston Medical College
Field, J. M., (M.D.), '68
Virginia
University of Virginia
Fisher, W. Frank, (M.D.), M.D., '69
Virginia
University of Virginia
Fitch, A. P., M.D., '71
Virginia
University of Virginia, (Professor Harrison)
Fitzgerald, Delano S., M.D., '77
Maryland
Fitzhugh, T., (M.D.), '69
Virginia
Medical College of Virginia
Fleet, Isaac M., '72
South Carolina
Foard, W. C. H., M.D., '72
Georgia
Dr. J. H. Allison
Folsom, I. W., M.D., '72
Choctaw Nation
Dr. Moore
Fooks, Frederick E., M.D., '74
Maryland
Foote, W. A., M.D., '74
North Carolina
Forbes, T. J., (M.D.), '71
Virginia
Ford, Newton, '71
Virginia
Forte, W. A., M.D., '69
North Carolina
Dr. C. E. Johnson
Foster, E. S., M.D., '69
North Carolina
Dr. P. S. Foster
Foster, H. L., '69
Alabama
Dr. William Reed
Foster, J. C., '67
Mississippi
Dr. E. Foster
Foster, Robert H., '70
Alabama
Dr. G. C. Howard
Foster, Whilden M., (D.D.S.), M.D., '75
Maryland
Foulkes, John Graham, '71
North Carolina
Fredericks, Alexander H., '72
Missouri
Freeland, H. Y., '69
Virginia
Dr. Alexander
Freeman, G. W., '68, '69
North Carolina
Dr. J. T. Reed
Freeman, Gideon M., '71
North Carolina
Freeman, Samuel, '70
Virginia
Dr. Harris
Fricks, A. J. (T.), M.D., '69
Georgia
Washington University
Frizzell, James W., '71
Maryland
Fuller, L. S., M.D., '69, '69
South Carolina
South Carolina Medical College
Fuqua, J. B., (M.D.), '69
West Virginia
Jefferson Medical College
Gaither, J. A. (B.), M.D., '69
North Carolina
Dr. W. W. Foote
Gallaway, W. L., '67
South Carolina
Dr. C. J. Flinn
Gal(l)oway, Walter C., M.D., '75
North Carolina
Gambell, Thomas B., '71
Maryland
Gannon, William H., M.D., '72
West Virginia
Dr. J. S. O'Donnell
Garey, Henry Foree, M.D., '76
Maryland
Garmendia, Henry F., '71, '72
Cuba
Garnett, Alfred H., M.D., '72
Virginia
Garnett, Judson W., M.D., '71
Virginia
University of Virginia
Germain, F. H., '67
Maryland
Dr. H. L. Byrd
Germa(o)n, Francis T. W., M.D., '70
Maryland
Dr. H. L. Byrd
Getzendanner, J. W., M.D., '68
Maryland
University of Maryland
Gibbons, J. E., M.D., '68
Maryland
University of Maryland
Gibbons, Robert C., '71
North Carolina
Gibson, C. W., '69
Virginia
Dr. Thornton
Gilbert, William T., '71
Alabama
Gilla(u)m, W. H., M.D., '69
Virginia
University of Virginia
Gilliss, Joseph A., M.D., '70
Maryland
Dr. W. H. Dashiell
Gilpin, Joseph Gideon, M.D., '76
Maryland

Glass, William A., '71
North Carolina
Glover, J., '67
North Carolina
Dr. Edward Warren
Godfrey, James Mallory, '71
Florida
Gold, S. McD., M.D., '69, '70
Virginia
University of Virginia
Goodwin, Thomas H., '71, '72
Maryland
Goolrick, P., (M.D.), '69
Virginia
Jefferson Medical College
Gordon, William Armistead, M.D., '76
Virginia
Grace, John C., M.D., '70
Virginia
St. Louis Medical College
Graham, George T., (M.D.). '71
Virginia
Graham, J. W. F., '67
Virginia
Dr. W. W. Smith
Graham, S. T., '70
Maryland
Grant, H. M., M.D., '68
Virginia
Dr. H. E. Noel
Graub, H. M., M.D., '74
Virginia
Gravatt, Charles V. (W.), M.D., '70, '70
Virginia
Dr. G. J. Gravatt
Graves, Henry C., '72
Mississippi
Graves, L., '67
Georgia
Dr. C. P. Gordon
Gray, J. (G.) D., M.D., '68
Arkansas
University of Louisiana
Gray, W. H., '69
North Carolina
Dr. Gilmer
Green, Isaac E., M.D.; '73
North Carolina
Green, J. H. C., '70
West Virginia
Green, William, (M.D.), '71
Maryland
Greentree, Winslow, M.D., '71
Maryland
University of Maryland
Gregg, S. Houston, '72
Texas
Gresham, Philip, M.D., '72
Virginia
Dr. H. Gresham
Griffin, J. S., '67
North Carolina
Dr. C. Smallwood
Gunn, W. B., M.D., '69
Mississippi
University of Virginia
Hale, James W., M.D., '71
West Virginia
Dr. J. Bell
Hall, Charles L., M.D., '76
Virginia
Hall, E. A., M.D., '68
North Carolina
Richmond Medical College
Hall, Isaac, '71
Virginia
Hall, J. W., '69
Virginia
Dr. J. Bee
Hall, Mc Intosh M., M.D., '74
Georgia
Hall, T. Briscoe, M.D., '74
Maryland
Hammond, G., (M.D.), '69
Maryland
Washington University
(See George Hammond, First Period)
Hardison, William H., M.D., '70
North Carolina
Drs. H. Hardison and W. W. Ward
Harman, A. H., '71
Maryland
Harne, Franklin Horatio, M.D., '76
Maryland
Harrell, C. W., M.D., '69
South Carolina
Dr. C. J. Flinn
Harrell, John B., '68
North Carolina
Dr. L. Harrell
Harris, Edmund I., '72
Maryland
Harris, J. J., (M.D.), '68
Georgia
Georgia Medical College
Harrison, J. A., M.D., '69
Virginia
University of Virginia
Harrison, Luther D., '70
Virginia
Washington University
Hart, R. S., M.D., '69
Alabama
South Carolina Medical College
Hartman, George A., M.D., '72
Maryland
Dr. Hartman
Harvey, Robert S., M.D., '72
West Virginia
Harwell, Robert B., M.D., '71
Virginia
Dr. J. H. Elder
Hassell, Alonzo, M.D., '72
North Carolina
Dr. R. S. Halsey
Hathook, W. H. H., M.D., '74
Maryland
Hayes, John W., M.D., '70
Tennessee
University of Louisville
Haywood, Mason C., '72
Florida

Heath, R. A., M.D., '68
Georgia
Richmond Medical College
Hebb, Henry J., M.D., '73
Maryland
Henderson, Charles E., '72
North Carolina
Henderson, William Francis, M.D., '77
Virginia
Henkle, Samuel T., M.D., '73
Maryland
Dr. E. J. Henkle
Henning, David N., '70
Maryland
Professor Dunbar
Henning, Thomas R., '68
Maryland
Washington University
Henry, Samuel Winston, '72
Texas
Herbert, John W., '71
Mississippi
Herman, J. R., M.D., '69
Alabama
Dr. J. T. Daniels
Hetrick, Jeremiah S., M.D., '73
Pennsylvania
Hill, Charles G., M.D., '70, '70
North Carolina
Washington University (Dr. Ellis Malone)
Hill, Joseph Spencer, '74
Tennessee
Hill, M. W., M.D., '69, '71
North Carolina
Dr. R. T. Campbell
Hill, Robert F., '71
Tennessee
Hill, William N. (A.), M.D., '75
Maryland
Hines, William C., '71
Georgia
Hodges, C. J., '69
Alabama
Dr. Campbell
Hodgson, Henry W., M.D., '71
Virginia
University of Virginia
Hoge, Robert H., M.D., '73
Virginia
Holbrook, W. H. H., M.D., '68, '69
Maryland
University of Maryland
Washington University
Holcomb, C. M., '68
North Carolina
Dr. D. F. Holcomb
Holland, Newton G., M.D., '72
Virginia
Dr. G. P. Terrell
Holland, R. A., '69
Kentucky
Dr. H. L. Bryd
Holliday, R. H., '67
North Carolina
Dr. J. B. Seavy
Holman, Thomas P., M.D., '69
Tennessee
Dr. H. H. Robinson
Holmes, William A., (M.D.), '71
Mississippi
Holt, J. W., '67
North Carolina
Hopkins, Walter C., '71
North Carolina
Hornaday, E. H., '68
North Carolina
University of New York
Houston, Thomas B., '72
Georgia
Howard, C. C., '70
Georgia
Dr. Holman
Howard, J. G., M.D., '68
Alabama
University of Louisiana
Howard, M., '67
Virginia
Dr. T. H. Howard
Hoyt, Henry T., (M.D.), '71
Kentucky
Hughes, Clement C., '72
Alabama
Hughes, R. K., '69
Virginia
Dr. William Clark
Hummer, J. C., '70
Virginia
Professor Bryd
Hunt, Christian J., '71
Virginia
Huss, Jacob C., M.D., '70
Alabama
Dr. Healey
Hutchi(n)son, H. G., M.D., '71
Virginia
W. T. Luck
Hutchison, Frederick, M.D., '76
Virginia
Hutchison, William P., '72
Tennessee
Hyde, George S., M.D., '71
Maryland
Washington University
Hyndes, Joseph H., '71
Tennessee
Iden, Benjamin F., M.D., '72
Virginia
Dr. Thomas L. Settle
Inloes, A. J., M.D., '69
Maryland
Dr. Edward Warren
Irvin, George H., (M.D.), '71
Tennessee
Jackson, Charles T., M.D., '74
Georgia
Jackson, James K., '72
Tennessee
Jackson, William B., M.D., '70
Mississippi
Philadelphia University of Medicine and Surgery
Jameson, Lewis Y., '72

Alabama
Jarnigan, Joseph E., M.D., '72
South Carolina
Dr. J. F. Culpeper
Johnson, C. T., '70
Georgia
Dr. Thruston
Johnson, E. H., M.D., '69
Alabama
Atlanta Medical College
Johnson, E. S., M.D., '69
Virginia
University of Virginia
Johnson, Isaac C., M.D., '73
West Virginia
Johnson, Isaac E., '71
West Virginia
Johnson, J. T., M.D., '68
Georgia
Atlanta Medical College
Johnson, Norman Mc., M.D., '77
North Carolina
Johnson, T. A., '69
Georgia
Dr. W. T. Taylor
Johnson, T. D., M.D., '69
Tennessee
University of Virginia
Johnston, John Henry, M.D., '74
North Carolina
Johnston, M. Tyler, '67, '68
Alabama
Dr. R. Whitfield
Jones, A. J. (G.), M.D., '68
North Carolina
Atlanta Medical College
Jones, A. S., M.D., '70
North Carolina
Dr. A. Wade
Jones, Charles A., (M.D.), '68
Virginia
Atlanta Medical College
Jones, Edward H., M.D., '72
North Carolina
Dr. S. A. Long
Jones, H. B., '67
North Carolina
Dr. J. J. Hardy
Jones, J., '70
South Carolina
Professor Warren
Jones, James T., M.D., '70
Tennessee
University of Louisville
Jones, M. T., M.D., '69
Mississippi
South Carolina Medical College
Jones, Robert K., M.D., '73
Mississippi
Jordan, E. C., '74
Illinois
Jordan, W. A., '71
North Carolina
Josey, John M., M.D., '73
South Carolina
Joyce, Pleasant H., M.D., '75
Tennessee
Keech, Edward P., (D.D.S.), M.D., '75
Maryland
Keech, Henry Hobart, (D.D.S.), M.D., '74
Maryland
Keeling, J. H., '69
Tennessee
Dr. Beaty
Kell, Thomas C., '70
Virginia
Professor Chancellor
Kendrick, J. E., '67
Alabama
Dr. J. C. Kendrick
Kennedy, E. M., '69
Georgia
Dr. M. D. Mooney
Kennedy, J. Henry, M.D., '74
Maryland
Kennedy, John B., '68
North Carolina
Drs. Davis and Kerby
Kern, J. S., '67
Virginia
Kerr, John P., M.D., '71
Virginia
University of Pennsylvania
Killough, James C., M.D., '70
Alabama
University of Virginia
Kimberley, Joseph, M.D., '76
Maryland
Kinabrew, William H., '70
Georgia
Dr. J. W. Kinabrew
King, J. E., M.D., '69
North Carolina
Dr. R. T. Campbell
King, J. W., M.D., '68
South Carolina
Charleston Medical College
King, T. P., '67
South Carolina
Dr. J. C. Flinn
Kirwan, George W., '71
Maryland
Knell, George, '74
Maryland
Lacy, Robert H., M.D., '71
Texas
University of Louisiana
Lander, , '69
Mississippi
Dr. Armstrong
Lane, H. C., '67
North Carolina
Dr. W. V. Lane
Latham, W. W., M.D., '68
North Carolina
New Orleans School of Medicine
Lawrence, John T., (M.D.), '72
Virginia
Laws, T. L., M.D., '68
Virginia
University of Maryland
Lawson, George K., '70

Virginia
Dr. J. G. Lewis
Lawson, Landon C., '71
West Virginia
Lawton, John C., '72
North Carolina
Laxton, J. L., M.D., '68
North Carolina
Richmond Medical College
Leary, John E., M.D., '73
North Carolina
Leas, Charles A., '70
Russia
Washington University
Leatherman, Marshall E., M.D., '73
Maryland
Leaverton, Enos C., '71
Maryland
Le Beau, Lewis A., M.D., '72
Louisiana
Legette, A. C., M.D., '69
South Carolina
South Carolina Medical College
Leggett, E. M. B., '70
Mississippi
Dr. N. E. Leggett
Lemon, George B., M.D., '69
Virginia
Dr. C. M. Stigleman
L'Engle, Henry A., '71
Florida
Lenoire, Francis T., '71
Texas
Lewis, Hiram S. (L.), M.D., '71
Kentucky
Dr. C. W. Chancellor
Lewis, Samuel B., '72
Virginia
Lindsay, Edward, M.D., '71
North Carolina
University of Virginia
Lindsey, James A., M.D., '73
Maryland
Dr. G. W. Bishop
Linthicum, D. D. (A.), (M.D.), M.D., '70
Arkansas
St. Louis University
Linthicum, James S., M.D., '72
Maryland
Dr. B. H. D. Bull
Little, Q. M., M.D., '72
North Carolina
Drs. Connor and Yount
Little, Thomas, '71
Tennessee
Long, G. W., '69
North Carolina
Dr. J. A. Walker
Long, James A., '72
North Carolina
Long, John Ignatius Theodore, M.D., '76
Maryland
Long, Joseph J. T., '74
Maryland
Love, H., '68
North Carolina
Love, Samuel J. (T.), M.D., '70
Maryland
Dr. John H. Turner
Lowry, H. L., '70
Alabama
Dr. Anderson
Luck, George S., M.D., '73
Virginia
Ludwig, James H., M.D., '70
Maryland
Baltimore Dental College
Lupton, J. L. F., M.D., '68
Virginia
University of Maryland
Lyman, J. A., '71
Maryland
Lynn, Calvin C., '71
West Virginia
Maddox, T. C., (M.D.), '68
Virginia
Winchester Medical College
Magruder, F. B., M.D., '71
Virginia
Dr. A. J. Nye
Malloy, J. H., '67
Alabama
Drs. Bledsoe and Lomax
Malone, George B., M.D., '72
Tennessee
Dr. L. L. Battle
Manard, S. A., M.D., '72
Tennessee
Drs. Fulton and Carriger
Mann, Ambrose W., '72
North Carolina
Mapp, J. E., M.D., '68
Virginia
University of Maryland
Marshall, J. A., M.D., '68
Virginia
University of Maryland
Marsteller, A. A., '71
Virginia
Mat(t)hews, J. E., M.D., '68
North Carolina
Richmond Medical College
Mat(t)hews, W. P., M.D., '68
Virginia
University of Virginia
Maxwell, Charles K., '72
North Carolina
Maynard, S. A., M.D., '72
Tennessee
Mayse, George, M.D., '69
Virginia
University of Virginia
McBrayer, Thomas Evans, M.D., '75
North Carolina
Dr. J. C. Gidney
McCain, J. H., M.D., '69
Alabama
Dr. T. Y. Nesbit (Nisbit)
McCally, Archie, '72
Alabama
McClelland, E. T., '72
North Carolina

McClelland, John R., M.D., '73
North Carolina
McClyment, J. B., M.D., '74 (?)
Maryland
McCoy, W. H., '67
North Carolina
Dr. E. Caldwell
McCravey, A. D., '69
Georgia
Dr. T. F. Jones
McDonald, A. D., '67
North Carolina
Dr. J. Black
McDonald, Alexander Donaldson, M.D., '77
North Carolina
McDowell, C. T., '68
Maryland
Dr. O. S. Mahon
McGuire, H. C., '67
Mississippi
Dr. A. J. Foard
McIntosh, James, (M.D.), '70
South Carolina
Medical College of South Carolina
McKie, N. W., M.D., '70
Mississippi
University of Louisiana
McLelland, John B., '71
North Carolina
McLendon, Walter J., M.D., '72
North Carolina
Dr. H. W. Houze
McLeod, A. S., '68
Maryland
Baltimore Dental College
McNider, V. St. Clair, M.D., '70, '70
North Carolina
Washington University
(Drs. Warren and H. L. Bryd)
McNutt, J. M., M.D., '69
Virginia
University of Virginia
McQueen, J. K., M.D., '69
Alabama
South Carolina Medical College
McWillie, J., M.D., '70
Mississippi
Merrick, Samuel K., '70
Maryland
Dr. S. Chapman
Millar, Maynard Nally, M.D., '76
Maryland
Miller, H. H., '69
North Carolina
Dr. B. Smith
Miller, Thomas Benton, '72
Missouri
Milles, Alphonse Leon, '74
France
Milliard, D. T., M.D., '68
North Carolina
University of Virginia
Montague, W. J., M.D., '70
Maryland
Washington University
Montgomery, C. H., M.D., '68
Georgia
Atlanta Medical College
Moore, J. W., M.D., '70
North Carolina
University of Pennsylvania
Moore, K. P., '67
Georgia
Dr. D. B. Searcy
Moore, Nathaniel C., '72
Tennessee
Moore, W. H., '69
Alabama
Dr. Moore
Morgan, Albert S., M.D., '69
North Carolina
University of Virginia
Morgan, Francis M., M.D., '69
North Carolina
University of Virginia
Morgan, J. H., '67
Virginia
Dr. B. C. Warwick
Morgan, James Barrenger, '71
Georgia
Morgan, W. S., M.D., '71
Georgia
Dr. R. B. Ridley
Morse, E. A., '68
North Carolina
Dr. M. T. Henderson
Moseley, A. (D.) P.O., M.D., '71
Alabama
Drs. T. H. Brashier and J. C. Blake
Moser, C. P., '67
Tennessee
Drs. Fulton and Magee
Moss, Edward A., M.D., '70
North Carolina
Dr. F. M. Henderson
Murphree, E. D., M.D., '69
Alabama
Atlanta Medical College
Musgrave, Simpson, J., '74
Pennsylvania
Neale, S. D., '71
Maryland
Nelson, Hugh, M.D., '77
Virginia
Nicholas, Dixon L., '72
Alabama
Ninde, Julien R., M.D., '73
Virginia
Noland, Stacy T., M.D., '73
Virginia
Norfleet, A. Jackson, '72
North Carolina
Norton, E., M.D., '69
South Carolina
Medical College of South Carolina
Oatis, Francis B., '70
Mississippi
Dr. C. E. Oatis
Oliver, William A., M.D., '73
North Carolina
Opie, T., (M.D.), '69
Maryland

University of Pennsylvania
Osmun, Charles J., M.D., '72
Virginia
Drs. Osmun and Barbour
Ossa, Luis Filipe, M.D., '76
Chile
Oursler, John T., '70
Maryland
Dr. Coonan
Owens, Robert B., '72
Virginia
Owens, T. L., (M.D.), '71
Maryland
Owens, W. M., '69
Alabama
Dr. G. W. Maddox
Pacetti, L. B., '70
Cuba
Dr. Gindrat
Painter, E., M.D., '69
Maryland
Long Island College Hospital
Palmer, A. J., (M.D.), '67, '69
Maryland
University of Pennsylvania
Parker, J. H., '67
North Carolina
Dr. J. G. Rose
Parkhill, J. H., M.D., '69
Maryland
Dr. Edward Warren
Parks, T. M., M.D., '68
North Carolina
College of Physicians and Surgeons
New York
Parks, W. P., M.D., '68
North Carolina
Atlanta Medical College
Parsons, Frederick, '74
North Carolina
Pate, Gabrial G., '71, '72
North Carolina
Patterson, F. W., '71
Maryland
Patterson, J. W., (M.D.), '69
Ohio
Medical College of Ohio
Patteson, A. Lee, '70
Virginia
Dr. J. A. Waddell
Paul, Isaac, (M.D.), '71
Virginia
Payne, C. M., M.D., '68
North Carolina
University of New York
Payne, J. P., M.D., '68
Virginia
University of Virginia
Pearson, J. W., M.D., '69
South Carolina
Dr. T. C. Hutchison
Peed, James A. (S.), M.D., '72
Maryland
Peeples, R. N., '69
Alabama
Dr. S. W. Harvill
Penrod, Hiram J., M.D., '73
Pennsylvania
Pentz, William F., Jr., M.D., '74
Maryland
Perry, B. B., M.D., '69
North Carolina
Dr. W. W. Greene
Perry, Henry Virgil, M.D., '76
New York
Perry, J. D., M.D., '68
North Carolina
University of Maryland
Peters, Andrew J., '72
Tennessee
Peters, W. H., '68, '69
Maryland
Dr. W. D. Hellam
Philips, H. G., '69
Virginia
Dr. Turner
Pierce, J. B., M.D., '68
Virginia
University of Virginia
Pierce, Lewis B., (M.D.), '70
Pennsylvania
Geneva Medical College
Pitts, Albert Brown, M.D., '76
Mississippi
Plank, Jacob R., M.D., '74
Pennsylvania
Pope, M. J., M.D., '71
Texas
University of Louisiana
Potter, Henry G., '72
North Carolina
Powell, R. C., M.D., '69
Virginia
University of Virginia
Powell, Thomas J., M.D., '70
Alabama
Dr. George Powell
Powers, Kinchen James, M.D., '76
North Carolina
Powers, Luther Milton, M.D., '77
North Carolina
Preston, James Henry, M.D., '77
Maryland
Price, John F., M.D., '75
Maryland
Price, O. K., '71
Maryland
Price, Samuel T., '72
Maryland
Prince, Henry (M.D.), '71
Alabama
Proctor, J. M., M.D., '70, '70
Maryland
Washington University
Dr. H. Richardson
Pugh, Edward N., M.D., '72
North Carolina
Dr. S. A. Bernard
Purnell, L. Dixon, M.D., '75
Maryland
Quidor, Leroy L., M.D., '71
Virginia

Dr. J. A. Harrison
Quinn, L. W. D., '70
Georgia
Dr. J. F. Wooton
Raiford, M. D., '68
North Carolina
Dr. E. H. Hornaday
Raines, S. L., M.D., '69
Tennessee
Medical College of South Carolina
Randolph, W. P. F., M.D., '74 (?)
Virginia
Ranni(e)lls, Charles Samuel, M.D., '76
Missouri
Rathbone, F. V., '71
West Virginia
Ray, Joseph M., M.D., '72
Maryland
Dr. D. S. Williams
Read, Henry C., '72
Virginia
Redden, Robert J., M.D., '72
Alabama
Reese, R. M., M.D., '68
Tennessee
University of Nashville
Reese, William P., '70
Virginia
Dr. S. G. Reese
Reeves, W. W., '68
North Carolina
Dr. J. O. Wilcox
Regester, W. G., M.D., '69, '70
Maryland
Washington University
Dr. F. Howard
Reves, William C., '70
North Carolina
Dr. E. B. Hampton
Reynolds, George B., M.D., '72
Virginia
Rhoads, Henry Wamsher, M.D., '76
Pennsylvania
Rhodes, William H., '71
Virginia
Rice, George L., M.D., '73
Maryland
Richards, Henry J., (M.D.), '72
Virginia
Richardson, B. F., '70
South Carolina
Dr. D. A. Richardson
Richardson, W. E., M.D., '68
North Carolina
University of Pennsylvania
Richey, Richard A., M.D., '72
Georgia
Richey, Robert A., '70
Maryland
Dr. T. H. Baker
Reddick, R. E., M.D., '69
Virginia
University of Virginia
Riddlemoser, J. A., M.D., '70
Maryland
Jefferson Medical College
Ridley, R. B., '67
Georgia
Dr. R. A. T. Ridley
Riggs, C. D., '67
Tennessee
Dr. G. T. Magee
Rives, N. T., (M.D.), '69
Virginia
University of Pennsylvania
Roberson, Calvin N., '71
North Carolina
Roberts, Hugh J., '72
Virginia
Roberts, S. T., '69
Virginia
Dr. Morrison
Roberts, Sudler Pool, M.D., '76
Maryland
Robinson, M. E., M.D., '70
North Carolina
Drs. Davis and Keeley, (Kerbey)
Rogers, H. A., '68
Maryland
University of New York
Rogers, James H., '71
Maryland
Ro(d)gers, James R., M.D., '69, '70
Maryland, (Virginia)
Washington University
Drs. Purnell and Parker
Ross, George Iverson, M.D., '77
Connecticut
Rowland, David T., M.D., '71
Virginia
Medical College of Virginia
Rucker, Edward H., '72
Tennessee
Russell, John Preston, '71
West Virginia
Rutledge, E. Hall, M.D., '72
Maryland
Dr. E. H. Richardson
Ryan, Daniel W., '71
Tennessee
Sabine, Alexander, (M.D.), '71
Ohio
Sadler, D. M., '70
Arkansas
Sale, C. J., '68
Virginia
Dr. R. B. Montague
Sale(s), J. Channing, M.D., '70
Virginia
Dr. W. G. Pollard
Sapp, Benjamin J., M.D., '75
North Carolina
Sauer, Francis A., '72
Maryland
Saunders, R. T., M.D., '68
North Carolina
Atlanta Medical College
Saunders, S. E., M.D., '70
Virginia
Dr. T. D. Saunders
Scarff, John Henry, M.D., '76
Maryland

Schuler, J. L., '68
South Carolina
Dr. J. A. Bruley
Schulte, Christian Moritz, M.D., '76
Maryland
Schulte, John Adolph, M.D., '75
Maryland
Scott, E. H., (M.D.), M.D., '69
Missouri
University of Virginia
Scott, Edward Waller, M.D., '71
Virginia
University of Virginia
Scott, H. R., '70
Maryland
University of Virginia
Scott, J. D., M.D., '68
Virginia
Dr. D. Wade
Scott, J. Ward, (M.D.), '67
Maryland
Jefferson Medical College
Scott, Walter, '68
North Carolina
Dr. B. F. Cobb
Seabrill, W. P., '67
North Carolina
Dr. J. W. Sherrod
Seawell, V. N., M.D., '68
North Carolina
University of Maryland
Seneker, A. D., M.D., '70
Tennessee
University of Virginia
Setzer, J. F., (D.D.S.), M.D., '69
North Carolina
Baltimore Dental College
Sexton, T. C., '67
Virginia
Dr. M. P. Watson
Sexton, Thomas C., M.D., '71
Nebraska
Dr. M. P. Watson
Shaw, H. M., M.D., '71
North Carolina
Washington University
Drs. Warren and Byrd
Shaw, R. M., (M.D.), '70
South Carolina
Shaw, Walter D., '71
North Carolina
Shepherd, J. W., M.D., '74
North Carolina
Shermer, Rev. David A., M.D., '73
Maryland
Shingler, F. J., '67
South Carolina
Dr. E. J. Oliveros
Shipley, William J., M.D., '73
Delaware
Dr. J. P. H. Shipley
Shuford, J. W., M.D., '68
North Carolina
Richmond Medical College
Shuler, Joseph L., M.D., '70, '70
South Carolina
Washington University
Dr. J. A. Berly
Sibley, H. C., '69
North Carolina
Dr. W. Jingle
Sills, Robert A., M.D., '73
North Carolina
Simms, Thomas J., '74
Maryland
Simpson, George W., '69, '70
Maryland
Philadelphia University of Medicine and Surgery
Dr. W. H. Clendinin
Sims, Alonzo, M.D., '69
Mississippi
Dr. W. B. Field
Slaughter, N. G., '67
Alabama
Dr. M. J. Slaughter
Slover, George, M.D., '69
North Carolina
Dr. E. F. Smallwood
Smiley, E. E., '67
Mississippi
Drs. McLean and Buill
Smith, Alexander G., '72
Alabama
Smith, Algernon G., M.D., '72
Maryland
Professor Clagett
Smith, David M., (M.D.), M.D., '72
Virginia
Snead, Edward F., M.D., '71
Virginia
Medical College of Virginia
Snoddy, S. T., '69
South Carolina
Dr. A. L. Moore
Sotherton, R. W., '67
Maryland
Dr. M. Stone
Sparrow, S. P., M.D., '68
North Carolina
University of Maryland
Speed, A. (E.) A., M.D., '69
North Carolina
Dr. E. Holt
Speed, Eugene T., M.D., '75
North Carolina
Sperry, Charles W., '72
Virginia
Sprinkle, George W., M.D., '70
Virginia
Dr. H. G. Garrett
Stallings, O. C., M.D., '70
North Carolina
Dr. J. M. Earle
Stark, George W., M.D., '77
Virginia
Stephen, Charles H., (M.D.), '70
Maryland
University of Maryland
Stewart, Wilberforce A., '72
Maryland
Stevens, R., '69

Georgia
Dr. W. H. Stevens
Stev(ph)enson, Samuel W., M.D., '73
North Carolina
Stick, Wesley C., M.D., '75
Pennsylvania
Stilley, Burton, '67
North Carolina
Dr. J. N. McDonald
Stine, Albert L., '72
Pennsylvania
Stire, William C., M.D., '71
North Carolina
Dr. J. R. Raine
Stith, Lawrence A., M.D., '73
North Carolina
Stonebraker, A. S., (M.D.), '69
Maryland
University of Maryland
Storey, J. C., (M.D.), '68
Virginia
Atlanta Medical College
Stout, Henry W., M.D., '76
Delaware
Stover, George, '71
North Carolina
Stover, J. M. H., M.D., '72
Virginia
Dr. J. A. Harrison
Strain, Horatio P., M.D., '72
Texas
Strawn, J. P., (M.D.), '71
California
Street, J. W., M.D., '69
Virginia
Dr. W. R. Gatewood
Stribling, George M., M.D., '74
Georgia
Strong, James D., '72
Pennsylvania
Strother, C. S., M.D., '69
Georgia
Dr. Nottingham
Strother, Clarence F., M.D., '76
South Carolina
Stubbs, J. Catlett, M.D., '74
Maryland
Stubbs, John C., '72
Virginia
Sturdivant, John Willis, '74
North Carolina
Suddarth, J. L., (M.D.), M.D., '68
Virginia
Summers, James A., '70
Tennessee
Dr. Magee
Swann, G. T., (M.D.), '69
Tennessee
Swigart, J., M.D., '73
Maryland
Philadelphia College of Medicine
Swindell, Charles A., M.D., '75
North Carolina
Sydnor, W. P., M.D., '75
Virginia
Tankard, J. W., M.D., '69
Virginia
Dr. W. E. Brickhurst
Tarbutton, William E., M.D., '74
Maryland
Tarrant, T. W., '67
Alabama
Dr. A. J. Foard
Tavener, R. V. (W.), M.D., '69
Virginia
Dr. J. W. Taylor
Taylor, A. S., '70
Virginia
Dr. Taylor
Taylor, Joshua, '69, '70
North Carolina
Drs. Harman and R. S. Halsey
Taylor, Joshua, (M.D.), '71
North Carolina
Taylor, K., M.D., '70
Virginia
Drs. Lupton and Harman
Taylor, W. C., (M.D.), '68
Virginia
Taylor, William P., M.D., '72
Maryland
Dr. J. C. Polk
Temple, Thomas P., (M.D.), '69
Virginia
Jefferson Medical College
Tewes, Wilhelm, M.D., '72
Prussia
Dr. Bates
Thomas, John H., M.D., '71
Tennessee
Dr. D. H. Thomas
Thomas, N. G., M.D., '68
Tennessee
University of Virginia
Thompson, J. B., '70
North Carolina
Dr. F. R. Freeman
Thompson, Rust, '71
Texas
Thornton, William Carter, '74
Virginia
Thorpe, H. B., (M.D.), '70
Maryland
Washington University
Thorpe, Henry W. (H.), M.D., '70
Maryland
Drs. Mitchell and Ellis
Threadgill, George A., '72
Alabama
Threadgill, J., '67
North Carolina
Dr. E. F. Ashe
Thruston, William G., '72
Tennessee
Thurmond, J. W. W., '68
Tennessee
Drs. Fuller and McGee
Tillotson, Robert S., M.D., '72
Mississippi
Dr. John A. Hall
Todd, Scott, '67
Alabama

Drs. Tate and Griggs
Tolosa, Henry F., M.D., '75
France
Tompson, Alfred E., '72
Virginia
Tonge, Samuel D., M.D., '72
Georgia
Dr. Claud Baxley
Toombs, R. S. (J.), M.D., '68
Mississippi
University of Louisiana
Towles, Robert H., M.D., '73
North Carolina
Dr. W. H. McKee
Travers, Edward, M.D., '70, '70
Maryland
University of Maryland
Washington University
Travers, Simon J., '72
Pennsylvania
Trent, J. W., '67
South Carolina
Dr. H. L. Byrd
Trent, R. O., '70
Maryland
Washington University
Triplett, J. S. (J.), M.D., '69
Virginia
University of Virginia
Tripp, Jonothan H., '71
Tennessee
Troxel(l), J. G., '67, '69
Maryland, (Pennsylvania)
University of Maryland
Turner, Josephus, M.D., '68
North Carolina
Richmond Medical College
Turner, R. H., '69
West Virginia
Dr. W. P. Smith
Turner, Robert Mason, '72
Virginia
Turner, S. W., (M.D.), '70
Louisiana
Turpin, Ferdinand A., M.D., '76
Maryland
Vernon, J. B., M.D., '68
Alabama
University of Louisiana
Vicks, J. W., '68
North Carolina
Dr. C. H. Harris
Wagg, A. W., '68
North Carolina
Dr. James Wagg
Wagg(a)(er)man, S. J. (G.), M.D., '69
Maryland: District of Columbia
Dr. S. C. Smoot
Waldo, S. P., M.D., '68
North Carolina
University of Maryland
Walker, George W., '70
Choctaw Nation
Dr. Moore
Walker, Henry P., '72
Virginia
Walker, R. E., Honorary M.D., '68
North Carolina
Dr. Edward Warren
Walker, T. E., '70
Alabama
Dr. J. Cook
Walls, Enoch G., M.D., '72
Maryland
Dr. Charles M. Morfit
Ward, W. F., '71
Maryland
Warfield, R. O. D., M.D., '70
Maryland
Dr. Edward Warren
Warner, Brinton Henderson, M.D., '77
Maryland
Warner, Michael Kimmel, M.D., '76
Maryland
Warr(e)ner, W. T. (S.), M.D., '70
Virginia
Dr. W. J. Cheatham
Washington, W. A., (M.D.), '70
South Carolina
Medical College of Virginia
Watkins, J. M., '67
Alabama
Dr. T. G. Slaughter
Watson, George S., '71
North Carolina
Watson, J. H., '68
South Carolina
Maryland College of Pharmacy
Wayson, W. A. N. (W.), '67, '68
Maryland
Dr. G. W. Wayson
Weaver, Henry B., M.D., '72
North Carolina
Dr. J. A. Reagan
Weddell, James D., M.D., '72
Maryland
Dr. J. K. Fleming
Wells, Marion C., M.D., '71
Tennessee
Professor Byrd: Drs. Henley and Harvey
Wels(c)h, Eberle G., M.D., '73
Maryland
West, S. T., '71
Virginia
Whipp, Oliver Shannon, M.D., '77
Maryland
White, S. G., (M.D.), '67
Georgia
University of Pennsylvania
White, Walter W., '68
Maryland
Maryland College of Pharmacy
Dr. Womble
Whiteford, Aloysius X., M.D., '73
Maryland
Dr. E. Hall Richardson
Wiley, George E., (D.D.S.), M.D., '75
Virginia
Wilhelm(n), J. T., M.D., '68
Maryland
University of Maryland
Wilkinson, J. E., '67

Alabama
Dr. Thomas Davis
Williams, E. J., M.D., '68
North Carolina
Charleston Medical College
Williams, E. L., '69
Alabama
Williams, Samuel A., (D.D.S.), '72
Maryland
Williamson, E. R., Jr., M.D., '69
Virginia
Virginia Medical College
Williamson, R. M. (n.), M.D., '71
North Carolina
University of Virginia
Wilson, David, M. D., '68
Maryland
University of Pennsylvania
Wilson, J. T., '69
Virginia
Baltimore Dental College
Wilson, Jacob J., M.D., '71
Maryland
Dr. W. H. McCormick
Wilson, Lawson B., '71
Maryland
Wilson, Lewis T., M.D., '72
Virginia
Wilson, P. S. (A.), M.D., '69, '70
South Carolina
Washington University
Professor J. E. Byrd
Wilson, W. A., '69
Missouri
Winder, Richard B., (D.D.S.), M.D., '74
Maryland
Winston, C., M.D., '69
North Carolina
Dr. D. C. White
Wintrode, John Henry, M.D., '76
Pennsylvania
Wise, John C., M.D., '69, '70
Virginia: United States Navy
University of Virginia
Washington University
Witherspoon, Robert G., M.D., '75
South Carolina
Wolf, J. H., M.D., '68
Virginia
University of Virginia
Wolfe, Alfred Lewis, M.D., '75
Virginia
Womersley, Henry P., M.D., '70, '70
England
Dr. C. W. Chancellor
Washington University
Wood, Julian E., M.D., '69
Virginia
University of Virginia
Wooley, C. L., '68
Alabama
Dr. G. S. Johnson
Woolfolk, Frank Leigh, M.D., '77
Virginia
Woolfolk, Robert T., M.D., '74
Virginia
Worsham, W. S., M.D., '70
Georgia
Washington University
Dr. W. J. Worsham
Worthington, Richard, '74
Maryland
Wright, Gustavis A., '71
North Carolina
Wright, W. A., M.D., '69
North Carolina
University of Maryland
Wright, W. P., M.D., '70
Georgia
Jefferson Medical College
Wysong, D. Preston, M.D., '72, '72
Maryland
Dr. Richard D. Lee
Yancey, Leyton B., M.D., '73
Virginia
Yates, , '68
Maryland
Dr. Yates
Yeates, Herbert, '74
Maryland
Yingling, George S., (M.D.), M.D., '71
Ohio
University of Maryland
Yost, George P., M.D., '71
Pennsylvania
Dr. W. A. Albaugh
Young, Edward C., '71
West Virginia
Young, H. B., M.D., '69
Virginia
Zeigler, Charles B., M.D., '76
Maryland
Zepp, Jesse (M.D.), M.D., '71
District of Columbia
Medical Department
Georgetown College
Zie(ei)gler, J. Henry, M.D., '74
Pennsylvania
Zimmerman, Michael J., M.D., '72
Maryland
Drs. Dunbar and Zimmerman

ACKNOWLEDGMENTS

Thanks are expressed to Miss Marion B. Savin and Mr. Kenneth V. Hahn, both of Philadelphia, for their large scale, patient efforts on my behalf.

I am also especially grateful to Miss Hilda E. Moore, Associate Librarian of the Health Sciences Library, University of Maryland, for her painstaking examination of a ledger in which are recorded, in handwriting, the names of persons who attended Washington University School of Medicine. (The ledger is in the office of the Dean of the School of Medicine, University of Maryland.) These records proved very difficult to read with any degree of satisfaction as to certainty of name, date, or status, and it therefore seemed wise not to use them in this study, particularly in view of the fact that during the course of gathering the needed sources, all of the names of graduates became available from a combination of the University Announcements and the files of the *Baltimore Sun.*

Mr. Charles Roos and Staff, of the National Library of Medicine, Mrs. Karl M. Koudelka, of the Welch Medical Library, Miss Gertrude L. Annan, Librarian, New York Academy of Medicine, Miss Florence Woods and Mrs. Elizabeth G. Sanford, of the Library of the Medical and Chirurgical Faculty of the State of Maryland, Miss Madeline Stanton, Librarian of Historical Collections, Yale Medical Library, Miss Dorothy Baker, of the Boston Medical Library, Mrs. Edith B. Hampel, of the Library of the University of Pennsylvania, Mr. P. W. Filby, of the Library of the Peabody Institute, of Baltimore, Mr. Clement G. Vitek, Librarian of the Baltimore Sun, Mr. Joseph Gordon, Director of the Bureau of Health Information, Baltimore City Health Department, Mr. Frank White, of The Hall of Records, Annapolis, Maryland, Miss Ruth D. Burton, State Library, Annapolis, Maryland, Miss Hester Rich and Mr. Thomas S. Eader, of the Library of the Maryland Historical Society, the library staff of the Enoch Pratt Free Library of Baltimore, Mr. Sanford Kotzen, Administrator, Franklin Square Hospital, Baltimore, and the staff of the Library of the College of Physicians of Philadelphia have all given valuable assistance in tracking down the documents and information needed for this study.

BIBLIOGRAPHY

Second Period

1. *Annual Announcements and Catalogues of the Washington University Medical Department, Baltimore, Maryland,* Sessions of 1867-68 to 1876-77.
2. Genevieve Miller: *A Nineteenth Century Medical School: Washington University of Baltimore,* Bulletin of the History of Medicine, Volume 14 (1943), pp. 14-29.
3. Eugene F. Cordell: (a) *The Medical Schools of Baltimore,* Transactions of the Medical and Chirurgical Faculty of the State of Maryland, 1881, pp. 320-356. (b) *Historical Sketch of the University of Maryland School of Medicine, 1807-1890.* Baltimore. 1891. (c) *The Medical Annals of Maryland,* 1799-1899, Baltimore, 1903.
4. William Frederick Norwood: *Medical Education in the United States before the Civil War.* University of Pennsylvania Press, Philadelphia, 1944.
5. G. Carroll Lockard: *Early Medical Education in Baltimore* Bulletin of the School of Medicine, University of Maryland, 1938-39, pp. 128-137.
6. John R. Quinan: *Medical Annals of Baltimore,* Baltimore, 1884.
7. H. Clay Dallam, Esq. *An Address Delivered at the Commencement of the Medical Department of the Washington University,* February 22, 1872.
8. *Baltimore Sun,* February 23, 1877.
9. Randolph Winslow: *Edward Warren, A.M., M.D., C.M., LLD.* Bulletin of the School of Medicine, University of Maryland, April 1927, Volume XI, pp. 161-171.
10. Isobel Stevenson: *American Medicine during the Sixties,* Ciba Symposia, 1941-43 Volumes 3-4, pp. 894-907.
11. Howard A. Kelly and Walter L. Burrage: *Dictionary of American Medical Biography,* New York, 1928.
12. Bernard C. Steiner: *History of Education in Maryland,* Washington, D. C., 1894.
13. Thomas J. Scharf: *History of Baltimore City and County,* Baltimore, 1881.

FOOTNOTES TO CHAPTER ONE

Second Period

(1) Examination of the lists of matriculates and graduates, as published in the Announcements of the University over the years given below enable us to arrive at the figures for these two categories, as follows:

MATRICULATES		GRADUATES	
1867	148	1868	55
1868	155	1869	82
1869	130	1870	48
1870	170	1871	38
1871	192	1872	57
1872	129	1873	35
1873	*	1874	34
1874	75	1875	26
1875	*	1876	32
1876	*	1877	17
		Total	424

* *The Announcements contain no lists of matriculates for these years.*

(2) All of the advertisements of the Washington University Hospital which have come to hand contain a line which reads: "Open for the Reception of all Classes of Patients, except those Suffering from Contagious Diseases", (or words to that effect).

(3) Cordell, *op. cit.*, (footnotes to p. 348), cites the following: *March 23, 1867* — The Legislature authorizes constructing or providing a building and establishing the Maryland Free Hospital.

March 30, 1868 — $10,000. appropriated for hospital building and furniture, for exclusive use of the University, but if diverted to other purposes, property to be sold at public auction and proceeds returned to the State. In addition, $2,500. to be given the University to sustain the hospital, provided that a certain number of patients are treated and a certain number of scholarships are made available. Later legislation limited the funds to a period of four years. (The University of Maryland also received $2,500. annually, for four years, on the same conditions.)

March 23, 1870 — Trustees authorized to raise $10,000. for enlarging the building, and *February 26, 1872* — Board of Visitors authorized to raise $15,000. by mortgage or creating a ground rent. Both acts fail, by a technical misuse of words.

April 11, 1874 — Legislature appropriates $10,000. to pay for the building "on condition that a full release of all claims against them be first exhibited by the Faculty, and that State beneficiary students be educated free so long as the property is used for college purposes". This amounts to a total appropriation of $30,000. It has been claimed that "a considerable proportion" of this sum was spent on "commissions".

(4) This list, taken from the Announcement for 1867, differs somewhat from that given by Cordell, who lists J. William Walls (Anatomy), Pascal A. Quinan (Physiology), and Henry St. George Hopkins (Diseases of Women and Children).

(5) *Abram B. Arnold*, an alumnus of Washington University School of Medicine, practiced in Carlisle, Pa. for a time. From 1873 to 1877 he was Professor of Principles and Practice of Medicine at his alma mater, then Professor of Nervous Diseases at the College of Physicians and Surgeons of Baltimore (1877-79), and Emeritus Professor until his death in 1904 at the age of 84. Dr. Arnold was consulting physician to the Hebrew Hospital of Baltimore until 1892, and was a president of the Maryland Medical and Chirurgical Faculty (1877-78). He wrote: *Manual of Nervous Diseases* (New York, 1855, 170 pp.).

(6) *Harvey L. Byrd*, born in North Carolina, was a surgeon in the Confederate Army. After graduating from the Medical Department of Pennsylvania College (1840), he taught Materia Medica at Savannah Medical College, and later, Theory and Practice of Medicine at Oglethorpe Medical College where he served as Dean. From 1867 until his death, he practiced medicine in Baltimore. He assisted Dr. Warren in re-organizing Washington University School of Medicine, and was also one of the founders of the College of Physicians and Surgeons of Baltimore (1872), as of the Baltimore Medical College (1881). Dr. Byrd was the first president of the Epidemiological Society of Maryland, editor (for three years) of the *Ogelthorpe Medical and Surgical Journal*, and of the *Independent Practitioner*, of Baltimore. (See, also, the chapter on the Baltimore University School of Medicine, footnote No. 1).

(7) *A. J. Foard* was a great-hearted and extraordinarily able administrator of Army medical service. He was Director of Medical Matters on the staffs of General Johnston and General Hood. During the greater part of the Civil War, he was Field and Hospital Medical Supervisor, Department of Tennessee. In this post he displayed great wisdom, dedication to duty, sympathy and understanding of his badly undermanned medical staff. After the heavy military engagements in the Tennessee Valley, his became the burden of transporting from battlefield to hospital, thousands of wounded and sick soldiers, and providing medical and surgical care for them. Because of his talents as an organizer and for successful handling of the men under him, his staff worked with notable efficiency under the severe conditions imposed by events effecting the rapid transport of the battle-wounded.

(8) *Francis T. Miles* taught Anatomy at his alma mater, the Medical College of South Carolina, a post which he left to serve as surgeon in the Confederate Army and to which he returned at the close of hostilities. In 1868 he joined the Faculty at Washington University, leaving at the end of the session to become Professor of Nervous Diseases and of Physiology at the University of Maryland. Dr. Miles was a president of the American Neurological Association. He wrote: *Diseases of the Peripheral Nerves*, in Pepper's System of Medicine, *Regional Diagnosis in Brain Dissease*, and *Electricity in Medicine*.

(9) *George Reuling* was a noted eye-surgeon. He was born in Germany, educated abroad (Germany, Austria and France), and served as a surgeon in the Prussian Army. He was the "first American ophthalmologist to remove a cataractous lens within its capsule". Dr. Reuling was surgeon-in-charge of the Maryland Eye and Ear Infirmary (1869), Professor of Eye and Ear Surgery at Washington University, and later, Professor of Ophthalmology and

Otology at Baltimore Medical College. (See, also, the chapter on the Baltimore University School of Medicine, section III, A. and B.).

(10) *Edward Warren* of Tyrrell County, North Carolina, was one of the most picturesque and romantic figures in the history of American medical practitioners. After graduating from Jefferson Medical College, he set himself up in medical practice in Edenton, North Carolina, for a brief period, then spent the years 1854-55 in Paris. In 1856 he was awarded the Fiske Fund Prize for his essay: *The Influence of Pregnancy on the Development of Tuberculosis.* In 1861 he edited the Baltimore Journal of Medicine.

Just before the outbreak of the Civil War, he was Professor of Materia Medica and Therapeutics at the University of Maryland. He left his post to serve the South as a medical inspector of the Confederate States (1861-65). Because of his efforts, early in the war, the Legislature of North Carolina appropriated $300,000. for the relief of sick and wounded soldiers. This resulted in a series of wayside hospitals near the principal lines of travel in North Carolina (Ashville, Greensboro, Raleigh, Wilmington). He is also credited with being responsible for the establishment of a soldiers' home where service men, on leave, could lodge. He was an able organizer. One feature of his medical department was a factory which produced artificial limbs for disabled soldiers of North Carolina. Ruined by the war, and in great destitution, he tried to regain his former post at the University of Maryland, but found it had been preempted. Thereupon he reorganized the Washington University School of Medicine with the help of other physicians (see text above).

In 1871 he forsook his professorship at that school and with other professors, founded the College of Physicians and Surgeons of Baltimore. Dr. Warren was thus, successively, a professor at three medical schools of Baltimore.

In the winter of 1871-72 a Mrs. Wharton was tried, in an Annapolis court, for the murder of General Ketchum by the alleged administration of an antimonial poison. Dr. Warren, chief medical expert for the defense, testified that the death was due to cerebro-spinal meningitis. This testimony resulted in the acquittal of Mrs. Wharton. During the trial Dr. Warren was cross-examined by the Attorney-General of Maryland who, losing his temper, provided the doctor with an opportunity to give evidence of his real talent for repartee — when the attorney sneered: "You doctors have the advantage of us lawyers. You bury your mistakes six feet under the Earth", the doctor retaliated with: "Yes, and you lawyers hang your mistakes in the air". The entire episode has since become a celebrated one. The acquittal placed Dr. Warren in the public eye in distant places, but the reaction in his city was unfavorable. In addition, the death of his son filled him with such deep grief that the familiar surroundings no longer held any joy for him, and he decided to leave Baltimore. He therefore sailed for Europe in 1873, which he traversed, finally journeying to Egypt. Here he found favor with the Khedive, Ismail Pasha, whom he served as chief surgeon of the general staff, displaying advanced medical knowledge, common sense, reliability and winning personality. At the moment, the Egyptian Minister of War was threatened with death due to a strangulated hernia, his case being considered hopeless by those in attendance. When Dr. Warren's skill and knowledge saved the Minister's life, the resulting acclaim brought the doctor fame and prosperity, but probably not unattended by jealousy. He evaded a plot by his enemies to send him south into the desert, making a trip, instead, to Paris, on a furlough (1875). A serious eye condition prevented his return to Egypt and when the efforts of Dr. Charcot resulted in Dr. Warren's being made a licentiate of the University of Paris, he decided to remain in that city, where he developed a highly successful practice and spent the rest of his life.

By reason of his detection of a case of arsenical poisoning of a prominent Spanish lady, the monarch of that country decorated him with knighthood in the "Order of Isabella, the Catholic".

He was the inventor of a splint for the treatment of fracture of the clavicle, and the claim has been made that he was the discoverer of hypodermic medication.

He wrote:

1) *An Epitome of Practical Surgery for Field and Hospital*, Richmond, 1863.
2) *A Doctor's Experience in Three Continents*, said to be a series of interesting letters to Dr. John Morris of Baltimore, and containing "charming and precious professional reminiscences".

The University of North Carolina bestowed the Degree of LL.D. upon him; the Khedive of Egypt made him a Bey, and he was also made a Chevalier of the Legion of Honor of France. He died in Paris in 1893 at the age of sixty-five, acclaimed in three continents as a great practitioner.

THE WOMAN'S MEDICAL COLLEGE OF BALTIMORE

In the year 1882 there were four medical schools for women in our country – Woman's Medical College of Pennsylvania (Philadelphia, Pa.); Woman's Medical College of Chicago, Illinois; New York Medical College and Hospital for Women (Homeopathic); and Woman's Medical College of the New York Infirmary for Women and Children.

On January 11, 1882, a meeting for the purpose of organizing a woman's medical school in Baltimore was held in a building at the corner of Hoffman Street and Druid Avenue, Mrs. Charles E. Waters, Mrs. John K. Carven and Mrs. Eugene F. Cordell attending.(1) In addition to a medical school were postulated a hospital and a training school for nurses. It was an unsettling idea for a somewhat conservative community, as reflected by the reluctance of prominent physicians, when offered posts on the Faculty, to accept them for fear of losing professional and social stature.

By late February of that year, however, seven physicians having signified their interest in such an undertaking, the trustees made formal application for incorporation by the Superior Court of Baltimore, and the request was granted. Thus there came into being the Woman's Medical College of Baltimore.

In the Announcement for the first session of the school (1882-1883), the reasons for establishing an institution for the "exclusive education of women in the art and science of medicine" are stated as follows:

1. Women are "peculiarly fitted" to treat the diseases of women and children.
2. Down through the ages, as well as today, women have been and are successful physicians and obstetricians, in successful competition with men.
3. It is only fair that women should have opportunities for education equal to those available to men, and in order to insure that this education shall take place without strain or embarrassment, there should be schools especially and exclusively for women.
4. The success of such schools in New York, Philadelphia and Chicago shows the desirability of establishing one in Baltimore, so as to provide such educational opportunity more conveniently for the ladies of the "South" and the adjacent Middle and Western States.
5. Baltimore, with a population of almost 400,000, has many advantages as a medical center, attracting a great many students who come here to study medicine. They come to Baltimore from all parts of the Union, and from foreign countries, the reasons being that not only are educational opportunities good, but in addition, board is low in cost, the climate is comparatively salubrious, the townspeople are genial, and there is an abundance of clinical material for medical instruction.

The Announcement for the second session (1883-1884) speaks of the "very flattering expressions of sympathy and good-will" which had arrived from far and near and of the first class of students who exhibited "intelligence, good deportment and earnest application to study". Thereafter the College grew and prospered.

After the college was firmly established as an institution where medical education for women was being adequately carried on, with clinical training in both Hospital and College clinic, additional expansion took place in the direction of nursing. The 1888 Announcement speaks of practical lectures on nursing at moderate rates, and lists the lectures of the previous year given at the College.(2) (See section II. Curriculum)

An interesting feature of this medical school was its medical society, organized in 1885, as the "Medical Society of the Women's Medical College," and remaining actively alive until the last days of the school. The membership included students, Faculty, assistants and the practicing physicians of Baltimore. There were meetings, monthly, during the session, and being of profit and pleasure to the members, were well attended. The officers of the Society were ladies who had already graduated or were still students of the College. Within a few years the Society matured to the point at which "eminent persons" were giving lectures, upon invitation, to the assembled members. In 1894 there were 104 members, divided into three classes: honorary, active, corresponding. Honorary members were certain distinguished physicians who had shown their interest in the Society, or in the medical education of women. Active members were students, members of the Faculty and assistants, and those women physicians practicing in Baltimore who had been duly elected. Corresponding members were active members now residing elsewhere than in Baltimore. The purposes of the Society were now two-fold – "intellectual and social". The well attended meetings were occasions of profit and pleasure. Papers were read during the two hours from 8 to 10 P.M., specimens were exhibited, and cases reported upon and discussed. These hours were followed by one hour spent in social enjoyment, simple refreshments being served. Twenty papers were read that year. During the past four years special lectures were given by Professors William H. Welch, James W. Bright, William T. Councilman and J. Edwin Michael, and Drs. William S. Thayer, Simon Flexner and Charles E. Simon. In February, 1894, the Society had begun the publication of its quarterly "Bulletin", of quarto size, containing eight or more pages, free to members, but fifty cents per annum, or fifteen cents per copy, to non--members. In 1895 Professors William Osler and George J. Preston gave lectures to the Society. Other famous persons spoke in later years.

The College was proud of the acceptance of its graduates by distant hospitals. The New England Hospital for Women and Children in Boston, Mass., annually appointed eight graduates of the various medical schools for women as internes, and by 1895 one graduate of this school had been so elected. The Thomas Wilson Sanitarium for children had, by the same date, appointed for the past ten years, a graduate of this school to the position of Resident Physician. The Philadelphia General Hospital (Blockley), based appointment to the position of Interne upon a competitive examination, open to graduates of all schools, and two graduates of this school, Dr. Claribel Cone and Dr. Flora Pollock, having passed the examination with high averages had, by 1895, held this position. By action of the Trustees of Bay View Hospital, Baltimore, about the year 1890, graduates were "admitted (for the first time), to the excellent advantages of this great institution, upon equal terms with men, as resident students", in consequence of which three graduates of the Woman's Medical College of Baltimore were accepted in 1891.

The College was also gratified by the fact that donations and subscriptions from friends of the College were received from time to time, thus giving evidence that its efforts to increase the sphere of women's usefulness were receiving tangible recognition.

The College took pride in the fact that it was one of the first institutions in the country and the first school in Maryland to adopt a three years' graded course, and that it early lengthened the course to four years, each of eight months. It stated that it aimed at giving a large amount of personal attention to each student, and to carry on its work "with all the advantages of private classes, combined with the dignity and college spirit so important in an institution of learning". Thus each student had the great advantage of the personal supervision of the professors, who could help each young lady in the special direction which she might need, a fact especially true in laboratory or clinic, where classes were so small that each student could be put through thorough drill. The College felt that the best assurance of the correctness of its educational methods was the brilliance of the records of its graduates achieved before the Boards of Medical Examiners in the various states.

Never a large school (there were less than thirty matriculates in most years), upon becoming a member of the Association of American Colleges in 1891, enrolment shrank for a time, partly because of the more rigid entrance requirements now in force.

We shall see, as we turn the pages of the record which follows, that the good people of Baltimore made a highly creditable effort to establish a medical school in which the young ladies of this city and surrounding areas could be trained so adequately as to enable them to take honorable places in the healing profession.

In the span of its life from 1882 to 1910 it rose to distinction as an educational institution, and during its twenty-eight years, graduated 116 women physicians. The Baltimore American for Sunday, June 24, 1894,(3) wrote as follows:

> *". . . Among the many admirable institutions in Baltimore designed for higher education, the Woman's Medical College on McCulloh Street, has taken a prominent rank and is notable not only because of the peculiar character of its special work but because of the high standing it has attained in comparatively little time. It has been a prominent factor in solving the problem of women's adaptability to professional pursuits and its graduates have at once an acknowledged position in the medical world."*

We have seen above that it was not easy to recruit a Faculty from among the male physicians of Baltimore in 1882. On the other hand, one of the graduates said, in later years, that it was a great mistake to found a college in which males staffed and steered "the craft on which women expected to reach shore. What has been inspired and produced by us, we must always nurture . . ." That trend had made its appearance in the later years, and while men greatly outnumbered women on the Faculty and Hospital staff, in the out-patient department there were eight women staff members, and only one man, in 1908.

The graduates did credit both to their alma mater and themselves, as may be seen from the record which appears under the name of each graduate in Section V of this study. That women could distinguish themselves in the field of medicine is shown by the life-work of Dr. Claribel Cone, who lectured on hygiene at Woman's Medical College of Baltimore, then was Professor of Pathology and later Pathologist at the Hospital. She was a pupil of William H. Welch at Johns Hopkins, then studied in Frankfort-on-Main and finally at the Pasteur Institute in Paris. She was a member of the Board of Trustees, serving as President in 1899-1900. She also served as Curator of the museum. Other graduates made their contributions in their turn. The Faculty was able and sincere, the excellent reading room and nearby medical libraries were very helpful factors in the education of the students, both the Alumnae Association (which was organized on May 2, 1884, and continued to function effectively throughout the life of the school), and the Medical Society were constructive and positive influences, and there were good internships available to graduates.

Why, then, did the school close its doors? The Baltimore Sun, May 31, 1910, reporting the Commencement Exercises of that date, quotes Dr. Guy L. Hunner, President of the Woman's Medical College of Baltimore, as saying that the lack of sufficient endowment prevented the school from meeting requirements of the American Medical Association, one of which was that during their first two years, students must be instructed only by paid professors, an expense which this institution could not afford, nor could it afford to meet another requirement – the purchase of expensive laboratory apparatus, now necessary for first-class work. The failure to survive, then, was caused by that same old beelzebub which "tormented most proprietary schools – the lack of attachment to a university, from which it could have derived financial stability. (Dr. Hunner went on to say that of the 116 graduates, all but four were living as of that date; thirty had married, most of their husbands being physicians; ninety per cent of the graduates were in active practice, as of that date.) About thirty of the students who had not yet attained graduation were going to enter the Woman's Medical College of Pennsylvania, and complete their medical education at that school. The Faculty of the Woman's Medical College of Baltimore, it was said, would help in the promotion of the South Baltimore Hospital.

The Commencement speaker, Dr. Eugene A. Nobel, President of Goucher College, commended the decision of the Trustees to close their college, rather than conduct a school which was not first-class. He expressed the wish that this splendid example of maintenance of high standards would be emulated by other institutions of learning, the country over.

The Maryland Medical Journal (Volume IX (1882), pages 267-275) contains the abstract of a remarkable address on the medical education of women, delivered at the opening of the first course of lectures at the Woman's Medical College of Baltimore, by Dr. Thomas A. Ashby, Professor of Obstetrics.

Dr. Ashby began by pointing out that this was the first attempt in Baltimore to establish a medical school exclusively for women students, an effort which would have run the risk of failure if made a decade ago, for public opinion and prejudice until that time, would have blighted the idea of liberating women "from the social fetters which for centuries have denied her a liberal scientific education." However, public sentiment was now sufficiently tolerant and liberal to favor the medical education of women. He told of the birth of the idea for such a school, in the minds of four gentlemen, some months earlier, and the gradual assembling of a Faculty, and the acquisition of a suitable college building, after which an Announcement was sent out, and "bid was made for patronage". He then reviewed the facts which favored its establishment, and the choice of Baltimore as a city in which to locate it. (Similar sentiments have already been presented above.)

The speaker then turned the pages of the history of the progress of the idea of woman's right to be admitted to the practice of medicine. In the dawn of history we find women assigned to ministering to the sick, presiding over childbirth, and performing "the necessary attentions to her sex." Ere yet "scientific thought and precision had molded a rational system of medicine", women had long been successful practitioners. Mythology assigns them the task of supervising the health of mankind, "of presiding over maternity and hastening delivery." Juno Lucina, Hygieia and Ocyroe are famed for medical skill and knowledge. Homer celebrates the skill and learning of female practitioners. In early Greece women were famous for their medical writings – Olympias of Thebes, Phaenarete (Socrates' mother), Agnodice, and Asphasia. Later Cleopatra is cited by Paulus Aegineta for her contributions to the literature of medicine. Mohammedan law prohibited the attending of females by males, in consequence of which women were the early obstetricians. Women students were admitted to the great school of Salerno, which flourished between the eleventh and thirteenth centuries, several women achieving wide distinction as professors. Trotula published a treatise in the thirteenth century, in which she tells us that many Saracenic women were obstetricians at Salerno. Italian Universities of the seventeenth and eighteenth centuries graduated women physicians, several women holding chairs in those schools. (J. R. Chadwick, M.D., of Boston, had written a valuable paper dated 1879: *The Study and Practice of Medicine by Women*, upon which Dr. Ashby drew for this part of his lecture.) La Dottoressa Laura Bassi, a graduate of the University of Bologna, held the chair of Natural Philosophy there, and Anna Morandi Mazzolina, famed for her knowledge of anatomy, "delivered her husband's lectures from behind a curtain", filling his chair at Bologna after his death, until 1774, when her own death occurred. Maria della Donne, another distinguished graduate of that school, became Professor of Midwifery ther in 1806, appointed thereto by the First Consul of France. History offers the names of many distinguished women in medicine, famous both for cures and for investigations. Madame La Chapelle and Madame Boivin of France were pre-eminent as accoucheurs, bequeathing us their great writings and observations, which provide material for statistical study and bedside instruction, even to this day. Although they won imperishable reputations as obstetricians, they also had a wide range of medical knowledge and were skilled in general medicine. The lives and work of these two women are excellent illustrations of woman's capacity for scientific work.

In France midwives have for a long time been entrusted with medical duties concerning the lying-in woman, and in England a few have so distinguished themselves as to have been employed in highest society. In America midwives are useful persons, presiding as chief or assistant accoucheurs in most deliveries – (up to 90% in one western city), which shows that "a proper delicacy and sentiment among women" requires the services of their own sex in the trying hours of childbirth, so that at best this phase of medical practice should be assigned to intelligent and educated women. Thus far few midwives have had intelligent training, having drifted into the profession as a result of the necessity of finding employment. This fact accounts for the accidents and mishaps which so often befall the lying-in woman, and the life-long misery which may result to mother and child because of ignorance at a time when scientific knowledge and skill are so urgently required.

The busy general practitioner, faced with the results of faulty practice in midwifery, must often have wished that there were educated and trained women who could offer such services to womankind. It is time that the system of practice by women be changed. As Dr. Chadwick remarks, it is not a question of whether women should be allowed to practice medicine, for hundreds of them already are so engaged. The only question now is: should they have the opportunity of studying medicine *before* they "avail themselves of the already acquired right of practicing it?" The most liberal and intelligent minds in the medical profession are beginning to show awareness of this problem.

We have seen above that the major part of the work of caring for the sick was, in past ages, done by women. Eventually such work was assumed by men, who gradually developed a rational and scientific system of practice. This very fact has been used as an argument to exclude women from the profession – the failure of the science of midwifery to advance in rational and exact knowledge, when it was almost exclusively in women's hands. However, their failure to formulate a system based upon clinical observation and experience was due to the circumstances which controlled their position in society, their mode of life and the failure of the educational system to train them to reason things out, being obliged, instead, to acquire their knowledge from ignorant instructors, or from rough and careless methods of observation.

It is also argued that woman is by nature more excitable, impulsive and physically weaker than man, and that in those qualities needed for success in practical medicine, "such as sound judgment, strong nerve and bold determination she is for the most part, deficient." While admitting these facts, it is not uncommon to find such virtues as will-power, endurance, calmness under trial, good judgment and practical intuition in women, making their services valuable to the sick, and when we make mention of patience, gentleness and sympathy we easily understand why their services are regarded as honorable and useful, and their instincts for loving-ministrations to mankind are viewed as both tender and appropriate. If we add the advantages of scientific medical training to all of these qualities, the sick-room would seem to offer an excellent field of action for woman's natural instincts.

Some persons argue that medical training would be degrading to woman, hardening and roughening her character and resulting in views which are at variance with present day civilization – encroachment upon man's privileges and encouragement of female suffrage and equal political rights. Medical education for woman is even opposed by members of the same sex, who argue that "woman is unsexed by a life of thought and action;" that she would thus be trained to experiences "which a refined and womanly instinct should escape." The arguments of the opposition are overdrawn and biased. Why not allow woman an opportunity to demonstrate her fitness for medical duties? Give her equal opportunity for education and training and let her show her skill and capacity.

As far as the claim that woman is robbed of her womanly characteristics by medical education, let us remember the teaching that:

"Honor and shame from no condition rise.
Act well your part; there's where the honor lies."

Turning to the growth of public opinion in favor of medical training for women, Dr. Ashby cited the fact that the first woman to obtain a medical degree in the United States was Elizabeth Blackwell, who graduated from Geneva Medical College in New York in 1849, having been previously denied admission to a number of medical schools. Feeling against such training for women ran so high that several years later, a Miss Adamson was unable to obtain a medical education at Geneva Medical College, which had been forced to close its doors, and no other "regular" medical school in our land was willing to admit her for a diploma course. She therefore attended and graduated from an Eclectic school at Syracuse, New York, in 1851. Soon thereafter Emily Blackwell entered Rush Medical College in Chicago, but was not permitted to take a second course because of a vote of censure passed by the Illinois State Medical Society. Cleveland Medical College awarded her the degree in medicine in 1854. By 1857 the two Drs. Blackwell, with Dr. Mary E. Zakrzewska, organized the New York Infirmary for Women and Children, where they instructed small classes of women students, and "laid the foundation" for the Woman's Medical College of the New

York Infirmary, which was chartered in 1865. Eminent physicians, such as Willard Parker, Austin Flint and Isaac E. Taylor made up the Faculty and Board of Examiners of this school. Five women, making up the first class, graduated in 1870, and since then the College has grown in size and influence, now ranking among the first of such schools in the world.

Philadelphia has the Female Medical College which opened in 1850, and established its hospital in 1861. The hospital now has a large endowment. Students of this college are admitted to the Philadelphia Hospital, Ophthalmic, the medical and surgical wards of Pennsylvania Hospital, and other medical institutions in the city. There were 276 alumnae in 1877.

The Chicago Hospital for Women and Children opened in 1865, and in 1870, in connection with this institution, the Woman's Hospital Medical College was organized, with Dr. W. H. Byford as President of the Faculty and Professor of Clinical Surgery of Women. The college requires three years of study (apprenticeship), and attendance upon two full courses of lectures. Its classes number from 20 to 35 students annually.

The Medical Department of the University of Michigan has admitted women since 1871, and has graduated more than one hundred to date. Syracuse University, incorporated in 1870, admits students irrespective of sex. It graduated three women in 1875, three in 1876 and none in 1879. Mixed classes at this school have not been successful. The University of California admits women on equal terms with men.

Dr. Chadwick designates Massachusetts as the place in which the first female medical school in the world was established, the Female Medical Educational Society having been organized in Boston, in 1848, and incorporated in 1850. There were twelve students at the beginning. The school merged with the School of Medicine of Boston University, in 1874, and is now under homoeopathic control.

Despite much discussion and division of Faculty opinion, numerous attempts by women to be admitted to Harvard University Medical School have thus far failed, and Dr. Chadwick thinks that the question is not settled, awaiting, instead, the time when some public-spirited person offers the University so large a sum of money as will overcome all such opposition.

Catalogues of the women's medical schools named above show annual gains in numbers of students and graduates, great improvement in facilities for instruction and clinical study and genuine effort by trustees, managers and teachers to advance the interests of the alumnae. On the Faculties of these schools are to be found many distinguished and conservative members of the medical profession, numbers of whom hold chairs in important all-male medical schools. Women have also qualified as holders of chairs in several female medical schools, and women practitioners are freely met in general practice in many localities. Women are admitted to membership in the American Medical Association, several State, and many local medical societies.

Thus we see that in thirty-four years' time the climate of public and professional opinion has undergone extensive change. Dr. T. Gaillard Thomas remarks upon the futility of resisting the "woman movement", which has won, in medicine, both consideration and respect, and says:

> *"The opportunity which is now offered to women for retrieving what has been lost in former ages is certainly all that the most exacting of modern reformers could require."*

Our country may claim the first medical school in the world for the exclusive education of women, but several universities in Europe awarded degrees in medicine to women as early as the middle of the eighteenth century. In France medical schools were nominally open to women, but none tried to be admitted until 1866, when the Faculty of Montpellier refused to accept one. It has since opened its doors to them. Miss Garrett, an English woman, was the first of her sex to graduate at Paris (June, 1870). Dr. Mary Putnam Jacobi, distinguished writer and accomplished physician, took honors upon her graduation in the next year. Enrollment of women in medical classes in France has increased in the last ten years, and they are eligible to the post of Internat of the hospitals. In Great Britain women have had great difficulty in obtaining registration and license to practice, because of the law requiring examinations and license from the government examining boards. The London School of Medicine for Women opened in 1874, there being twenty-three students and a strong Faculty, among which were such well known figures as Dr. Burdon-Sanderson, Dr. Bastian, Mr. Ernest Hart and Professor Huxley, and in 1877 the school was on the official list of schools recognized by the Irish College of Physicians. Registered women physicians are now admitted to practice in many London hospitals. Still there is very strong opposition in England to women medical students and practitioners, and the Royal College of Physicians, the Obstetrical Society of London and the British Medical Association refuse to admit women to membership. In Germany few women apply, but are generally admitted to study medicine. The Universities of Vienna and Leipsic admit them, and the University of Zurich in Switzerland began to do so in 1864, the first medical diploma being granted to a woman in 1867. In 1872 there were sixty-three women medical students at that University and shortly thereafter the number rose to eighty-eight, with twenty-five women students in the Department of Philosophy. In Russia women study and practice medicine on equal terms with men. The University of Moscow began to accept women medical students in 1871. In the session for 1874-75 one hundred and seventy-one women were studying medicine at the Imperial Academy of Medicine, one hundred and two of whom were of noble birth, seventeen of the commercial class, fourteen of shop-keeper class, and twelve the daughters of clergymen; twenty-three were married women. The State universities of Italy, Denmark and Sweden admit women on equal terms with men. We thus see that both at home and abroad social and educational reform have in some measure overcome the centuries-old prejudice which has denied to woman an opportunity to make her contribution in an area for which she is so eminently fitted.

Turning now to another side of the question of woman in medicine, Dr. Ashby addressed himself to the influence of her entry into the medical profession upon the main currents in her life – her professional and financial success, her duties as wife and mother, her social, physical and moral being. Dr. Rachel L. Bodley, in a valedictory address to the twenty-ninth graduating class of the Woman's Medical College of Pennsylvania, had answered these questions so fully and so well, that Dr. Ashby drew upon her excellent speech for replies to these questions. Dr. Bodley had sent printed questionnaires to 276 alumnae, inquiring about the life work of a woman physician. Only 189 replied, as follows:

Question number one:
Are you engaged in active medical practice?
Affirmative, 166; Negative, 23 – distributed as follows:

Domestic duties	8	Retired	3
Philanthropic work	1	No reason assigned	5
Ill-health	6		

Question number two:
Predominating character of medical practice?

Gynecological	32	General practice without discrimination	37
Obstetrical	10	Gynecological and Surgical	16
Medical	10	Obstetrical and Medical	9
Surgical	3	Surgical and Medical	7

Question number three:
Social status of the woman physician in the community?
Of 157 replied to this question –
Cordial social recognition: Yes, 150; No, 7.

Question number four:
Character of work accomplished by the woman physician as a resident or visiting physician to medical institutions?

Prominently identified with, or attached to, leading hospitals and medical institutions in New York, Philadelphia, Boston and Chicago	60
Consulting and Visiting Physicians to State asylums and charitable retreats	"Several" – no exact number given.
City Health Officer, (City of Charlotte, Michigan)	1
Physician to State Industrial School, (Lancaster, Massachusetts)	1

Question number five:
Monetary value of the medical practice, per annum?
Of 76 replies to this question – number of Alumnae who had collected

$ 1,000, but less than $ 2,000	24	$ 5,000, but less than $15,000	3
$ 2,000, but less than $ 3,000	20	$15,000, to $20,000	4
$ 3,000, but less than $ 4,000	10	Less than $1,000	10
$ 4,000, but less than $ 5,000	5		

Miscellaneous replies:

Number of Alumnae who were professors in the medical schools of Philadelphia and New York	7

Number of Alumnae who were lecturers and instructors 14

Members of County, State or other local medical society 68

(The distribution was as follows:

California	4	Minnesota	1
Connecticut	1	Missouri	1
Delaware	1	New Hampshire	1
Illinois	4	New York	16
Indiana	1	Ohio	7
Kansas	3	Pennsylvania	15
Massachusetts	2	Rhode Island	3
Michigan	5	Wisconsin	2

Tennessee, the only Southern State represented, reported . . . . 1)

Influence of study and practice upon domestic relations as wife and mother?

Fifty-two married Alumnae replied as follows:

Favorable 45

Not entirely favorable 6

Unfavorable 1

One Alumna wrote: "The study of medicine is of great benefit, but the practice often interferes with my duty to my family".

Another wrote: "I think if the history of the families of woman physicians were written it would be found that their children are all well cared for, well trained, well educated, all this and the household duties not neglected."

Three Alumnae stated that the study and practice of medicine had prevented marriage, and one wrote: "Never married but have found time and means to care for several orphan children".

Dr. Bodley drew the following conclusions:

1. . . . . That woman is physically equal to the duties and life of a "hard-worked practitioner" is attested by the fact that in 30 years there were but 32 deaths among the 276 Alumnae.

2 . . . . . That women physicians address themselves to the practice of medicine as a life-work; marriage does not interfere with this work, as it might in theory do.

3 . . . . . That woman physicians show the same zeal, interest and fidelity, the same devotion to domestic, social and religious obligations as their non-medical sisters, while displaying patience, earnestness, sincerity in the discharge of their duties to the sick, honorableness, and loyalty to medical ethics.

In review, Dr. Ashby cited the following: As late as 1850 the number of female graduates in medicine in the United States could be counted on the fingers of one hand. Today, estimates run over one thousand, with the number increasing in progressive ratio annually. It would be as well to try to stop the progress of the tides, as to endeavor to arrest a reform which gives woman a useful place in society, an opportunity to earn an honorable living, and pursue a benevolent calling. It was a rugged road which the early woman practitioner was obliged to travel. Prejudices constituted formidable barriers to progress. It took hard pounding upon the doors to gain admission, which was only won grudgingly. The doors are now open. A woman may obtain a medical education, and enter upon a medical career. She may now compete with man in a profession which taxes physical and mental powers severely, and in which the ranks are so filled that the "struggle for place and support is sharp and contested". Each year standards rise, and ultimate success in the profession rests upon education, training and experience. The future of medical education for woman therefore rests with her skill, knowledge and adaptability. She must master the science and demonstrate her ability to do scientific work. Otherwise the movement to win recognition of woman in medicine will fail.

I. BUILDINGS AND EQUIPMENT

The first home of the College was in a building at 126 North Eutaw Street (near Franklin Street), a central and convenient location, as two lines of street cars passed the building, and three other lines were within "a square" of it, thus making it of easy access to all parts of the city. A dispensary for treatment of the poor was established within a few days of the opening of the first session. It was soon noted that larger accommodations would be needed, which led an unnamed member of the Faculty to establish, and defray the costs of, a one-room children's hospital. From this small beginning grew the Women's and Children's

Hospital, for other rooms were added by other members of the Faculty. Eventually, a board of "lady managers" headed by Mrs. William Reed was set up, and steps taken to make the hospital comfortable and attractive.

Dr. Elizabeth Mason-Hohl tells us *(Woman's Medical College of Baltimore)*, in Medical Woman's Journal, December, 1946, pp. 58-63) that the Hiss property on McCulloh Street was secured in 1885, and that it had "three lecture rooms, laboratories, reception, drug, faculty, dissection and private consultation rooms for the various members of the faculty, a museum and a students' parlor". There were two lines of cable cars nearby.

Thoughts about the best type of medical education for women soon led to the conclusion that a hospital exclusively for women and children was not ideal, and the decision to have a general hospital for men, women and children, contagious diseases alone being excluded, was reached. The result was the Hospital of the Good Samaritan.

In order to give the students every advantage to acquire a high-grade education in medicine, the Faculty established "a normal and pathological museum, and started a library of standard medical authors", in the first year of its existence. There was a study and rest room associated with the library. Students were also welcome to use the facilities of the nearby Peabody Institute and Enoch Pratt libraries (which had large numbers of medical books and journals), and the fine library of the State Medical Faculty.

There was a comfortable reception room for the use of students and visitors.

The second Announcement stated that the dissecting room (well lighted and heated), was located in a separate building, and was open from 5 to 7 P.M. daily. There was a demonstrator to instruct students, and an abundant supply of anatomical material, furnished free of charge.

The Announcement for 1885-86 mentions a laboratory for histology, well supplied with microscopes and materials for a thorough laboratory course in this subject.

The same Announcement tells of the change of the name of the hospital to The Hospital of the Good Samaritan. (The hospital was no longer located in the College building.) It was described as occupying an entire "square", (including adjoining ground) in the northwestern part of the city. The rooms were large, well-ventilated, and lighted. A porch, the entire width of the building, on each floor, permitted patients unable to walk outside, as well as convalescents and chronic cases, to get the benefits of country air and surroundings amongst the trees and shrubbery of the extensive grounds. A board of "lady visitors" managed the institution, showing great devotion to responsibility, and sparing no expense to render its sanitary condition perfect. By that year the number of patients in the "Out-Door Department" had risen to 5,451. Both the State and the City maintained free beds in the Hospital, by annual monetary appropriation, and there was also a private fund in the hands of the Faculty, all of which made possible the facilities of the Hospital both as an institution for treatment of the sick and for clinical instruction.

The Out-Door Department was now located in the College building, and was the College dispensary. This was so located because of convenience and in order to allow students the advantages of instruction in pharmacy. The clinical material thus provided was utilized to best educational advantage. Each professor had one or more clinical assistants, and his own private apartment, thus allowing smooth functioning of each department, without interference of the others. Those patients who required in-door treatment had been transferred to the Hospital.

The Announcement for 1887 tells of a chemical laboratory, fitted up under the direction of the professor of that subject, so that students would have ample opportunity to become thoroughly acquainted with its principles.

In 1888 the College had a new home at the Southeast Corner of Hoffman Street and Druid Hill Avenue, a central and convenient location, accessible, by street car, from the various parts of the city. The out-patient or College dispensary was located here, the in-patients being treated at The Hospital of the Good Samaritan.

By 1895 the College occupied a group of buildings (its final home), on the corner of McCulloh and Hoffman Streets, two of which it owned. The location was convenient, being accessible to all parts of the City by means of cable and electric cars. The College building had a southern exposure, was well-lighted, and had three lecture rooms, a suite of rooms, microscopes et al, for instruction in normal and pathological histology, and all the other appurtenances already mentioned in this study, or discussed below. In addition to private clinic rooms for the various departments, there were reception rooms for patients and other means for ample medical instruction. The general hospital had twenty-five beds, and a lying-in hospital (The Maternité Hospital), separated from the College building by only the width of a street (410 W. Hoffman Street), had twelve beds. There were also the dispensary, and the large out-door obstetric clinic, discussed elsewhere, to afford a great deal of clinical study. In addition, the Presbyterian Eye, Ear and Throat Charity Hospital (one of the largest in the country), was available for instruction in the departments of the Hospital, the cases at St. Mary's Asylum could be studied by the students, and Professor Trimble made available ample opportunity to see injuries of all kinds which had resulted from railroad accidents on the Belt Line, Baltimore and Lehigh.

In 1882 equipment included drawings, specimens and manikin, for obstetrics; drawings, models, casts, anatomical and pathological preparations in surgery; plates, models and various instruments for teaching diseases of throat and chest; models, plates, drawings, preparations and dissections in anatomy and operative surgery; "a well-selected series of materia medica and pharmaceutical preparations". (The College purchased a complete set of anatomical models, made by Bock of Leipzig, in 1883.)

By 1886 the College could boast "several microscopes . . . imported from Germany, especially for use of the laboratory, which is provided with all facilities for . . . Normal and Pathological Histology", thus providing modern medical instruction.

Later an osteological cabinet, containing an abundant supply of bones was assembled, for study by the students.

In 1895 the library had several hundred choice books including many modern text-books, which circulated, and current journals.

By 1898 the laboratory of bacteriology was equipped with a thermostat, dry air and steam sterilizer, microscopes with oil immersion lenses and Abbe' condensers, and other necessary apparatus.

The school made acknowledgment, in its Announcement for that year, to the following persons who had subscribed to a fund for the purchase of the equipment for the laboratory of bacteriology:

Professor William Osler	Mr. Herman Cone
Professor Edward N. Brush	Mr. Sol. N. Cone
Professor Ralph Robinson	Mr. Ceasar Cone
Mr. Isaac Guggenheimer	Mrs. Moses H. Cone
Mrs. I. N. Guggenheimer	Mrs. Helen Cone
Miss Clara Guggenheimer	Mr. H. J. Lobe
Professor Eugene F. Cordell	Mrs. J. Mann
Mrs. Rose W. Rosenfeld	Mrs. Louis K. Gutman
Mr. Nathan Ullman	Dr. Anngenette Fowler-Noble

The College also acquired a full set of crude drugs and a fine collection of chemicals at about this time. These, with the earlier collections of specimens, were displayed in a special room, to which students could have access.

II. CURRICULUM

The first session was that of 1882-1883, and ran from October 2 until the following May 1, with intermissions at Christmas and all legal holidays. The College favored a seven months rather than a "crowded" five months term.

There was a full series of lectures upon each of the following subjects:

PRINCIPLES AND PRACTICE OF MEDICINE

The lectures were supplemented by clinical instruction on the diseases commonly met by the general practitioner. Special attention was given to diagnosis, and the distinctive signs of the several diseases pointed out. The combination of didactic and chemical instruction was held by the College to be the best kind of preparation for becoming a practitioner.

DISEASES OF WOMEN

The course began with the study of the surgical anatomy of the female genito-urinary organs. Various methods and instruments for diagnosis of diseases of uterus and appendages were thoroughly explained. Diseases and displacements of the uterus were illustrated by drawings and models, and ample clinical opportunities were provided for practical instruction. Therapeutic resources and the technicalities of gynecology were taught with care, as were surgical procedures for cure and repair of the various diseases and injuries of women. Instruction was both clinical and didactic.

OBSTETRICS

The aim was to be as thorough and practical as possible. The anatomy and physiology of the female reproductive organs were considered, after which the subject of embryology was presented, in the light of current knowledge. Pregnancy, gestation and labor were discussed, with special emphasis upon instruction on the mechanical phenomena of labor and the "necessary attentions to the mother during and after the act of parturition" and management of the new-born child. Malformations, malpositions and diseases incident to the pregnant and lying-in state were given attention, as were the accidents which result during parturition and the operative procedures for correcting these. Stress was laid upon the fact that a knowledge of the principles of obstetrics must be accompanied by the necessary skill needed to apply such principles in successful practice. Illustrative material included the use of drawings, specimens and the manikin. Whenever possible, clinics for illustrating practical obstetrics were held.

SURGERY

Surgical pathology and practice were taught in a clear and practical manner. After a study of inflammation and its results came consideration of the various constitutional diseases, as erysipelas, septicemia, and others, then the disorders of special organs and regions. Illustrative materials included drawings, models, casts, anatomical and pathological preparations, and clinical demonstrations of the diseases under discussion.

MATERIA MEDICA AND THERAPEUTICS

This was a course on the materials of medicine with special emphasis upon therapeutics or the application of remedies to disease. The student acquired a practical familiarity with drugs and the art of compounding prescriptions, in the Drug Room.

PHYSIOLOGY AND DISEASES OF CHILDREN

This was a course in those established facts of physiology as were of service to the physician, and it avoided doubtful or theoretical questions. Attention was given to histology.

The course on the diseases of children was both clinical and didactic, every effort being made to familiarize students with the peculiarities of disease as it affects children.

DISEASES OF THROAT AND CHEST

There were both didactic and clinical lectures, illustrated by plates, models and other aids. There was much practical instruction in the use of rhinoscope, laryngoscope and the various methods of physical diagnosis.

ANATOMY AND OPERATIVE SURGERY

This was an illustrated course, made as practical as possible by the professor, who used models, plates, drawings, preparations and dissections. There were demonstrations of surgical operations and application of instruments and apparatus. All surgical maneuvers were carefully performed and clearly explained.

CHEMISTRY

This was a rather elementary course, aimed at meeting the practical needs of the medical practitioner. Emphasis was upon tests for impurities in water, milk and "other articles of domestic consumption"; antidotes for poisons; the "physical and vital properties" of the chemical agents used in medicine and surgery; urine analysis.

The first Announcement also promised lectures upon diseases of eye and ear, diseases of children. Emphasis was laid upon supplementary clinical lectures on the practical branches, and the fact that there would be laboratory work in chemistry, materia medica and pharmacy, and demonstrations in anatomy and histology. The second Announcement promised lectures upon hygiene and upon medical jurisprudence.

CLINICS

During its first year (1882-1883), the Hospital had 3,000 visits in the Out-Door Department, and patients requiring operation had been admitted to the Wards.

GYNECOLOGICAL AND OBSTETRIC CLINICS

These were active from the beginning, and nearly all the ordinary diseases of women, and those complicating pregnancy were treated, thus providing good opportunities to learn.

CLINICAL MEDICINE

A good opportunity was afforded to become acquainted with the acute and chronic diseases common in our climate. There were many patients.

SURGICAL CLINIC

The many interesting and instructive cases included those of spinal diseases, diseases of joints, wounds, abscesses, ulcers, hernia, fistula, necrosis, aneurism, fractures and dislocations, hemorrhoids, syphilis, etc. The John Hopkins Asylum furnished interesting surgical cases, operated upon in the presence of the class. The House of Refuge did likewise.

THROAT AND CHEST CLINIC

The large number of patients in this clinic and the careful teaching by the professor made each student familiar with the physical signs presented by the healthy chest and then, by the various diseases of lungs and heart. After sufficient training, each student was permitted to diagnose cases in the presence and under supervision of the professor. Students were also trained in making examinations with laryngoscope and other means. The number of patients was large.

PEDIATRICS CLINIC

The department of diseases of children was made into a separate clinic apart from that of clinical medicine. It provided ample training in diagnosis and treatment.

OUT-DOOR OBSTETRICAL DEPARTMENT

By registering name and address, poor women could obtain the services of competent assistant physicians during confinement, at their homes, free of charge and, in case of difficulty, the professors attended in person. Students thus saw a large number of cases, and learned midwifery in a practical manner – diagnosis, judgment as to stages of labor, its progress, and mechanism. In addition to normal labor, students also frequently saw application of the forceps version, and other approved methods for relief of difficult and unnatural labor. The class was subdivided into small classes of two or three, each group "privileged to witness the accouchment", and when competent, took charge of the case. Students thus saw from two to six cases of obstetrics per session.

HOSPITAL

In the gynecological wards, set apart for the purpose, the professor demonstrated the surgical procedures necessary for the cure and repair of diseases and injuries, such as lacerations of the perineum and cervix, various forms of fistulae, removal of tumor, etc. Nearly all of the gynecological operations were performed each session. Therapeutic resources and technicalities of gynecology, such as use of pessaries, sponge tents, tampons, curettes, and intra-uterine applications were fully explained.

In obstetrical wards women were "delivered" in the presence of the class, the professor teaching the various obstetric operations and demonstrating the physiological changes "which the maternal system undergoes during the puerperal period."

GENERAL WARDS

These were for any illness, except those which were contagious, and for accident cases.

DAILY ORDER OF LECTURES

Session 1882-1883

Hour	Monday	Tuesday	Wednesday	Thursday	Friday	Saturday	Hour
9 A.M.	Prof. Cordell	Prof. Thomas	Prof. Cordell		Prof. Thomas		9 A.M.
10 A.M.	Prof. Jay	Prof. Ashby	Prof. Winslow	Prof. Jay	Prof. Winslow	Prof. Ashby	10 A.M.
11 A.M.	Prof. Booker	Prof. Browne	Prof. Lynch	Prof. Booker	Prof. Lynch	Prof. Browne	11 A.M.
2 P.M.	Clinic Prof. Winslow	Dispen-sary	Dispen-sary	Clinic Prof. Lynch	Clinic Prof. Browne	Clinic Prof. Jay	2 P.M.
3 P.M.	Chemistry Dr. Piggot	Prof. Cordell	Clinic Prof. Thomas	Clinic Prof. Ashby	Chemistry Dr. Piggot		3 P.M.

DAILY ORDER OF LECTURES

SESSION OF 1883-84

MONDAY

9	Materia Medica	Prof. Cordell
10	Anatomy	Prof. Jay
11	Physiology	Prof. Booker
+ 2	Surgery	Prof. Winslow
* 3½	Hygiene	Dr. Thomas
* 3½	Medical Jurisprudence	Dr. Quinan

TUESDAY

9	Diseases of Throat and Chest	Prof. Thomas
10	Obstetrics	Prof. Ashby
11	Diseases of Women	Prof. Browne
+ 2	Surgery	Prof. Jay
+ 3	Clinical Medicine	Prof. Cordell
4	Diseases of Eye and Ear	Prof. Murdoch

WEDNESDAY

9	Materia Medica	Prof. Cordell
10	Chemistry	Dr. Piggot
11	Prin. and Practice of Medicine	Prof. Lynch
+ 2	Diseases of Children	Prof. Booker
+ 3	Diseases of Throat and Chest	Prof. Thomas

THURSDAY

10	Anatomy	Prof. Jay
11	Physiology	Prof. Booker
2	Surgery	Prof. Winslow
+ 3	Obstetrics and Diseases of Women	Prof. Ashby
+ 4	Diseases of Eye and Ear	Prof. Murdoch

FRIDAY

10	Surgery	Prof. Winslow
11	Prin. and Practice of Medicine	Prof. Lynch
+ 2	Diseases of Women	Prof. Browne
4	Diseases of Throat and Chest	Prof. Thomas

SATURDAY

9	Chemistry	Dr. Piggot
10	Obstetrics	Prof. Ashby
11	Diseases of Women	Prof. Browne

+ Clinics   *Alternate Mondays   Dissections Daily

THE CHANGING CURRICULUM

In 1884-85, the College offered a choice of a three-year graded curriculum, or a two-year graded course, provided that a student had studied for one year under a preceptor, could furnish the following certificate, signed by a physician in good standing, and had complied with the other regulations:

CERTIFICATE

"This is to certify that .... has faithfully pursued her medical studies under my personal direction for twelve months.

.... M.D."

THREE YEAR COLLEGIATE COURSE

First or Junior Year – Anatomy, Physiology, Chemistry, Materia Medica and Pharmacy. These branches were taught not only by lectures, but by practical laboratory work, dissections and recitations. At the end of this year final examinations were held on

Anatomy, Chemistry, Physiology and Practical Pharmacy.

Second or Intermediate Year – Regional Anatomy by Dissections, Materia Medica, Obstetrics, Practice, Gynecology, Surgery, Diseases of Throat and Chest, Operative Surgery, and Medical Jurisprudence. During this year attendance on all the clinics were required. At the end of this year final examinations were held on Regional Anatomy, Materia Medica and Operative Surgery.

Third or Senior Year – Practice, Gynecology, Obstetrics, Surgery, Diseases of Throat and Chest, Diseases of Children, Diseases of Eye and Ear, Hygiene and Pathology. Clinical Practice. Examinations at the end of this year on all these branches except Hygiene and Pathology.

TWO YEAR COURSE

First Year – Anatomy, Physiology, Chemistry, Materia Medica, Practice, Gynecology, Obstetrics, Surgery, Diseases of Throat and Chest, Operative Surgery, Medical Jurisprudence, Dissections and attendance on Clinics. Examinations at the end of this year on Operative Surgery.

Second Year – The same except that Medical Jurisprudence and Operative Surgery were dropped, and Diseases of Children, Diseases of Eye and Ear, Hygiene and Pathology were added. Dissections. Clinical Practice in all branches. Examination on all the above branches except Hygiene, Medical Jurisprudence and Pathology.

The course in physiology was described as "advanced physiology", supplemented by recitations in elementary physiology, demonstrations and practical histology. The work on diseases of children, which was also a part of this chair, remained the same as in 1883-84.

Materia Medica and Therapeutics – The emphasis was now upon natural history of drugs and opportunity to test theoretical views of lectures in the clinic. There were recitations, lectures; there was training in practical pharmacy. New courses appeared: diseases of eye and ear, hygiene, medical jurisprudence, general pathology.

DISEASES OF EYE AND EAR

By didactic and clinical lectures students acquired the needed knowledge of these diseases, and the practical use of ophthalmoscope, trial glasses, otoscope, Eustachian catheter, Politzer bag, head mirror speculum, and other methods of physical diagnosis.

HYGIENE

The lectures emphasized the practical application of this study to daily life.

MEDICAL JURISPRUDENCE

The course consisted of lectures, embracing the usual topics, with practical instruction (illustrated from American authorities), on the duties of the general practitioner, "when occupying the responsible role of a medical jurist."

GENERAL PATHOLOGY

A course of lectures, intended for advanced students.

PRACTICAL ANATOMY

This has been discussed in section I, Buildings and Equipment.

EYE AND EAR CLINIC

This clinic supplied ample opportunity to become familiar with diseases of these organs, and with the practical use of ophthalmoscope and other instruments.

In addition to hospital clinics, and the surgical cases of the John Hopkins Asylum and the House of Refuge mentioned earlier, the graduates were given the privilege of a month's gratuitous "residence" at the Thomas Wilson Sanitarium, where there were many opportunities to observe children's diseases.

In other respects the course contents remained the same as in the previous session.

SESSION OF 1885-86

Three year course: Microscopy was added to the first year schedule. Physiology, chemistry, diseases of children, hygiene and general pathology were added to the second year course. The studies for the third year students remained the same.

Two year course: Same as in 1884.

The philosophy underlying the educational plan was that after a thorough grounding in the principles of medical science, during the earlier years, the student could be led to the advanced branches, with special attention to individual student advancement, to training in "various methods of physical diagnosis, and treatment."

SESSION OF 1886-87

Emphasis was now upon much activity in laboratory, drug room and dissecting room for beginning students, as a means of acquiring background for future studies, and upon recitations from text-books in the elementary branches, instructors being in charge of recitations. Professors held quizzes in the more advanced branches.

There were a few changes in the order in which subjects were taught – for example, diseases of eye and ear were now in the second year curriculum, while diseases of throat and chest were taught in the third year.

By regulations, each junior student was required to spend one afternoon each week in the drug room, where she was given instruction in pharmacy and assisted in making pharmaceutical preparations and filling prescriptions. Regular recitations were held, and the final examination, on theory and practice of pharmacy, held at the close of the year, counted toward the calculation of the student's standing at a given time.

The out-door department of the obstetrical clinic had become so well patronized that the time of the senior students was being taxed to the utmost. In the in-door department (the hospital wards), students were being instructed in touch, in ausculting the fetal heart, in the practice of abdominal palpation, and in the physiological changes connected with pregnancy, as well as those elements of practice mentioned earlier.

At the surgical clinics in dispensary and hospital, all sorts of operations were being performed (extirpation of various forms of tumors, amputations, circumcision, tapping of hydrocele, and so on).

At the medical clinic a great variety of acute and chronic diseases were being treated. Records and notes were made, and advanced students were required to examine cases, give diagnoses and treatments, thus calling for an exercise of judgment and practical use of acquired knowledge. Hospital practice allowed for "follow-up" of acute cases, an advantage not possible from study limited to dispensaries.

TRAINING SCHOOL FOR NURSES
Session of 1887-88

Lectures on practical nursing were given, as follows:

- Duties of nurses in special cases.
- Surgical emergencies.
- Medical emergencies and the administration of drugs.
- Care of the mother and child.
- Bandaging and the treatment of wounds.
- Hygiene.
- Care of the sick and of invalids.
- Care of children, and physiology in daily life.

In connection with this "Training School for Nurses", a directory for Nurses was established at the Hospital building. Competent nurses could be furnished promptly, at any hour of the day.

1889: Emphasis was upon the training of junior students in the use of the microscope and methods of preparing and examining material for microscopic study of the normal structures of the body. Senior students were grounded in pathology.

Chemistry now advanced in standing, from an elementary course to "a general survey of the entire field of inorganic chemistry, particularly as applied to medicine . . . general principles of toxicology and urinalysis." In the laboratory the students had an opportunity to verify facts learned in the lectures, and to become familiar with modern laboratory methods. The first half of the course was devoted to general chemical phenomena, and properties of non-metals and their compounds. The second half of the course was devoted to qualitative analysis, concluding with identification of unknowns.

Thus students were now doing laboratory work in chemistry, histology and pathology.

By 1893 Chemistry lectures and laboratory work were extended over a period of two years. The lectures of the first half of each session presented a general survey of the entire field of "chemico-physics"; general inorganic compounds and those metals which are important to the physician. The second half of each term was devoted to general organic chemistry (homologous series, etc.), urinalysis, toxicology, and micro-chemistry. The laboratory work dealt with verification of principles, familiarization with chemical manipulations, reactions of the principal metals, acids and compounds, qualitative analysis, urinalysis and toxicology, (in detail). There were two lectures and six hours of laboratory per week, the class being divided "into suitable sections". There were frequent recitations and general quizzes.

Pharmacy was now being taught, in theoretical and practical aspects, by formal lectures, which included treatment of the theories, laws and principles controlling the extemporaneous practices of pharmacy, production of the various officinal preparations, preparation of galenicals and compounding of prescriptions, and opportunity to acquire thorough acquaintance with "physical and chemical characteristics of the materia medica, especially in combination".

1894: The work in histology laboratory provided every first year student with the opportunity to learn techniques of selecting, hardening, cutting, staining and mounting specimens of the various normal tissue. There were four to six hours per week on practical work, and examinations (theoretical and practical), were held from time to time. Third year students were taught pathological histology with the same thoroughness.

The course in physiology consisted of two weekly lectures, illustrated by suitable experiments: digestion, blood, circulation, respiration, metabolism, animal heat, excretion, muscle tissue, the peripheral and central nervous system, the special senses, reproduction and development, all in detail. There were recitations, practical work in the laboratory, and a monthly examination. The course was obligatory for first and second year students and was believed to be of especial value to the physician in the diagnosis and treatment of disease.

Hygiene consisted of about twenty lectures (with recitations and demonstrations when possible). The topics were: Personal hygiene of the four periods of life – a) infancy, childhood, youth; b) the young man; c) the man; d) the old man.

School pathology – a) the construction of school houses; exercise; school quarantine; air; ventilation; methods of heating; water, sewerage, plumbing, house drainage, baths and bathing, clothing, dietetics, prophylaxis, antiseptics, bacteriology, sterilization, disinfection and deodorants.

In 1895 there were marked changes in the curriculum. The session was reduced to six months in length (October 1 to April 1), but the school, one of the first in the nation, and the first in Maryland, to give a three year course, inaugurate a preliminary examination, lengthened annual courses, a graded curriculum, and other improvements in methods of medical education, proposed to make a further improvement by lengthening the required period of study to four annual courses, while continuing to improve its facilities, corresponding with the exacting demands of the day, and enabling it to prepare its graduates for a creditable professional career. The College claimed (Announcement for 1895, pg. 5) that:

> *Before the action of the American Medical College Association in May, 1894, making a four-year term compulsory in 1895, this College had lengthened its annual term of lectures to eight months, making the course 24 months. Ever ready to adopt improvements and to strengthen the influence of the College Association (the inception of which originated in its Faculty), it cheerfully complies with the requirement to add the additional year to its course.*

By rule of the Faculty it was required that one-fourth of the time be devoted to quizzing. Another requirement obliged all senior students to assist for one year at operations in the hospital.

Bacteriology was now being taught (to third year students). The lectures and laboratory work were so arranged that students prepared the culture media and staining fluids, cultivated and differentiated the important pathogenic bacteria, and inoculated and examined the organisms in the tissues.

ANATOMY

The following is quoted from the Announcement for 1895:

> *The first half of the year is devoted to the study of bones and attachment of muscles and ligaments and their relation to the joints. Advanced students are required to make joint preparations. The second half is devoted to work on the subject. The new preparations for demonstrations are worked out with the class. Muscles, arteries, veins, lymphatics, the brain, cerebrospinal and sympathetic nervous systems, viscera, thoracic cavity and regional anatomy are thoroughly studied.*
>
> *The demonstrator of osteology works with the students until they*

thoroughly master the bones and attachment of muscles. Students are not allowed to dissect until they know this part of the anatomical course. A full dissection of a subject is required of each student during the course. After dissection on each part the student is examined orally by the Professor.

OPERATIVE SURGERY

After the various operations were demonstrated on the subject, each student was required to perform them herself.

PATHOLOGY AND CLINICAL MICROSCOPY

There were lectures and demonstrations in general pathology and pathological histology, with the demonstration of gross lesions, where possible. Lectures on clinical microscopy embraced consideration of blood, sputum, urine, feces and gastric juice. Seniors could perform laboratory experiments relating to the points made in the lectures, practical instruction being given on two afternoons of each week throughout the College term.

MEDICAL JURISPRUDENCE

There were two parts to the course:

1 . . . State Medicine, ten lectures: origin and development of medical jurisprudence; functions of the State and the administration of law (with special reference to woman's position as a member of society); State and local laws affecting the practice of medicine and dispensing of drugs; the constitution and functions of Boards of Health; legislation with respect to contagious diseases, including quarantine laws and vital statistics; disposition and care of the insane; preventive medicine and the law; principles of evidence in relation to medical testimony.

2 . . . Forensic medicine, eight lectures (later increased to twelve): impotence and sterility; rape; pregnancy; legitimacy; infanticide; wounds; poisons; insanity; feigned diseases; survivorship; malpractice.

In 1896 the graded curriculum lengthened to four years, each of eight months duration, shaped up as follows:

First year: Anatomy, Osteology, Physiology, Chemistry, Pharmacy, and Embryology. These branches are taught not only by lecture but by practical laboratory work, dissections and recitations. At the end of this year final examinations are held in Osteology, Embryology, and Pharmacy.

Second year: Anatomy, Physiology, Chemistry, Materia Medica and Therapeutics, Hygiene, Bacteriology, Normal Histology, and Dissections. At the end of this year final examinations are held on Anatomy, Physiology, Chemistry, Hygiene, Bacteriology, and Normal Histology.

Third year: Materia Medica and Therapeutics, Practice, Surgery, Obstetrics, Diseases of Women, Diseases of Children, Diseases of Eye and Ear, Operative Surgery, Physical Diagnosis, with instruction in bandaging and fracture dressing, and Clinics, Pathology, and Medical Jurisprudence. At the end of this year final examinations are held on Materia Medica and Therapeutics, Operative Surgery, Pathology, and Medical Jurisprudence.

Fourth year: Practice, Surgery, Obstetrics, Diseases of Women, Diseases of Children, Diseases of Eye and Ear, Diseases of Chest, Throat and Nose, Clinical Microscopy, Orthopaedics, Dermatology, Mental Diseases, Neurology, and Clinics. At the end of this year final examinations are held on all these branches. During the year opportunity will be afforded to review the earlier subjects of the course in order that the students may be better prepared to undergo successfully the State Examinations.

In 1899 the program reproduced from the Announcement for that year, was as follows:

First Year – Anatomy, Chemistry, Dissections, Embryology, Materia Medica, Osteology, Pharmacy, and Physiology. These branches are taught not only by lectures, but by practical laboratory work and recitations. At the end of the year examinations are held:

FINAL	PRIMARY
Embryology	Anatomy
Materia Medica	Chemistry
Osteology	Physiology
Pharmacy	

Second Year – Anatomy, Bacteriology, Chemistry, Dissections, Histology (Normal), Hygiene, Pathology, Physiology, and Therapeutics. At the end of the year examinations are held:

FINAL	PRIMARY
Anatomy	Pathology
Bacteriology	Therapeutics
Chemistry	
Histology (Normal)	
Hygiene	
Physiology	

Third Year – Children, Diseases of; Eye and Ear, Diseases of; Gynaecology; Medical Jurisprudence; Obstetrics; Pathology; Physical Diagnosis; Practice of Medicine; Surgery; Surgery (Operative); Therapeutics. Instruction is given in bandaging and fracture dressing. Attendance on the Clinics at Hospital and Dispensary are required. At the end of the year examinations are held:

FINAL	PRIMARY
Medical Jurisprudence	Children, Diseases of
Pathology	Eye and Ear, Diseases of
Physical Diagnosis	Gynaecology
Surgery (Operative	Obstetrics
Therapeutics	Practice of Medicine
	Surgery

Fourth Year – Children, Diseases of; Dermatology; Eye and Ear, Diseases of; Gynaecology; Mental Diseases; Microscopy (Clinical); Neurology; Nose, Throat and Chest; Obstetrics; Practice of Medicine; Surgery. Attendance on the Clinics at Hospital and Dispensary is required. At the end of the year final examinations are held on all the above named branches.

(For an explanation of the terms "primary" and "final", please see under "Requirements for Graduation", 1896, at the end of section II, Curriculum.)

SCHEDULE OF LECTURES
1898-1899

FIRST YEAR

MONDAY

10 A.M.	Chemistry	Prof. Kintzing
11 A.M.	Physiology	Prof. Batchelor
12 M.	Anatomy	Prof. Trimble

TUESDAY

11 A.M.	Anatomy	Prof. Trimble
3 P.M.	Chemical Laboratory	Dr. Holmes
4 P.M.	Chemical Laboratory	Dr. Holmes

WEDNESDAY

9 A.M.	Embryological Laboratory	Prof. Pollack till Feb. 1st
10 A.M.	Embryological Laboratory	Prof. Pollack till Feb. 1st

THURSDAY

9 A.M.	Materia Medica	Dr. Abercrombie
11 A.M.	Physiology	Prof. Batchelor
2 P.M.	Pharmaceutical Laboratory	Mr. McAvoy

FRIDAY

9 A.M.	Osteology	Dr. Davis
10 A.M.	Embryological Laboratory	Prof. Pollack till Feb. 1st
11 A.M.	Embryological Laboratory	Prof. Pollack till Feb. 1st
3 P.M.	Chemical Laboratory	Dr. Holmes
4 P.M.	Chemical Laboratory	Dr. Holmes

SATURDAY

9 A.M.	Pharmacy, (Didactic)	Prof. Blades
10 A.M.	Chemistry	Prof. Kintzing
12 M.	Anatomy	Prof. Trimble

SECOND YEAR

MONDAY

10 A.M.	Chemistry	Prof. Kintzing
11 A.M.	Physiology	Prof. Batchelor
12 M.	Anatomy	Prof. Trimble

TUESDAY

9 A.M.	Pathology (Didactic)	Prof. Cone
10 A.M.	Hygiene	Dr. Eareckson
11 A.M.	Anatomy	Prof. Trimble
12 M.	Materia Medica	Prof. Smith
4:30 P.M.	Normal Histology (Didactic)	Prof. Lewis till Feb. 1st

WEDNESDAY

3 P.M.	Bacteriological Laboratory	Dr. Hamburger after Feb. 1st
4 P.M.	Bacteriological Laboratory	Dr. Hamburger after Feb. 1st

THURSDAY

11 A.M.	Physiology	Prof. Batchelor
12 M.	Materia Medica	Prof. Smith

FRIDAY

1.30 P.M.	Histological Laboratory	Prof. Lewis till Feb. 1st.
3 P.M.	Bacteriological Laboratory	Dr. Hamburger after Feb. 1st
4 P.M.	Bacteriological Laboratory	Dr. Hamburger after Feb. 1st.

SATURDAY

10 A.M.	Chemistry	Prof. Kintzing
12 M.	Anatomy	Prof. Trimble

THIRD YEAR

MONDAY

11 A.M.	Practice	Prof. Cordell
2 P.M.	Clinic Surgery	Prof. Jay
4 P.M.	Obstetrics	Dr. ________

TUESDAY

9 A.M.	Pathology (Didactic)	Prof. Cone
10 A.M.	Surgery	Prof. Jay
11 A.M.	Diseases of Women	Prof. Browne
12 M.	Materia Medica	Prof. Smith
2 P.M.	Clinic Medicine	Profs. Cordell Smith, Batchelor
4 P.M.	Diseases Eye and Ear	Prof. Harlan

WEDNESDAY

9 A.M.	Pathological Laboratory	Prof. Cone
10 A.M.	Pathological Laboratory	Prof. Cone
11 A.M.	Diseases of Women	Prof. Browne
12 M.	Operative Surgery	Prof. Trimble after Feb. 1st.
1:30 P.M.	Clinic Children	Prof. O'Donovan
4 P.M.	Obstetrics	Prof. Riley

THURSDAY

9 A.M.	Pathological Laboratory	Prof. Cone
10 A.M.	Pathological Laboratory	Prof. Cone

11 A.M.	Diseases of Children	Prof. O'Donovan
12 M.	Materia Medica	Prof. Smith
2 P.M.	Clinic Stomach	Prof. Kintzing
3 P.M.	Clinic Surgery	Prof. Trimble
4 P.M.	Medical Jurisprudence	Prof. Lee after Nov. 1st.

FRIDAY

10 A.M.	Surgery	Prof. Jay
11 A.M.	Practice	Prof. Cordell
2 P.M.	Clinic Women	Prof. Browne
3 P.M.	Physical Diagnosis	Dr. Johnson till Feb. 1st.
4 P.M.	Obstetrics	Prof. Riley

SATURDAY

11 A.M.	Diseases of Children	Prof. O'Donovan
2 P.M.	Clinic Eye and Ear	Prof. Harlan (Presbyterian Hospital)

FOURTH YEAR

MONDAY

9 A.M.	Clinical Microscopy	Prof. Lewis after Feb. 1st.
10 A.M.	Clinical Microscopy	Prof. Lewis after Feb. 1st.
11 A.M.	Practice	Prof. Cordell
2 P.M.	Clinic Surgery	Prof. Jay
3 P.M.	Clinic Nose and Throat	Dr. Bernstein
4 P.M.	Clinic Obstetrics	Dr. ________

TUESDAY

10 A.M.	Surgery	Prof. Jay
11 A.M.	Diseases of Women	Prof. Browne
2 P.M.	Clinic Medicine	Profs. Cordell, Smith, Batchelor
4 P.M.	Diseases Eye and Ear	Prof. Harlan
2 P.M.	Clinical Microscopy	Prof. Lewis after Feb. 1st.

WEDNESDAY

11 A.M.	Diseases of Women	Prof. Browne
1:30 P.M.	Clinic Children	Prof. O'Donovan
3 P.M.	Psychiatry	Prof. Brush
4 P.M.	Obstetrics	Prof. Riley

THURSDAY

11 A.M.	Diseases of Children	Prof. O'Donovan
2 P.M.	Clinic Stomach	Prof. Kintzing
3 P.M.	Clinic Surgery	Prof. Trimble

FRIDAY

10 A.M.	Surgery	Prof. Jay
11 A.M.	Practice	Prof. Cordell
2 P.M.	Clinic Women	Prof. Browne
3 P.M.	Neurology	Dr. Deetjen after Feb. 1st.
4 P.M.	Obstetrics	Prof. Riley

SATURDAY

11 A.M.	Diseases of Children	Prof. O'Donovan
2 P.M.	Clinic Eye and Ear	Prof. Harlan (Presbyterian Hospital)

DISSECTIONS DAILY

Psychiatric Clinic .... by Prof. Brush, as announced.

In 1900 histology and pharmacy exchanged places in the first and second year programs. The fourth year course in mental diseases was now psychiatry.

Diseases of children were taught in two lectures and one clinic per week. The condition of the child in health and in disease, from birth to adolescence, best method of preserving health or curing its maladies, the preparation and administration of artificial food, were all considered, and the clinic was drawn upon for illustrative purposes in the lectures. The students also profited from the opportunity of learning differential diagnosis in the clinics. (In 1904 fourth year students took lectures and quizzes, based upon the text-book by Holt. These students took histories, made examinations, and presented cases to the class.)

The principles of surgery, so dependent upon the numerous day to day investigations and discoveries pertaining to the etiology and pathology of surgical diseases, and progressive improvement in technique, undergo frequent revision. Consequently the professor taught both those principles and methods which had stood the test of time and research and, as well, all most modern and most useful knowledge in this field.

CLINICS

In the previous year (1899), 3,253 patients were treated in the In-and-Out-patient departments. There were clinics for the following: diseases of children, cutaneous diseases, gynecology, acute and chronic affections, nose and throat, obstetrics, surgery. These continued throughout the year, and were a source of the most valuable medical education for students. The work of these clinics has been discussed above.

1901: Psychiatry lectures, one at the College, weekly, and one clinical lecture at the Springfield State Hospital, monthly, provided an opportunity to become acquainted with the different phases of insanity.

In the clinics 5,123 in-and out-patients had been treated in the previous year (1900), an increase of almost 1,900 over the year before that (1899).

1903: Gynecology (two lectures and two clinics per week, with recitations and quizzes), covered principles of this and allied subjects, with opportunity for students to acquire experience in the examination and management of gynecological cases by direct contact with patients, and familiarity with normal and diseased pelvic organs; the gynecological operations performed in the hospital demonstrated important conditions such as abdominal and plastic surgery, particular attention being paid to: urinary affections, urethral, ureteral, renal, and all vesical diseases connected with or dependent on the special organs of generation in women; gynecological pathology and bacteriology – diagnosis from uterine scrapings and tissues removed for this purpose; examination of micro-organisms from the genital and uropoietic organs. In the clinics nearly every important gynecological operation was performed (laparotomy removal of ovarian and other tumors, etc.).

Cutaneous diseases were carefully taught and illustrated by typical cases and by microscopical sections.

In orthopedics, the didactic and clinical lectures made students familiar with diagnosis and treatment of congenital and acquired deformities, and the fitting of mechanical appliances; each student was required to make and apply plastic dressings.

In physical diagnosis the effort was to prepare students for the clinical work of third and fourth years. The students learned to take histories and the methods of examination for physical diagnosis of diseases of thoracic and abdominal organs.

Histology was a four hour per week laboratory course.

Practice of medicine consisted of lectures and two clinics per week on a great variety of acute and chronic diseases. Records of cases for thorough analysis, and note-taking, were prominent features of the learning process. Advanced students examined, diagnosed and treated, learning to exercise judgment and apply knowledge earlier acquired. The same care was exercised in the departments of neurology, gastric affections and general medicine. There was "follow-through" on acute cases in the hospital.

Physiology was much the same course as that described above (1894).

Psychiatry consisted of weekly lectures and quizzes. The Sheppard and Enoch Pratt Hospital, near Baltimore, furnished cases in ample supply for clinical demonstration and study.

Principles of Surgery and Operative Surgery have been discussed above (1900).

Therapeutics, in the second and third years, reviewed the materia medica, but was largely devoted to a consideration of practical therapeutic measures – the more common and useful drugs, method of administration, dosage, and effect upon the human system. Methods of prescription writing, use of hydro-therapy and massage, diet in health and disease, and the treatment of special cases by rest, climate and other means, were features of the course. The clinical work of the medical dispensary, in the fourth year, furnished abundant opportunity to apply the knowledge acquired in the course.

In 1903 nearly 5,000 patients were treated in the dispensary.

REPORT
of the
HOSPITAL OF THE WOMAN'S MEDICAL COLLEGE
(Hospital Good Samaritan)
from
January 1, 1899 to January 1, 1900

Number of Patients in Hospital, Jan. 1, 1899	25
Number of Patients in Hospital, Jan. 1, 1900	13
Number admitted during year	318
Number discharged during year	305
Number of Medical Cases during year	120
Number of Gynaecol. Cases during year	61
Number of Surgical Cases during year	129
Number of Obstetrical Cases during year	10
Number of Private Cases during year	36
Number of Deaths during year	20
Number of Surgical Operations during year	95
Number of Gynaecol. Operations during year	52
Number of Private Patients during year	36
Number of City Patients during year	233
Number of State Patients during year	16

GYNAECOLOGICAL

Abscess, Post-uterine	3
Abscess, Vulval	1
Amenorrhea	1
Antiflexion	1
Ascites with Uterine Fibroids	1
Carcinoma (Uterine)	1
Cervical and Perineal Laceration	1
Cervical Laceration	1
Encysted Dropsy of Peritoneum	1
Endometritis	19
Fistula, Urethro-Vaginal	1
Fistula, Recto-Vaginal	1
Fibroids (Abdominal)	1
Gonorrheal Inflam. Bartholini's Glands	1
Oophoritis with Salpingitis	1
Pyosalpynx	5
Retroflexion	5
Retroversion	1
Salpingitis	1
Sarcoma (Uterine)	1
Syphilitic Vulval Condylomata	1
Pregnancy with Fibroid Uterus	1
Pregnancy Threatened Abortion	1
Urethral Caruncle	3
Vaginismus	1
Vulval Growth	1

MEDICAL

Acute Dilatation of Heart, Lung Apoplexy	1
Acute Alcoholism, Neuritis	1
Acute Enteritis	1
Acute Gastritis	1
Arterio-Sclerosis, Heart dilatation	1
Ascites	3
Bright's Disease	6
Bronchitis	4
Colitis	1
Chorea	1
Constipation	10
Chronic Constipation	5
Dyspepsia	1
Febricula	3
Goitre	2
Gastritis	4
Gastritis Chronic	1
Gastralgia	1
Gonorrheal Rheumatism	3
Heart Dilatation, Valvular insufficiency	1
Hemiplegia (left)	1
Hemiplegia (right)	3
Hydrothorax, Tricuspid Murmur	1
Hysteria	1
Inflammatory Rheumatism	4
Indigestion	1
Influenza	5
Interstitial Keratitis, Syphilitic	1
Marasmus	1
Malaria	4
Malaria after Confinement	1
Malaria after Typhoid	1
Melancholia	1
Moribund	1
Nausea and Indigestion	1
Nervous Prostration	4
Neurasthenia	5
Opium Habit	1
Ophthalmia	1
Ophthalmia (Gonorrheal)	1
Paralysis	2
Paraplegia	1
Pleurisy	1
Pneumonia	5
Pleurodynia	1
Prostration from Senility	1
Ptyalism	1
Rheumatism	4
Rheumatic Fever	1
Sciatica and Rheumatism	1

Syphilitic Keratitis	1
Tonsillitis (Follicular)	2
Tonsillitis (Parenchymatous)	1
Tuberculosis	6
Typhoid	4
Unknown	6

SURGICAL

Abscess (Knee)	1
Abscess under Chin	2
Abscess Ischio-Rectal	1
Abscess Thigh	1
Amputation Thumb	1
Amputation (Fingers)	6
Amputation (unhealed)	2
Ankyloglossia	1
Appendicitis	2
Ascites	3
Burns (Leg)	1
Burns (Arm)	1
Carcinoma (Nose)	1
Carcinoma (R. Breast)	2
Cellulitis	2
Cellulitis (Finger)	5
Cellulitis (Foot)	2
Cleft Palate	1
Colles' Fracture	2
Crushed and Lacerated Hand	1
Enlarged Glands (Cervical)	1
Elbow injured by a fall	1
Epididymitis	1
Erysipelas	1
Fingers Crushed	1
Fistula in Ano	3
Fracture, ext. end l. Clavicle	1
Fracture, Leg	2
Fracture, Femur	3
Fracture, Metacarpus	1
Fracture, Rib	1
Fracture, Skull	1
Furuncular eruption	1
Furuncles, head and face	1
Gall Stone	1
Gangrene (foot)	2
General Septic Peritonitis	1
Gonorrhea	1
Gun shot wound	1
Hand Crushed	1
Hemorrhoids and Fistula	1
Hip Anyklosed	1
Housemaid's Knee	1
Incised wound (arm)	1
Incised wound (finger)	1
Incised wound (forehead)	4
Incised wound (hand)	7
Incised wound (leg)	1
Incised wound (scalp)	7
Incised wound (under eye)	1
Impervious urethra	1
Infected hand	3
Injured by a fall	1
Inflammation (Cervical Glands)	1
Inflammation (Inguinal Glands)	2
Inflammation (Gall Bladder)	1
Laceration (Arm)	1
Laceration (Muscles of Arm)	1
Laceration (Leg and Foot)	1
Laceration (Toes, with Cellulitis)	1
Laryngeal Growth	1
Leg hurt by a fall	1
Mastitis	2
Ostitis (finger)	1
Osteo-periostitis, ankylosis, (knee)	1
Orchitis	1
Papilloma (hand)	1
Paralysis (muscles of bladder)	1
Pistol shot wound (hand)	1
Pott's Disease	1
Rachitis	1
Relaxed ligaments (foot and ankles)	1
Sarcoma (sup. maxillary)	1
Sebaceous Cyst (cheek)	1
Shock and injuries from a fall	1
Symptoms of appendicitis	1
Syphilitic ostitis (both legs)	1
Phimosis	2
Pin in throat	1
Post axillary tumor	1
Tuberculosis abscess, breast	1
Tumor, ear (fatty)	1
Tumor, cheek (fatty)	1
Ulcer (Leg)	4
Ulcer (Foot)	1
Varicose Ulcer	1
Wart on Nose	1

DISPENSARY REPORT

Total number of Patients	2835
Total number of Prescriptions	3528
Total number of New Patients	1721
Total number of Old Patients	1114

The curriculum during the last years of the school (1907-1910), was as follows:

1907: OUTLINE OF THE COURSES OF INSTRUCTION

FIRST YEAR

Anatomy – Three hours lectures and recitations per week throughout the term. Ten hours dissection weekly during two periods of eight weeks each.
Osteology – Two hours lectures and recitations per week, October 1st to February 1st.
Histology – One hour lecture and three hours laboratory instruction per week throughout the term.
Embryology – Two hours lectures and four hours laboratory instruction per week, February 1st to May 15th.
Physiology – Three hours per week lectures throughout the term.
Chemistry and Toxicology – Three hours lectures and six hours laboratory instruction per week throughout the term.
Materia Medica – Two hours lectures and one hour laboratory instruction per week, October 1st to February 1st.

Final examinations held in Osteology, Embryology, Histology, Materia Medica, Organic and Inorganic Chemistry. Primary examinations held in Anatomy and Physiology.

In order to be promoted to the second year a student must pass at least a majority of the required examinations of the first year.

SECOND YEAR

Anatomy – Three hours lectures and recitations per week throughout the term. Ten hours dissection weekly during two periods of eight weeks each.
Physiology – Three hours lectures and recitations, four hours laboratory instruction per week throughout the term.
Pharmacology – Two hours lectures and one hour laboratory instruction per week, February 1st to May 15th.
Pathology – Three hours lectures and six hours laboratory instruction throughout the term.
Bacteriology – Two hours lectures and five hours laboratory instruction per week, October 1st to January 1st.
Hygiene and Public Health – Two hours lectures and recitations per week, February 1st to May 15th.
Physical Diagnosis – Two lectures per week, March 1st to May 15th.

Final examinations held in Anatomy, Physiology, Physiological chemistry, Pharmacology, Bacteriology, Hygiene and Public Health and Pathology.

In order to be promoted to the third year a student must have passed all of the required examinations of the first year and at least a majority of those of the second year.

THIRD YEAR

Medicine – Three hours lectures and recitations. Six hours clinical instruction per week throughout the term.
Surgery – Three hours lectures and recitations and four hours clinical instruction per week throughout the term.
Gynecology – Two hours lectures and recitations. Two hours clinical instruction per week throughout the term.
Obstetrics – Two hours lectures and recitations. One hour clinical instruction per week throughout the term.
Therapeutics – Three hours lectures and recitations per week throughout the term.
Electrotherapeutics – One hour lecture and two hours clinical instruction per week, October 1st to April 1st.
Eye and Ear – One hour lecture and recitation per week throughout the term.
Nose and Throat – One hour lecture and recitation per week throughout the term.
Pediatrics – Two lectures per week January 1st to May 15th.
Dietetics – Two lectures per week October 1st to January 1st.
Clinical Microscopy, Medical Zoology – One hour lecture and two hours laboratory instruction per week throughout the term.
Physical Diagnosis – Three hours clinical instruction per week, October 1st to March 1st.

Examinations held in the Practice of Medicine, Practice of Surgery, the Principles and Practice of Obstetrics, Gynecology, Therapeutics, Physical Diagnosis, Electrotherapeutics, Eye and Ear, Nose and Throat, Pediatrics, Dietetics, Clinical Microscopy.

In order to be promoted to the fourth year a student must have passed all the required examinations of the first and second years and at least a majority of those of the third year.

FOURTH YEAR

Medicine – Three hours lectures and recitations. Six hours clinical, dispensary and bedside instruction per week throughout the term.
Surgery – Three hours lectures and recitations. Four hours clinical, dispensary and bedside instruction per week throughout the term.
Gynecology – Two hours lectures and recitations and two hours clinical and bedside instruction per week throughout the term.
Obstetrics – Two hours lectures and recitations and one hour clinical instruction per week throughout the term.
Eye and Ear – Two hours clinical instruction every other week throughout the term.
Nose and Throat – Two hours clinical instruction every other week throughout the term.
Pediatrics – Two hours clinical instruction per week throughout the term.
Genito-urinary Diseases – One hour lecture and one hour clinical instruction per week throughout the term.
Mental Diseases – One hour lecture and one hour clinical instruction per week throughout the term.
Nervous Diseases – One hour lecture and one hour clinical instruction per week throughout the term.
Medical Jurisprudence – One hour lecture per week throughout the term.
Dermatology – One hour lecture and one hour clinical instruction per week, October 1st to March 1st.
Orthopedic Surgery – Two hours clinical instruction per week throughout the term.

Examinations held at the end of the term in all the above-named branches.

The Faculty reserve the right to alter or amend the course of study if in their judgment it is deemed desirable.

Further changes were made in the last years of the life of the school:

Anatomy – Emphasis was now upon the phase of medical education. Embryology, osteology, arthrology and myology were completed in the first year, then a "primary"* examination was given. In the second year, angiology, neurology and splanchnology were taught, and at the end of that year a final examination was given on the entire course in anatomy. The second half of the first year, and the first half of the second year were devoted to work on the cadaver – muscles, arteries, veins, lymphatics, brain, cerebrospinal and sympathetic nervous system, viscera, thoracic cavity and regional anatomy were studied. Each student was required to make a full dissection, using atlases and text-books as guides. Students were encouraged to make the dissecting room their study room. There were lectures and recitations, in modified form of the old didactic lecture. In the study of the skeleton students were required to make drawings of the bones, in order to fix in the mind of the students the shape of the bones, attachment of muscles, location of the various foramina, tuberosities, tubercles, etc.

Bacteriology – Lectures and laboratory work were designed to make this a practical laboratory course of training in preparation of culture media, principles of sterilization and disinfection, methods of cultivating, staining and studying bacteria, the biological examination of air, water and soil, and the recognition of the important species of known pathogenic micro-organisms. The hygiene, as well as the pathologic relations of bacteriology were considered.

Chemistry – First year students took three lectures and three laboratory hours, per week, on elementary inorganic chemistry. In laboratory students learned to identify metals and acids. They acquired a general familiarity with compounds used by physicians. Second year students had two hours of lecture and two of laboratory on organic chemistry – alcohols, aldehydes, acids, esters, ethers, carbohydrates, fats, soaps, proteins, alkaloids and other substances. The time from January until the end of the session was devoted to chemical physiology – theory and laboratory work on blood, urine, foods. There were oral quizzes and a "written review" at the end of April. *Halliburton's Essentials of Chemical Physiology* was used as a guide in the second year course.

Dermatology – Forty lectures and clinics, dealing with the more common diseases of the skin, met with in our country, illustrated by charts and photographs. A great many cases were exhibited and discussed. The course was for members of the senior class.

Pathology – In addition to the lectures on general pathology and pathological histology, discussed above (1895), students prepared and studied illustrative tissues, microscopically,

*An oral examination not exceeding twenty minutes for each student, with the passing grade 70 on the basis of 100.

and saw laboratory and lecture demonstrations of the processes discussed. Special pathology of the various organs, with reference to pathological physiology of each, and development of symptoms of diseases, were taken up systematically in combined lectures and demonstrations.

Practice of Medicine – In addition to the course outlined above (1903), there was also a systematic course of lectures on nervous and mental diseases, as part of this department. There was one lecture and one clinic per week, for senior students, who were permitted to examine the cases presented. There were frequent quizzes upon both the didactic lectures and the clinical cases.

Genito-urinary Diseases – The course consisted of weekly clinics and frequent didactic lectures. The didactic lectures were devoted to a systematic study of the entire field of genito-urinary surgery. A large number of cases of the genito-urinary diseases of the female was presented to students, and each student was thoroughly drilled in the use and manipulation of various instruments. Special attention was given to the study of diagnosis with the various urethral and bladder instruments, including cystoscope and endoscope.

(The contents of the other courses are not discussed here, since there was little difference between them and that of the same courses, as outlined above, in the preceding years.)

Nearly 8,000 patients were treated in the dispensary in 1907. The students of the fourth year class had an abundance of clinical experience at the Hospital, and Dispensary, and saw demonstrations at the very large Presbyterian Eye, Ear and Throat Charity Hospital, and at the forty bed Hospital for the Relief of Crippled and Deformed Children (general orthopedic cases and lateral curvature of the spine).

The competitive examinations for resident physician at the New York Infant Asylum, the Charity Hospital at Norristown, Pa., the Methodist Episcopal Hospital of Philadelphia, Blockley Hospital of Philadelphia, and the Manhattan State Hospital for the Insane were open to graduates of this school.

COLLEGE PRIZES

In the early years a gold medal was given annually to the student who attained the highest grade in the final examination, provided that her average was 90 or over. From 1888 on, an average of 93 was required for this prize.

The student standing second in the graduating class was awarded second honor, on the same conditions.

In 1885 announcement was made of a prize in Practice for the student attaining the highest grade in the final examination in this subject.

MEDALS AND PRIZES

Year	GOLD MEDAL	PRIZE IN PRINCIPLES AND PRACTICE OF MEDICINE
1884	First Honor and Gold Medallist Mayne M. Pile Second Honor Hattie B. Jones	----
1885	First Honor and Gold Medallist Marie E. Thalwitzer Second Honor Alice S. Parkhurst	Marie B. Thalwitzer
1886	----	PRIZE IN SURGERY Marie White PRIZE IN MATERIA MEDICA AND THERAPEUTICS Jasmine McAlpine
1887	----	PRIZE IN PRINCIPLES AND PRACTICE OF MEDICINE Jasmine McAlpine

1888	First Honor Mary P. Dole Second Honor M. Lizzie Zimmerman	Mary P. Dole
1889	Jessie Brevitt	– – – –
1891	Flora Pollack	Annie R. Houston
1892	Clara S. Eirley	Clara S. Eirley
1893	Anngenette L. Fowler	Ida Pollack
1894	Ella J. Reed	– – – –
1895	Vida Ziegler Baerecke	Vida Ziegler Baerecke
1896	Mattie Ingold	Mattie Ingold
	There were no seniors in 1898 due to the change to the four year curriculum. There were therefore no graduates in that year, hence no medallists.	
1899	Mary Augusta Waters	– – – –
1900	Willena Abby Peck	– – – –
1901	Mary Lois Jones Honorable Mention Jessie Ella Sweet	– – – –
1902	Jennie Nicholson Browne	– – – –
1904	Harrietta M. Thomas	– – – –
1910	Palmira Monserrate Gatell	– – – –

REQUIREMENTS FOR ADMISSION

1882:

In the early years of the school a candidate for admission was required to pass an examination "on the usual elementary English branches taught in the public schools."

1884:

A student must either present a diploma from a "respectable institution of learning", or pass an examination on English grammar, history, geography, arithmetic, elementary physics and composition (writing at least twenty lines upon some subject dictated by the Committee of the Faculty).

1885:

In addition to earlier requirements a candidate for admission had to present "a creditable certificate of good moral character." (A few years later it was stipulated that the certificate be signed by two physicians of good standing.) A first-grade teacher's certificate could be substituted for the required diploma from a respectable institution.

1892:

Graduates or matriculates of recognized liberal arts colleges or normal schools (graduates of academies and high schools also included, but not actually mentioned), were admitted without examination. All others had to pass a preliminary entrance examination, consisting of the following: a) the writing of an English composition of not less than two hundred words, b) the translating of easy Latin prose, c) an examination in higher arithmetic, d) an examination in elementary physics. (A deficiency in the Latin required could be corrected in the junior years, arrangements having been made for giving instruction in Latin to those first year, i.e. junior, students who could not pass the entrance examination upon that subject.)

The following regulations appeared in the Announcement for 1895.

This College being a member of the American Medical College Association, the following rules governing the admission of Colleges to membership in the American Medical College

Association, will henceforth be enforced:

"That the following classes of students be recognized as entitled to apply for advanced standing in colleges, members of this body.

a. Such graduates of recognized universities and colleges as have completed the prescribed courses in chemistry and biology therein.

b. Graduates and matriculates of colleges of homeopathy.

c. Graduates and matriculates of colleges of eclectic medicine.

d. Graduates and matriculates of colleges of dentistry requiring two or more courses of lectures before conferring the degree of D.D.S.

e. Graduates and matriculates of colleges of pharmacy.

f. Graduates and matriculates of colleges of veterinary medicine.

It is provided, however, that the above classes of students be required to comply with the provisions of the entrance examination, and to prove their fitness to advanced professional study by an individual examination upon each branch below the class he or she may desire to enter.

It is provided that students availing themselves of these provisions be required to comply with the provisions of the four years' course.

That the colleges, members of this Association, require of student-matriculates not otherwise exempt, an examination as follows:

I. – 1. In ENGLISH, a composition on some subject of general interest. This composition must be written by the student at the time of the examination, and should contain at least 200 words. It should be criticised in relation to thought, construction, punctuation, spelling and handwriting.

2. In ARITHMETIC, such questions as will show a thorough knowledge of common and decimal fractions, compound numbers, and ratio and proportion.

3. In ALGEBRA, such questions as will bring out the student's knowledge of the fundamental operations, factoring, and simple quadratic equations.

4. In PHYSICS, such questions as will discover the student's understanding of the elements of mechanics, hydrostatics, hydraulics, optics and acoustics.

5. In LATIN, an examination upon such elementary work as the student may offer, showing a familiarity usually attained by one year of study; for example, the reading of the first 15 chapters of Caesar's Commentaries, and the translation into Latin of easy English sentences involving the same vocabulary.

II. – In place of this examination, or any part of it, colleges, members of this Association, are at liberty to recognize the official certificates of reputable literary and scientific colleges, academies, high schools and normal schools, and also the medical student's certificate issued by any State examining board covering the work of the foregoing entrance examination.

III. – Colleges, members of this Association, may allow students who fail in one or more branches in this entrance examination the privilege of entering the first year course, but such students shall not be allowed to begin the second course until the entrance requirements are satisfied.

IV. – Colleges, members of this Association, are free to honor official credentials issued by medical colleges of equal requirements, except in the branches of study embraced in the last year of their own curriculum.

V. – Colleges, members of this Association, are free to give to students who have met the entrance requirements of the Association additional credit for time on the four years' course as follows: (a) To students having the A.B., B.S., or equivalent degree from reputable literary colleges one year of time. (b) To graduates and students of colleges of homeopathic or eclectic medicine, as many years as they attended those colleges, provided they have met the previous requirements of the Association and that they pass an examination in materia medica and therapeutics. (c) To graduates of reputable colleges of dentistry, pharmacy and veterinary medicine, one year of time, i.e., the first year.

A course of instruction for those desiring to fit themselves for the entrance examination is given at the College, August 1st to September 30th. Terms, $20. Address the Secretary."

A calendar of College dates (1896) may be of interest:

CALENDAR

Examination for Admission and Advanced
Standing, 10 A.M., September 30, 1896.
Introductory Lecture, 8 P.M., October 1, 1896.
Annual Meeting of Medical Society, October 6, 1896.
Thanksgiving Holiday, November 26, 1896.
Christmas Holiday begins December 19, 1896.
Lectures Resumed, January 4, 1897.

Washington's Birthday, February 22, 1897.
College Day, February 24, 1897.
Good Friday Holiday, April 16 and 17, 1897.
Final Examinations begin May 10, 1897.
Alumnae Meeting, 8 P.M., May 31, 1897.
15th Commencement Day, June 1, 1897.
Alumnae Banquet, 8 P.M., June 2, 1897.
Annual Meeting of Board of Trustees, June 7, 1897.

All communications should be addressed to
EUGENE F. CORDELL, M.D., Secretary,
2032 Maryland Ave., Baltimore, Md.

In 1903, the following notice appeared in the Announcement:

In accordance with the action of the American College Association taken at its meeting in New Orleans in May, 1903, after July 1st, 1905, the entrance requirements will be raised so as to be equivalent to an average high school education. Due notice of details will be given.

Sometime around the year 1906 the regulations governing the entrance examinations were as follows:

An examination in the following branches:

(a) Required subjects to 16 points as follows: Mathematics, 4 points; English, 4 points; History, 2 points; Latin, 4 points; Physics, 2 points.

(b) Optional subjects to 14 points as follows: English, 4 points; History, 6 points; Language, 8 points; Drawing, 1 point; Natural Science (botany, biology, zoology), 2 points; Physical Science (chemistry, physics), 2 points; Trigonometry, 1 point; Astronomy, 1 point; Civics, 1 point; Geology, 1 point; Physical Geography, 1 point; Physiology and Hygiene, 1 point; Solid Geometry, 1 point.

(One point in any subject in a high school or academic course demands not less than one period per week of forty-five minutes each for thirty-six weeks.)

(c) Certificates of principals of accredited high schools, normal schools, academies; of superintendents of public schools; of reputable instructors recognized by superintendents of public instruction of district, city or State; or of any State Board of Medical Examiners will be accepted in lieu of any part of, or all of the above examination.

A student may be allowed to enter on her medical work conditioned in not more than six points, and these conditions must be removed by satisfactory examination before she is allowed to enter on the second year of her medical course.

REQUIREMENTS FOR GRADUATION

1882: The candidate:

Must be at least twenty-one years of age.

Must have attended at least two full courses of lectures at this school, or one in this after one in some other respectable medical school.

Must present evidence of having attended the clinics.

Must have made at least one creditable dissection of the usual divisions of the cadaver.

Must pass an examination (see below).

Must present a thesis of her own composition and in her own handwriting, upon some medical subject.

The Faculty reserved the right to inquire into the moral qualifications of a candidate.

(A candidate would be permitted to appear for examination at the end of her second year, and be graduated, if she passed the examination (in addition to meeting the other requirements). However, the Faculty strongly recommended that students attend three sessions instead of two and, as a special inducement, would remit the fee for the third year, except for the matriculation fee, which must be paid each year. If a student chose to attend for three years, she was permitted to appear, at the end of the second year, for examination upon: anatomy, physiology, chemistry, materia medica, therapeutics and operative surgery and, if successful, would be excused from attending lectures upon those branches during her third year.)

(To obtain credit for a lecture course it was required that a student enter before November 1, and remain until the close of the session, "except by express permission of the Faculty."

Examinations were held in all branches and were both written and oral.)

1884: The requirements were:

The candidate must be at least twenty-one years of age, and have attended three full courses of lectures at this school, or two full courses after one year's study under a preceptor, in which case a certificate (mentioned above), must be presented. Persons who presented such a certificate and passed an examination in anatomy, physiology, chemistry and practical pharmacy were permitted to enter the intermediate, i.e., second year, class.

The candidate must present a certificate from the demonstrator of anatomy, evidencing one creditable dissection of the usual divisions of the cadaver.

(Credit for attendance upon a full course of lectures required that the person enter the course on or before November 1, etc., as above. A record of attendance was maintained for both didactic and clinical lectures, and according to this record the Faculty would instruct the Dean whether or not to sign the certificate of attendance. The Faculty could exercise its discretion as to excuses for absence.)

The candidate must pass the examinations, which were both written and oral, to attaining a grade of 70, out of a possible 100 in order to receive the degree of M.D., (to advance from one class to the next, it was also necessary to attain a grade of 70 in the examinations).

The Faculty had the right to inquire into the moral qualifications of a candidate.

1892: The dissection requirement was now that two creditable dissections of the usual divisions of the cadaver be made.

1896: Students shall hereafter be divided into four classes, called 1st year, 2nd year, 3rd year and 4th year.

In courses of lectures extending over two or more years, or such courses as are attended by two or more classes, two examinations shall be held at the end of each year; one to be called a Primary Examination, and one to be called a Final Examination.

The Primary Examination shall be oral and shall not exceed twenty minutes for each student, and students shall obtain a grade of seventy on a basis of one hundred, in order to pass such Examination.

The passing of such Primary Examination as above provided for shall be necessary to admit a student to advanced standing, but grades made in primary examinations shall not be reckoned in determining the standing of students at graduation.

Students shall be required to pass final examinations upon all branches and courses required by the curriculum; such final examinations shall be both written and oral, and the length of such written examination shall not exceed three hours for the entire class, and oral examination shall not exceed fifteen minutes for each student, and in grading students on any such final examination, the written portion shall count as 3/4ths, and the oral portion as 1/4th of the examination; and students shall obtain a grade of seventy-five to pass such final examination, which grade shall count in determining the standing of the student at graduation.

Students failing to attain such grades shall be considered as "Conditioned."

"Conditioned" students shall not receive on any re-examination a grade to exceed that established by the Faculty as necessary to pass such examination, that is, 70 p.c. in Primary and 75 p.c. in Final Examinations.

Students, other than candidates for graduation at the next succeeding commencement, shall be required to pass such examinations in which they have been conditioned, within twenty days of the opening of the session, next succeeding such failure. In case of a second failure, the matter shall be referred to the Faculty for action.

Students not appearing at the appointed examination unless excused in writing by the Dean, shall be considered to have failed such examination, and be subject to the rules for re-examination.

Candidates for Diplomas shall attain an average grade of seventy-five in all Final Examinations in branches required by the curriculum. If a student shall fail to attain a grade of seventy-five in any one branch in the examinations immediately preceding her graduation, she shall be allowed to graduate if her general average for the course amounts to seventy-five, providing such one grade shall not fall below fifty. In case such general average falls below seventy-five, or in case of one grade falling below fifty, or in case a student fails to attain the required grade in two or more branches, then the standing of such student shall be referred to the Faculty for action.

No final examinations are permitted until the close of the term; nor will students be excused from any regular examination, except by express permission of the Faculty.

Every student on matriculating will be required to present a certificate of character signed by at least two physicians of good standing in the State from which she comes.

Students who have previously attended one or more courses of lectures in other recognized medical schools will be assigned positions according to their proficiency and the length of such attendance.

The estimate of the standing of each student shall be based upon the general character of her work, her attendance during the year, and upon the results of the examinations, the standing to be determined by the teachers in charge of the various departments. In addition all regulations relating to age, certificate of two creditable dissections of the usual divisions

of the cadaver, record of full attendance each year, Faculty certificate of attendance and right of inquiry into the moral character of candidates for graduation, remained the same.
1903: Candidates for graduation must, (1) be at least 21 years of age and (2) be of good moral character: have studied medicine at least four full years of nine months each, including four satisfactory courses of at least six months each in four different calendar years in accredited medical schools; the last year of which must have been in this school. No allowance is made for work not done in an accredited school. Graduates in dentistry, in veterinary medicine, in pharmacy, and from other professional and technical schools, under no circumstances, receive M.D. degree in less time.*

During the past year this College has entered into affiliation with the Medical Department of the University of West Virginia to this extent, that it will receive students from that institution into the second or third year's course without further examination, provided such students come with credentials as to character and with certificates showing that they have taken the full course of study required for the first one or two years and have passed satisfactory examinations in the subjects studied. Such students will not be required to study over again any branch properly completed at the University of West Virginia.

Candidates for graduation will be required in addition to passing the required examinations, to present a certificate from the Demonstrator of Anatomy of having made at least two creditable dissections of the usual divisions of the Cadaver.

The Faculty reserves the right to make inquiry into the moral as well as the scientific qualifications of candidates for examination.

(In 1907 the "four full years" of requirement (2) had to be of thirty teaching weeks each, with nothing said about "including four satisfactory courses of at least six months each", in regard to accredited medical schools.)

FEES

1882:

Professors' Tickets	$ 75.00
Matriculation, Yearly	5.00
Practical Anatomy	10.00
Graduation	30.00
Total	$120.00

Tickets for one or any number of departments could be taken out separately. If a lady wished to acquire education upon certain subjects without wishing to pursue a medical career, she could register as a special student and attend lectures on chemistry, anatomy, obstetrics, physiology, materia medica, hygiene, medical jurisprudence, pharmacy and microscopy by matriculating, and paying $10. per ticket, in addition.

A limited number of pupils unable to pay full rates were received at a reduced rate.

The demand for medical women as missionaries caused the Faculty to reduce the rates for students who could furnish satisfactory evidence of their sincere intentions to serve in that field.

1884: In order to encourage students to take the full three year graded course, twenty per cent, each year, was deducted from the charges for any student entering the junior year.
1885: Professors' tickets were reduced to $50.00, the other fees remaining the same.
1886: Tuition was now $60.00, other fees remaining the same.
1888: Tuition was raised to $75.00, matriculation and graduation fees remained the same, and no stipulation was made about the fee in practical anatomy.
1891: Two free scholarships became available. A candidate for a scholarship must be at least eighteen years old and must present a certificate, signed by two reputable persons, that she was of good character and was unable to pay the fees. She was required to pay matriculation and diploma fees, to have had a good English education, and have the ability to read German, French or Latin. The scholarship could be revoked, for improper conduct, at the discretion of the Faculty.
1892: The tuition rates were now the same as they had originally been, (i.e., 1882, when they totalled $120.).

The scholarship program was extended – one free student would be accepted from each Congressional District of Maryland, upon the same conditions as the other scholarships mentioned above. Appointments to these scholarships were to be made by State Senators.

*Note — Exception. The medical statute of the State of New York amended 1902, provides that the University may accept as the equivalent of the first year in a medical school registered as maintaining a satisfactory standard, evidence of graduation from a registered college course that includes not less than the minimum requirements prescribed by the Regents for admission to advanced standing. The Woman's Medical College of Baltimore will act in accordance with this provision.

1895: Tuition was raised to $85.00, other fees remaining unchanged. For persons preparing for missionary work the fee for a course was $75.00. There was a breakage fee, for all students, of $5.00, returnable if there were no charges against the student.
1896: Tuition was raised to $100.00 for the complete course of lectures. The other fees remained the same as in 1895.

A certain number of students were elected annually as "Internes and Externes", which gave them special facilities for clinical observation and study in the Hospital. The fees were $100. and $50. per annum, respectively.
1898: The tuition fee was now $100.00 yearly for the first three years and $50.00 for the fourth year. Tickets for special courses were $15.00 each. The other fees remained the same.

In 1900 the College announced that the Faculty had authorized the appointment of a scholarship in fifteen "literary institutions or colleges" for persons who were of sufficiently high standing, were unable to pay the usual fees, and conformed to the rules governing such cases.

In 1903 there was an annual charge of a library fee of $1.00, the money being used for the purchase of books. Upon payment of a fee of $5.00, a student could have exclusive use of a microscope, assuming responsibility for its safe keeping and return at the end of the session. (This microscope-rental fee was raised to $10.00, after about 1906.)

"Excellent rooms with board" could be had in the immediate neighborhood of the College, at from $3.00 to $5.00 a week, by applying to the Dean for a list of desirable boarding houses (1882-1908).

Fees, from 1906 to 1909, were as follows:

Matriculation, (yearly)	$ 5.00
Tuition, (yearly), first three years	100.00
Tuition, fourth year	50.00
Final Examination, (fourth year)	30.00
Each special course	15.00
Breakage fee, (returnable)	5.00
Library fee	1.00

DATA for COMPARISON and EVALUATION

A retrospective view of the Woman's Medical College of Baltimore reveals that medical education had come a long way from the days of the middle decades of the nineteenth century. Requirements for admission were now clearly drawn, and must be met by those who aspired to enter the profession. (This school claimed to be one of the first institutions in the country, and the first in Maryland to require a preliminary examination.) The requirements for graduation likewise underwent an extension, a three "year" course, which soon evolved into one of four "years" duration being required. The college "year" itself had seen a development from the original fourteen to eighteen week span of pre-Civil War days to a "year" of thirty teaching-weeks by the turn of the century. The college claimed to have been a pioneer in the movement to lengthen the "year", provide a graded curriculum, and improve the methods of medical instruction. While an attached hospital was a rarity in earlier times, this school had both hospital and college dispensary, in addition to the usual "guest" privileges at the other hospitals of the city. Thus the opportunity to acquire a good, practical medical education through an abundance of clinical experience was clearly present.

The nature, number and content of the courses show a great evolution from the almost primitive character of earlier decades. Specialization, the advances of the frontiers of knowledge and a new philosophy of medical education and practice which elevated its sights, had, in half a century, proliferated the six-to-eight-chair curriculum of the era of the extinct medical schools of Philadelphia into one at least three times that size. One may gain a clearer idea as to what had happened in five decades to the content of the individual courses by glancing at a "synopsis of instruction" in the College Announcement for 1908. Anatomy had evolved into a two-year course, in each year of which there were three hours of lectures and recitations per week throughout the year, and ten hours of dissection weekly during sixteen weeks of each year. In addition to the professor of anatomy, the staff included a lecturer on embryology, a lecturer on osteology and the usual demonstrator of anatomy. The staffs in gynecology and in diseases of children each had three members, dermatology two, histology four, obstetrics two, orthopedics two, pathology two, practice of medicine seven, surgery five, therapeutics, materia medica and pharmacology four. Bacteriology, dermatology, ophthalmology, otology and psychiatry would have been among other strange sounds in the ears of the earlier Philadelphia professors. (A better idea of the development which had taken place in the medical curriculum can be formed by referring to section II, than from this random sampling.) Certain it is that the lengthened day, week and number of years were now making possible a far fuller theoretical education in medicine than in ante-bellum days.

The Faculty of the Woman's Medical College was a notable one, and both its dedication to the cause, and the fact that classes at this school were small, conspired to provide each student with instruction tailored to her individual needs. (With such small classes, the total number of graduates during the life-span of this school was also obviously small, by comparison with the number of graduates of most of the extinct medical schools of Philadelphia.)

Other differences are to be noted: students were held to high standards of attainment during the years of study, there was an abundance of clinical experience, requirements for graduation included two creditable dissections of the usual divisions of the cadaver, laboratory work, as part of the education of a physician in this school, had become relatively extensive, a satisfactory record of attendance must be maintained, and a possible inquiry into the moral qualifications of each candidate might be conducted. Other features of this school, which had no parallel in the schools with which we have been comparing it, were an active student-faculty medical society, an active association of graduates, and an effort to train nurses.

Despite what has been said above about the efforts of the College to provide excellent schooling, the educational standards of the American Medical Association relative to various kinds of equipment and a salaried Faculty for first and second year students could not be met, for lack of endowment, and the school closed its doors. Yet the training which it offered showed a great advance over that available at some earlier schools. (See Appendices F-1 and F-2.)

III. (A) FACULTY

SESSIONS OF 1882-83* AND 1883-84

JOHN S. LYNCH, M.D.
Professor of Principles and Practice of Medicine
B. BERNARD BROWNE, M.D.
Professor of Diseases of Women
THOS. A. ASHBY, M.D.
Professor of Obstetrics
RANDOLPH WINSLOW, A.M., M.D.
Professor of Surgery
EUGENE F. CORDELL, M.D.
Professor of Materia Medica and Therapeutics
WM. D. BOOKER, M.D., DEAN
Professor of Physiology and Lecturer on the Diseases of Children
RICH'D HENRY THOMAS, M.D., SECRETARY
Professor Diseases of Throat and Chest
JOHN G. JAY, M.D., TREASURER
Professor of Anatomy and Operative Surgery
CAMERON PIGGOT, M.D.
Lecturer on Chemistry and Pharmacy
THOMAS P. MC CORMICK, M.D.
Demonstrator of Anatomy

CLINICAL ASSISTANTS

B. A. TURNER, M.D.
Chief of Clinic to Diseases of Women
J. RUSSELL MARTENET, M.D.
AMANDA E. TAYLOR, M.D.
Chiefs of Clinic to Diseases of Throat and Chest
GEO. R. GRAHAM, M.D.
Chief of Clinic to Surgery
HIRAM WOODS, JR., M.D.
Chief of Clinic to Diseases of Eye and Ear

HORACE M. SIMMONS, M.D.
Chief of Clinic to Obstetrics
HENRY J. BERKLEY, M.D.
Chief of Clinic to Diseases of Children
W. H. NOBLE, M.D.
Chief of Clinic to Clinical Medicine
W. GRAY SMITH, M.D.
Chief of Clinic to Operative Surgery

*The Announcement for 1882-83 makes no mention of clinical assistants nor demonstrator of anatomy, nor does it give the name of the lecturer on chemistry.

SESSION OF 1884-85

B. BERNARD BROWNE, M.D.
Professor of Diseases of Women
THOS. A. ASHBY, M.D.
Professor of Obstetrics
RANDOLPH WINSLOW, A.M., M.D.
Professor of Surgery
EUGENE F. CORDELL, M.D.
Professor of Principles and Practice of Medicine
WM. D. BOOKER, M.D., DEAN
Professor of Physiology and Lecturer on Diseases of Children

RICH'D. HENRY THOMAS, B.A., M.D. Sec'y.
Professor of Diseases of Throat and Chest
JOHN G. JAY, M.D., Treasurer
Professor of Anatomy and Operative Surgery
RUSSELL MURDOCH, M.D.
Professor of Diseases of Eye and Ear
CAMERON PIGGOT, M.D.
Lecturer on Chemistry
AMANDA TAYLOR-NORRIS, M.D.
Lecturer on Materia Medica and Therapeutics

LECTURERS ON SPECIAL SUBJECTS

JAS. CAREY THOMAS, A.M., M.D.
Hygiene

JOHN R. QUINAN, M.D.
Medical Jurisprudence

PROF. JOHN S. LYNCH, M.D., General Pathology

DEMONSTRATORS AND INSTRUCTORS

THOMAS P. MC CORMICK, M.D.
GEORGE R. GRAHAM, M.D.
Demonstrators of Anatomy
GEORGE H. SCHONE, PH. G.
Instructor in Practical Pharmacy

C. H. JONES, M.B., C.M.
Instructor in Physiology
....
Instructor in Materia Medica and Therapeutics

...................., Instructor in Chemistry

CLINICAL ASSISTANTS

B. A. TURNER, M.D.
J. M. HUNDLEY, M.D.
GERTRUDE SCOTT, M.D.
Gynecology and Obstetrics
J. FUSSELL MARTENET, M.D.
A. C. ABBOT, M.D.
Diseases of Throat and Chest
GEORGE R. GRAHAM, M.D.
Surgery

A. KERR BOND, B.A., M.D.
M. ELIDA ENGLISH, PH.B., M.D.
Diseases of Children
GEORGE C. SHANNON, M.D.
S. J. FORT, M.D.
Clinical Medicine
MACTIER WARFIELD, B.A., M.D.
Diseases of Eye and Ear

SESSION 1885-86

The same as in 1884-85, with the following exceptions:
Joseph T. Smith, M.D., replaced John R. Quinan, M.D., in Jurisprudence; Thomas P. McCormick, M.D., was no longer one of the demonstrators of anatomy; M. Elizabeth Hargraves, M.D., replaced George H. Schone, Ph.G., an instructor in pharmacy; Marie E. Thalwitzer, M.D., became instructor in anatomy. The clinical assistants for 1885-86 are given below:

CLINICAL ASSISTANTS

JAMES M. CRAIGHILL, M.D.
A. KERR BOND, B.A., M.D.
GERTRUDE SCOTT, M.D.
MARIE E. THALWITZER, M.D.
Gynecology and Obstetrics
J. FUSSELL MARTENET, M.D.
ALICE S. PARKHURST, M.D.
Diseases of Throat and Chest

GEORGE R. GRAHAM, M.D.
Surgery
A. KERR BOND, B.A., M.D.
M. ELIDA ENGLISH, PH.B., M.D.
Diseases of Children
CAROLINE E. SMITH, M.D.
Clinical Medicine
MACTIER WARFIELD, B.A., M.D.
Diseases of Eye and Ear

CLARA STEINBRENNER, M.D., Librarian

SESSION OF 1886-87

B. BERNARD BROWNE, M.D.
Professor of Diseases of Women and Clinical Midwifery

THOS. A. ASHBY, M.D.
Professor of Obstetrics and Clinical Gynecology

RANDOLPH WINSLOW, A.M., M.D.
Professor of Surgery

EUGENE F. CORDELL, M.D.
Professor of Principles and Practice of Medicine

WM. D. BOOKER, M.D.
Professor of Diseases of Children

RICH'D HENRY THOMAS B.A., M.D., Dean
Professor of Diseases of Throat and Chest

JOHN G. JAY, M.D., Treasurer
Professor of Anatomy and Operative Surgery

RUSSELL MURDOCH, M.D.
Professor of Diseases of Eye and Ear

AMANDA TAYLOR-NORRIS, M.D. Secretary
Professor of Materia Medica and Therapeutics

ALONZO L. THOMSEN, B.A.
Professor of Chemistry

C. HAMPSON JONES, M.B., C.M.
Lecturer on Physiology

LECTURERS ON SPECIAL SUBJECTS

JAS. CAREY THOMAS A.M., M.D.
Hygiene

JOS. T. SMITH, M.D.
Medical Jurisprudence

DEMONSTRATORS AND INSTRUCTORS

GEORGE R. GRAHAM, M.D.
Demonstrator of Anatomy

M. ELIZABETH HARGRAVES, M.D.
Assistant in Chemistry

EDWARD E. MACKENZIE, M.D.
Instructor in Pharmacy

ANNIE L. ALEXANDER, M.D.
Instructor in Anatomy and Curator

CLINICAL ASSISTANTS

GERTRUDE SCOTT, M.D.
ANNIE E. KUHN, M.D.
Gynecology and Obstetrics

J. FUSSELL MARTENET, M.D.
CLARA STEINBRENNER, M.D.
Diseases of Throat and Chest

GEORGE R. GRAHAM, M.D.
LAURA M. EWING, M.D.
Surgery

A. KERR BOND, B.A., M.D.
M. ELIZABETH HARGRAVES, M.D.
Diseases of Children

CAROLINE E. SMITH, M.D.
Clinical Medicine

MACTIER WARFIELD, B.A., M.D.
Diseases of Eye and Ear

MISS JULIA T. HENDERSON, Librarian

SESSION OF 1887-88

The Faculty was the same as in 1886-87, with the following exceptions:
Russell Murdock, M.D., M. Elizabeth Hargraves, M.D., and Annie L. Alexander, M.D. were no longer on the Faculty.
Clara Steinbrenner, M.D., became demonstrator of pharmacy. The clinical assistants are given below:

CLINICAL ASSISTANTS

ANNIE E. KUHN, M.D.
Gynaecology and Obstetrics

GEORGE R. GRAHAM, M.D.
LAURA M. EWING, M.D.
Surgery

MRS. HEMMETER, Librarian

SESSION OF 1888-89

The Faculty was the same as in 1886-87, with the following exceptions:
Hiram Woods, Jr., M.D., was professor of diseases of eye and ear, and secretary of the

Faculty; C. Hampson Jones' rank became associate professor; John R. Winslow, M.D., was assistant demonstrator of anatomy; J. Fussell Martenet, M.D., was lecturer adjunct on diseases of throat and chest.
The clinical assistants are given below:

CLINICAL ASSISTANTS

CLARA STEINBRENNER, M.D.
Gynaecology and Obstetrics
INDIA M. COCHEL, M.D.
Diseases of Throat and Chest
M. LIZZIE ZIMMERMAN, M.D.
Clinical Medicine

JOHN R. WINSLOW, M.D.
LAURA M. EWING, M.D.
Surgery
C. O. MILLER, M.D.
Diseases of Children

SESSION OF 1889-90

B. BERNARD BROWNE, M.D.
Professor of Diseases of Women
and Clinical Midwifery
THOS. A. ASHBY, M.D.
Professor of Obstetrics and
Clinical Gynaecology
RANDOLPH WINSLOW, A.M., M.D.
Professor of Surgery
EUGENE F. CORDELL, M.D.
Professor of Principles and
Practice of Medicine
WM. D. BOOKER, M.D.
Professor of Diseases of Children
RICH'D HENRY THOMAS
B.A., M.D., DEAN
Professor of Diseases of Throat
and Chest

JOHN G. JAY, M.D.
Professor of Anatomy and
Operative Surgery
AMANDA TAYLOR-NORRIS, M.D.
Professor of Materia Medica
and Therapeutics
HIRAM WOODS, JR., B.A., M.D.
Secretary
Professor of Diseases Eye and Ear
GEORGE J. PRESTON, B.A., M.D.
Professor of Physiology
JOSEPH T. SMITH, M.D.
Professor of Hygiene and
Medical Jurisprudence
JOHN R. WINSLOW, B.A., M.D.
Lecturer on Chemistry
C. O. MILLER, M.D.
Lecturer on Histology and Pathology

DEMONSTRATORS AND INSTRUCTORS

GEORGE R. GRAHAM, M.D.
Demonstrator of Anatomy
JESSIE BREVITT, M.D.
Demonstrator of Chemistry
EDWARD E. MACKENZIE, M.D.
Instructor in Pharmacy

J. FUSSELL MARTENET, M.D.
Lecturer Adjunct on Diseases of
Throat and Chest
INDIA M. COCHEL, M.D.
Demonstrator of Obstetrics

CLINICAL ASSISTANTS

HORACE R. WINCHESTER, M.D.
ISABELLA K. GODFREY, M.D.
Gynaecology and Obstetrics
INDIA M. COCHEL, M.D.
Diseases of Throat and Chest
C. O. MILLER, M.D.
Diseases of Children

JOHN R. WINSLOW, M.D.
LAURA M. EWING, M.D.
Surgery
E. J. BERNSTEIN, M.D.
JESSIE BREVITT, M.D.
Diseases of the Eye and Ear

SESSION OF 1891-92

B. BERNARD BROWNE, M.D.
Professor of Diseases of Women
THOS. A. ASHBY, M.D.
Professor of Obstetrics and
Clinical Gynaecology
RANDOLPH WINSLOW, A.M., M.D., Dean
Professor of Principles of Surgery
EUGENE F. CORDELL, M.D.
Professor of Principles and
Practice of Medicine

WM. D. BOOKER, M.D.
Professor of Diseases of Children
RICH'D HENRY THOMAS, B.A., M.D.
Professor of Diseases of Throat
and Chest
JOHN G. JAY, M.D.
Professor of Practice and Surgery
AMANDA TAYLOR-NORRIS, M.D.
Professor of Practical Obstetrics

HIRAM WOODS, JR., B.A., M.D.
Professor of Diseases of Eye and Ear
JOSEPH T. SMITH, M.D.
Professor of Materia Medica
and Therapeutics
JOHN R. WINSLOW, B.A., M.D.
Secretary
Professor of Physiology
I. R. TRIMBLE, M.D.
Professor of Anatomy
CHARLES W. MITCHEL, M.D.
Lecturer on Normal and
Pathological Histology

PEARCE KINTZING, B.Sc., M.D.
Lecturer on Chemistry
HENRY P. HYNSON, Ph.G.
Lecturer on Pharmacy
J. FUSSELL MARTENET, M.D.
Lecturer on Hygiene and Medical
Jurisprudence, and Lecturer
Adjunct on Diseases of Throat
and Chest

DEMONSTRATORS

WM. ROYAL STOKES, B.A., M.D.
Demonstrator of Anatomy

JESSIE BREVITT, M.D.
Demonstrator of Chemistry

J. W. WESTCOTT, Ph.G., Demonstrator of Pharmacy

CLINICAL ASSISTANTS

BENJ. A. TURNER, M.D.
HATTIE M. FRIST, M.D.
Gynaecology and Obstetrics
J. F. SHEMWELL, M.D.
H. E. GALE, B.A., M.D.
Surgery
WM. S. LOVE, M.D.
ISABELLA K. GODFREY, M.D.
W. MILTON LEWIS, M.D.
Clinical Medicine

JESSIE BREVITT, M.D.
MARY PENROSE, M.D.
Diseases of Children
FLORA POLLACK, M.D.
Diseases of Throat and Chest
JESSIE BREVITT, M.D.
Diseases of Eye and Ear

SESSION OF 1892-93

The Faculty was the same as in 1891-92, with the following exceptions:
J. W. Westcott, Ph.G., was no longer demonstrator of pharmacy. William S. Love, M.D., and W. Milton Lewis, M.D., replaced J. F. Shemwell, M.D., and H. E. Gale, M.D., as clinical assistants in surgery; William T. Watson, M.D., replaced Drs. Brevitt and Penrose as clinical assistants in diseases of children, and W. McLean Yost, M.D., became clinical assistant in diseases of throat and chest.

SESSION OF 1893-94

B. BERNARD BROWNE, M.D.
Professor of Diseases of Women
THOS. A. ASHBY, M.D.
Professor of Obstetrics and
Clinical Gynaecology
EUGENE F. CORDELL, M.D.
Professor of Principles and
Practice of Medicine
JOHN G. JAY, M.D.
Professor of Principles and
Practice of Surgery
AMANDA TAYLOR-NORRIS, M.D.
Professor of Practical Obstetrics
HIRAM WOODS, JR., B.A., M.D.
Professor of Diseases of Eye and Ear
JOSEPH T. SMITH, M.D., DEAN
Professor of Materia Medica and
Therapeutics and Clinical
Professor of Diseases of Chest
JOHN R. WINSLOW, B.A., M.D.
Professor of Physiology and
Clinical Professor of
Diseases of Throat and Nose

I. R. TRIMBLE, M.D.
Professor of Anatomy and
Clinical Surgery
CHAS. W. MITCHELL, B.A., M.D.
Professor of Diseases of Children
PEARCE KINTZING, B.Sc., M.D.
Professor of Chemistry
HENRY P. HYNSON, Ph.G.
Lecturer on Pharmacy
J. D. FARRAR, B.A., M.D.
Lecturer on Histology
and Pathology
CLARIBEL CONE, M.D.
Lecturer on Hygiene
JULIAN STUART JONES, L.L.B.
Lecturer on Medical Jurisprudence
T. BRICE MARDEN, B.A., M.D.
Demonstrator of Anatomy
and Chemistry

CLINICAL ASSISTANTS

H. BURTON STEVENSON, M.D.
HATTIE FRIST-EMMART, M.D.
Gynaecology and Obstetrics
T. BRICE MARDEN, B.A., M.D.
F. W. KRUM, M.D.
Clinical Surgery
W. MILTON LEWIS, M.D.
Clinical Medicine

JOSEPH A. SELIGMAN, M.D.
Diseases of Children
BESSIE RENSHAW, M.D.
Diseases of Throat and Nose
MARION A. WATSON, M.D.
Diseases of Eye and Ear
ROBERT FAWCETT, M.D.
Diseases of Chest

SESSION OF 1894-95

B. BERNARD BROWNE, M.D.
Professor Gynaecology
THOS. A. ASHBY, M.D.
Professor of Obstetrics
EUGENE F. CORDELL, M.D.
Professor of Principles and Practice of Medicine
JOHN G. JAY, M.D.
Professor of Principles and Practice of Surgery
HIRAM WOODS, JR., B.A., M.D.
Professor of Diseases of Eye and Ear
JOSEPH T. SMITH, M.D.
Professor of Materia Medica and Therapeutics and Clinical Medicine
JOHN R. WINSLOW, B.A., M.D.
Clinical Professor of Diseases of Throat and Nose
I. R. TRIMBLE, M.D., DEAN
Professor of Anatomy and Clinical Surgery
PEARCE KINTZING, B.Sc., M.D.
Professor of Chemistry

CHARLES E. SIMON, B.A., M.D.
Professor of Physiology, Normal Histology and Clinical Medicine
CHAS. O'DONOVAN, B.A., M.D.
Professor of Diseases of Children
HENRY P. HYNSON, Ph.G.
Lecturer on Pharmacy
B. B. LANIER, B.A., M.D.
Lecturer on Pathology and Pathological Histology
CLARIBEL CONE, M.D.
Lecturer on Hygiene
RALPH ROBINSON, B.A., L.L.B.
Lecturer on Medical Jurisprudence
T. B. MARDEN, B.A., M.D.
Demonstrator of Anatomy and Chemistry
IDA POLLACK, M.D.
Demonstrator of Obstetrics
LOUISE EATON, M.D.
Assistant Demonstrator of Obstetrics
PROF. SIMON & DR. W. MILTON LEWIS
Curators of Museum

CLINICAL ASSISTANTS

SUE RADCLIFF, M.D.
Gynaecology
HUGH FORSYTHE, M.D.
S. GRIFFITH DAVIS, M.D.
Clinical Surgery
W. MILTON LEWIS, M.D.
Clinical Medicine

EDITH EARECKSON, M.D.
Diseases of Children
JOHN GIRDWOOD, M.D.
Diseases of Throat and Nose
JESSIE BREVITT, M.D.
Diseases of Eye and Ear

SESSION OF 1895-96

B. BERNARD BROWNE, M.D.
Professor of Gynaecology
THOS. A. ASHBY, M.D.
Professor of Obstetrics
EUGENE F. CORDELL, M.D.
Professor of Principles and Practice of Medicine
JOHN G. JAY, M.D.
Professor of Principles and Practice of Surgery
HIRAM WOODS, JR., B.A., M.D.
Professor of Diseases of Eye and Ear
JOSEPH T. SMITH, M.D.
Professor of Materia Medica and Therapeutics and Clinical Medicine

JOHN R. WINSLOW, B.A., M.D.
Clinical Professor of Diseases of Throat and Nose
I. R. TRIMBLE, M.D., DEAN
Professor of Anatomy and Clinical Surgery
PEARCE KINTZING, B.Sc., M.D.
Professor of Chemistry
CHAS. O'DONOVAN, B.A., M.D.
Professor of Diseases of Children
RALPH ROBINSON, B.A., L.L.B.
Professor of Medical Jurisprudence
CLARIBEL CONE, M.D.
Professor of Pathology and Pathological Histology

HENRY P. HYNSON, Ph.G.
Lecturer on Pharmacy
B. B. LANIER, B.A., M.D.
Lecturer on Operative Surgery
W. MILTON LEWIS, M.D.
Lecturer on Normal Histology
G. M. LINTHICUM, B.A., M.D.
Lecturer on Physiology
EDITH EARECKSON, M.D.
Lecturer on Hygiene
T. B. MARDEN, B.A., M.D.
Demonstrator of Chemistry
IDA POLLACK, M.D., and
LOUISE EATON, M.D.
Demonstrators of Obstetrics

S. GRIFFITH DAVIS, M.D.
Demonstrator of Anatomy and Osteology
G. CLINTON BLADES, Ph.G.
Demonstrator of Pharmacy
J. WILLIAM FUNCK, M.D., and
LOUISE ERICH, M.D.
Assistants in Histology
PROF. CONE and DR. W. MILTON LEWIS
Curators of Museum

CLINICAL ASSISTANTS

LOUISE EATON, M.D.
Gynaecology
HUGH FORSYTHE, M.D.
S. GRIFFITH DAVIS, M.D.
Clinical Surgery
CHRISTIAN DEETJEN, M.D.
Clinical Medicine

EDITH EARECKSON, M.D.
Diseases of Children
JOHN GIRDWOOD, M.D.
Diseases of Throat and Nose
LOUISE ERICH, M.D.
Diseases of Eye and Ear

SESSION OF 1896-97

B. BERNARD BROWNE, M.D.
Professor of Gynaecology
THOS. A. ASHBY, M.D.
Professor of Obstetrics
EUGENE F. CORDELL, M.D.
Professor of Principles and Practice of Medicine
JOHN G. JAY, M.D.
Professor of Principles and Practice of Surgery
JOSEPH T. SMITH, M.D.
Professor of Materia Medica and Therapeutics and Clinical Medicine
JOHN R. WINSLOW, B.A., M.D.
Professor of Diseases of Throat and Nose
I. R. TRIMBLE, M.D.
Professor of Anatomy and Clinical Surgery
PEARCE KINTZING, B.Sc., M.D.
Professor of Chemistry
CHAS. O'DONOVAN, M.A., M.D.
Professor of Diseases of Children
RALPH ROBINSON, B.A., L.L.B.
Professor of Medical Jurisprudence
HERBERT HARLAN, M.A., M.D.
Professor of Diseases of Eye and Ear
M. MAGDALENE WARNER, M.D.
H. H. ARTHUR, M.D.
Demonstrators of Obstetrics
S. GRIFFITH DAVIS, M.D.
Demonstrator of Anatomy and Osteology
G. CLINTON BLADES, Ph.G.
Demonstrator of Pharmacy
CHRISTIAN DEETJEN, M.D.
Instructor in Neurology

CLARIBEL CONE, M.D.
Professor of Pathology and Pathological Histology
G. MILTON LINTHICUM, B.A., M.D.
Professor of Physiology
HENRY P. HYNSON, Ph.G.
Professor of Pharmacy
THOS. C. GILCHRIST, M.R.C.S., L.S.A.
Clinical Professor of Diseases of the Skin
R. TUNSTALL TAYLOR, B.A., M.D.
Clinical Professor of Orthopaedic Surgery
EDWIN N. BRUSH, M.D.
Clinical Professor of Psychiatry
KEMP B. BATCHELOR, M.D.
Associate Professor of Obstetrics
W. MILTON LEWIS, M.D.
Lecturer on Normal Histology
EDITH EARECKSON, M.D.
Lecturer on Hygiene
FLORA POLLACK, M.D.
Lecturer on Embryology
IDA POLLACK, M.D.
Lecturer on Bacteriology
T. B. MARDEN, B.A., M.D.
Demonstrator of Chemistry
FRANCIS E. BROWN, B.A., M.D.
Instructor in Physical Diagnosis
H. FORSYTHE, M.D., and
J. A. MELVIN, M.D.
Assistants in Histology
LOUISE ERICH, M.D.
Assistant in Pathology
PROF. CONE and DR. LEWIS
Curators of Museum

CLINICAL ASSISTANTS

J. A. MELVIN, M.D.
Gynaecology
WM. H. BLOCK, M.D.
Clinical Surgery
CHRISTIAN DEETJEN, M.D.
FRANCIS E. BROWN, B.A., M.D.
JOHANNA T. ZELWIS, M.D.
Clinical Medicine

EDITH EARECKSON, M.D.
Diseases of Children
LOUISE ERICH, M.D.
Diseases of Eye and Ear
JESSIE BREVITT, M.D.
Diseases of Stomach and Intestines
N. E. B. IGLEHART, M.D.
Orthopaedic Surgery

SESSION OF 1898-99

B. BERNARD BROWNE, M.D.
Professor of Gynaecology
EUGENE F. CORDELL, M.D.
Professor of Principles and Practice of Medicine
JOHN G. JAY, M.D.
Professor of Principles and Practice of Surgery
JOSEPH T. SMITH, M.D.
Professor of Materia Medica and Therapeutics and Clinical Medicine
I. R. TRIMBLE, M.D.
Professor of Anatomy, Operative and Clinical Surgery
PEARCE KINTZING, B.Sc., M.D.
Professor of Chemistry and Clinical Prof. Diseases Stomach and Intestines
CHAS. O'DONOVAN, M.A., M.D.
Professor of Diseases of Children
HERBERT HARLAN, M.A., M.D.
Professor of Diseases of Eye and Ear
CLARIBEL CONE, M.D.
Professor of Pathology
EDWARD N. BRUSH, M.D.
Professor of Psychiatry
CHARLES H. RILEY, M.D.
Professor of Obstetrics
S. GRIFFITH DAVIS, M.D.
Demonstrator of Anatomy and Osteology
LOUISE D. HOLMES, A.B., M.D.
Demonstrator of Chemistry
G. MILTON LINTHICUM, B.A., M.D.
Professor of Physiology and Clinical Professor of Rectal Surgery

G. CLINTON BLADES, Ph.G.
Professor of Pharmacy
KEMP B. BATCHELOR, M.D.
Associate Professor of Clinical Medicine
W. MILTON LEWIS, M.D.
Associate Prof. of Normal Histology and Clinical Microscopy
FLORA POLLACK, M.D.
Associate Professor of Embryology and Physical Diagnosis
EDITH EARECKSON, M.D.
Associate Professor of Hygiene
E. J. BERNSTEIN, M.D.
Clinical Professor of Diseases of Eye, Ear, Nose and Throat
JOHN R. ABERCROMBIE, M.D.
Lecturer on Materia Medica
CHRISTIAN DEETJEN, M.D.
Lecturer on Neurology
SYLVAN LIKES, M.D.
Clinical Lecturer on Dermatology
JOHN L. G. LEE, B.A., L.L.B.
Lecturer on Medical Jurisprudence
LOUIS HAMBURGER, B.A., M.D.
Lecturer on Bacteriology
M. J. MC AVOY, Ph.G.
Demonstrator of Pharmacy
R. H. JOHNSTON, M.D.
Instructor in Physical Diagnosis
PROFS. CONE AND LEWIS
Curators of Museum

CLINICAL ASSISTANTS

J. A. MELVIN, M.D.
Gynaecology
S. GRIFFITH DAVIS, M.D.
NATHAN HERMAN, M.D.
Clinical Surgery
CHRISTIAN DEETJEN, M.D.
MARIE E. THALWITZER, M.D.
Clinical Medicine

A. C. HEARN, M.D.
Diseases of Children
SAMUEL KAHN, M.D.
Diseases of Stomach and Intestines

SESSION OF 1899-1900

The Faculty was the same as in 1898-99, with the following exceptions:
Drs. O'Donovan, Linthicum, Batchelor, Johnston, and Thalwitzer were no longer on the Faculty.

A. C. Harrison, M.D., became professor of physical diagnosis and Jennie N. Browne, A.B., became adjunct professor of physiology.

SESSION OF 1900-1901

B. BERNARD BROWNE, M.D.
Professor of Gynaecology
EUGENE F. CORDELL, M.D.
Professor of Principles and Practice of Medicine
JOHN G. JAY, M.D.
Professor of Principles and Practice of Surgery
JOSEPH T. SMITH, M.D.
Professor of Materia Medica and Therapeutics and Clinical Medicine
PEARCE KINTZING, B.Sc., M.D.
Professor of Anatomy, Operative and Clinical Surgery
HERBERT HARLAN, M.A., M.D.
Professor of Diseases of Eye and Ear
CLARIBEL CONE, M.D.
Professor of Pathology
W. MILTON LEWIS, M.D.
Associate Prof. of Normal Histology and Clinical Microscopy
JENNIE N. BROWNE, A.B.
Adjunct Professor of Physiology
S. GRIFFITH DAVIS, M.D.
Adjunct Prof. of Operative Surgery and Demonstrator of Anatomy
LOUISE ERICH, M.D.
Adjunct Professor of Hygiene
F. M. CHISOLM, M.D.
Adjunct Professor of Diseases of Eye and Ear
JOHN R. ABERCROMBIE, M.D.
Lecturer on Materia Medica

CHARLES H. RILEY, M.D.
Professor of Obstetrics
JOHN L. G. LEE, B.A., L.L.B.
Professor of Medical Jurisprudence
RICHARD HENRY THOMAS, M.D.
Professor of Diseases of Nose Throat and Chest
JOSEPH CLEMENT CLARK, M.D.
Professor of Psychiatry
G. CLINTON BLADES, Ph.G., M.D.
Professor of Pharmacy
A. DuVAL ATKINSON, M.D.
Professor of Diseases of Children
M. EKSTROMER, M.D.
Professor of Chemistry
A. C. HARRISON, M.D.
Professor of Physical Diagnosis and Clinical Medicine
SYLVAN LIKES, M.D.
Clinical Lecturer on Dermatology
T. L. SAVIN, M.D.
Lecturer on Embryology
HENRY LEE SMITH, M.D.
Lecturer on Bacteriology
M. J. MC AVOY, Ph.G., M.D.
Demonstrator of Pharmacy
MARY A. WATERS, M.D.
Assistant in Pathology
PROFS. CONE and LEWIS
Curators of Museum

CLINICAL ASSISTANTS

NATHAN HERMAN, M.D.
Clinical Surgery

SAMUEL KAHN, M.D.
MARIE E. THALWITZER, M.D.
Gynaecology

SESSION OF 1901-1902

B. BERNARD BROWNE, M.D.
Professor of Gynaecology
EUGENE F. CORDELL, M.D.
Professor of Principles and Practice of Medicine
JOHN G. JAY, M.D.
Professor of Principles and Practice of Surgery
JOSEPH T. SMITH, M.D.
Professor of Materia Medica and Therapeutics and Clinical Medicine
PEARCE KINTZING, B.Sc., M.D.
Professor of Anatomy, Operative and Clinical Surgery
HERBERT HARLAN, M.A., M.D.
Professor of Diseases of Eye and Ear
CLARIBEL CONE, M.D.
Professor of Pathology

CHARLES H. RILEY, M.D.
Professor of Obstetrics
JOHN L. G. LEE, B.A., L.L.B.
Professor of Medical Jurisprudence
F. M. CHISOLM, M.D.
Adjunct Professor of Diseases of Eye and Ear
JOHN R. ABERCROMBIE, M.D.
Lecturer on Materia Medica
....
Clinical Lecturer on Dermatology
FRANCES A. CARPENTER, M.D.
Lecturer on Embryology
W. S. SKILLMAN, M.D.
Lecturer on Diseases of the Digestive Tract
LOUISE ERICH, M.D.
Lecturer on Orthopedics

RICHARD HENRY THOMAS, M.D.
Professor of Diseases of Nose
Throat and Chest
JOSEPH CLEMENT CLARK, M.D.
Professor of Psychiatry
HENRY P. HYNSON, Ph.G.
Professor of Pharmacy
HENRY LEE SMITH, M.D.
Professor of Diseases of Children
and Lecturer on Bacteriology
M. EKSTROMER, M.D.
Professor of Chemistry
W. MILTON LEWIS, M.D.
Associate Prof. of Normal Histology
and Clinical Microscopy
JENNIE N. BROWNE, A.B.
Adjunct Professor of Physiology

S. GRIFFITH DAVIS, M.D.
Adjunct Prof. of Operative Surgery
and Lecturer on Osteology
LOUISE ERICH, M.D.
Adjunct Professor of Hygiene
H. A. B. DUNNING, Ph.G.
Demonstrator of Pharmacy
H. WARREN BUCKLER, M.D.
Demonstrator of Obstetrics
HENRY W. KENNARD, M.D.
Demonstrator of Anatomy
S. T. DARLING, M.D.
Demonstrator of Chemistry
MARY P. VOEGLEIN, M.D.
Assistant in Pathology
PROFS. CONE and LEWIS
Curators of Museum

CHIEFS OF CLINICS

W. S. SKILLMAN, M.D.
Practice

SAMUEL KAHN, M.D.
MARIE E. THALWITZER, M.D.
Gynaecology

MARY P. VOEGLEIN, M.D.
Diseases of Children and Diseases
of the Nose and Throat

SESSION OF 1902-03

The Faculty was the same as in 1901-02, with the following exceptions:
Drs. Harlan, Chisolm and Darling were no longer on the Faculty. Dr. Erich became professor of orthopedics; James Bordley, Jr., M.D., became clinical professor of diseases of eye and ear; Mary A. Waters, M.D., adjunct professor of hygiene; John A. Luetscher, B.S., M.D., lecturer on normal physical diagnosis; Charlotte S. Murdock, A.B., M.D., instructor in pathology, and Leonard A. Beach, M.D., assistant in normal histology and clinical microscopy. In the clinics Drs. Kahn and Thalwitzer were replaced in gynaecology by Mary N. Browne, M.D., and Drs. S. DeMarco and M. Ekstromer were in charge of surgery. Dr. Ekstromer was no longer professor of chemistry.

SESSION OF 1903-04

B. BERNARD BROWNE, M.D.
Professor of Gynaecology
EUGENE F. CORDELL, M.D.
Professor of Principles and Practice of Medicine
PEARCE KINTZING, B.Sc., M.D.
Professor of Surgery
CLARIBEL CONE, M.D.
Professor of Pathology
CHARLES H. RILEY, M.D.
Professor of Obstetrics
JOHN L. G. LEE, B.A., LL.B.
Professor of Medical Jurisprudence
RICHARD HENRY THOMAS, B.A., M.D.
Professor of Diseases of Nose
Throat and Chest
LOUISE ERICH, M.D.
Professor of Orthopedics
S. GRIFFITH DAVIS, M.D.
Professor of Anatomy and
Operative Surgery
H. WARREN BUCKLER, A.B., M.D.
Professor of Therapeutics and
Clinical Medicine
HENRY P. HYNSON, Ph.G.
Professor of Pharmacy

HENRY LEE SMITH, M.D.
Professor of Diseases of Children
and Lecturer on Bacteriology
JENNIE N. BROWNE, A.B., M.D.
Professor of Physiology
W. MILTON LEWIS, M.D.
Professor of Normal Histology
and Clinical Microscopy
CHARLES MAYER FRANKLIN, A.M., M.D.
Professor of Psychiatry
GEORGE A. FLEMING, M.D.
Professor of Diseases of Eye and Ear
H. L. TROXEL, Ph.G.
Professor of Chemistry
JOHN R. ABERCROMBIE, M.D.
Professor of Materia Medica
and Dermatology
MARY A. WATERS, M.D.
Adjunct Professor of Hygiene
THOMAS J. TALBOTT, M.D.
Adjunct Professor of Anatomy
and Osteology
FRANCES A. CARPENTER, M.D.
Lecturer on Embryology

W. F. SKILLMAN, M.D.
Lecturer on Diseases of the Digestive Tract
W. J. LOWERY, Ph.G.
Demonstrator of Pharmacy
MARY N. BROWNE, A.B., M.D.
Demonstrator of Obstetrics
J. I. FRANCE, M.D.
Demonstrator of Anatomy

MARY P. VOEGLEIN, M.D.
Assistant in Pathology
LEONARD E. BEACH, M.D.
Assistant in Normal Histology and Clinical Microscopy
PROFESSOR CONE
Curator of Museum

CHIEFS OF CLINICS

MARY N. BROWNE, M.D.
Gynaecology
EVA SEAL THOMPSON, M.D.
Practice

MARY A. WATERS, M.D.
Diseases of Children and Surgery
F. M. WILCOX, M.D.
Surgery

MARY P. VOEGLEIN, M.D.
Diseases of the Nose and Throat

SESSION OF 1904-05

B. BERNARD BROWNE, M.D.
Professor of Gynaecology
PEARCE KINTZING, B.Sc., M.D.
Professor of Surgery
CLARIBEL CONE, M.D.
Professor of Pathology
CHARLES H. RILEY, M.D.
Professor of Obstetrics
JOHN L. G. LEE, A.B., LL.B.
Professor of Medical Jurisprudence
RICHARD HENRY THOMAS, A.B., M.D.
Professor of Diseases of Nose Throat and Chest
JOSEPH I. FRANCE, A.B., A.M., M.D.
Lecturer on the Anatomy of the Nervous System
W. J. LOWERY, Ph.G.
Lecturer on Pharmacy

MAURICE LAZENBY, A.B., M.D.
Lecturer on Bacteriology
LOUIS HAMMAN, A.B., M.D.
Demonstrator of Normal Physical Diagnosis
MARY N. BROWNE, A.B., M.D.
Demonstrator of Obstetrics
H. E. ASHBURY, M.D.
Demonstrator of Anatomy
MARY P. VOEGLEIN, M.D.
Assistant in Pathology
BERTHA BERGER, M.D.
Assistant in Histology and Clinical Microscopy
J. C. HODGES, M.D.
Assistant Demonstrator of Anatomy
PROFESSOR CONE
Curator of Museum

CHIEFS OF CLINICS

MARY A. WATERS, M.D.
Dispensary Physician
MARY N. BROWNE, M.D.
Gynecology
MARY P. VOEGLEIN, M.D.
Surgery
HENRIETTA M. THOMAS, M.D.
Diseases of the Nose and Throat
BERTHA BERGER, M.D.
Diseases of Children

In 1906 John Staige Davis, M.D., was professor of surgery; Albert J. Underhill, M.D., associate professor of surgery; Bertha D. Berger, M.D., lecturer on histology and clinical microscopy, and assistant in pediatrics, and Calvin D. Crist, M.D., assistant in anatomy.

SESSION OF 1907-08

FACULTY

B. BERNARD BROWNE, M.D.
Professor of Gynaecology
CLARIBEL CONE, M.D.
Professor of Pathology
CHARLES H. RILEY, M.D.
Professor of Obstetrics

COL. JOHN L. G. LEE, A.B., LL.B.
Professor of Medical Jurisprudence
LOUISE ERICH, M.D.
Emeritus Professor of Orthopedic Surgery

S. GRIFFITH DAVIS, M.D.
Professor Anatomy, and Dean
H. WARREN BUCKLER, A.B., M.D.
Professor of Clinical Medicine
J. H. MASON KNOX, Jr., Ph.D., M.D.
Professor of Pediatrics
GEORGE A. FLEMING, M.D.
Professor of Diseases of the Eye and Ear
HENRY LEE SMITH, M.D.
Professor of Medicine
JENNIE N. BROWNE, A.B., M.D.
Professor of Physiology
W. MILTON LEWIS, M.D.
Professor Normal Histology and Clinical Microscopy
JOHN R. ABERCROMBIE, A.B., M.D.
Professor of Therapeutics, Materia Medica and Dermatology
GUY L. HUNNER, S.B., M.D.
Professor of Genito-Urinary Diseases
CHARLES M. FRANKLIN, A.M., M.D.
Professor of Psychiatry
ROBERT TUNSTALL TAYLOR, A.B., M.D.
Professor of Orthopedic Surgery
CHARLES W. LARNED, M.D.
Professor of Clinical Medicine
ALEXIUS MC GLANNAN, M.D.
Professor of Surgery
WM. BURGESS CORNELL, A.B., M.D.
Professor of Neurology
H. COOK DAVIS, M.D.
Clinical Professor of Diseases Nose and Throat
J. I. FRANCE, A.M., M.D.
Clinical Professor of Diseases of Nervous System

MARY P. VOEGLEIN, M.D.
Associate Professor Hygiene, Instructor in Surgery and Assistant to the Dean
MAURICE LAZENBY, A.B., M.D.
Associate Professor of Surgery
FRANCES A. CARPENTER, M.D.
Lecturer on Embryology
H. E. ASHBURY, M.D.
Lecturer on Electrotherapeutics and Instructor in Orthopedic Surgery
J. HOWARD IGLEHART, M.D.
Lecturer on Osteology and Demonstrator of Obstetrics
MARY COOK WILLIS, M.D.
Lecturer on Materia Medica
HARRY C. HOUCK, M.D.
Lecturer on Histology and Clinical Microscopy
J. KONRAD UHLIG, A.B., M.D.
Lecturer on Chemistry
HENRIETTA M. THOMAS, M.D.
Lecturer on Bacteriology and Assistant in Pediatrics
RONALD T. ABERCROMBIE, A.B., M.D.
Lecturer on Pharmacology
A. LEE ELLIS, A.B., M.D.
Demonstrator of Anatomy
J. HARRY ULLRICH, Ph.G., M.D.
Assistant in Anatomy
H. H. HAZEN, M.D.
Instructor in Medicine

SESSION OF 1908-09

The new members of the Faculty were:

Carroll D. Partridge, M.D., lecturer on chemistry
Bertha E. Tapman, M.D., Assistant in gynecology
Anna D. Schultze, M.D., demonstrator of histology
Josephine M. Stransky, M.D., demonstrator of clinical microscopy
W. Warren Buckler, M.D., professor of clinical medicine
John H. King, M.D., associate professor of medicine
George W. Mahle, M.D., associate in medicine
Bertha E. Tapman, M.D., assistant in medicine
George W. Hemmeter, M.D., lecturer on physiology.

SESSION OF 1909-10

The Faculty was the same as in 1907-08, with the following exceptions: the following were no longer on the Faculty:

W. Warren Buckler, M.D.
Jennie N. Browne, M.D.
J. I. France, A.M., M.D.
Harry C. Houck, M.D.
J. Konrad Uhlig, M.D.
J. Harry Ullrich, Ph.G., M.D.
H. H. Hazen, M.D.

The new members of the Faculty were:

Grace Lotz, Ph.G., lecturer in chemistry
Matthew S. Hopkins, lecturer in chemistry
A. Lee Ellis, A.B., M.D., associate professor of anatomy (instead of demonstrator of anatomy).

III. (B) ALPHABETIZED LIST OF MEMBERS OF THE FACULTY

(For Faculty grouped by year, see previous pages)

Abbott, A. C., M.D. 1884-86
Abercrombie, John R., M.D. 1898-04, 1907-10
Alexander, Annie L., M.D. 1886-87
Arthur, H. H., M.D. 1896-97
Ashbury, H. E. 1904-05, 1907-10
Ashby, Thomas A.,[4] M.D. 1882-97
Atkinson, A. DuVal, M.D. 1900-01
Batchelor, Kemp. B., M.D. 1896-99
Beach, Leonard A., M.D. 1902-04
Berkley, Henry J., M.D. 1882-84
Berger, Bertha, M.D. 1904-06
Bernstein, E. J., M.D. 1889-90, 1898-00
Blades, G. Clinton, Ph.G. 1895-01
Block, William H., M.D. 1896-97
Bond, A. Kerr, B.A., M.D. 1884-89
Booker, William D.,[5] M. D. 1882-93
Bordley, James, Jr., M.D. 1902-03
Brevitt, Jessie, M.D. 1889-92, 1894-97
Brown, Francis E., B.A., M.D. 1896-97
Browne, B. Bernard, M.D. 1882-05, 1907-10
Browne, Jennie N., A.B. 1899-04, 1907-09
Browne, Mary N., M.D. 1902-05
Brush, Edward N., M.D. 1896-00
Buckler, H. Warren, M.D. 1901-04, 1907-09
Carpenter, Frances A., M.D. 1901-04, 1907-10
Chisolm, F. M., M.D. 1900-02
Clark, Joseph Clement, M.D. 1900-03
Cochel, India M., M.D. 1887-90
Cone, Claribel, M.D. 1893-05, 1907-10
Cordell, Eugene F.,[6] M.D. 1882-04
Cornell, William Burgess, A.B., M.D. 1907-10
Craighill, James M., M.D. 1885-86
Crist, Calvin D., M.D. 1906
Darling, S. T., M.D. 1901-03
Davis, H. Cook, M.D. 1907-10
Davis, John Staige, M.D. 1906
Davis, S. Griffith, M.D. 1894-04, 1907-10
Deetjen, Christian, M.D. 1895-00
DeMarco, S., M.D. 1902-03
Dunning, H., A.B., Ph.G. 1901-03
Eareckson, Edith, M.D. 1894-00
Eaton, Louise, M.D. 1894-96
Edstromer, M., M.D. 1900-03
Ekstromer, M., M.D. 1901-02
Ellis, A. Lee, A.B., M.D. 1907-10
English, M. Elida, Ph.B., M.D. 1884-86
Erich, Louise, M.D. 1895-97, 1900-04, 1907-10
Ewing, Laura M., M.D. 1886-90
Farrar, J. D., B.A., M.D. 1893-94
Fawcett, Robert, M.D. 1893-94
Fleming, George A., M.D. 1903-04, 1907-10
Forsythe, Hugh, M.D. 1894-97
Fort, S. J., M.D. 1884-85
France, J. J., M.D. 1903-05, 1907-09
Franklin, Charles Mayer, A.M., M.D. 1903-04, 1907-10
Frist, Hattie M., M.D. M.D. 1891-93
Frist-Emmart, Hattie, M.D. 1893-94
Funck, J. William, M.D. 1895-96
Gale, H. E., B.A., M.D. 1891-92
Gilchrist, Thomas C., M.R.C.S., L.S.A. 1896-97
Girdwood, John, M.D. 1894-96
Godfrey, Isabella K., M.D. 1889-93
Graham, George R., M.D. 1882-90
Hamburger, Louis, B.A., M.D. 1898-99
Hamman, Louis, A.B., M.D. 1904-05
Hargraves, M. Elizabeth, M.D. 1885-89
Harlan, Herbert, M.A., M.D. 1896-02
Harrison, A. C., M.D. 1899-01
Hazen, H. H., M.D. 1907-09
Hearn, A. C., M.D. 1898-00
Hemmeter, George W., M.D. 1908-09
Hemmeter, Mrs. 1887-88
Henderson, Miss Julia T. 1886-89
Herman, Nathan, M.D. 1898-01
Hodges, J. C., M.D. 1904-05
Holmes, Louise D., A.B., M.D. 1898-00
Hopkins, Matthew S. 1909-10
Houck, Harry C., M.D. 1907-09
Hundley, J. M., M.D. 1884-86
Hunner, Guy L., S.B., M.D. 1907-10
Hynson, Henry P., Ph.G. 1891-97, 1901-04
Iglehart, N. E. B., M.D. 1896-97, 1907-10
Jay, John G., M.D. 1882-1903
Johnston, R. H., M.D. 1898-99
Jones, C. Hampson, M.B., C.M. . . . 1884-89
Jones, Julian Stuart, LL.B. 1893-94
Kahn, Samuel, M.D. 1898-03
Kennard, Henry W., M.D. 1901-03
King, John H., M.D. 1908-09
Kintzing, Pearce, B.Sc., M.D. 1891-05
Knox, J.H. Mason, Jr., Ph.D., M.D. . 1907-10
Krum, F. W., M.D. 1893-94
Kuhn, Annie E., M.D. 1886-89
Lazenby, Maurice, A.B., M.D. 1904-05, 1907-10
Lanier, B. B., B.A., M.D. 1894-96
Larned, Charles W., M.D. 1907-10
Lee, John L. G., B.A., LL.B. 1898-05, 1907-10
Lewis, W. Milton, M.D. 1891-04, 1907-10
Likes, Sylvan, M.D. 1898-01
Linthicum, G. Milton, B.A., M.D. . 1895-99

Lotz, Grace, Ph.G. 1909-10
Love, William S., M.D. 1891-93
Lowery, W. J., Ph.G. 1903-05
Luetscher, John A., B.S., M.D. . . . 1902-03
Lynch, John S., M.D. 1882-86
McAvoy, M. J., Ph.G. 1898-01
McCormick, Thomas P., M.D. 1882-85
McGlannan, Alexius, M.D. 1907-10
Mackenzie, Edward E., M.D. 1886-90
Mahle, George W., M.D. 1908-09
Marden, T. Brice, B.A., M.D. 1893-97
Martenet, J. Fussell, M.D. 1882-93
Melvin, J. A., M.D. 1896-00
Miller, C. O., M.D. 1887-90
Mitchel, Charles W., M.D. 1891-94
Murdoch, Russell,(7)M.D. 1884-87
Murdock, Charlotte S., A.B., M.D. . 1902-03
Noble, W. H., M.D. 1882-84
O'Donoval, Charles, B.A., M.D. . . . 1894-99
Parkhurst, Alice S., M.D. 1885-86
Partridge, Carroll D., M.D. 1908-09
Penrose, Mary, M.D. 1891-92
Piggot, Cameron, M.D. 1882-86
Pollack, Flora, M.D. 1891-93
1896-00
Pollack, Ida, M.D. 1894-97
Preston, George J., B.A., M.D. 1889-90
Quinan, John R.,(8)M.D. 1884-85
Radcliff, Sue, M.D. 1894-95
Renshaw, Bessie, M.D. 1893-94
Riley, Charles H., M.D. 1898-05
1907-10
Robinson, Ralph, B.A., LL.B. 1894-97
Savin, T. L., M.D. 1900-01
Schone, George H., M.D. 1884-85
Schultze, Anna D., M.D. 1908-09
Scott, Gertrude, M.D. 1884-89
Seligman, Joseph A., M.D. 1893-94
Shannon, George C., M.D. 1884-86
Shemwell, J. F., M.D. 1891-92
Simmons, Horace M., M.D. 1882-84
Simon, Charles E., B.A., M.D. 1894-95
Skillman, W. F., M.D. 1901-04
Smith, Caroline E., M.D. 1885-89
Smith, Henry Lee, M.D. 1900-07
1908-10
Smith, Joseph T., M.D. 1885-03
Smith, W. Gray, M.D. 1882-84
Steinbrenner, Clara, M.D. 1885-89
Stevenson, H. Burton, M.D. 1893-94
Stokes, William Royal, B.A., M.D. . 1891-93
Stransky, Josephine M., M.D. 1908-09
Talbott, Thomas J., M.D. 1903-04
Tapman, Bertha E., M.D. 1908-09
Taylor, Amanda E., M.D. 1882-84
Taylor-Norris, Amanda, M.D. 1884-94
Taylor, Robert Tunstall,B.A.,M.D. 1896-97
1907-10
Thalwitzer, Marie E., M.D. 1885-86
1898-03
Thomas, Henrietta M., M.D. 1904-05
1907-10
Thomas,James Carey,(9)A.M.,M.D. 1884-89
Thomas, Richard Henry, M.D. 1882-93
1900-05
Thompson, Eva Seal, M.D. 1903-04
Thomsen, Alonzo L., B.A. 1886-89
Trimble, I. R., M.D. 1891-00
Troxel, H. L., Ph.G. 1903-04
Turner, Benj. A., M.D. 1882-86
1891-93
Uhlig, J. Konrad, A.B., M.D. 1907-09
Ullrich, J. Harry, Ph.G., M.D. 1907-09
Underhill, Albert J., M.D. 1906
Voeglein, Mary P., M.D. 1901-05
1907-10
Warfield, Mactier, B.A., M.D. 1884-89
Warner, M. Magdalene, M.D. 1896-97
Waters, Mary A., M.D. 1900-05
Watson, Marion A., M.D. 1893-94
Watson, William T., M.D. 1893
Westcott, J. W., Ph.G. 1891-92
Wilcox, F. M., M.D. 1903-04
Willis, Mary Cook, M.D. 1907-10
Winchester, Horace R., M.D. 1889-90
Winslow, John R., B.A., M.D. 1888-97
Winslow, Randolph, A.M., M.D. . . 1882-93
Woods, Hiram, Jr., M.D. 1882-84
1888-96
Yost, W. McLean, M.D. 1892-93
Zelwis, Johanna T., M.D. 1896-97
Zimmerman, M. Lizzie, M.D. 1888-89

IV. TEXT BOOKS USED

The first named book in each branch is preferred.

1883
PRACTICE OF MEDICINE – Bristowe, Niemeyer, Flint.
DISEASES OF WOMEN – Thomas, 5th Edition. Emmet's Gynecology, 2nd Edition. Barnes.
OBSTETRICS – Lusk, Playfair, Leishman, Cazeaux.
SURGERY – Bryant, Erichsen, Agnew, Stimson Operative Surgery.
MATERIA MEDICA – Biddle, Farquharson, Bartholow, Ringer.
PHYSIOLOGY – Martin, Foster, Kirke, Dalton.
DISEASES OF CHILDREN – Smith.
DISEASES OF THROAT AND CHEST – Cohen, Mackenzie, Flint, Loomis.
ANATOMY – Gray, Quain.
CHEMISTRY – Attfield, Youmans.
1884
DISEASES OF WOMEN – Thomas, 5th Edition. Emmet's Gynecology, 2nd Edition. Barnes. Goodell.
OBSTETRICS – Lusk, Playfair, Leishman, Cazeaux.
SURGERY – Bryant, Erichsen, Ashhurst, Stimson's Operative Surgery.
PRACTICE OF MEDICINE – Flint, Bartholow, Hartshorne's Essentials.
PHYSIOLOGY – Elementary, Yeo, Klein's Elements of Histology; Advanced, Foster.
DISEASES OF CHILDREN – Smith, Meigs and Pepper.
DISEASES OF THROAT – Cohen, Mackenzie.
DISEASES OF CHEST AND PHYSICAL DIAGNOSIS – Flint, Loomis, DaCosta's Medical Diagnosis.
ANATOMY – Gray, Quain.
DISEASES OF EYE AND EAR – Soelberg Wells on the Eye. Politzer on the Ear.
CHEMISTRY – Attfield, Youmans.
MATERIA MEDICA – Wood, Bartholow, Farquharson.
HYGIENE – Huxley & Youmans.
MEDICAL JURISPRUDENCE – Beck, Tidy.
PHARMACY – Parrish.
1885, 1886
Same as in 1884, with the following exceptions:
DISEASES OF CHILDREN – J. Lewis Smith, Eustace Smith.
DISEASES OF THE THROAT – Ingals added.
MEDICAL JURISPRUDENCE – Beck, Tidy replaced by Taylor.
1887
Same as in 1885, with the following exceptions:
DISEASES OF THE THROAT, CHEST AND PHYSICAL DIAGNOSIS – Ingals, for Intermediate Class; Cohen; Mackenzie; DaCosta's Physical Diagnosis.
ANATOMY – Weisse added.
CHEMISTRY – Youmans abandoned; Hill's Qualitative Analysis and Fresenius added.
MATERIA MEDICA – Farquharson replaced by Biddle.
1888
Same as in 1887, with the following exceptions:
DISEASES OF WOMEN – Emmett, 3rd edition.
OBSTETRICS – Playfair replaced by Parvin.
SURGERY – Bryant, Erichsen replaced by Wyeth.
DISEASES OF EYE AND EAR – Wells, Politzer replaced by Jular on the Eye; Roosa on the Ear.
1889
Same as in 1888, with the following exceptions:
DISEASES OF EYE AND EAR – Jular on the Eye replaced by Meyer.
CHEMISTRY – Youmans, Attfield, Hill replaced by Remsen's Elementary, Miller's, Stoddard's Qualitative Analysis.
1891
DISEASES OF WOMEN – Hart and Barbour. Thomas, 5th Ed. Emmet's Gynaecology, 3rd Edition. Skene.
OBSTETRICS – Lusk, Parvin, Leishman, Cazeaux.
SURGERY – Wyeth, Ashhurst, Stimson's Operative Surgery.
PRACTICE OF MEDICINE – Flint, Strümpel, Bristowe, Hartshorne's Essentials.
PHYSIOLOGY – Elementary, Yeo, Klein's Elements of Histology; Advanced, Foster,

Martin's Human Body.
DISEASE OF CHILDREN – J. Lewis Smith, Eustace Smith.
DISEASE OF THROAT, CHEST AND PHYSICAL DIAGNOSIS – Ingals, for Intermediate Class; Cohen, Mackenzie, DaCosta's Physical Diagnosis.
ANATOMY – Gray, Quain, Weisse.
HISTOLOGY AND PATHOLOGY – Klein, Schafer; Ziegler, Green, Cornil and Ranvier.
DISEASES OF EYE AND EAR – Noyes on the Eye; Buck on the Ear.
CHEMISTRY – Remsen's Elementary, Thorpe's Non-Metals, Muter's Analytical Chemistry.
MATERIA MEDICA – Wood, Bartholow, Farquharson by Woodbury.
HYGIENE – Huxley and Youmans.
MEDICAL JURISPRUDENCE – Taylor.
PHARMACY – Remington.
WORKS ON SPECIAL SUBJECTS – Bumstead and Taylor on Venereal Diseases; Gowers on Diseases of Nervous System; Bulkley's Manual of Diseases of Skin. Seifert and Müller's Manual of Clinical Diagnosis by Canfield; Canfield's Urinary Analysis.

1892

Same as in 1891, with the following exceptions:
DISEASES OF WOMEN – Thomas, 6th edition; Emmett abandoned.
SURGERY – Ashhurst preferred.
PRACTICE OF MEDICINE – Osler added.
PHYSIOLOGY – Klein abandoned; Kirke added.
DISEASES OF THROAT, CHEST AND PHYSICAL DIAGNOSIS – Ingals abandoned.
ANATOMY – Hollman added.

1893

Same as in 1892, with the following exceptions:
SURGERY – American Textbook of Surgery, Wyeth, Stephen Smith.
PRACTICE OF MEDICINE – Osler, Flint, Strümpel, Pepper's American Text Book.
PHYSIOLOGY – Kirkes, Foster, Yeo.

1894

DISEASES OF WOMEN – Hart and Barbour. Thomas and Mundé. Skene.
OBSTETRICS – Lusk, Parvin, Davis, Cazeaux.
SURGERY – American Text Book of Surgery, Wyeth, Stephen Smith.
PRACTICE OF MEDICINE – Osler, Flint, Strümpel, Pepper's American Text Book.
PHYSIOLOGY – Foster, Martin, Landois and Sterling, Herman.
DISEASES OF CHILDREN – J. Lewis Smith, Eustace Smith.
DISEASES OF THROAT – Cohen, Mackenzie.
ANATOMY – Gray, Quain, Weisse, Hollman.
HISTOLOGY AND PATHOLOGY – Schäfer, Ziegler, Green, Cornil and Ranvier, Quain.
DISEASES OF EYE AND EAR – Noyes and Fuchs on the Eye; Politzer (Last Ed.) and Roosa, on the Ear.
CHEMISTRY – Remsen's Elementary, Thorpe's Non-Metals, Muter's Analytical Chemistry.
MATERIA MEDICA – Wood, Bartholow, Farquharson by Woodbury.
HYGIENE – Parkes' Hygiene and Public Health, Rohé's Text Book of Hygiene.
MEDICAL JURISPRUDENCE – Reese.
PHARMACY – Remington.
WORKS ON SPECIAL SUBJECTS – Bumstead and Taylor on Venereal Diseases; Gowers on Diseases of Nervous System; Bulkley's Manual of Diseases of Skin; Von-Jaksch on Clinical Diagnosis; Ewald on Digestive Diseases; Canfield's Urinary Analysis; Flint's Diagnosis.

1895

Same as in 1894, with the following exceptions:
PRACTICE OF MEDICINE – DaCosta's Medical Diagnosis added.
PHYSIOLOGY – Kirkes, Foster and Yeo.
HISTOLOGY AND PATHOLOGY – Green, Cornil and Ranvier, Quain abandoned. Delafield and Prudden added.
MEDICAL JURISPRUDENCE – Ewell added.
PHARMACY – Caspari, Remington.

1896

Same as in 1895, with the following exceptions:
DISEASES OF CHILDREN – Eustace Smith abandoned. Keating's Cyclopaedia added.
HISTOLOGY AND PATHOLOGY – Schäfer; Piersol; Ziegler; Thoma and Green.
CHEMISTRY – Thorpe abandoned. Withaus' Elements of Chemistry and Purdy's Uranalysis added.
MATERIA MEDICA – Shoemaker added.
WORKS ON SPECIAL SUBJECTS – Canfield, Flint, Bulkley abandoned. Malcolm Morris on Skin Diseases, Bradford and Lovett on Orthopaedic Surgery, Clouston on Mental Diseases, Tyson's Urinary Analysis, Manton's Embryology were added.

1898

DISEASES OF WOMEN – Hart and Barbour, Thomas and Mundé, Garriques, 2d Ed.
OBSTETRICS – Lusk, Parvin, Davis, Cazeaux.
SURGERY – American Text-Book of Surgery, Principles of Surgery, Senn, Operative Surgery, J. D. Bryant.
PRACTICE OF MEDICINE – Osler, Wood & Fitz, Flint, Strümpel, DaCosta's Med. Diagnosis, Pepper's American Text-Book.
PHYSIOLOGY – Stewart's Manual, Foster, Waller, American Text-Book.
DISEASES OF CHILDREN – J. Lewis Smith, Keating's Cylopaedia, Holt.
DISEASES OF THROAT – Cohen, Mackenzie.
ANATOMY – Gray, Quain, Weisse, Hollman.
HISTOLOGY, PATHOLOGY AND BACTERIOLOGY – Marden's Manual, Schäfer, Piersol, Ziegler, Thoma, Delafield & Prudden, Mallory & Wright's Pathological Technique, Abbott.
DISEASES OF EYE AND EAR – DeSchweinitz and Fuchs on the Eye, Politzer (last Ed.) and Roosa on the Ear.
CHEMISTRY – Remsen's Elementary, Withaus' Elements of Chemistry, Muter's Analytical Chemistry, Purdy's Urinalysis.
MATERIA MEDICA – Wood, Bartholow, Shoemaker, Butler.
HYGIENE – Parke's Hygiene and Public Health; Rohé's Text-Book of Hygiene.
MEDICAL JURISPRUDENCE – Reese, Ewell.
PHARMACY – Caspari, Remington.
WORKS ON SPECIAL SUBJECTS – Ewald on Digestive Diseases, Simon on Clinical Diagnosis, Malcolm Morris on Skin Diseases, Bradford and Lovett on Orthopaedic Surgery, Clouston on Mental Diseases, Tyson's Urinary Analysis, Gowers on Nervous Diseases, Bumstead and Taylor on Venereal Diseases, Manton's Embryology.

1899-1900

ANATOMY – Gray; Quain; Weisse; Hollman.
BACTERIOLOGY – Abbott.
CHEMISTRY – Withaus' Elements of; Remsen's Elementary; Muter's Analytical; Purdy's Urinalysis.
CHILDREN, DISEASES OF – J. Lewis Smith; Holt, Rotch; Keating's Cyclopaedia.
EYE AND EAR, DISEASES OF – DeSchweinitz & Fuchs on the Eye; Politzer & Roosa on the Ear.
GYNAECOLOGY – 1899 Garriques, 2d ed; Penrose, Sutton and Giles; Greig Smith (Abdominal Surgery).
1900 Dudley, Diseases of Women; Byford, Manual of Gynaecology; Greig Smith, (Abdominal Surgery).
HISTOLOGY (Normal) – Schaefer; Marden, Piersol; Stohr.
HYGIENE Parke's Hygiene and Public Health; Rohé's Text-Book of Hygiene; Coplin & Bevan's Practical Hygiene.
MATERIA MEDICA AND THERAPEUTICS – Wood; Hare; Butler; Shoemaker; Bartholow.
MICROSCOPY, CLINICAL – Clinical Diagnosis, Simon, V. Jaksch; Urine, Hofman & Utzman; Blood, Cabot.
MEDICAL JURISPRUDENCE – Reese; Ewell.
NOSE AND THROAT – Lennox Browne, Bosworth.
OBSTETRICS – Lusk; Parvin; Davis; Hirsh; Cazeaux.
PATHOLOGY – Ziegler; Stengel; Mallory & Wright (Pathological Technique).
PHARMACY – Caspari; Remington.
PHYSIOLOGY – Stewart's Manual; Foster; Waller; American Text-Book.
PRACTICE OF MEDICINE – Osler; Wood & Fitz; Strümpel; DaCosta's Medical Diagnosis; Pepper's American Text-Book.
SURGERY – American Text-Book; Principles of Surgery; Senn; DaCosta; Operative Surgery, I. D. Bryant.

SPECIAL SUBJECTS

DIAGNOSIS, PHYSICAL – Tyson.
EMBRYOLOGY – Manton.
DIGESTIVE DISEASES – Ewalt.
MENTAL DISEASES – Mental Diseases – Clouston; Compendium of Insanity – Chapin; Manual of Insanity – Spitzka; Nervous Diseases – Gowers; Skin Diseases – Malcolm Morris; Venereal Diseases – Bumstead & Taylor.

1901

Same as in 1900, with the following exceptions:
ANATOMY – Hollman abandoned; Added: Holden; Morris.
CHEMISTRY – Simon; (all earlier books abandoned).

EYE AND EAR – On the Eye: Swanzy, Thorington added. On the Ear: Howell, Dench added.
GYNECOLOGY – Garriques restored.
HISTOLOGY (Normal) – Bohm, Davidoff and Huber added.
HYGIENE – Coplin and Bevan's Practical Hygiene abandoned. Egbert added.
MICROSCOPY, CLINICAL – Jaksch replaced by Levy and Klemperer.
PRACTICE OF MEDICINE – Anders added.

1902

Same as in 1901, with the following exceptions:
GYNECOLOGY – Byford replaced by Penrose: Diseases of Women.
OBSTETRICS – Hirsch preferred.

1903

Same as in 1902, with the following exceptions:
EYE AND EAR, DISEASES OF – Eye – Fuchs; Ear – DeSchweinitz, Politzer, Dench.
HISTOLOGY (Normal), Bohm, Davidoff and Huber; Schaefer.
MATERIA MEDICA – Butler; Shoemaker, both abandoned. Yeo's Manual of Treatment; American Text-book of Applied Therapeutics. (both added.)
MICROSCOPY (Clinical) – Levy and Klemperer; Cabot, both abandoned.
NOSE AND THROAT – Ingalls; Burnett, Ingalls and Newcomer replaced Lennox Browne, Bosworth.
OBSTETRICS – Williams added.
PHYSIOLOGY – Stewart; Waller, both abandoned. Kirke's Handbook, Raymond's Human Physiology added.
PRACTICE OF MEDICINE – DaCosta abandoned.

1904

Same as in 1903, with the following exceptions:
CHILDREN, DISEASES OF – Holt Preferred.
SPECIAL SUBJECTS – Berkeley (mental diseases) added.
MEDICAL DICTIONARY – Dorland added.

1906-1907

Same as in 1904, with the following exceptions:
HISTOLOGY (NORMAL) – 1907 – Marden, Schaefer.
MATERIA MEDICA, THERAPEUTICS AND PHARMACOLOGY – Bartholow; Yeo's Manual of Treatment; both abandoned. 1907 – Stevens; Butler; Cushny added.
PHYSIOLOGY – The following were used: Howell's Textbook of Physiology; Brubaker's Textbook, 2d ed.; Kirke's Handbook; Ott's Human Physiology; Raymond's Human Physiology.
SPECIAL SUBJECTS – 1907: All previous works on Mental Diseases were replaced by De Fursac's Manual of Psychiatry; Burr's Psychology and Mental Diseases; Mendel's Textbook of Psychiatry.
SKIN DISEASES 1907: Crocker; Stelwagon; Pusey; Wolff were added.
DIETETICS – 1907: Friedenwald and Ruhrah on Dietetics.

1908

Same as in 1907, with the following exceptions:
CHEMISTRY – Remsen; Halliburton; both added.
MATERIA MEDICA – U. S.Pharmacopoeia added.
PRACTICE OF MEDICINE – Wood and Fitz; Pepper's American Text-book; both abandoned. Tyson added.
SPECIAL SUBJECTS
DIAGNOSIS PHYSICAL – Tyson abandoned. Butler; Musser (both added).
SKIN DISEASES – Van Harlingen added.

V. LISTS OF a). GRADUATES, and b). MATRICULATES OF THE WOMAN'S MEDICAL COLLEGE OF BALTIMORE, MARYLAND

The data for the graduates to the year 1908 are taken from the College catalogue for 1909-1910, which also contains a list of the graduates of 1909, without biographical data. The names of the graduates of 1910 were located in the *Baltimore Sun*, for May 31, 1910.

V. a). Alphabetical List of Graduates of the Woman's Medical College of Baltimore, Maryland. (See separate list for names of matriculates who did not graduate).

ABERLE-BARTOLS, LILLIE A., M.D., 1901, Massachusetts
Prepared at Girl's Latin School, Boston; Visiting Physician to Boston Dispensary and Trinity Dispensary, 1901; Member Massachusetts Medical Society. Married. Retired. 186 Boylston Street, Boston, Mass.

ALLEN, LIDA T., M.D., 1906, New Jersey
Resident Physician, Jewish Maternity Hospital, Phila., Pa., 1906-07. Private practice, Collingwood, New Jersey.
*BACON, MARGARET, M.D., 1886, Maryland
BAERECKE-ZIEGLER, VIDA, M.D., 1895, Alabama
Prepared at Woman's College, Haarlem, Holland. College Physician for Women in Jno. B. Stetson University. General practice, DeLand, Florida.
BEMENT, LUCY P., M.D., 1897, Ohio
Prepared by private tutor; Physician in charge of Sarah C. Parker Memorial Hospital for Women and Children, Shaowu, China; Member Medical Association of China, Shaowu, China.
BOYD, LOIS, M.D., 1907, North Carolina
Prepared by private schools, and North Carolina State Normal College. Resident Physician, Good Samaritan Hospital, 1906-1907. Resident Physician, Sanitary Officer and Professor of Physiology, Winthrop Normal, and Industrial College. Rock Hill, S. C.
BREVITT, JESSIE, M.D., 1889, Maryland
Retired. 144 Wilson Street, Baltimore, Maryland.
BROWNE, JENNIE NICHOLSON, M.D., 1901, Maryland
Prepared at Bryn Mawr School, Baltimore; Holder of Bryn Mawr Scholarship, 1894-98; A.B., 1898; Visiting Physician to Evening Dispensary for Working Women and Girls of Baltimore, 1902; Visiting Physician to the City Medical Agency of South Baltimore; Clinical Assistant in Gynecology, Johns Hopkins Hospital, 1902; Member American Medical Association, Medical and Chirurgical Faculty of Maryland; Adjunct Professor of Physiology, 1899 to 1901; Professor Physiology, 1902-07. Private practice, 510 Park Avenue, Baltimore, Maryland.
BROWNE, MARY NICHOLSON, M.D., 1902, Maryland
Prepared at Bryn Mawr School, Baltimore; Holder of Bryn Mawr School Scholarship, 1895-99; A.B., 1899; Clinical Assistant in Gynecology Johns Hopkins Dispensary, 1902-04; Chief of Clinic in Gynecology, Women's Medical College 1902-06; Demonstrator of Obstetrics, 1903-06; Visiting Physician to Evening Dispensary for Working Women and Girls of Baltimore, 1906. Private practice, 510 Park Avenue, Baltimore, Maryland.
BURGESS-BARROW, M. L., M.D., 1890, Tennessee
Medical Missionary in China.
CAMPBELL-SHAW, EMMA F., M.D., 1907, Maryland
Prepared at the Girl's Latin School, Baltimore. Retired, Marquette, Mich.
CASEY, ELSIE M., M.D., 1905, Virginia
Prepared at the Clifton Forge Seminary. Private practice, Lynchburg, Va.
CASTLE, SARA ALLEN, B.L., M.D., 1900, Mississippi
Prepared by private tutor; M.D., Cornell Medical School, 1901; Resident Physician Hospital Woman's Medical College, 1902; Resident Physician Evening Dispensary for Women and Working Girls; Post-Graduate Work, Johns Hopkins, May and June, 1900, and February to July, 1902; Resident Physician Meridian Female College, 1902-05; Member Lauderdale County, Mississippi State, and American Medical Societies; City Bacteriologist. Private practice, Meridian, Miss.
COALE, EDITH SE VILLE, M.D., 1908, Ohio
Prepared in high school. Assistant Resident Physician, State Hospital, Retreat, Pa.
COCHEL-HEWES, INDIA M., M.D., 1887, Maryland
Prepared at Western Maryland College; Demonstrator of Obstetrics, Woman's Medical College, 1888; Post-graduate work, Johns Hopkins, 1891; Physician in Charge, Aroostook Springs, 1892-1900; Medical Examiner, Boys' Industrial Club, Malden, Mass.; Retired. 221 Harvard St., Brookline, Mass.
COHON, EUGENIA, M.D., 1910, Baku, Russia
COLER, IDA C., M.D., 1888, Ohio
Prepared at the Ohio State University; Post-Graduate Work, University of Michigan, 1898-99 Private practice, 1316 Washtenow Street, Ann Arbor, Mich.
CONDIT, GERTRUDE SCOTT, M.D., 1884, Virginia
CONE, CLARIBEL, M.D., 1890, Maryland
Prepared at Western Female High School; Lecturer on Hygiene, Woman's Medical College, 1893-95; Professor Pathology, 1895; Pathologist, Hospital Woman's Medical College; Post-Graduate Work, Johns Hopkins Pathological Laboratory under Dr. W. H. Welch, 1893–1903; Post-Graduate Work in Pathology at Seactenburger Institute, Frankfort-on-Main, and Pasteur Institute, Paris, 1903-05; Member Society Woman's Medical College; Member Medical and Chirurgical Faculty of Maryland; Member American Medical Association. Baltimore, Maryland.
COOK, MARY, M.D., 1903, New Jersey

Prepared at Hackettstown Seminary; Resident Physician Hospital Woman's Medical College, June to September, 1903; Assistant in Dispensary and Infirmary for Women and Children, New York. Member of Essex County Medical Society and Medical Club of Newark, N. J. Private practice, 83 Third Avenue, Newark, N. J.

COTTON, JULIA C., M.D., 1908, Pennsylvania
Prepared in High School; Assistant Resident Physician, State Hospital, Norristown, Pa.

CRUTTENDEN, MABEL C., M.D., 1909, Connecticut

CURTIS, BELLE D., M.D., 1895, Massachusetts
Member Everett Medical Society. Private practice, Everett, Mass.

DALY, KATHERINE L., M.D., 1897, Pennsylvania
Private practice, 132 S. St. Clair St., Pittsburgh, Pa.

DOLE, MARY P., M.D., 1888, Massachusetts
Prepared at Mt. Holyoke College; Interne at the New England Hospital, 1890-91; Visiting Physician Franklin County Hospital, 1897-1905; Post-Graduate Work Paris and Berlin, 1894-95 and 1901; Member of Massachusetts Medical Society. Private practice, Greenfield, Mass.

EARECKSON, EDITH, M.D., 1893, Maryland
Lecturer on Hygiene, 1895-98; Associate Professor Hygiene, 1898-1900; Member Medical and Chirurgical Faculty. Private practice, 953 Madison Avenue, Baltimore, Maryland.

EATON-SEEBUR, LOUISE, M.D., 1894, New Jersey
Prepared at Jersey City High School; Assistant Resident Physician Hospital Woman's Medical College, 1894-95; Resident Physician Maternity Hospital. Woman's Medical College, 1895-96; Post-Graduate Work Johns Hopkins Hospital, 1895-96; Connected with New York Health Department, 1897-1904. Retired. Waterloo, Wisconsin.

EIRLEY, CLARA S., M.D., 1892, Pennsylvania
Prepared at private school. Private practice, Hagerstown, Md.

ENGLISH, M. ELIDA, Ph.B., M.D., 1884, Illinois

ERDMAN, CARRIE D., M.D., 1907, Pennsylvania
Prepared at Shamokin High School, Pennsylvania. Assistant in Histology, Woman's Medical College, 1907-1908; Post graduate Johns Hopkins Medical School, 1907-1908. Shamokin, Pa.

ERICH, LOUISE, M.D., 1895, Maryland
Assistant in Pathology and Histology; Chief of Eye Clinic, 1895-97; Professor of Orthopedics, 1901-05; Physical Examiner Gymnasium, Y.W.C.A.; Physician to Evening Dispensary for Working Women; Orthopedist to the N. E. City Dispensary and to the Hospital Woman's Medical College; Member Medical and Chirurgical Faculty. Private practice, 613 Park Avenue, Baltimore, Maryland.

EVERS, FLORENCE B., M.D., 1908, West Virginia
Prepared in High School of Martinsburg, W. Va. Private Practice, Martinsburg, W. Va.

EWING-READING, M.L., M.D., 1885, Maryland
Prepared at Chestnut Hill School, Pa., and at State Normal School, Baltimore, Md.; Post-Graduate Work Woman's Medical College and Johns Hopkins Hospital; Physician-in-Charge Oglethorpe-by-the-Sea Sanitarium, Tampa, Florida, 1902. Hayden, Maryland.

FAUGHNAN, ROSE CECELIA, M.D., 1910, New Jersey

FENDLER, AMELIA M., M.D., 1892, New York
Visiting Physician to Mt. Sinai Hospital; Member of Harlane Medical Association; Member of Medical Society, County of New York; Delegate to and Member of Medical Society, State of New York; Expert Medical Counsel to the Supreme Court, New York. Private practice, 1391 Madison Avenue, New York City.

FIFIELD, EMILY W., M.D., 1884, Nebraska
Interne N. W. Hospital, Minneapolis, 1887; Visiting Physician to Asbery Hospital and City Hospital, Minneapolis; Post-Graduate Work, 1885 and 1893; Johns Hopkins Hospital, 1901; Member Hennepin County Medical Society. Private practice, Gynecology, 210 Pillsbury Building, Minneapolis, Minnesota.

FLETCHER, HILDA, M.D., 1907, Indiana
Prepared at Indianapolis High School. Private practice, 510 Meridan St., Indianapolis, Ind.

FOWLER-NOBLE, A.L., M.D., 1893, Massachusetts
Prepared at Westfield High and Normal School; Member Massachusetts State Medical Society and American Medical Association. Private practice, Westfield, Mass.

FRIST-EMMART, HATTIE, M.D., 1890, Maryland
Retired. 817 Fremont Avenue, Baltimore, Maryland.

FULLER, FLORENCE C., M.D., 1910, Iowa

GATELL, PALMIRA MONSERRATE, M.D., 1910, Porto Rico

GODFREY, ISABELLA K., M.D., 1890, Maryland
Private practice, 1431 Park Avenue, Baltimore, Maryland.

GREANY-DOYLE, ANNIE G., M.D., 1901, Massachusetts
Prepared at Fall River Grammar and High School; Interne, Fall River Hospital, 1901-02. Private practice. Grafton, West Virginia.

HANN, LAURA W. COOK, M.D., 1892, New Jersey
Prepared at the Centenary Collegiate Institute, Hackettstown, N. J. Private practice, Washington, N. J.

HARRIS-GLASCOCK, JOY, M.D., 1896, North Carolina
Member Guilford County and North Carolina Medical Societies. Private practice, Greensboro, N. C.

HEFFNER, ALICE M., M.D., 1891, New York
Private practice, 244 Carl St., Buffalo, N. Y.

HILL-CRAWFORD, JULIA T., M.D., 1886, Missouri
Private practice, York, Pennsylvania.

HOFFNAGLE-VAN DYKE, DAISY C., M.D., 1907, New York
Prepared at Westport High School, New York. Private practice, Malone, N. Y.

HOOPES, FANNIE E., D.D.S., M.D., 1893, Maryland
D.D.S., Pennsylvania College Dental Surgery; Visiting Physician to Evening Dispensary for Working Women and Girls, 1898-1901; Member Medical and Chirurgical Faculty, Md. Private practice, 906 N. Calvert St., Baltimore, Maryland.

HOUSTON-PATTERSON, A. R., M.D., 1891, Virginia
Medical Missionary at Suchien, China.

HOWE-ANTHONY, M. ANNIE, M.D., 1900, Massachusetts
Resident Physician Hospital Woman's Medical College, 1900-01; Woman Resident Markleton Sanitarium, 1901-02; Resident Physician, Dr. Green's Sanitarium, 1902-07. Private practice, Nervous and Mental Diseases, Church St., Moravia, N. Y.

HOYER, LUCIA, M.D., 1908, Wisconsin
Prepared by private tutor; Assistant Resident Physician, N. Y. Infirmary for Women and Children, 1908–.

INGOLD-TATE, MATTIE BARBARA, M.D., 1896, South Carolina
Medical Missionary in Chunju, Korea.

JACQUES, J. EUGENIA, M.D., 1897, New York
Visiting Physician to Christ's Hospital Dispensary, Jersey City, 1897-99; The Dispensary for Women and Children, New York, 1898; Member Hudson County Medical Society. Private practice, 74 Waverly St., Jersey City, N. J.

JANER, ANITA, M.D., 1909, Porto Rico

JANES-TOWNSEND, ELMA L., M.D., 1899, Wisoncsin
Private practice, 34 Campbell Building, Hartford City, Indiana.

JONES, HARRIET B., M.D., 1884, West Virginia
Prepared at private school; Assistant Superintendent West Virginia Hospital for the Insane, 1888-91; Post-Graduate Work, N. Y. Post-Graduate School, 1888; Chicago Post-Graduate 1894; Member Ohio County and W. Va. Medical Societies; Member American Medical Association. Private practice, 80 Fifteenth St., Wheeling, W. Va.

JONES, MARY LOIS, M.D., 1901, Pennsylvania
Prepared at private school and Pittsburg School of Anatomy; Member Butler County Medical Society. Private practice, 434 Pacific Ave., Pittsburg, Pa.

JONES, MAY-FARINHOLT, M.D., 1897, Virginia
Prepared at Mary Baldwin Seminary and Mt. DeSales Convent; Resident Physician Hospital Woman's Medical College, 1897; Resident Physician Tom Franklin Hospital, Miss., 1897-1908; Member Sounds County and Mississippi State Medical Societies; Post-Graduate Work Johns Hopkins Hospital, 1900; Post-Graduate Work in Bacteriology and Clinical Microscopy, 1900-02-03-04; Vice-President Mississippi State Society, 1903; Professor Anatomy Physiology and Physical Culture, Mississippi Industrial Institute and College, Columbus, Miss., 1897-1908; Resident Physician Eastern State Hospital, Williamsburg, Va., 1908–.

JOHNSON-DURRETT, LADY M., M.D., 1897, Maryland
Prepared at private schools; Member W. Va. State Medical Society. Private practice Women and Children, Fairmount, W. Va.

KEAY, ELIZABETH A., M.D., 1910, Maine

KELLY, KATHERINE DE SALES, M.D., 1899, Maryland
Prepared at Mt. DeSales College; Dispensary Physician to the Dispensary Woman's Medical College, 1900-04; Visiting Physician to the N. W. City Medical Agency, 1905-08. Private practice, 2122 Pennsylvania Avenue, Baltimore, Md.

LATIMER, CAROLINE W., M.D., 1890, Maryland
Prepared at private school; Member of Medical and Chirugical Faculty; Post-Graduate Work at Johns Hopkins Hospital, 1890-91. Retired. 25 W. Chase St., Baltimore, Md.

LIGG, E. CAMILLE, M.D., 1895, Pennsylvania
Westfield, N. Y.

MC ALPIN, JASMIN, M.D., 1887, Ohio
Prepared at private schools; Resident Physician Hospital Woman's Medical College, 1887; Post-Graduate Work at New York Eye and Ear Infirmary, 1889. Private practice, Butler, Pa.

MC KAY, MARY E., M.D., 1897, Georgia
A.B.; Resident Physician Hospital Woman's Medical College, 1898-99; Assistant Resident Physician Dispensary for Working Women and Girls, 1898-1901; Member Macon Medical Society; Member Georgia State Medical Association. Private practice, The Grand, Macon, Ga.

MC MILLAN, KATHERINE, M.D., 1896, New Brunswick
Resident Physician Hospital Woman's Medical College, 1896-97. Medical Missionary, Wonsan, Korea.

MARTIN, CAROLINE R., M.D., 1908, Maryland
Prepared by Private Tutor. Private practice.

MILLER, LILLIAN G., M.D., 1906, Maryland
Resident Physician, Hospital for Consumptives, Towson, Md., 1906-07. County Physician, Yellowstone Co. Private practice, Babcock Building, Billings, Mont.

MURDOCK-YOUNG, CHARLOTTE S., M.D., 1902, Maryland
Prepared at the Miss Adams School, Baltimore; A.B., Woman's College, Baltimore, 1897; Graduate Student Romance Languages and Philology, Bryn Mawr College, 1897-99; Scholar in Romance Philology, 1897-98; A.M., Woman's College, Baltimore, 1898; Instructor in Pathology Woman's Medical College, 1902-03; Superintendent Presbyterian Deaconess Home, 1903; Hospital Work, Hfi-an-fu, Shensi Province, China.

NORRIS, GRACE, M.D., 1904, New York
Prepared at High School, Richfield Springs, N. Y., and New York State University. Resident Physician, State Industrial School for Girls, Mitchellville, Iowa, 1907–.

OWEN-BRILL, K. ROSE, M.D., 1896, New York
Prepared at Girls High School, Brooklyn; Ph.G., Brooklyn College Pharmacy, 1893; Physician in Manhattan State Hospital for the Insane, Central Isle, N. Y., since 1902; Member Suffolk County Medical Society, 100 W. Seventy-eighth St., New York City, N.Y.

OWEN, MARY R., M.D., 1883, New York
Resident Physician Hospital Woman's Medical College, 1884; Seven years in Eastern District Hospital, Brooklyn; Post-Graduate Work in Post-Graduate School, New York City; Member N. Y. State Pathological Brooklyn, and Kings County Medical Societies. Private practice, 153 S. Fourth St., Brooklyn, N. Y.

PAK, ESTHER KIM, M.D., 1900, Korea
Medical Missionary, Pyeng Yang, Korea.

PARKHURST, ALICE S., M.D., 1885, Maryland
Private practice, 1410 Park Avenue, Baltimore, Maryland.

PECK, WILLENA A., M.D., 1900, Massachusetts
Resident Physician Hospital Woman's Medical College, 1900-01; Assistant in Laryngology, Dispensary Woman's Medical College; Resident Physician Blue Mountain College, Blue Mountain, Miss.

PENROSE-APPELGARTH, MARY, M.D., 1891, Maryland
Prepared at Friend's High School, Baltimore. Retired, Huntingdon, Pa.

PILE, MAYNE, M., M.D., 1884, Pennsylvania
Member of Medical Society and Medical Association of Washington, D. C., Private practice, 1328 R St., N. W., Washington, D. C.

PLATT-WHITE, BELLE J., M.D., 1893, Massachusetts
Post-Graduate Work at N. Y. Post-Graduate College and Polyclinic, 1898; Member Massachusetts Medical Society. Retired. 182 Sumner Avenue, Springfield, Mass.

POLLACK, FLORA, M.D., 1891, Maryland
Prepared at Public and Private Schools; Interne Blockley Hospital, Philadelphia, 1891-92; Associate Professor Embryology and Physical Diagnosis, 1897; Assistant in Gynecology, Johns Hopkins Dispensary, 1902–; Member Medical and Chirurgical Faculty. Private practice, Baltimore, Maryland.

POLLACK-BERNSTEIN, IDA, M.D., 1893, Maryland
Prepared at Western Female High School, Baltimore; Resident Physician Hospital Woman's Medical College, 1894-95; Post-Graduate Work Johns Hopkins Hospital in Medicine, Surgery, Gynecology, Clinical Microscopy, Pathology and Bacteriology, 1893-94. Retired. Kalamazoo, Michigan.

PRICE, SUSAN ALEXANDER, M.D., 1903, West Virginia
Prepared at Lewisburg, W. Va. Woman's College; Resident Physician Hospital Woman's Medical College, 1903-04; Visiting Physician to Marlington Sanitarium and Dispensary, 1904-05; Member W. Va. State Medical Society. Woman Resident, State Hospital for the

Insane, Weston, West Virginia.

PRUITT, OLGA VALERIA, M.D., 1910, South Carolina

PUETT, BESSIE V., M.D., 1909, Georgia

RADCLIFFE, SUE, M.D., 1894, New York

Prepared at Yonkers High School; Assistant in Gynecology, Woman's Medical College, 1894-95; Post-Graduate Work Johns Hopkins Hospital, 1894-95; Resident Physician Hospital Woman's Medical College, 1895-96; Member West Chester County Medical Society; Member Woman's Medical Association, New York City. Private practice, 279 S. Broadway, Yonkers, N. Y.

*REED-MARTENET, ELLA J., M.D., 1894, Virginia

RENSHAW, ELIZABETH, M.D., 1893, Maryland

Post-Graduate work in Baltimore, 1907-09. Baltimore, Md.

RIEGLEMAN, LAURIE M. L., M.D., 1897, New York

Prepared at Chicago High School, Ill.; M.D., New York Medical College for Women, 1890; Visiting Physician to S. 3d Street Hospital, Brooklyn, N. Y.; Member of Kings County Medical Society. Private practice, 43 Lee Ave., New York City.

RIVERA, ELISA, M.D., 1909, Porto Rico

ROCHE, MARY E., M.D., 1908, Connecticut

Prepared in High Schools; Graduate of Connecticut Training School for Nurses, 1902; Assistant Superintendent, Carbondale Hospital, Pa., 1902-1904; Assist. Dr. Simon's Laboratory. Baltimore, 1908-1909.

RUSSELL, MINNIE A., M.D., 1896, Illinois

Prepared at Illinois Normal University; Post-Graduate Work, School of Electricity and Diagnosis at Mary Thompson Hospital. Private practice, Armington, Ill.

SCHULTZE-ABERCROMBIE, ANNA D., M.D., 1908, Maryland

Prepared at Zion School and by private tutor; Graduate Lying In Department, University of Maryland, 1893; Graduate, Philadelphia General Hospital Training School for Nurses, 1895; Superintendent of Connecticut Training School for Nurses, 1900-1902; Superintendent, Englewood Hospital, Chicago, 1902-1904; Resident Student, Good Samaritan Hospital, 1907-1908; Resident Physician, Good Samaritan Hospital, 1908-1909.

SEILER, MINNIE M., M.D., Pennsylvania

Private practice, 1008 White St., Key West, Florida.

SHIPLEY, ANNIE C., M.D., 1902, Delaware

Prepared at Seaford High School, Del.; Resident Physician Hospital Woman's Medical College, 1902-03; Consulting Physician United Charities Hospital, Cambridge, Md.; Member Sussex County Medical Society. Resident Physician, College for Women, Columbia, S. C.

SMITH, LOUISE Z., M.D., 1890, Nebraska

Private practice, Chattanooga, Tenn.

STEINBRENNER, CLARA, M.D., 1885, Maryland

Private practice, 223 W. 105th St., New York City.

STERLING, E. BLANCHE, M.D., 1905, Maryland

Prepared at Western Female High School, Baltimore; Graduate Boston Normal School of Gymnastics; Assistant in Medical Gymnastics, Johns Hopkins Hospital; Instructor in Gymnastics at Oldfield School, Physician, 819 Park Ave., Baltimore, Md.

STRANSKY, JOSEPHINE M., M.D., 1908, Maryland

Prepared by private tutor. Private practice, 2309 Ashland Avenue, Baltimore, Md.

SWEET-SAVIN, JESSIE ELLA, M.D., 1901, Arkansas

Prepared at St. Louis, Mo., and Pine Bluff, Ark., High Schools; Visiting Ophthalmologist to Jefferson County Alms House, Ark.; Post-Graduate Work at Presbyterian Eye, Ear and Throat Charity Hospital, Baltimore; Member Jefferson County and Arkansas State Medical Societies; Member American Medical Association; U. S. Pension Examiner. Private practice, Specialty Eye, Ear, Nose and Throat, Pine Bluff, Ark.

TAPMAN, BERTHA E., M.D., 1907, Maryland

Prepared at the Western High School, Baltimore. Post-Graduate Work, Johns Hopkins Dispensary. Physician to the Crittendon Home, 1907. Assistant in Clinical Microscopy, Woman's Medical College, 1907-1908. Private practice, 2725 York Road, Baltimore, Md.

TAYLOR, LOLA D., M.D., 1909, Illinois

TEDFORD, ADA B., M.D., 1908, Nova Scotia

Graduate High School, Salem, Mass. Assistant Resident Physician in New England Hospital for Women, 1908. Private practice, Woburn, Mass.

THALWITZER, MARIE E., M.D., 1885, Germany

Retired. Baltimore, Md.

THOMAS, HENRIETTA M., M.D., 1904, Maryland

Assistant in Pediatrics Woman's Medical College; Post-Graduate Work Polyclinic College for Medical Graduates, London, England. Lecturer on Bacteriology, Woman's College. Private practice, 1718 John St., Baltimore, Md.

THORNTON-SCOTT, JESSIE M., M.D., 1901, Virginia
Prepared by private tutor; Resident Physician Hospital Woman's Medical College, June to November, 1901; Second Assistant Resident Physician Woman's Group, Springfield State Asylum for Insane, 1902; Post-Graduate Work Gynecology, Johns Hopkins Hospital; Resident Physician Evening Dispensary for Working Women and Girls, 1903-1906; Woman Resident, State Hospital for the Insane, Staunton, Va., 1906-1907. Member Medical and Chirurgical Faculty, Md.; Member American Medical Association. Private practice, Charleston, W. Va.

THORNTON, IRENE, M.D., 1908, North Carolina
Prepared at High School of Fayetteville, N. C.; Graduate of Training School for Nurses, Highsmith Hospital; Resident Physician, Highsmith Hospital, Fayetteville, N. C., 1908.

TIFFANY, BESSIE L., M.D., 1908, Pennsylvania
Prepared at High School; Regent's Certificate, Pa.; Assistant in Dr. Simon's Laboratory, Baltimore, 1908-1909; Hop Bottom, Pa.

VOEGLEIN, MARY P., M.D., 1901, Maryland
Prepared at Notre Dame, Md. Assistant in Presbyterian Eye, Ear, Nose and Throat Hospital, Baltimore, 1901-03; Visiting Physician to Evening Dispensary for Working Women and Girls, 1901-04; Assistant in Pathology, Surgery, Medicine and Gynecology, Woman's Medical College Dispensary; Visiting Physician, St. Francis Academy, Baltimore, 1906; Member Medical and Chirurgical Faculty of Md.; Member American Medical Association. Private practice, 1028 Valley St., Baltimore, Md.

WALDRAN, DONNA ANN, M.D., 1890, Tennessee
Attending Physician Southern Homeopathic College Dispensary, 1893-1902; Post-Graduate Work Southern Homeopathic College; Member Tristate Medical Society in Memphis, Tenn., and Maryland State Homeopathic Society. Private practice, 917 Madison Avenue, Baltimore, Md.

WARNER-SHUVELL, MAGDALENE, M.D., 1896, Maryland
Glen Rock, Pa.

WATERS, MARY AUGUSTA, M.D., 1899, Maryland
Resident Physician Hospital Woman's Medical College, 1899-1900; Assistant in Pathology, Woman's Medical College, 1900-01; Adjunct Professor Hygiene, 1902; First Assistant Resident Physician, Springfield State Hospital for the Insane, 1901-02; Member Medical and Chirurgical Faculty, and American Medical Association; Dispensing Physician to Dispensary Woman's Medical College, 1904-08; Resident Physician Tom Franklin Hospital, and Professor Physiology and Hygiene, Mississippi Industrial Institute and College, Columbus, Miss., 1908–.

WATSON, MARIAN ANNIE, M.D., 1890, Maryland
Westfield, New York.

WHITE, MARIA, M.D., 1886, Pennsylvania
Prepared State Normal School and Grove City College; Post-Graduate work in N. Y. Post-Graduate School; Medical Missionary in charge of Memorial Hospital, Sialkat, North India.

WILLIAMS, ALICE D., M.D., 1891, Ohio

WILLIS, MARY COOK, M.D., 1901, Maryland
Prepared at Western Boarding School; Resident Physician Hospital Woman's Medical College, 1901-02; Resident Physician Evening Dispensary for Working Women and Girls, 1902-03; Member Medical and Chirurgical Faculty; Visiting Physician to Crittenden Home; Chief of Medical Clinic, Woman's Medical College, 1905-06; Visiting Physician to the N. W. City Agency, 1908–; Lecturer on Materia Medica, and Assistant in Pediatrics and Dermatology. Private practice, 810 Hanover St., Baltimore, Md.

WILTON-LITTLE, T. CLAIRE, M.D., 1893, Maryland
Latonia, New Hampshire.

WINSLOW, ISABELLA M., M.D., 1896, Pennsylvania
Private practice, 6009 Penna. Avenue, Pittsburg, Pa.

WOOD, ELIZABETH, M.D., 1891, Ohio
Medical Staff Toledo Hospital, 1894-1901; Post-Graduate Work Philadelphia Polyclinic, 1900, and at Chicago Post-Graduate School, 1903; Member Toledo Academy of Medicine, Ohio State Medical Society, and American Medical Association. Private practice, 305 Wayne Building, Toldeo, Ohio.

WOODS, SOPHIA L., M.D., 1893, Illinois

ZELWIS, JOHANNA T., M.D., 1896, Maryland
Member Luzerne County Medical Society. Private practice, Church St., Plymouth, Pa.

*ZIMMERMAN-FORD, M. L., M.D., 1888, Maryland

*Deceased.

V. b). MATRICULATES WHO DID NOT GRADUATE

Name	Years	State
Allee, Katharene W.	'93, '94, '97, '98	Pennsylvania
Bacon, Ida M.	'88	Maryland
Baker, G. D.	'94	Maryland
Baker, Maude C.	'03	Dist. of Columbia
Barry, Mary J.	'98, '99	Maryland
Bartlett	'98	Maryland
Bealor, Quilla E.	'07	Pennsylvania
Bean, Anna K.	'01	Virginia
Benkard, Kate	'82	Germany
Bennett, Bessie	'00	Maryland
Berger, Bertha D.	'99, '00, '01	Maryland
Berry, Matta L.	'01	Pennsylvania
Birmingham, Mary E.	'07, '08	New York
Blotkamp, Mary E.	'82	Maryland
Bobart, Ethel S.	'01	Maryland
Bosley, Mary R.	'01, '02	
Bouchelle, Eliz. T.	'08	Maryland
Brace, Hazel	'08	New York
Brewster, Cora Belle	'83	New York
Brewster, Flora A.	'82	Illinois
Briscoe, Henrietta E.	'03	Maryland
Brush, Edith	'99	Florida
Cain, Maud F., Ph.G.	'95	Massachusetts
Carter, Grace	'85	Maryland
Chalfant, Estalee M.	'00	West Virginia
Church, Ella R.	'02	Indiana
Clark, Rebecca F.	'99, '00, '01, '02	Maryland
Clayton, Mary	'91, '92	Pennsylvania
Coplan, Annie R.	'99, '00, '01	Virginia
Cordell, Martha F.	'00	Maryland
Cox, Anna L., Ph.B.	'90	West Virginia
Cunning, Hattie W.	'94, '95	New York
Darby, Elizabeth A.	'95	New Jersey
Dies, Marie A.	'00	Pennsylvania
Douglas, Marion	'88	Maryland
Downs, Julia	'91, '92	Maryland
Drought, Carrie A.	'90, '94	Maryland
Dunlap, Hattie	'92	Tennessee
Dutton, Mary L.	'06	Ohio
Ellis, Harriett S.	'93	Maryland
Emory, Elizabeth	'95	New York
Ernsberger, Emma	'94, '95	Tennessee
Flanagan, Katie E.	'93, '94	Massachusetts
Flyborg, Hanna G.	'97	Sweden
Fuller, Ethelyn A.	'00	New York
Gardner, Emily E.	'88	Maryland
Garmong, Leona	'07	Iowa
Garrett, Hallie, A. B.	'00, '01	Mississippi
Gillen, Carrie S.	'86, '87	Maryland
Goold, F. Mary	'86	Ohio
Gover, Mary E.	'83	Maryland
Green, Sara E.	'01	New York
Hart, Elizabeth	'01	Maryland
Hedges, Edith V.	'90, '91, '92	Maryland
Heller, Beulah May	'02, '03	Pennsylvania
Heston, Mary E.	'90, '91	Ohio
Hockaday, Agnes	'07, '08	Maryland
Holmes, Emily	'87	Maryland
Humphrey, Minnie	'07, '08	New York
Hunter, Lillian	'00	Ohio
Israel, Mary Anna	'03	Dist. of Columbia
Jarvis, Louise	'95	Ohio
Jones, Mary E.	'98, '99, '00, '01, '02, '03	Maryland
Kelley, Julielma M.	'90, '91	Maryland

Name	Year(s)	Place
Kennedy, Mamie V. C.	'94, '95	North Carolina
Kernodel, G. W.	'91	North Carolina
Kilbourne, Lillian	'94	Louisiana
King, Victoria T.	'01	Maryland
Kleiner, Annie M.	'03	Georgia
Knappe, Idean	'95	Dist. of Columbia
Knowland, Carolyn	'90	Pennsylvania
Kuhn, Annie E., M.D.	'83	Maryland
Langley, Sallie R.	'91	Virginia
Leatherman, Katherine	'91	Pennsylvania
Levandoski, Julia M.	'07, '08	Massachusetts
Lewis, Sarah S.	'82	Maryland
Littlejohn, Susan	'97	South Carolina
Long, Viola M.	'94	New York
Magill, Annie	'82	Maryland
Magill, Harriet	'82, '83	Maryland
Marshall, Elizabeth P.	'82, '83	Maryland
McAlpine, A. d.L. H.	'82, '85	Canada
McClellan, Mary Oarswell	'03	Kentucky
McGary, Vina	'88	Pennsylvania
Meisner, Ida	'83	Maryland
Mellier, DeB.	'00	Maryland
Merrington, Ruth	'03	New York
Monks, Georgiana	'06	Pennsylvania
Morgan, Grace	'08	New York
Morrow, Mary G.	'03	Maryland
Norton, Annie	'94, '95	New Mexico
Nuebling, Sophie D.	'00, '01	Pennsylvania
Ockerman, Sarah S.	'02	Maryland
Onnen, Julia A.	'83	Germany
Otto, Lellia B.	'08	Maryland
Palmer, Edwina	'08	Virginia
Pinero, Dolores	'08	Porto Rico
Plum, Amy E.	'93, '95	Maryland
Powers, Lelia H.	'94	Maryland
Richardson, Gretchen	'03	Maryland
Roberts, Edith G.	'92	New York
Rowley, Caroline C.	'95	New York
Rudolph, Frida	'99	Maryland
Russell, Flora S.	'85	Massachusetts
St. Clair, Emma M.	'93, '94, '97, '98	Maryland
Schell, Ida L.	'98	Iowa
Schneckenburger, Carrie	'06	Louisiana
Scott, Gertrude	'82, '83	Maryland
Seager, M. E.	'91	Maryland
Shafer, Marinda L.	'90, '91	West Virginia
Shotwell, Laura H.	'06, '07	New Jersey
Shrive, Susan	'94	New York
Shuter, Mary	'87, '88	Maryland
Sloan, Elizabeth	'00	Maryland
Smith, Margaret	'87, '88	Maryland
Spencer, Eleanor Lee	'94	Maryland
Steffian, Alice	'01	Mexico
Stephens, Edith M.	'07	New York
Szlupas, Luisa	'93, '97	Pennsylvania
Talbot, Ada E.	'01	Minnesota
Tallon, Lucy	'82	Maryland
Taylor, Anna L.	'94, '95	West Virginia
Taylor, Annie W.	'94	Virginia
Thorne, M. R.	'82, '85	Ohio
Tilghman, Winifred P.	'83, '85	Maryland
Twining, Bessie A.	'98	Connecticut
Urdang, Ruth	'06	New York
Van Antwerp, J. Carrie	'85	Maryland
Van Der Veer, Julia T.	'97, '98	Kansas
Van Meter, Lillian	'91	Maryland

Villafarie, Josefina	'06, '07, '08	Porto Rico
Walker, Clara	'99	Pennsylvania
Waring, Amy M.	'94	South Carolina
Watson, Helen	'06	Massachusetts
Weiss, Josephine	'83, '84	Hungary
Weitzman, F. E.	'99, '00, '01	New York
Welch, Lina B.	'94	Ohio
Wescott, Bessie	'94	Massachusetts
Whitehead, Margaret L.	'94	Virginia
Whiteside, Margaret	'08	South Carolina
Worth, Laura D., B.S.	'99	North Carolina
Yellott, Mary	'99	Maryland
Young, Harriet M. (Mrs. J. T.)	'02, '03, '06	New York
Yuskosky, Felelet	'06	Maryland
Zalneraitis, Antonia	'97	Maryland

BIBLIOGRAPHY

1. *Announcements of the Woman's Medical College of Baltimore, from 1882 to 1909-10, except those for 1890, 1897, 1905, 1906.*
2. Bernard C. Steiner: *History of Education in Maryland*, Washington, D. C., 1894.
3. *Baltimore Sun, May 31, 1910.*
4. Elizabeth Mason-Hohl: *Woman's Medical College of Baltimore.* Medical Woman's Journal, December 1946, pp. 58-63.
5. Thomas A. Ashby: *Abstract of an Address on the Medical Education of Women, delivered at the . . . Woman's Medical College of Baltimore.* Maryland Medical Journal, 9:267-275 (1882)
6. Howard A. Kelly and Walter L. Burrage: *Dictionary of American Medical Biography*, New York, D. Appleton and Co., 1928.

ACKNOWLEDGMENTS

Thanks are expressed to Miss Marion B. Savin and Mr. Kenneth V. Hahn, both of Philadelphia, for their untiring efforts to help, and to the following librarians and staffs: Miss Gertrude L. Annan, New York Academy of Medicine; Mr. Charles Roos, National Library of Medicine; Miss Hilda E. Moore, Health Sciences Library, University of Maryland; Miss Madeline Stanton, Yale Medical Library; Miss Dorothy Baker, Boston Medical Library; Mrs. Karl Koudelka, Welch Medical Library; Mr. Elliott H. Morse, College of Physicians of Philadelphia; and Mrs. Freida Chapman and Miss Barbara Knapczyk, both of the Midwest Inter-Library Center of Chicago.

FOOTNOTES TO CHAPTER TWO

(1) Elizabeth Mason-Hohl: Woman's Medical College of Baltimore, in *Medical Woman's Journal*. Volumes 52-53, December 1946, pp. 58-63. However, Bernard C. Steiner, op. cit., p. 300, states that Drs. Randolph Winslow and Thomas A. Ashby originated the idea in December, 1881.

(2) By 1889 the 25 bed hospital was full, and there were two resident physicians (graduates of the school), and three trained nurses.

(3) Quoted by Elizabeth Mason-Hohl (op. cit.).

(4) *Thomas A. Ashby*, said by Bernard C. Steiner to have been one of the originators of the idea of organizing the Woman's Medical College of Baltimore, was a surgeon and author, as well as teacher. He had his preliminary education at Washington College in Virginia, under General Robert E. Lee, then graduated in Medicine from the University of Maryland (1873). With several colleagues he founded the *Maryland Medical Journal*, which he edited for fourteen years. He was likewise one of the founders of the Woman's Medical College of Baltimore, where he taught until he succeeded Dr. William T. Howard, at the University of Maryland, as professor of diseases of women. He was president of the Medical and Chirurgical Faculty of the State of Maryland, in 1890. The manuscript of his book on the diseases of women was destroyed in a fire in 1904. He later published:

TEXT BOOK OF GYNECOLOGY
THE LIFE OF TURNER ASHBY
THE VALLEY CAMPAIGN

(5) *William D. Booker* enlisted and served in the Third Virginia Cavalry during the Civil War, and after being mustered out, attended, and graduated in medicine from the University of Virginia (1867). He was professor of clinical pediatrics at the Johns Hopkins Medical School (1897-1909). His studies of the diseases of children (especially summer diarrhea), involved careful research on the colon bacillus, and were carried on in the laboratory at Johns Hopkins Hospital. He wrote a bacteriological and anatomical study of the summer diarrhea of infants. He was one of the founders of the American Pediatrics Society, of which he was president in 1901.

(6) *Eugene F. Cordell*, well known as a teacher and medical historian, was born and educated in Virginia. He enlisted as a private in the Confederate Army, was wounded in 1865, and held prisoner of war during the spring of 1865. (He was eventually commissioned a Lieutenant.) After taking his medical degree from the University of Maryland Medical School in 1868 and spending one year as assistant resident at the University Hospital, he entered practice in Baltimore in 1869, and early became a leader in the medical life of his city. In addition to his efforts on behalf of the founding of the Woman's Medical College of Baltimore, he served this school for many years as professor of medicine. He was instrumental in bringing about the lengthening of the duration of medical instruction from two to three years, in establishing the examination for preliminary education of students of medicine, and in the formation of the Association of American Medical Colleges.

Dr. Cordell was librarian of the Medical and Chirurgical Faculty of the State of Maryland for a total of eight years, and its president in 1903-04.

His deep interest in history of medicine is reflected in his service as professor of the history of medicine at the University of Maryland and in his important work:

MEDICAL ANNALS OF MARYLAND, 1799-1899

the centennial volume of the Medical and Chirurgical Faculty of the State of Maryland, published in 1903. He also wrote:

HISTORICAL SKETCH OF THE UNIVERSITY
OF MARYLAND SCHOOL OF MEDICINE, 1807-1890
THE MEDICINE AND THE DOCTORS OF HORACE

in Johns Hopkins Hospital Bulletin, Volume XII, pp. 233-40,

THE MEDICINE AND DOCTORS OF JUVENAL

in Medical Library and Historical Journal, Volume I, pp. 8-17,

ARETAEUS, THE CAPPADOCIAN

in Johns Hopkins Hospital Bulletin, Volume XX, pp. 371-77, and

LIBRARY OF A COLONIAL PHYSICIAN

(dealing with Upton Scott's library) in Old Maryland, Volume VIII, pp. 98-101. With Thomas A. Ashby, he was one of the co-founders of the Maryland Medical Journal, and he was editor of *Old Maryland*.

(7) *Russell Murdoch*, distinguished ophthalmologist, had his collegiate education at the University of Edinburgh, then studied medicine at the University of Virginia, where he won his medical degree in 1861. After serving as resident physician at the Baltimore Almshouse and as attending physician to the Baltimore General Dispensary, he was appointed surgeon in the Corps of engineers of the Confederate Army, where he continued to serve until the end of the Civil War, and was with General Lee at Appomattox. The war over, he studied ophthalmology both at home and abroad, and, upon his return to Baltimore, lectured on diseases of eye and ear at the University of Maryland. He declined the invitation of Dr. C. R. Agnew to become his associate in New York. He was one of the founders of the Eye, Ear and Throat Charity Hospital, and an attending physician there until his death. From 1884 to 1887 he held the chair in ophthalmology and otology at the Woman's Medical College of Baltimore. He created works in sculpture displaying marked talent in this field, as well as an invention of medical instruments, his best known of several contributions being his eye speculum, and various forms of bandages to be applied following eye operations. His knowledge of botany and zoology was extensive, and he was actively interested in the Maryland Academy of Sciences. His special field of concern was the comparative anatomy of the eye, in which he was an authority.

(8) *John R. Quinan*, noted as a medical historian, studied medicine with Dr. John K. Mitchell, of Philadelphia, then took his medical degree at Jefferson Medical College in 1844. He practiced medicine first in Calvert County, Maryland, then moved to Baltimore in 1869. He was president of the Medical and Chirurgical Faculty of the State of Maryland in 1885. His writings were many and are listed in the *Transactions of the Faculty* for 1891. He was the author of:

MEDICAL ANNALS OF BALTIMORE FROM 1608-1880, INCLUDING
EVENTS, MEN AND LITERATURE; TO WHICH IS ADDED
A SUBJECT INDEX AND RECORD OF PUBLIC SERVICES.

He was one of the editors of F. P. Foster's *MEDICAL DICTIONARY*. He served briefly as lecturer on Medical Jurisprudence at the Woman's Medical College of Baltimore.

(9) *James Carey Thomas*, educator and philanthropist, entered the practice of medicine in Baltimore, after graduating from the University of Maryland in 1854, and continued to practice for forty-six years. His own education, high educational ideals, and dedication to belief in women's intellectual capacity were reflected in his efforts in helping to organize the School of Medicine of Johns Hopkins University, where standards of admission and graduation were higher than elsewhere, and where women were admitted on equal terms with men. Dr. Thomas was a Trustee of Johns Hopkins University, a charter member of the Board of Trustees of Bryn Mawr College, member of the Board of Managers of Haverford College (where he won his A.M. in 1851) and a minister of the Society of Friends. His many philanthropies exceed the limits of this brief note.

Limitations of space prohibit the inclusion of additional biographical footnotes. The foregoing selection is based upon the fact that those persons were among the pioneer members of the Faculty.

MARYLAND MEDICAL COLLEGE OF BALTIMORE

The Maryland Medical College of Baltimore, chartered under the laws of Maryland in August, 1898,[1] published its first Announcement for the session 1898-1899. The Directors and Faculty of this college stated their philosophy as follows: a student can acquire as much professional training and knowledge in three longer sessions as in four shorter ones. They therefore proposed to hold eight-month sessions (by making summer vacations shorter), requiring three such sessions for graduation, instead of the more commonly required four sessions, of six months each. They believed that the long interval between sessions (i.e. the vacation period) was actually a disadvantage, and that a student who had vacations only sufficiently long enough to recuperate between sessions, would be better fitted to enter upon his professional duties, upon being graduated, than a student who has had longer periods of resting time, which have only allowed him to forget more of his acquired knowledge. The truth of this belief was all the more apparent now that it was recognized that medicine must be learned at the dissecting table, in the laboratories of chemistry, physiology, pathology, bacteriology and at the bedside of the patient, while lectures and books were merely guides and adjuncts. Seeing no advantage in a four year curriculum of six months study and six months vacation per year, which only served to delay the time of graduation by an unremunerated year, without any countervailing profit the College authorities decided in favor of distributing the twenty-four months in three sessions of eight months each, rather than in four sessions of six months each.[2].

Two aims were kept in view by the College – first, that of thoroughly equipping the student for his medical career and second, preparing him for his final examination and for the State Board. The first aim, that of a proper medical education, was to be achieved by so organizing the curriculum that most of the early instruction was devoted to laboratory work, and the later months to clinical and bed-side instruction. The second aim, that of preparing students for examinations, would be achieved by giving frequent quizzes and intermediate examinations, which not only helped in the acquisition of knowledge and training, but in the expression and useful application of these.[3]

In the Announcement for 1901-02 the College made recognition of the fact that many men were prevented from studying medicine by the excessive costs, and that this was a loss to medical science and to society, as well as a misfortune to such students. For that reason the College had determined to provide a thorough, systematic and comprehensive medical education, at a minimum cost. (Yet the same Announcement states the tuition fee for a full course to be $65.00, an increase of $15.00 over the previous years.)

On April 11, 1902, John Walter Smith, Governor of Maryland, signed an act previously passed by the General Assembly, to enlarge and extend the powers of the Maryland Medical College, by which the directors of the College, Bernard P. Muse, John B. Schwatka, J. William Funck, Joseph H. Branham, G. Milton Linthicum, Frederick Caruthers, William S. Smith, C. Urban Smith, J. Charles Linthicum, and Harry Gross, as successors of the original incorporators, were authorized to annex schools, confer degrees, and purchase grounds and buildings for educational, scientific and hospital purposes to the limit of $300,000. (See Acts, January Session, 1902, Chapter 560.)

Early in the life of the school the students organized and published "an excellent monthly, *The Medical Observer*, which (took) high rank among the best college publications". An Alumni Association was also organized. (See section II – Curriculum).

The College proudly announced, as early as 1899, that one of its graduates of that class had passed an examination for appointment to the United States Marine Hospital Service, "standing third in his class", and that of the sixty-one graduates to date, only two had failed the State Board examination to date.

A branch of the city Y.M.C.A. was maintained at the College. Religious activity of students was directed by the Y., and classes for Bible study and devotional meetings were regularly held. The Association also extended welcome to new students at the opening of each session and maintained a list of suitable boarding houses for them. It issued a handbook of information, having value to students, in the Fall of each year. (For a statement concerning gymnasium privileges at the West Branch of the Y., see near the end of section II, Curriculum.)

In later years there were College football and baseball teams. (See section II, Curriculum.)

The Announcement for 1912-13 states that the school is co-educational, the Faculty, with endorsement of the Board of Trustees having opened the doors of the College to women on the same terms as to men. The curriculum, it was claimed, offered to both sexes superior facilities for acquiring a thorough medical training of highest order.

Two excerpts from addresses made at the Commencement of 1910 are of interest:

Speaking to the graduates on the importance of upholding the honor of the medical profession, Dr. Joseph H. Branham, professor of principles and practice of surgery, having in mind the recent suit for $50,000. against Dr. John D. Blake, said:

"Only the other day one of the most eminent physicians in the city was before the bar of justice, in a suit alleging malpractice. Many of the leading members of the profession went to the fore and gave him their support, with the result that he was acquitted. If you are to uphold the honor of your profession that is what you must do."

In the address of the evening, Congressman Finis J. Garett, of Tennessee, said:

"You have heard a lot about evolution, but I refuse to accept any theory that seeks to prove that humanity sprang from something lower than man. The first man was perfect in every way. He was complete mentally, he knew all law, he knew the bird song, the passion of the crouching tiger, and he was complete spiritually for he discussed matters with God. By the force of his perfection he held dominion over the earth. He held the power to destroy and by this power he destroyed his own perfection."

At the Commencement exercises of May 27, 1913, Dr. Lewis M. Grundy announced that the College would re-open in the Fall. However, this promise was in vain, the school failing to resume sessions, and the Maryland Medical College became extinct in 1913. (The Baltimore Sun for September 23, 1912, had reported that the Maryland Medical College, rated a class C school, might be forced to close, because of its lack of endowment, and the issue of that newspaper for September 9, 1913, reported that the Trustees had, indeed, decided to close the school.)

I. BUILDINGS AND EQUIPMENT

The College edifice was situated at 1114 to 1120 West Baltimore Street (near Carrollton Avenue), in a popular and growing section of town, "with car lines in close proximity, one line passing the door". The building was guarded against traffic noises from the fact that it stood well back from the street, thus insuring a quiet and tranquil atmosphere for study. The large front yard produced by locating the building well back on the grounds provided a place where students could engage in a program of athletics, which was to receive encouragement from the Faculty.

There were two lecture halls, the seating capacities being 400 and 100 respectively. There were laboratories for chemistry, pathology and bacteriology, all of which were fully equipped for practical instruction in these studies. The dissecting room was convenient, well warmed, ventilated and lighted.

The college dispensary, where indigent patients in large numbers were treated, furnished an abundance of clinical material for the instruction of the students. The out-door department of the dispensary provided advanced students with the opportunity to visit, diagnose and treat patients, under supervision of the dispensary physician.

In later years arrangements were made with the Northeastern Dispensary, by which students of the Maryland Medical College could attend that large clinic and profit from its instructional opportunities, in addition to those already available.

For a few years the College also controlled the National Temperance Hospital, and patients could be brought from the wards directly before the class in the amphitheatre. This hospital was "conducted purely upon temperance principles in accordance with the most recent deductions of medical science." It, too, (like the College) was located in a part of the city which supplies clinical material in great abundance, as it was the only hospital in the western section of the city, and there was a diversity of cases. The Temperance Hospital was eminently fitted to carry on the work of a high class, well equipped hospital.(4)

One room in the College building was set aside for the use of student-athletics.

The Announcement for 1901-02 tells of the acquisition of a building on the corner of Calhoun and Fayette Streets, facing Franklin Square, an open park, and the refitting of this building for hospital purposes, "according to the most approved modern ideas at a cost of $15,000." The location of the Franklin Square Hospital, as it was named, was ideal, affording the patients "an abundance of fresh air and a pleasant outlook". A new clinical amphitheatre and dispensary adjoining the hospital on the west was erected at a cost of $5,000. The College claimed that the one hundred and forty seat amphitheatre, with the new hospital and enlarged laboratories gave it clinical facilities which were "second to none". Once again it claimed that the hospital, under management of the Faculty, was so arranged that patients could be brought from wards directly before class in the amphitheatre. This hospital was also "conducted upon temperance principles, in accordance with the most recent deductions of medical science", and its location, also in the western section of the city, offered a superabundance of clinical material. The Franklin Square Hospital, it was claimed, was also eminently fitted to carry on the work of a high class, well-equipped institution. Later Announcements (1907) emphasized the modern facilities for care of patients – heating, lighting, plumbing and sanitary arrangements, all of the most advanced order; well-furnished, and attractive private rooms; pleasant, well lighted and well ventilated public wards; well-equipped operating room; amphitheatre; clinical, pathological and X-ray laboratories, the X-ray apparatus being of the latest design, embodying the latest advances in this field, and superior to any other apparatus in Baltimore. The Hospital was so planned that advantage was taken of the latest ideas without resorting to those extremes which might seem theoretically excellent, but are found without benefit in actual practice. Simplicity, utility and thoroughness were kept in mind when the Hospital was planned, and it was hoped that the new Hospital would long serve as a model institution.

The Announcement for 1901-02 also speaks of the West-End Maternite Hospital of Baltimore, ("its new building") situated at 112 North Calhoun Street, in close proximity to the College, and under the supervision of the Faculty, where there was ample opportunity for bedside instruction in diagnosis and care of patients during pregnancy, labor and the puerperal state. Absolute privacy could be had for private patients, rates being moderate, and varying according to location and size of room. The incorporators had tried to make it a model institution of its kind, equipped in a manner to meet the advanced requirements for a lying-in hospital.

Equipment included manikin for obstetrics, models and preparations (both wet and dry) in anatomy, plates and charts in physiology, drawings, charts, mounted specimens, one imported microscope for each student and a private, locked drawer containing a complete outfit of glassware, staining reagents and instruments in histology.

The Announcement for 1907-08 tells of the expansion of facilities:

"ENLARGEMENT"

> "The necessity for enlarging the equipment of the College became apparent in 1902, and at the close of that session arrangements were made for increasing the capacity of the laboratories and for the addition of new facilities. This work has been completed, and places within reach of the student ample and complete facilities for the extensive laboratory work now recognized as the primary essential in the acquisition of a modern medical education."

("The Histologic, Pathologic, Bacteriologic, Chemic and Anatomic Laboratories were fully equipped for practical work" said this Announcement – for example, microtome charts, plates, mounted sections and treatises for work in histology and so on.)

If this was an honest statement, the most charitable view would be that a very great decline must have set in before Dr. Abraham Flexner visited this school in March, 1909, and reported conditions in his *Medical Education in the United States and Canada*, (New York, 1910), page 237:

> "The school building is wretchedly dirty. Its so called laboratories are of the worst existing type: one neglected and filthy room is set aside for bacteriology, pathology, and histology: a few dirty test-tubes stand around in pans and old cigar boxes. The chemical laboratory is perhaps equal to the teaching of elementary chemistry. The dissecting room is foul. This description completely exhausts its teaching facilities. There is no museum or library and no teaching accessories of any kind."

A year or two later there were further improvements. There was a new dissecting room, embodying the most modern ideas of convenience and efficiency, and a new lecture hall. The clinical amphitheatre was completely remodeled. The Hospital had a new clinical amphitheatre, along the most modern lines, two new laboratories, and a sun parlor which rivalled "that of any hospital in Baltimore". The Faculty felt that these additions to the plant enabled it to fulfill the exacting demands of modern medical education, and in passing, took pride in the fact that the College offered individual teaching, not mass education. The Board of Managers had so shown like-minded progressiveness in not only adding to the comfort and well-being of the patients, but in greatly facilitating diagnosis, clinical research and clinical teaching." This policy of expansion has been pursued from year to year and recently a well equipped laboratory for clinical diagnosis, including a Wasserman Outfit, has been installed and successfully operated during the past session."

The Announcement for 1912-13 tells of a "splendid new College building being erected on the grounds adjacent to the Franklin Square Hospital . . . ready for occupancy in October next." The building had been carefully planned to meet the requirements of a modern medical school, and would be complete in every detail and furnished with every facility for carrying out its purposes. The lecture rooms were to be well-lighted and ventilated, of ample size and furnished with comfortable chairs. There would be seven spacious laboratories, each furnished with tables, drawers and lockers of the latest design, and water, gas and electricity where needed. The convenience of arrangement and the completeness of the equipment would greatly facilitate the work of the expert laboratory teachers.

(The size of the dispensary was more than doubled, and each of its eight departments now had ample floor space and hot and cold water.)

II. CURRICULUM

After the preliminary course, which began on September 1, 1898, (free of charge to all students of medicine), the first regular session started on September 20th, and was scheduled to close about May 20th following, with November 24th off for Thanksgiving, a Christmas recess from December 23rd until the following January 3rd, and another holiday on Washington's birthday, February 22. Subsequent Announcements repeat the fact that the first class to complete the prescribed course, and win the degree of M.D., graduated in 1899, but do not explain how this was arranged.

The calendar for the sessions which followed immediately was very similar. By 1901 the sessions were a few weeks shorter and there were more holidays. Some years later the session ran from October 1 until about June 1.

There was to be a three year graded curriculum, the fundamental medical sciences being, for the most part, taught earlier, in laboratory and lecture room, and the study of practical medicine, surgery, obstetrics and various specialties taught later, in dispensary, hospital ward and clinical laboratories.

In the first year students attended lectures on anatomy, physiology, chemistry and materia medica, and had laboratory work in chemistry, histology and anatomy. At the end of that year they were required to pass examinations on osteology, histology, inorganic chemistry and materia medica.

Second year studies were a continuation of first year studies except those on osteology, histology, materia medica and inorganic chemistry, and, in addition, students had courses in therapeutics, obstetrics, general medicine, general surgery, diseases of children, diseases of the eye, diseases of the ear, diseases of women, diseases of nervous system and mind, diseases of nose, throat and chest, pathology and hygiene and laboratory work in pathology, chemistry and anatomy. At the end of the second year students were required to pass a final examination on anatomy, chemistry, therapeutics, physiology, pathology and hygiene and must show evidence that his work in the different laboratories had been satisfactory. Attendance at clinics was optional.

If a student failed any first or second year examination, another examination was available before the opening of the next session.

Third year studies included general surgery, obstetrics, diseases of children, general medicine, diseases of women, of eye, of ear, of nervous system, nose, throat and chest, skin, medical jurisprudence and clinical microscopy. Attendance at the various clinics, of which there were two daily, was obligatory. At the end of the third year the student was admitted to the final examinations upon all of the third year subjects listed immediately above.

The College reserved the right to make such alterations in the course of instruction as experience or expedience might prove to be necessary.

After October 1, 1902, another year was added to the curriculum and it became obligatory to take a four year course at this College.

By 1909 the stated educational philosophy ran as follows: the organizers of the College believed in individual as opposed to mass education, such as is the order of the day in many large colleges and universities. The professors and teachers at this school were therefore given ample latitude to employ such methods as experience has shown to be preferable rather than being compelled to systems which tradition had sanctified and time had fossilized. Such a philosophy required a corps of teachers larger in proportion to the number of matriculates than was true at other medical schools.

"The teacher stamps his individuality upon the student with whom he comes into intimate personal contact, and the student is not embarrassed by fruitless discussions of methods and measures radically opposed, the efficiency of which is stoutly maintained by various professors in the same college, as is unfortunately too often the case, in our American institutions of learning. The teacher is, nevertheless, encouraged to keep fully abreast of the times in every particular that pertains to his branch, to visit and investigate the methods employed by other institutions, both in our own country and abroad, for the purpose of broadening his views and perfecting his methods, and, when necessary, the college provides funds for such purposes.

Likewise, the entire energy of the Board of Trustees and the Faculty is expended in an endeavor to provide a MEDICAL education, solely, and no attempt is made to maintain a quasi University with faculties of law, dentistry and the like.

Experience has demonstrated the value of conferences, case reports, discussions and examinations as methods of teaching; hence these forms are generally followed, and, as a rule, monthly written examinations are held in all save the minor and unimportant branches, while class conferences, case reports and critical discussions are so arranged that each student, in rotation, is given ample opportunity to display his attainments. Progress is judged largely by these methods instead of being based solely upon final or yearly examinations. Recitations and quizzes, conducted by the professors and teachers, have, to a large extent, replaced the formal didactic lecture of older days, and we believe that not only the graduate of today, but the public, is reaping the benefit of the change."

The courses were described as follows:

OBSTETRICS

Instruction in clinical and operative obstetrics was given to advanced students under the personal supervision of the professor. The course included bedside instruction in diagnosis of pregnancy, diagnosis of presentations and positions, management of labor and the puerperal state, abdominal palpation, pelvimetry, etc. There were unusual opportunities for study of practical obstetrics in the daily dispensary clinics and the out-door service. The various obstetric operations, instrumental and manual, were taught by demonstration and practice upon cadaver and manikin, supplemented by clinical demonstrations in lying-in chamber. Confinement cases were assigned to members of the class, which was divided into two sections, each student receiving direct personal instruction.

DISEASES OF CHILDREN

The professor aimed to give the course "in the most attractive manner possible, both in didactic and clinical lectures". Students had ample opportunity to become thoroughly familiar with diagnosis and treatment of these diseases because of the large amount of material presented in the dispensaries.

DISEASES OF THE EYE

There were regular didactic lectures on the anatomy, physiology and diseases of the eye, and there were practical demonstrations in the amphitheatre, hospital and dispensary clinics, all of which supplied abundant illustrative material. The professor gave to the students every possible opportunity for personal observation and examination of cases, the student having direct contact with the patient so that he became familiar, in a most practical manner with the diagnosis, prognosis and treatment of eye diseases. There were frequent quizzes and several intermediate examinations.

PRINCIPLES AND PRACTICE OF SURGERY

The aim was to achieve a thorough understanding of the broad principles of this science and render the student fit for successful practice in this field. There were to be two didactic lectures per week, for second and third year students, and frequent quizzes and intermediate examinations, to insure a thorough understanding of the subject.

Clinical surgery was taught in amphitheatre, hospital, dispensary and out-door department. Advanced students were permitted to diagnose surgical cases, assist in operations and dress wounds. Careful attention was given to the method of preparing patients, sterilization of instruments, dressings, etc.

There was a course in operative surgery which included a regular course of didactic lectures, including demonstrations on bandaging, application of splints on the living subject, and operations done on the cadaver by the students, under direction of the professor.

RECTAL SURGERY

The second Announcement states that in recognition of the prevalence of cases of diseases of the lower bowel, and the dependence upon this organ for the maintenance of the health of the human system, a special chair had been created for instruction in such diseases and abnormalities. The course would be mainly clinical, but there would be didactic lectures.

CHEMISTRY AND TOXICOLOGY

The course ran for two years. In the first year the time was devoted to chemical physics, chemical philosophy, descriptive inorganic chemistry, and laboratory exercises. This was followed by an examination at the end of the session, in order to determine the student's fitness to enter the second year, which was devoted, first to a review of laws and principles and the chemistry of the metals, then to organic chemistry and toxicology, embracing symptoms, treatment, and chemical detection. There were lectures, recitations and laboratory work, student fitness for advancement or graduation being determined by his standing in class throughout the session.

ANATOMY

This was a two year course, an examination being held at the end of each year. There were lectures, recitations, and dissections. Illustrative aids included models, and wet and dry preparations from the museum. The aim was to demonstrate the application of anatomy to practical medicine. There was an ample supply of material in the dissecting room, which was under supervision of demonstrators. Each student was examined after the completion of the part dissected. There were lectures upon the brain and spinal cord in regard to localization.

MATERIA MEDICA AND THERAPEUTICS

Lectures and recitations on this subject taught the origin, physical properties, preparation and methods of administration of drugs. There was emphasis upon physiological action and therapeutic uses. Lectures were supplemented by instruction in prescription writing. There were blackboard illustrations.

PHARMACY

There were lectures on weighing, measuring, and compounding drugs, how to make powders, pills and solutions, and on "those practical details so essential to a physician's success, especially those intending to locate in rural districts".

DISEASES OF THE NOSE, THROAT AND CHEST

The students were instructed in the use of laryngoscope, stethoscope and all methods of examining patients. Examinations and operations were conducted before the class, in order to familiarize students with practical work and give them an opportunity to examine and diagnose cases themselves. Thus there were both didactic and clinical lectures.

PHYSIOLOGY

There were two lectures per week, illustrated by experiments, plates and charts, and reviewed by quizzes and written examinations. There was a detailed consideration of the physiology of blood, circulation, respiration, digestion, absorption, metabolism, secretion and excretion, muscle tissue, the peripheral and central nervous system, the special senses, generation and development. The course was intended to deal with that which would be of especial value in diagnosis and treatment. It extended throughout the first and second years and was obligatory for students of those years. There was an examination at the end of each year.

(The preamble to the description of this course, in the second Announcement, emphasizes the importance of the new treatment of disease, "serum therapy", a development resulting from researches in physiology, a most important branch in the study of medicine, a thorough conception of which was absolutely necessary as a foundation for understanding of the great advances made in medicine during the past few years. The professor promised that there would be experiments upon the lower animals.)

HISTOLOGY

This was both a theoretical and practical course. There were lectures, illustrated by drawings, charts and mounted specimens, covering all the important points of normal histology. The first lectures dealt with the use of the microscope, and methods of fixing, staining and mounting specimens. The remainder of the session was given to a consideration of the normal tissues and fluids of the body. Laboratory work was a prominent feature of the course and was under the charge of the demonstrator and his assistants. Every member of the class was assigned to a private locked drawer, completely furnished with glassware, staining reagents and instruments, and a microscope of the best make, and he was held responsible for all of these while in his possession. The first laboratory lessons were devoted to becoming familiar with the actual use of microscope and other equipment, and to examination of simple cells and fibres. This was followed by study of the simpler forms of human tissue. The more highly organized and complex tissues were studied in the second half of the term. There was a final examination, written and practical, at the end of the session.

DISEASES OF EAR; HYGIENE

The course on the ear emphasized that which was of direct and practical importance to the general practitioner. Advanced students were given clinical instruction in diagnosis and treatment.

The course in hygiene dealt with that of the individual, the home and the community at large – the principles of sanitation, as they bear upon the management of public institutions, sewerage, infection, quarantine regulations, drainage and cleanliness of cities and towns, and similar matters.

In 1901 hygiene became an independent chair at this school, under Alan W. Smith, M. D., lecturer.

PRINCIPLES AND PRACTICE OF MEDICINE

Teaching was by didactic lectures, recitations, clinical and bedside instruction, augmented "by microscopical and by bacteriological investigation". The professor's philosophy was that the lecture method alone, in vogue only a generation ago, was now inadequate and insufficient for a practical physician. Didactic instruction did have its strengths even if it had weaknesses, and it was still very useful to arrange and summarize the observations and opinions of mature thinkers and workers, and present these in lecture form. Because of lack of time or opportunity to have contact with the literature of his profession, a student's reading may be limited to a single text-book. By bringing student and patient together in clinic and at bed-side, it was hoped, the mental faculties could be developed and the powers of observation trained, and the student thus learn to recognize disease, to differentiate and to draw conclusions, i.e., to think out a situation. Students were given individual, thorough practical instruction in physical diagnosis by another member of the Faculty. For purposes of bedside instruction the class was subdivided. In 1901, with the chair now occupied by Professor C. Urban Smith, diseases of the stomach became part of this course. Students were instructed in modern methods of diagnosis and treatment embracing physical, chemical and microscopical analysis of test meals, stomach contents, etc.

DISEASES OF WOMEN

The professor aimed to make his course as thorough, comprehensive and practical as possible. There were didactic lectures covering the entire subject of gynecology and weekly clinics, at which the various major and minor operations were performed and demonstrated in detail. Routine office treatments – use and application of technical therapeutic resources, such as douches, pessaries, tents, tampons, dilators, vaginal and intra-uterine medication, and related treatments, were fully and carefully taught. Advanced students had special opportunity to practice the various manipulations necessary in diagnosis and treatment, and this training was on an individual basis, as it was thus thought to be of greatest value. There was practical instruction in the gynecological department of the dispensary, and students observed operations in the hospital on other than the regular clinic days.

MEDICAL JURISPRUDENCE

There were general and practical lectures, "students being taught how to testify in court", "how to conduct themselves under cross examination on the witness stand", "how to answer hypothetical questions in giving expert testimony", and the existing legal relations between physician, State and patient.

PATHOLOGY AND BACTERIOLOGY

There were didactic lectures, illustrated by demonstration of gross lesions, whenever practical. There were also two periods per week, during the second and third years, devoted to the preparation and study, under the microscope, of the more common lesions of the various organs. Newer methods of diagnosis were taught – blood, urine, feces, sputum, gastric juice, various exudates and transudates were studied in detail, and the knowledge thus gained applied to diagnosis of disease.

Methods of cultivating, isolating and identifying micro-organisms, in relation to clinical pathology, were taught.

DISEASES OF THE NERVOUS SYSTEM AND MIND

This was a systematic course of weekly lectures for one year, and a weekly clinic, in which there were presented cases of familiar, and also many more rare forms, of these diseases. Students were permitted to examine the patients. There were frequent quizzes on both didactic lectures and clinical studies.

DERMATOLOGY

Advanced students had exceptional advantages for observation of skin diseases. Dispensary and hospital wards had an abundance of material for presentation to the class by the professor and his assistants, who recognized the fact that knowledge of these diseases could only result from frequent examination of patients and therefore aimed "to furnish a thorough drill in symptomatology and diagnosis".

PRACTICAL ANATOMY

Dissection was carried on under direction of the demonstrator, in a convenient, well warmed, ventilated and lighted room, to which access could be had at all hours of the day and until 10 P.M. There was an abundance of dissecting material. Tickets must be countersigned by the demonstrator, in evidence that the student had performed satisfactory dissection.

For a statement about graduate work, see under Requirements for Admission, below.

DENTAL SURGERY

In 1901 advanced students began receiving practical instruction in dental surgery by demonstrations in extracting and other minor dental operations.

No private quizzes or classes were held by any member of the Faculty of the Maryland Medical College, nor by a member of the adjunct Faculty on the branch or branches upon which he conducted final examinations.

SPRING SESSION

After the close of the regular winter course, a course of lectures and clinics was given by the professors and lecturers upon their respective branches. All students, matriculates and practitioners, were admitted to this spring course free of additional charge. The dispensary was open throughout the year, and students who remained in the city could avail themselves of the opportunity to learn in the medical and surgical clinics in both dispensary and hospital, free of charge.

The West Branch of the Y.M.C.A. was but one square of the College building, and students could obtain ticket privileges at two dollars for the duration of the college session. The building had a well-lighted and ventilated, very completely equipped gymnasium, "offering special advantages to athletics and physical improvement, both of which (were) encouraged by this college".

1902-03: The session for 1902-03 began with a preliminary clinical course on September 15, all students of medicine being invited to take the course free of charge. The regular session ran from October 1 until about May 1 following.

OBSTETRICS

In addition to the previous specifications the course included instruction in anatomy of the pelvis, and embryology.

DISEASES OF THE EAR, NOSE AND THROAT

This was a change in the old grouping. The course was taught from the standpoint of the general practitioner. There were regular didactic lectures, supplemented by clinics and practical instruction in the use of the otoscope, laryngoscope and other instruments. The class was divided into small sections, to insure that each student benefit from personal supervision of the instructor.

MATERIA MEDICA

The student examined crude drugs and various preparations made from them, thus becoming familiar with their properties. All official drugs and their preparations were studied, as were many of the newer remedies. Doses were taught in both apothecaries' and metric systems. Special attention was given to prescription writing. Therapeutics was now a separate course, embracing pharmacology, toxicology and therapeutics proper. Special attention was given to physiological action of drugs and a study of their effect upon the lower animals. The practical application of remedial agents to disease was given thorough and systematic treatment.

GENITO-URINARY DISEASES

There was now a department of these diseases. There was a weekly clinic, in which students could see a large number of cases and various operations. Each student was individually trained in the use and manipulation of the various instruments. Special attention was given to the study of diagnosis by means of all kinds of urethral and bladder instruments, including cystoscope and endoscope.

Following are the curricular structure and regulations which came into effect with the four year course. In the main this structure continued to be the same over the years, with a few variations.

"FOUR-YEAR GRADED COURSE"

During the first year the student is required to attend lectures on Anatomy, Physiology, Chemistry and Materia Medica, and work in the Chemical, Histological and Anatomical Laboratories.

At the end of the first year the student will be expected to pass final examinations on Osteology, Histology, Elementary Physiology, Inorganic Chemistry and Materia Medica.

During the second year the studies of the first year, except Osteology, Histology, Materia Medica and Inorganic Chemistry are continued, and in addition the course in Therapeutics, Obstetrics, General Medicine, General Surgery, Diseases of Children, Diseases of the Eye, Diseases of the Ear, Nose and Throat, Diseases of Women, Diseases of the Nervous System and Mind, Pathology and Hygiene, and work in the Pathological, Chemical and Anatomical Laboratories. The attendance on the clinics will be optional.

At the end of the second year the student will be expected to pass final examinations on Anatomy, Chemistry, Therapeutics, Physiology, Pathology and Hygiene, and must also show evidence that his work in the different laboratories has been satisfactory.

The studies of the third year embrace General, Operative and Special Surgery, Obstetrics, Diseases of Children, General Medicine, Diseases of Women, of the Eye, of the Ear, Nose and Throat, of the Nervous System and Mind, Medical Jurisprudence, Diseases of the Skin and Clinical Microscopy.

At the end of the third year the student will be admitted to the final examinations in all the studies of the year.*

The fourth year will be devoted mainly to practical work, consisting of clinical instruction at the Hospitals and Dispensary, special lectures, clinical conferences, recitations, etc.

At the end of the fourth year the student shall be required to pass examinations on Clinical Surgery, Clinical Obstetrics, Clinical Diseases of Children, Clinical Medicine, Clinical Gynecology, Clinical Diseases of the Eye, Ear, Nose and Throat, Clinical Diseases of Nervous System and Mind, Clinical Diseases of Skin, Special Surgery and advanced Clinical Microscopy.

Should a student fail to pass a successful examination in any of his first, second or third year branches, another opportunity will be afforded him before the opening of the next regular session.

Students who have attended one or more courses of lectures in any accredited medical college or colleges are placed upon the same footing with our own students, and the same privileges as regards examinations (as previously described) for advance standing are extended to them. Examination will not be required on subjects for which proper credentials are exhibited.

After October 1, 1902, all students matriculating at this College will be required to take a four-year course.

All matriculates under the four-year graded course will be required to present credentials showing that they are matriculates or graduates of recognized colleges of literature, science or arts, of high schools, normal schools, academies or equivalent schools, or the regents' certificates as required by the statute of New York, or those of any State Examining Board covering the work of the following entrance examination.

Matriculates not presenting such credentials will be required to pass an entrance examination as follows:

1. An English composition of at least two hundred words.
2. Translation of easy Latin prose.

*Those students matriculating prior to October 1, 1902, will be considered candidates for graduation after passing the examinations of this year (i.e., session of 1902-03)."

3. In elementary arithmetic, algebra and physics.

Students failing in one or more of these subjects may register and pursue their studies for one year, but must meet the entrance requirements before the second course of study.

Students having the degree A.B. or B.S., or equivalent degrees from reputable literary colleges, also graduates of dentistry, pharmacy or veterinary medicine, will be given one year advanced standing.

Graduates or students of homeopathic or eclectic medical schools will be allowed as many years as they have attended such colleges, provided they have met the requirements of the entrance examination and pass an examination in Materia Medica and Therapeutics.

The right is reserved to make such alterations in the course as experience or expedience may prove to be necessary.

We have seen above that all students who matriculated after October 1, 1902, were obliged to take a four year curriculum of studies, the session running from October 1 until about the following June 1. With the session of 1905-06 a rearrangement of subjects went into effect. The following statement is taken from the Announcement for 1907-08:

"Experience has shown that a logical arrangement of the subjects in such a manner as to place the correlated groups in the same periods greatly increases the amount of time which can be devoted to such subject, and likewise permits the student to concentrate his energies to much greater advantage than when his attention is divided among numerous diverse subjects. An examination of the schedule shows the arrangement of studies and the amount of time which students are required to devote to each branch.

A minimum of 1000 hours' work is required of each first-year student; of 1000 hours is required for each second-year student; of 1100 hours is required of each third-year student; of 1360 hours is required of each fourth-year student.

Courses will be offered adapted to the student who desires to become a general practitioner, and also courses adapted to those who desire to become specialists or teachers of medicine.

A series of written and practical examinations on all the required subjects of medical instruction is distributed throughout the four years' course of study. Every candidate for the degree of Doctor of Medicine must pass these examinations in a satisfactory manner as well as fulfill the admission requirements and all the other requirements of the curriculum.

No student is permitted to enter upon the work of the fourth year until he has passed all first and second year examinations. A special examination, to enable students to pass upon conditioned branches, is held during November of each session. In addition to the regular courses, a preliminary course of clinical medicine is given each year, which is open to all students and practitioners of medicine and for which no charge is made.

Laboratory technique, clinical teaching and research work, combined with didactic teaching and stated recitations upon each subject furnish the basis of the teaching methods employed in this College. Individually and collectively the Faculty stands ready to advise students in regard to the studies which they should pursue and the best methods of attaining the ends sought.

The degree of Doctor of Medicine cum laudi is given to candidates who obtain an average of 95 per cent or over, in all the required examinations."

THE CHANGING CURRICULUM

ANATOMY

1907

First and Second Years:

There were lectures, extensive dissections, demonstrations upon wet and dry preparations of the museum and anatomical models, supplemented by recitations and demonstrations in the anatomy laboratory. Preliminary work embraced thorough courses in osteology, syndesmology, and anatomic histology. Dissecting was under supervision, and the student exhaustively examined upon completion of the part dissected. Material was liberally supplied, and there was no limitation upon the amount of work which the student was permitted to do. A special course of lectures upon brain and spinal cord was included. The department had a professor (anatomy) and an associate professor (osteology and syndesmology).

PRACTICAL ANATOMY

First and Second Years:

(See earlier description of this course).

Each student was required to dissect three parts. First year students were required to devote 420 hours to the work, and second year students no less than that number of hours. One professor.

HISTOLOGY

First Year:

The course was little different from that already described earlier. The Announcement now mentions the microtome, and freedom from a fee for use of the microscope. The Histological museum included a very large collection of mounted sections, charts and plates, and there were many pertinent treatises on the subject available, so that there were ample facilities not only for elementary and advanced work, but also for original investigation.

The class was divided into sections, thus facilitating individual supervision. A final written examination was held at the end of the year. One professor.

CHEMISTRY

First and Second Years:

The course remained the same as described above, except that in the second year, physiological chemistry was included. One professor.

MATERIA MEDICA AND THERAPEUTICS

First Year:

Materia medica, (as taught earlier).

Second and Third Years:

Toxicology and therapeutics, (as taught earlier).

The department had one professor of materia medica and one professor of therapeutics.

PHYSIOLOGY

First and Second Years:

There were two lectures each week, illustrated by charts, plates and the classical experiments of this science grouped in instructive sequence. There were experiments upon the lower animals, illustrating the laws of this science, in the laboratory, the experiments being selected to show the relation of physiological processes to clinical medicine, and of value to the physician in diagnosis and treatment. There were conferences, recitations and written examinations at intervals. The theory, development and application of serum therapy was carefully studied. The remaining specifications of this course are given in the earlier discussion above. There was one professor.

EMBRYOLOGY AND BIOLOGY

Second Year:

In addition to the lectures and demonstrations, there was in the second half of the session, a laboratory course, in which students carried out experiments under teacher supervision.

PATHOLOGY AND BACTERIOLOGY

Second and Third Years:

The course was described as follows: lectures and recitations, throughout the second year, on general and special pathologic anatomy, on histology and on bacteriology, with three afternoons per week devoted to study by use of the microscope.

I. *BACTERIOLOGY* – each student learned to prepare culture media, the principles of sterilization and disinfection, methods of cultivating and staining the more important organisms, and biological examination of air, soil and water. Infection and immunity, in relation to curative and preventive medicine were given thorough consideration.

II. *PATHOLOGY* – there were lectures, conferences and recitations on various aspects of the subject. In the laboratory, the students cut, mounted and studied the various lesions of the human tissues, under the microscope. There was a demonstration once per week, on gross morbid anatomy, using specimens from the museum and post-mortems. Students of second, third and fourth years attended and assisted at autopsies. One professor.

PRINCIPLES AND PRACTICE OF MEDICINE AND GASTRO-ENTEROLOGY
Third and Fourth Years

Third Year: didactic and clinical lectures
Fourth Year: clinical lectures, demonstrations, conferences and recitations. Advanced students, in sections, visited patients in the Hospital ward and were drilled in taking histories and in examination of blood, urine, sputum and gastric contents.

Students had close contact with patients in Hospital and Dispensary, took active part in the clinics, made records and reports of their observations, differentiated diseases, and treated suitable cases (under direction of the staff). The Class was divided into small sections, in order that each student have individual practical instruction.

There were special clinical courses in diseases of the stomach. In these courses there was instruction in the newer methods of diagnosis and treatment, embracing physical, chemical and microscopic examination of test meals, stomach contents, and so on.

There was one professor of theory and practice of medicine and gastro-enterology and one associate in medicine.

SURGERY

Second and Third Years:

There were systematic lectures, recitations, lecture demonstrations and clinical lectures, to divided classes, in wards and the out-patient department, augmented by laboratory work in surgical pathology. Didactic lectures were given each week by the professor, supplemented by the work of assistants, associates and demonstrators. There were recitations at stated intervals and intermediate examinations.

Clinic surgery was taught in amphitheatre, hospital, dispensary, in the out-door department and at the bedside. Daily operations and demonstrations illustrated the lectures, supplemented the laboratory work, and afforded unusual opportunity to acquire the necessary knowledge and technique of this subject.

Third year students examined and diagnosed cases, were required to assist in operations, dress wounds and make reports on cases. The reports might be discussed at the conferences at the discretion of the professors.

Surgical technique – preparation of dressings, sterilization of instruments and the necessary preparation of the patient for an operation was repeatedly taught and demonstrated, in order to make students thoroughly familiar with these techniques. There were yearly and final examinations. Elective courses in surgery were available to graduates and those desiring advanced work. There were one professor, three associates and one demonstrator.

OPERATIVE AND CLINICAL SURGERY

There was one didactic lecture per week, various surgical procedures being described and illustrated. There was also one regular clinic per week, at the Hospital, where various major operations were performed.

Until January 1 the seniors were given one hour per week of clinical instruction, in the Hospital, by the professors and assistants. This included diagnosis and operative technique and bedside observation of post-operative cases, with special attention to the after-treatment of cases operated upon at the clinic. After January 1 the time was given to practical work on the cadaver, at the College building, seniors being required to perform various operations and surgical manipulations. There were one professor, two associate professors and one associate.

OBSTETRICS

Third and Fourth Years:

There were lectures, recitations, conferences and clinical teaching. Students were required "to take charge of at least five cases of labor, to receive clinical instruction in at least three cases, to care for patients during convalescence, and to make a full written report of at least one case". Instruction in embryology, anatomy of the pelvis, presentations, positions, abdominal palpation, pelvimetry and management of labor was included. Obstetrical operations, instrumental and manual were taught by demonstration and practice upon manikin and cadaver, as well as upon the patient in the lying-in chamber. There were one professor and two associates.

DISEASES OF WOMEN

Third and Fourth Years:

In addition to the description of the course given above (section II. Curriculum, earlier years) it may be added that in later years small sections of the class took charge of gynecological cases in the Hospital, each member of the section making examinations, taking histories and assisting in operations. There was also practical instruction in the gynecological department of the dispensary, and students could also observe operations in the Hospital on other than the regular clinic days.

There was a systematic course in gynecological pathology, which thoroughly familiarized students with the techniques of the various methods of hardening, cutting, staining and mounting specimens for microscopic study and permanent preservation. There were intermediate examinations, and a final examination at the end of the fourth year. Special graduate courses were available. There were one professor, one associate professor and two associates.

DISEASES OF CHILDREN

Third and Fourth Years:

There were lectures for third year students and clinics for those of the fourth year. The lectures were on special topics which prepared students for the clinical instruction to follow in the next year. Students were required to take an active part in examination and discussion of cases. There were recitations upon selected subjects.

There were many cases of contagious diseases in the out-patient department. Each student was taught the technique of intubation and had the opportunity of seeing this operation performed. Especial attention was given to clinical therapeutics. The examinations were held at the end of each year. Instruction was given by one professor and one chief of clinic.

DISEASES OF NERVOUS SYSTEM AND MIND

Fourth Year:

(See same department above.) One professor.

DISEASES OF THE EYE

Fourth Year:

There were didactic lectures, demonstrations, operations, recitations, practice in use of ophthalmoscope and examination of patients for errors of refraction. Students had abundant opportunity to work with the ample material in hospital and dispensary clinics, examining the cases, making personal observation of the diseases, and becoming familiar, in a practical way, with diagnosis, prognosis and treatment (i.e. to produce well-trained practitioners, but not specialists). There were examinations at stated intervals, to measure the progress of the students. One professor.

DISEASES OF EAR, NOSE AND THROAT

Fourth Year:

(See same department, 1902-03, above.) One professor and one associate.

DERMATOLOGY

Fourth Year:

Lectures, demonstrations, recitations, and a weekly clinic. Out-door department and hospital wards furnished abundant and varied material. The pathological histology of skin diseases and the various parasites were fully discussed. There was one professor and one associate.

GENITO-URINARY DISEASES

Fourth Year:

One clinic, weekly, with clinical lectures, clinical demonstrations and frequent illustrative operations. There was individual instruction in the use of diagnostic instruments for exploration of urethra and bladder, including cystoscope and endoscope, with direct contact between student and patient. The aim was to allow the student to acquire dexterity by using various instruments for diagnosis and treatment, by assisting in the clinics, and by performing the different manipulations himself. There were special and elective courses open to physicians and post-graduate students. Instruction was given by one professor and one chief of clinic.

PROCTOLOGY

Fourth Year:

There were clinical and didactic lectures, illustrated by operations in the amphitheatre. There were recitations and conferences, at intervals. Advanced courses were open to post-graduates "upon compliance with the required conditions". There was one professor and one chief of clinic.

CLINICAL DIAGNOSIS

Third Year:

Work in the clinical laboratory was considered the culmination of all laboratory studies and therefore highly important to the student. All the work done was from the clinical standpoint. There were special courses upon blood, urine, sputum, dejecta stomach contents from the viewpoints of their chemistry, bacteriology and microscopy. All of these studies were under a demonstrator, who was a specialist in the field. An examination was given at the end of the year's work. The course was intended as preparatory for fourth year practical clinical work. There were special and elective courses available to graduate students. The staff consisted of one professor and one demonstrator.

PHYSICAL DIAGNOSIS

Third Year:

Didactic lectures, clinical demonstrations, conferences and recitations. Students examined patients, made diagnoses and made reports on their findings. Specially assigned cases had to be examined and written reports made, the latter being then made the subjects of discussions at the conferences. Progress of students was measured by frequent recitations and examinations, and there was a final examination at the close of the third session. The course was in charge of one professor, one associate and one demonstrator.

MEDICAL JURISPRUDENCE

Third and Fourth Years:

(See same department above.) Also considered was the question of expert testimony, the status of the medical expert and the nature of the hypothetical question. There was one professor.

PRACTICAL PHYSIOLOGY

This department, equipped with a laboratory for demonstrations on applied physiology, experimental surgery and applied and experimental therapeutics, supplemented didactic courses. Research in theoretical therapeutics could be carried on in this laboratory. Demonstrations in experimental surgery were evaluated. There were two demonstrators.

DENTAL SURGERY

(See same department above.)

Chemistry, Pharmacy, Hygiene. These courses were essentially the same as in earlier years, and have been described above. Each of these departments had a staff of one person.

There is sufficient difference between the specifications of the 1907 and 1910 courses in operative and clinical surgery to be worthy of a note here.

OPERATIVE AND CLINICAL SURGERY (1910)

Two hours per week were devoted to describing, illustrating and demonstrating the various surgical procedures, at the College building. The class was divided into sections to perform operations and work out the topographical anatomy of the different parts of the cadaver, under direction of the professor or his associate. There was also experimental work on animals. One hour weekly was also devoted to performing operations at Franklin Square Hospital. Ward classes were assigned and rotated at intervals, to take histories and make diagnosis of the clinical patients. These diagnoses were read by the student and carefully discussed by the professor before each operation. Students studied after-treatment, and daily noted the condition of these patients, change in diet, dressing and drugs, then reported the results to the whole class.

REQUIREMENTS FOR ADMISSION

Matriculates in medicine, graduates in dentistry or pharmacy, matriculates or graduates of colleges of literature, science and arts, or graduates of high schools of the first grade or various State normal schools were admitted without examination. All other candidates for matriculation were required to pass a preliminary entrance examination. This examination comprised "the writing of an English composition of not less than two hundred words, the translation of easy Latin prose, a knowledge of the elements of algebra or arithmetic and of elementary physics. These examinations (were) reasonable and (were) given to ascertain whether students (were) sufficiently educated to profit by medical study". A student who had failed one or more subjects of the entrance examination was allowed one year to qualify, during which time they could matriculate and pursue first year studies, but had to pass the entrance examination before beginning the second year studies.

Physicians who were graduates of medical colleges in good standing could take any course given at this school and, if they so desired, would be given a certificate of their actual attendance. Those who wished to become "familiar with any of the special departments", were afforded an opportunity to take a six-weeks course at any time during the year, "provided due inquiry be made previously concerning the same. The facilities for acquiring knowledge of laboratory technique as well as operative skill are unexcelled and worthy of consideration". Visiting physicians were always welcome and cordially invited to inspect College, Hospital and Clinical Amphitheatre.

Requirements for Admission – 1907

"The requirements for admission to the Medical course are as follows: I. Moral. A certificate of good moral character, signed by one or more reputable physicians. II. Age. Evidence that the applicant is at least seventeen years of age. III. Educational. One of five alternatives as follows:

(1) A Bachelor's degree from an approved college or university.

(2) A diploma from a recognized high school, normal school or academy requiring for admission evidence of the completion of an eight years course in primary and intermediate grades, and for graduation not less than four years of study.

(3) A certificate from the regularly constituted authorities of any State authorized to pass on the qualifications of students to study Medicine.

(4) An examination to be conducted by a duly chosen examiner, not connected with the College, extending over 30 points, of which at least 18 must be from list (A). A point represents a half-session's work on any one subject. For this examination a fee of $5.00 is exacted.

(5) A certificate from a reputable instructor recognized as such by the State, county or city superintendent of schools, from which the applicant comes, or a certificate issued by any State board of Medical examiners, will be accepted in lieu of the whole or a part of this examination. Such certificate shall set forth by subject and points the ground which has been covered by the student, and shall be duly signed with the name and title of the person issuing it, and witnessed.

(A) Mathematics, 4 points; English, 6 points; History, 2 points; Language, 4 points (Latin, 2 or 4 points); Science, 5 points. Total, 21 points.

(B) English, 2 points; History, 6 points; Language, 6 points; Manual Training, 2 points; Mechanical Drawing, 1 point; Science, 5 points; Trigonometry, 1 point; Astronomy, 1 point; Civics, 1 point; Physical Geography, 1 point; Physiology, 1 point; Hygiene, 1 point; Political Economy, 1 point. Total, 29 points.

NOTE – A student may be allowed to enter conditioned on not more than 10 points. These conditions must be removed by satisfactory examination before he is allowed to enter on the second year of the course.

Graduates or students of homeopathic or eclectic medical schools will be granted an allowance equal to the number of years they have attended such colleges, provided they can meet the requirements of the entrance examinations and pass examinations in Materia Medica and Therapeutics.

The right is reserved to make such alteration in the course of instruction as experience or expedience may prove to be necessary.

Students who have attended one or more courses of lectures in any accredited medical college or colleges, are placed upon an equal footing with our own students, and the same privileges as regards examinations (previously described) for advanced standing, are extended to them. Examination will not be required on subjects for which proper credentials are exhibited by the student, showing that he has passed such examination."

REQUIREMENTS FOR GRADUATION(5)

1. Candidates must be of good moral character, and correct in deportment.
2. They must be at least twenty-one years of age.
3. They must have attended three full courses of lectures, the last of which must have been at the College, and passed examinations in the various branches of medicine taught in the school. After October 1, 1902, four full courses were required.
4. They must pass a satisfactory examination before the Faculty.
5. Tickets for completed courses would be issued by the Dean, at the end of the session. Laboratory tickets and tickets for practical anatomy must be countersigned by the proper demonstrators and directors, and, unless properly countersigned, a ticket would not be accepted as evidence of a completed course, the student then being considered as not having met the requirements in practical anatomy and other laboratory courses.
6. Attendance upon all clinical lectures was obligatory.
7. The judgment of the Faculty upon the fitness of a candidate was based upon the professors' knowledge of his general attendance, industry, character and habits, as well as upon the outcome of his final examination.
8. Candidates who failed some parts of the final examination were not required to reappear for examination in the branches in which they had obtained the required percentage, except in the major branches, which they were required to take again.
9. Candidates who absented themselves from the Commencement exercises without special permission of the Faculty would not have the degree conferred upon them. (In the appointment of officers, assistants and additional teachers, other things being equal, the graduates of this school were to have preference.)

   With the establishment of the four year curriculum the requirements for graduation included attendance upon four full courses of lectures, "except those matriculating before October 1, 1902".

FEES

Tuition for full course	$50.00
Matriculation fee	5.00
Graduation fee	30.00
Laboratory fees	
First year Chemistry	5.00
First year Histology	5.00
First year Practical Anatomy	10.00
Second year Chemistry	5.00
Second year Pathology	5.00
Second year Practical Anatomy	10.00
Third year Clinical Microscopy	5.00

A special student could take single tickets for any departments desired. These cost $25.00 each for lecture courses, and $10.00 per laboratory courses. Graduates of other medical schools, who wished to take special post-graduate courses, were expected to pay a matriculation fee of $5.00, as well as the fees to be quoted by the Dean, for such work as they wished to do.

Board in the vicinity of the College could be had at $3.00 to $5.00 per week, fire and light included. A list of boarding houses was available at the Dean's office.

In 1901 the tuition for a full course was raised to $65.00, and a deposit of $2.00 for each laboratory course was required, the money being returnable to the student at the close of the session except for deductions charged for breakage.

In 1902 the fee for the full course of lectures was raised to $75.00, and the laboratory fee for fourth year advanced microscopy was announced as $15.00. All other fees remained the same. Students who had completed three full courses in this College would not be required to pay lecture fees for the fourth year. The laboratory fees for matriculates who were not following the regular courses were double those paid by full time students.

By 1909 the fee for the full course of lectures was $100., and the special fees for matriculates who were not following the regular course were to be ascertained by consulting the Dean.

(The fee to be paid by internes is given below, in the discussion on hospital appointments.)

In 1912 the tuition fee for the first three years became $125.00 per year for the full course of lectures, the fee for the fourth year remaining $100.

FACULTY PRIZES

In order "to stimulate zealous study among the candidates for graduation", the Faculty established the following prizes, in 1898:

First Highest General Average, a gold medal.

Second Highest General Average, a gold medal.

Third Highest General Average, a gold medal.

In 1899 two additional prizes were announced: For the best examination in Professor Baxley's course, . . . a gold medal.

For the best examination in Professor William S. Smith's course, a case of instruments.

In 1901 Professor Gross offered a case of instruments, as a prize for the best examination in his branch.

In 1902 Professor Muse announced a prize (obstetrical forceps) for the best examination in his branch.

The prize for the third highest general average was not awarded after 1903, and that for the second highest was also abolished later, as was also Dr. Baxley's medal, so that there was only one medal during the last years of the life of the College. However, all students who attained a general average of 90, or over were "entitled to honorable mention".

To be eligible for these prizes a student must take all the studies of the third year.

At the close of each session, one graduate was appointed as resident physician, and several graduates as dispensary physicians, to the National Temperance Hospital. Beginning 1901, these appointments were to the Franklin Square Hospital. In 1902 the College announced that two resident physicians would be appointed to the Franklin Square Hospital, the other numbers of appointments remaining unchanged.

In later years three were appointed to the Franklin Square and one to the West End Maternite. One graduate was also appointed resident physician to the Maryland Hospital for Consumptives.

Graduates were also eligible to annual appointment at other Baltimore hospitals.

About 1907 the Faculty decided to appoint a number of "Internes of the Franklin Square Hospital and West End Maternitē from among the graduating class, in order that students of this college obtain all the advantages resulting from the extended facilities of the Hospital. Internes were housed in a building convenient to both hospitals and received appropriate certificates at the end of their terms of service. The fee, including room, heat and light was one hundred dollars per year, or fifty dollars per half year.

ATHLETICS

The College authorities in later years (ca 1907) expressed their regret that in former times the three year curriculum allowed no time for proper exercise, but now that the years of study had been lengthened the student had ample time to engage in out-door athletics in season, or gymnasium work in the rest of the year. There were College football and baseball teams each year, in which students were encouraged by the Faculty, to participate, in the belief that a well-rounded body would house an evenly-balanced brain. The Athletic Association arranged to have the football team spend two weeks at the seashore, for preliminary training.

ALUMNI ASSOCIATION

All alumni in good standing, the Faculty and Adjunct Faculty were eligible for membership in the College Alumni Association, the purposes of which were: to advance the influence of the College, to encourage better educational methods and to secure intellectual, social and professional benefit to the members. The annual meeting was held on or about Commencement Day, an address being made by a member who had been selected for the purpose by the Executive Committee. The fee for membership was fifty cents per year.

"THE MEDICAL OBSERVER"

Reference has been made, on a very early page in this study, to the *Medical Observer of the Maryland Medical College*, the student monthly publication. This was a soft cover journal, measuring about nine by twelve inches, and consisting of three sheets, eighteen by twelve, folded once, and printed on both sides, resulting in a twelve paper page. The front cover of the first issues bore a photograph of the College building, the inside surface of the cover being devoted to advertisements. The next eight pages were given over to textual material, the inside of the back cover to additional advertisements, and the outside of that cover to the names of the Faculty and Chiefs of Clinics. It was published throughout the year, and the price was $1.00, (or ten cents per single issue). The editors and managers of Volume I were F. N. Tannar, of Pennsylvania, and H. C. Hess, of West Virginia, presumably under the watchful eye and friendly counsel of Drs. Pearce, Kintzing and Haughton Baxley, the Faculty Committee of the *Medical Observer*.

The issue of December 20, 1898 (Volume I, number I), contained:
"A Case of Lumbar Abscess", by Professor Branham, (one page).
"Superstition and Education", by John C. Rudolph, (about one page).
"Lead Palsy", by Richard L. McNeer, (about one and a half pages).
Short items, statistics, quips and book reviews filled the remaining pages:
"Question: Define delirium tremens. Answer – a tight fit.

Medical Facts and Statistics

Short women live longer than tall ones.
The married live longer than the single.
Tall men live longer than short ones. (no pun)
There are more insane among farmers than any other laborers.
Between the ages 16 and 45 there are more females than males.
One half of the people die before the age of 17; one fourth before 7.
Opium is eaten in the world by one hundred and twenty million people.
Only one person in a thousand reaches his allotted years – three score and ten."

DATA for COMPARISON and EVALUATION

Unlike any of the extinct Philadelphia Schools, or those of Baltimore thus far discussed, the Maryland Medical College, during the major portion of its existence, was a four-year-school. Again, unlike the other schools, with the exception of the Penn Medical University, it adopted a co-educational philosophy in its later years.

It was not alone in its claim to providing individual instruction, for the Women's Medical College also emphasized a similar ideal, but, with this exception, the Maryland Medical College stands out alone in this respect, claiming that the student was treated as an individual by his teachers, and the teachers in turn allowed to grow, by visiting other schools, both at home and abroad, in order to gain wider views, and to perfect their teaching methods. (Even the College itself remained an "individual", refusing to dissipate its energies in an effort to become a quasi University.) Through the student-professor conference, the individual student case report and the discussions, each student, in rotation, was permitted to develop his potentialities, and his progress was judged largely by the evidence of his growth which was manifested in these activities, and not by examinations, alone.

The amount of bedside and clinical training was very great, constituting a most significant improvement upon the early Philadelphia schools, as it was, indeed, upon such schools everywhere in our country. There was also a great deal of laboratory work.

Concern for the best educational procedures seems to have been very marked at this school, as shown in its logical arrangement of subjects so as to "place correlated groups in the same periods", thus allowing more time to the particular subject, while also permitting the student to apply himself, to better advantage, to a limited number of fields, (rather than distracting him by dividing his attention among many diverse subjects).

Courses were planned not only for the education of general practitioners, but, as well, for those who wished to become specialists or teachers of medicine. The Faculty, individually and collectively, stood ready to advise students regarding the studies which they should pursue, and how to attain their goals. Graduate work was offered and encouraged.

It was the policy of the school to maintain a program of constant improvement of the courses, (content and method of presentation), and expansion of facilities and equipment, (i.e., establishment of courses in proctology, dental surgery, enlarged laboratory of histology, etc.). Things seemed constantly to be "abuilding" in this school.

Both Faculty and student body were very large in comparison with the earlier schools.

An interesting, and not altogether unimportant departure from the usual pattern, was the presence of a program of athletics at this school. The gymnasium, football and baseball activities stemmed from what must have been a dedication to the ideal of "mens sana in corpore sano", an appropriate one for an institution devoted to the education of those who serve humanity by helping to preserve its health.

ALL OF THESE CLAIMS FOR THE MARYLAND MEDICAL COLLEGE OF BALTIMORE SHOULD BE READ WITH DR. FLEXNER'S REPORT OF 1910 IN MIND. (See the quotation near the end of Section 1-Buildings and Equipment, above.)

III. (A) FACULTY

SESSION OF 1898-99

BERNARD PURCELL MUSE, M.D., Dean
Professor of Obstetrics
J. B. SCHWATKA, M.D.
Professor of Diseases of Children and Clinical Medicine
J. WM. FUNCK, M.D.
Diseases of the Eye
JOSEPH H. BRANHAM, M.D.
Professor of Principles and Practice of Surgery and Abdominal Surgery
EDMUND A. MUNOZ, Ph.G., M.D.
Professor of Chemistry and Toxicology
FRED. CARUTHERS, M.D.
Professor of Anatomy and Genito-Urinary Surgery
HENRY M. BAXLEY, Ph.G., M.D.
Professor of Materia Medica, Therapeutics and Clinical Medicine
HAUGHTON BAXLEY, M.D.
Professor of Diseases of Nose, Throat and Chest, and Physical Diagnosis
G. MILTON LINTHICUM, B.A., M.D.
Professor of Physiology and Rectal Surgery
W. WAYLAND FRAMES, Ph.G., M.D.
Professor of Diseases of the Ear and Hygiene
PEARCE KINTZING, B.Sc., M.D.
Professor of Principles and Practice of Medicine
WM. S. SMITH, M.D.
Professor of Diseases of Women
W. MILTON LEWIS, M.D.
Professor of Pathology, Bacteriology and Clinical Medicine
A. L. HODGDON, M.D.
Professor of Diseases of the Nervous System and Mind
CHAS. F. HARLEY, A.M., B.C.L.
Professor of Medical Jurisprudence
S. GRIFFITH DAVIS, M.D.
Associate Professor and Demonstrator of Anatomy
WILLIAM HERBERT PEARCE, M.D.
Clinical Professor of Diseases of the Skin

FRANK A. HANCOCK, A.B.
Lecturer and Demonstrator of Chemistry
RICHARD L. MC NEAR, M.D.
Demonstrator of Pathology and Histology
J. W. LEITCH, M.D.
Assistant Demonstrator of Anatomy
H. A. WILSON, D.D.S.
Lecturer on Dental Surgery

CHIEFS OF CLINIC

Chief of Clinic to the Chair of Surgery
JAMES C. HOLDSWORTH, M.D.
Chief of Clinic to the Chair of Obstetrics
J. MORGAN DIX, M.D.
Chief of Clinic to the Chair of Principles and Practice of Medicine
CHARLES R. DAVIS, M.D.
Chief of Clinic to the Chair of Diseases of Children
W. D. F. BLANEY, M.D.
Chief of Clinic to the Chair of Genito-Urinary Surgery
JAMES C. HOLDSWORTH, M.D.
Chief of Clinic to the Chair of Diseases of the Eye
M. K. GWYNN, M.D.
Chief of Clinic to the Chair of Diseases of the Ear
W. H. SCHWATKA, M.D.
Chief of Clinic to the Chair of Diseases of the Nervous System
W. H. KOEHLERT, M.D.
Chief of Clinic to the Chair of Diseases of Rectal Surgery
- - - - - -
Chief of Clinic to the Chair of Diseases of the Nose, Throat and Chest
JOSEPH E. MUSE, M.D.
Chief of Clinic to the Chair of Diseases of Women
P. E. CRAIG, M.D.

BOARD OF DIRECTORS

JOSEPH H. BRANHAM, M.D.
J. B. SCHWATKA, M.D.
J. WM. FUNCK, M.D.
BERNARD PURCELL MUSE, M.D.
FRED. CARUTHERS, M.D.
EDMUND A. MUNOZ, M.D.
HENRY M. BAXLEY, M.D.
HAUGHTON BAXLEY, M.D.
G. MILTON LINTHICUM, M.D.
W. WAYLAND FRAMES, M.D.

OFFICERS OF THE BOARD

J. B. SCHWATKA, M.D., *President*
FRED. CARUTHERS, M.D., *Vice President*
W. WAYLAND FRAMES, M.D., *Secretary*
J. WM. FUNCK, M.D., *Treasurer*
CHARLES F. HARLEY, ESQ., *Counsel*

SESSION OF 1899-1900

BERNARD PURCELL MUSE, M.D.
Professor of Obstetrics and Dean
J. B. SCHWATKA, M.D.
Professor of Diseases of Children and Clinical Medicine
J. WM. FUNCK, M.D.
Professor of Diseases of the Eye
JOSEPH H. BRANHAM, M.D.
Professor of Principles and Practice of Surgery and Abdominal Surgery
EDMUND A. MUNOZ, Ph.G., M.D.
Professor of Chemistry, Toxicology and Dermatology
FRED CARUTHERS, M.D.
Professor of Anatomy and Genito-Urinary Surgery
HENRY M. BAXLEY, Ph.G., M.D.
Professor of Materia Medica, Therapeutics and Clinical Medicine
HAUGHTON BAXLEY, M.D.
Professor of Diseases of Nose, Throat and Chest, and Physical Diagnosis
G. MILTON LINTHICUM, A.B., M.D.
Professor of Physiology and Rectal Surgery
W. WAYLAND FRAMES, Ph.G., M.D.
Professor of Diseases of the Ear and Hygiene
PEARCE KINTZING, B.Sc., M.D.
Professor of Principles and Practice of Medicine
WM. S. SMITH, M.D.
Professor of Gynecology
A. L. HODGDON, M.D.
Professor of Diseases of the Nervous System and the Mind
CHAS. F. HARLEY, A.M., LL.B.
Professor of Medical Jurisprudence
S. GRIFFITH DAVIS, M.D.
Associate Professor of Anatomy and Operative Surgery
WILLIAM HERBERT PEARCE, M.D.
Associate Professor of Materia Medica
RICHARD L. MC NEER, M.D.
Associate Professor of Histology, Pathology and Bacteriology
FRANK A. HANCOCK, A.B.
Lecturer and Demonstrator of Chemistry
ELIJAH J. RUSSELL, M.D.
Demonstrator of Anatomy

J. W. LEITCH, M.D.
J. W. BURKHALTER, A.B., M.D.
Assistant Demonstrators of Anatomy

ASSISTANTS TO THE DEMONSTRATOR OF ANATOMY

PAUL ENGEL	R. F. TARR
HARRY PALMER	H. B. HOECHST
W. K. BELL	J. R. VERMILLION

CHIEFS OF CLINIC

JAMES C. HOLDSWORTH, M.D.
Chief of Clinic to the Chair of Surgery
J. MORGAN DIX, M.D.
Chief of Clinic to the Chair of Obstetrics
W. D. F. BLANEY, M.D.
Chief of Clinic to the Chair of Diseases of Children
JOSEPH E. MUSE, M.D.
Chief of Clinic to the Chair of Diseases of Women
I. H. GARDINER, A.M., M.D.
Chief of Clinic to the Chairs of Diseases of the Eye and of the Ear
W. M. WHELAN, M.D.
Chief of Clinic to the Chair of Principles and Practice of Medicine
JNO. C. TRAVERS, M.D.
Chief of Clinic to the Chair of Diseases of Nose, Throat and Chest
JAMES L. TRUAX, M.D.
Chief of Clinic to the Chair of Diseases of the Nervous System
GEORGE B. M. ADAMS, M.D.
Chief of Clinic to the Chair of Dermatology
T. A. CALLAHAN, M.D.
Chief of Clinic to the Chairs of Genito-Urinary Surgery and Rectal Surgery
G. C. BLADES, Ph.G.
Assistant to the Chair of Diseases of Women
E. W. PARKINS
Druggist
J. E. MC CLAIN
Janitor

SESSION OF 1900-01

FACULTY

BERNARD PURCELL MUSE, M.D.
Professor of Obstetrics
J. B. SCHWATKA, M.D.
Professor of Diseases of Children and Clinical Medicine
J. WM. FUNCK, M.D.
Professor of Diseases of the Eye and Dean
JOSEPH H. BRANHAM, M.D.
Professor of Principles and Practice of Surgery and Abdominal Surgery
FRED. CARUTHERS, M.D.
Professor of Anatomy and Clinical Surgery
HENRY M. BAXLEY, Ph.G., M.D.
Professor of Materia Medica Therapeutics and Clinical Medicine
G. MILTON LINTHICUM, A.B., M.D.
Professor of Physiology and Rectal Surgery
W. WAYLAND FRAMES, Ph.G., M.D.
Professor of Diseases of the Ear, Nose and Throat and Hygiene
WM. S. SMITH, M.D.
Professor of Diseases of Women
A. L. HODGDON, M.D.
Professor of Diseases of the Nervous System and the Mind
CHAS. F. HARLEY, A.M., LL.B.
Professor of Medical Jurisprudence

C. URBAN SMITH, A.B., Ph.G., M.D.
Professor of Principles and Practice of Medicine and Diseases of the Stomach
HARRY GROSS, M.D.
Professor of Operative and Clinical Surgery
ERNEST E. QUANDT, Ph.G.
Professor of Chemistry and Toxicology
WILLIAM HERBERT PEARCE, M.D.
Associate Professor Materia Medica
RICHARD L. MC NEER, M.D.
Associate Professor of Histology, Pathology and Bacteriology
ELIJAH J. RUSSELL, M.D.
Lecturer on Diseases of the Skin and Demonstrator of Anatomy
JAMES H. BAKER, D.D.S., M.D.
Demonstrator of Dental Surgery
ALEX. MC KEE, A.B., M.D.
Demonstrator of Obstetrics
CHAS. H. BEETEM, Ph.G., M.D.
Demonstrator of Histology
JOEL J. BARNET, Ph.G.
Demonstrator of Chemistry
ALAN W. SMITH, M.D.
Demonstrator of Pathology and Bacteriology
H. B. HOECHST, M.D.
Assistant Demonstrator of Anatomy

DISPENSARY STAFF

JOSEPH E. MUSE, M.D.
Dispensary Physician
A. G. HUBBARD, Ph.G., M.D.
Assistant Dispensary Physician
W. D. F. BLANEY, M.D.
Chief of Clinic to the Chair of Diseases of Children
W. M. WHELAN, M.D.
Chief of Clinic to the Chair of Principles and Practice of Medicine
JAMES L. TRUAX, M.D.
Chief of Clinic to the Chair of Diseases of the Nervous System
G. C. BLADES, Ph.G., M.D.
Chief of Clinic to the Chair of Diseases of Women
JNO. C. RUDOLPH, A.B., M.D.
Chief of Clinic to the Chair of Surgery

H. B. HOECHST, M.D.
Chief of Clinic to the Chair of Operative and Clinical Surgery
ELLIOTT GARDNER, M.D.
Chief of Clinic to the Chairs of Genito-Urinary Surgery and Rectal Surgery
A. G. HUBBARD, Ph.G., M.D.
Chief of Clinic to the Chair of Diseases of the Ear, Nose and Throat
SAM'L. J. HERMAN, M.D.
Chief of Clinic to the Chair of Diseases of the Eye
J. C. MORTON, M.D.
Chief of Clinic to the Chair of Diseases of the Skin

SESSION OF 1901-02

Same as that of 1900-01, with the following exceptions:

Drs. Baxley, Hodgdon, Harley, Beetem, and Hoechst were no longer on the Faculty. J. Charles Linthicum was professor of medical jurisprudence, W. McLean Yost, M.D. was associate professor of materia medica and clinical diagnosis, P. Eugene Craig, M.D. was associate professor of diseases of children, Dr. McKee was lecturer on osteology and embryology and demonstrator of obstetrics, Dr. A. W. Smith lecturer on hygiene, Jacob S. Parr,

Ph.G. was lecturer on practical pharmacy and B. K. Stumberg, A.B., M.D. was demonstrator of pathology and bacteriology.

The dispensary staff was as follows:

J. W. BARTON, M.D.
Dispensary Physician
A. G. HUBBARD, Ph.G., M.D.
Assistant Dispensary Physician, and Chief of Clinic
to the Chair of Diseases of the Ear, Nose and Throat
J. C. MORTON, M.D.
Chief of Clinic to the Chair of Diseases of the Skin
H. C. HESS, M.D.
Chief of Clinic to the Chair of Diseases of Women
CHAS. L. BOYERS, M.D.
Chief of Clinic to the Chair of Surgery
J. W. BARTON, M.D.
Chief of Clinic to the Chair of Operative and Clinical Surgery
GUSTAV A. THIEDE, M.D.
Chief of Clinic to the Chairs of Rectal Surgery
and Genito-Urinary Surgery
CLARENCE P. ERKENBRACK, M.D.
Chief of Clinic to the Chair of Principles and
Practice of Medicine
WM. J. SULLIVEN, M.D.
Chief of Clinic to the Chair of Diseases of the Eye
....
Chief of Clinic to the Chair of Diseases of the
Nervous System

SESSION OF 1902-03

BERNARD PURCELL MUSE, M.D.
Professor of Obstetrics
J. B. SCHWATKA, M.D.
Professor of Diseases of Children
and Clinical Medicine
J. WM. FUNCK, M.D.
Professor of Diseases of the Eye
and Dean of the Faculty
JOSEPH H. BRANHAM, M.D.
Professor of Principles and Practice
of Surgery and Abdominal Surgery
FRED. CARUTHERS, M.D.
Professor of Anatomy and
Genito-Urinary Surgery
G. MILTON LINTHICUM, A.B., M.D.
Professor of Histology, Physiology
and Rectal Surgery
W. WAYLAND FRAMES, Ph.G., M.D.
Professor of Diseases of the Ear,
Nose and Throat
WM. S. SMITH, M.D.
Professor of Diseases of Women
C. URBAN SMITH, A.B., Ph.G., M.D.
President,
Professor of Principles and Practice
of Medicine and Diseases
of the Stomach
HARRY GROSS, M.D.
Professor of Operative and
Clinical Surgery
ERNEST E. QUANDT, Ph.G.
Professor of Chemistry and Toxicology
WILLIAM HERBERT PEARCE, M.D.
Vice-President,
Professor of Materia Medica,
Therapeutics and Clinical Medicine
J. CHAS. LINTHICUM, LL.B., M.D.
Professor of Medical Jurisprudence

L. H. GUNDRY, M.D.
Professor of Diseases of the Nervous
System and the Mind
RICHARD L. MC NEER, M.D.
Associate Professor of Pathology
and Bacteriology
ALEXANDER MC KEE, A.B., M.D.
Associate Professor of Obstetrics and
Lecturer on Osteology
A. D. MC CONACHIE, D.D.S., M.D.
Associate Professor of Materia Medica
WILBUR M. PEARCE, A.M., M.D.
Associate Professor of Clinical
Medicine and Physical Diagnosis
ALAN W. SMITH, M.D.
Lecturer on Hygiene
JACOB S. PARR, Ph.G.
Lecturer on Practical Pharmacy
H. C. HESS, M.D.
Lecturer on Diseases of the Skin
THOS. H. BRAYSHAW, M.D.
Lecturer on Climatology
ELIJAH J. RUSSELL, M.D.
Demonstrator of Anatomy
JAMES BAKER, D.D.S., M.D.
Demonstrator of Dental Surgery
CHAS. H. HUDSON, Phar.D.
Demonstrator of Chemistry
B. K. STUMBERG, A.B., M.D.
Demonstrator of Pathology and
Bacteriology
JOSIAH J. GOFF, M.D.
Demonstrator and Prosector of Anatomy
CHAS. H. BUBERT, M.D.
Demonstrator of Minor Surgery
and Bandaging

DISPENSARY STAFF

F. E. SMITH, M.D.
Dispensary Physician
A. G. HUBBARD, Ph.G., M.D.
Chief of Clinic to the Chair
of Surgery
G. C. BLADES, Ph.G., M.D.
Chief of Clinic to the Chair of
Operative Surgery
CLARENCE P. ERKENBRACK, M.D.
Chief of Clinic to the Chair of
Diseases of Women
L. H. EPHRAIM, M.D.
Chief of Clinic to the Chair of
Diseases of the Ear,
Nose and Throat

WM. J. SULLIVAN, M.D.
Chief of Clinic to the Chair
of Diseases of the Eye
GUSTAV A. THIEDE, M.D.
Chief of Clinic to the Chairs of
Rectal Surgery and
Genito-Urinary Surgery
W. T. KIRK, M.D.
Chief of Clinic to the Chair of
Diseases of the Nervous System
J. H. RAVENSCROFT, M.D.
Chief of Clinic to the Chair of
Principles and Practice
of Medicine

BOARD OF DIRECTORS

President: JOHN B. SCHWATKA, M.D.
Vice-President: FRED. CARUTHERS, M.D.
Secretary: G. M. LINTHICUM, M.D.
Treasurer: W. S. SMITH, M.D.
Counsel: J. C. LINTHICUM, LL.B., M.D.
BERNARD P. MUSE, M.D.
J. WM. FUNCK, M.D.
JOSEPH H. BRANHAM, M.D.
C. URBAN SMITH, M.D.
HARRY GROSS, M.D.

SESSION OF 1903-04

Same as that of 1902-03, with the following exceptions:

Dr. McNeer became clinical professor of orthopedic surgery, Dr. Wilbur Pearce became associate professor of diseases of children and clinical medicine, George B. Scholl, A.B., M.D., became associate professor of pathology and bacteriology, and Gustavus C. Dohme, A.B., M.D., became demonstrator of chemistry. The following were no longer on the Faculty: Drs. McKee, A. W. Smith, Hudson, Stumberg and Goff.

The dispensary staff was as follows:

DISPENSARY STAFF

E. L. MORTIMER, M.D.
Dispensary Physician
A. G. HUBBARD, Ph.G., M.D.
Chief of Clinic to Chair of
Diseases of Eye
CLARENCE P. ERKENBRACK, M.D.
Chief of Clinic to the Chairs of
Rectal Surgery and
Genito-Urinary Surgery
E. L. MORTIMER, M.D.
Chief of Clinic to Chair of
Surgery
A. C. SMINK
Chief of Clinic to the Chair
of Operative Surgery

J. C. CAHOON, M.D.
Chief of Clinic to the Chair of
Diseases of the Ear, Nose
and Throat
WALTER A. COX, M.D.
Chief of Clinic to the Chair of
Diseases of the Ear, Nose
and Throat
W. T. KIRK, M.D.
Chief of Clinic to the Chair of
Diseases of the Nervous System
E. C. J. MILLER, M.D.
Chief of Clinic to the Chair of
Diseases of Women

SESSION OF 1904-05

Same as in 1903-04, with the following exceptions:

C. P. Erkenbrack, M.D., was lecturer on osteology, L. E. Beach, M.D., was demonstrator of obstetrics, Charles N. Branin, M.D., was demonstrator of minor surgery and bandaging, E. C. Lehnert was lecturer on materia medica. The resident physicians of Franklin Square Hospital were Drs. O. H. McNemar and L. C. Hodges. Dr. Hubert was no longer on the Faculty.

SESSION OF 1905-06

The changes were as follows: Dr. Schwatka, dermatology, Dr. William H. Pearce, diseases of children and clinical medicine, Dr. McNeer added associate professor of anatomy to his rank, Dr. McConachie added the chair of clinical professor of eye and ear, Dr. Wilbur Pearce was no longer on the Faculty, Pearce Kintzing, B.Sc., M.D., became professor of physical diagnosis and diseases of the heart, Dr. Scholl added clinical microscopy, Dr. Dohme became associate professor of chemistry, Dr. Erkenbrack, associate professor of medicine and lecturer on osteology and syndesmology, Dr. Hess, associate professor of hygiene and State medicine, Gilman P. Evans, M.D., associate in surgery, Thomas J. Talbot, M.D., associate professor of gynecology, Thomas J. O'Donnell, M.D., associate in surgery (and chief of the clinic to the chair of operative surgery), A. G. Barrett, M.D., associate professor of operative and clinical surgery, Maurice Lazenby, A.B., M.D., associate in histology, biology and embryology, Henry M. Baxley, Ph.G., M.D., associate in eye, nose and throat, Charles R. Davis, M.D., lecturer on bandaging and minor surgery, B. A. Knorr, M.D., demonstrator of clinical diagnosis, A. C. Smink, M.D., associate in operative surgery, F. N. Tannar, M.D., demonstrator of special surgery, F. W. Hachtel, M.D., chief of the clinic to the chair of diseases of ear, nose and throat, A. T. vonSchultz, B.Sc., M.D., demonstrator of histology, H. Lee Franks, M.D., assistant demonstrator of anatomy, and Eldridge Baskin, D.D.S., M.D., lecturer on dental histology and pathology.

SESSION OF 1907-08

BERNARD PURCELL MUSE, M.D.
Professor of Obstetrics

J. B. SCHWATKA, M.D., DEAN
Professor of Clinical Medicine

J. WM. FUNCK, M.D.
Professor of Diseases of the Eye

JOSEPH H. BRANHAM, M.D.
Professor of Principles and Practice of Surgery and Abdominal Surgery

FRED. CARUTHERS, M.D.
Professor of Anatomy and Genito-Urinary Surgery

G. MILTON LINTHICUM, A.B., M.D.
Professor of Diseases of the Colon and Rectum

W. WAYLAND FRAMES, Ph.D., M.D.
Professor of Diseases of the Ear, Nose and Throat

W. S. SMITH, M.D.
Professor of Diseases of Women

C. URBAN SMITH, Ph.G., M.D.
Professor of Theory and Practice of Medicine and Gastro-Enterology

HARRY GROSS, M.D.
Professor of Operative and Clinical Surgery

J. CHARLES LINTHICUM, LL.B., M.D.
Professor of Medical Jurisprudence

L. H. GUNDRY, M.D.
Professor of Diseases of the Nervous System and the Mind

A. D. Mc CONACHIE, D.D.S., M.D.
Professor of Therapeutics, and Clinical Professor of Diseases of the Eye and Ear

WILLIAM HERBERT PEARCE, M.D.
Professor of Diseases of Children and Clinical Medicine

PEARCE KINTZING, B.Sc., M.D.
Professor of Physical Diagnosis and Diseases of the Heart

GEORGE B. SCHOLL, A.B., M.D.
Professor of Pathology, Bacteriology and Clinical Microscopy

GUSTAVUS CHARLES DOHME, A.B., M.D.
Professor of Chemistry

CHRISTIAN DEETJEN, M.D.
Professor of Electro-Therapeutics

WM. S. LOVE, M.D.
Professor of Materia Medica

MAURICE LAZENBY, A.B., M.D.
Professor of Clinical Pathology and Clinical Diagnosis

E. H. HUTCHINS, A.B., M.D.
Associate Professor of Physiology, Histology and Embryology

THOMAS H. BRAYSHAW, M.D.
Associate Professor of Climatology

H. C. HESS, M.D.
Clinical Professor of Dermatology

THOMAS J. O'DONNELL, M.D.
Associate Professor of Surgery and Chief of Clinic in the Chair of Operative Surgery

EDWARD GREMPLER, M.D.
Associate Professor of Surgery

L. E. BEACH, M.D.
Associate in Obstetrics

THOMAS J. TALBOTT, M.D.
Associate Professor of Gynecology

A. G. BARRETT, M.D.
Associate Professor of Operative and Clinical Surgery

HENRY M. BAXLEY, Ph.G., M.D.
Associate in Ear, Nose and Throat

CHARLES T. BRANIN, M.D.
Associate Professor of Osteology and Syndesmology

E. L. MORTIMER, M.D.
Associate in Surgery

O. C. SMITH, Ph.G.
Associate Professor of Practical Pharmacy

ALBERT T. CHAMBERS, M.D.
Associate in Gynecology and
Demonstrator of Anatomy
A. C. SMINK, M.D.
Associate in Operative Surgery
F. N. TANNAR, M.D.
Associate in Obstetrics and
Gynecology
HOWARD W. JONES, M.D.
Associate in Medicine
F. W. HACHTEL, M.D.
Associate in Physical Diagnosis,
Demonstrator of Clinical
Diagnosis and Pathology

ELDRIDGE BASKIN, D.D.S., M.D.
Lecturer on Dental Histology and
Pathology
C. L. MORTIMER, M.D.
Assistant to Chair of Surgery
A. T. vonSCHULTZ, M.Sc., M.D.
Associate in Dermatology
JOSEPH LUTHER SHEPPE, A.B., M.D.
Lecturer on Hygiene
R. V. GLANN, M.D.
Lecturer on Minor Surgery and
Bandaging

FRANKLIN SQUARE HOSPITAL

Visiting Staff

SURGEONS

PROF. J. H. BRANHAM, M.D.
PROF. J. WM. FUNCK, M.D.
PROF. F. CARUTHERS, M.D.
PROF. G. M. LINTHICUM, M.D.
PROF. W. W. FRAMES, M.D.
PROF. WM. S. SMITH, M.D.
PROF. HARRY GROSS, M.D.
PROF. A. D. MC CONACHIE, M.D.

PHYSICIANS

PROF. J. B. SCHWATKA, M.D.
PROF. C. URBAN SMITH, M.D.
PROF. WM. H. PEARCE, M.D.
PROF. PEARCE KINTZING, M.D.
PROF. L. H. GUNDRY, M.D.
Neurologist
PROF. GEO. B. SCHOLL, M.D.
Pathologist
PROF. MAURICE LAZENBY

Resident Physicians

H. C. IRWIN, M.D.
Superintendent of Hospital
J. PAGE STRONG, M.D.
Associate Resident Physician

HARRY GOLDBERG, M.D.
Associate Resident Physician
REV. GEORGE SCHOLL, D.D.
Business Manager

WEST END MATERNITE

PROF. B. P. MUSE, M.D., Visiting Obstetrician
F. W. TANNER, M.D., Associate in Obstetrics
L. E. BEACH, M.D., Demonstrator of Obstetrics

DISPENSARY STAFF

E. A. DICKEY, M.D.
Dispensary Physician
E. A. DICKEY, M.D.
Chief of Clinic to the Chair
of Diseases of the Eye
C. L. MORTIMER, M.D.
Chief of Clinic to the Chair
of Surgery
F. N. TANNAR, M.D.
Chief of Clinic to the
Chairs of Proctology and
Genito-Urinary Surgery

ALBERT T. CHAMBERS, M.D.
Chief of Clinic to the Chair of
Diseases of Women
HOWARD W. JONES, M.D.
Chief of Clinic to the Chair of
Practice and Clinical Medicine
FRANK W. HACHTEL, M.D.
Chief of Clinic to the Chair
of Physical Diagnosis
T. J. O'DONNELL, M.D.
Chief of Clinic to the Chair of
Operative Surgery

SESSION OF 1909-10

WILLIAM HERBERT PEARCE, M.D.
Emeritus Professor of Diseases
of Children and Clinical Medicine
BERNARD PURCELL MUSE, M.D.
Professor of Obstetrics

J. WM. FUNCK, M.D.
Professor of Diseases of the Eye
JOSEPH H. BRANHAM, M.D.
Professor of Principles and
Practice of Surgery and
Abdominal Surgery

FRED. CARUTHERS, M.D.
Professor of Genito-Urinary Surgery
W. WAYLAND FRAMES, M.D.
Professor of Diseases of the
Ear, Nose and Throat
W. S. SMITH, M.D., Assistant Dean
Professor of Diseases of Women
C. URBAN SMITH, Ph.G., M.D.
Professor of Theory and Practice
of Medicine and Gastro-Enterology
HARRY GROSS, M.D., Dean
Professor of Operative and
Clinical Surgery
L. H. GUNDRY, M.D.
Professor of Diseases of the
Nervous System and the Mind
A. D. MC CONACHIE, D.D.S., M.D.
Professor of Therapeutics, and Clinical
Professor of Diseases of the
Eye and Ear
PEARCE KINTZING, B.Sc., M.D.
Professor of Physical Diagnosis and
Diseases of the Heart
GEORGE B. SCHOLL, A.B., M.D.
Professor of Pathology, Bacteriology
and Clinical Microscopy
GUSTAVUS CHARLES DOHME, A.B., M.D.
Professor of Chemistry and
Associate in Medicine
WM. S. LOVE, M.D.
Professor of Materia Medica
and Clinical Medicine
MAURICE LAZENBY, A.B., M.D.
Professor of Embryology and Biology
HARRY M. BAXLEY, Ph.G., M.D.
Professor of Hygiene and Associate
Professor of Diseases of Ear,
Nose and Throat
E. MILLER REID, M.D.
Professor of Medical Jurisprudence
J. HARRY ULRICH, Ph.G., M.D.
Professor of Physiology and Assistant
Professor of Gynecology
ALBERT T. CHAMBERS, M.D.
Professor of Anatomy

.............................., M.D.
Professor of Diseases of Children
H. C. HESS, M.D.
Clinical Professor of Dermatology
THOMAS J. O'DONNELL, M.D.
Associate Professor of Surgery
and Chief of Clinic in the
Chair of Operative Surgery
EDWARD GREMPLER, M.D.
Associate Professor of Surgery
L. E. BEACH, M.D.
Associate in Obstetrics and
Instructor in Electro-Therapeutics
and Radiography
THOMAS J. TALBOTT, M.D.
Associate Professor of Gynecology
HENRY G. BRANHAM, M.D.
Associate in Osteology and
Syndesmology
C. L. MORTIMER, M.D.
Associate in Surgery
CHARLES L. MEYER, Ph.G.
Associate Professor in
Practical Pharmacy
H. D. LEWIS, M.D.
Associate Professor of Operative Surgery
WALTER A. COX, M.D.
Associate in Gynecology
J. GILBERT SELBY, M.D.
Demonstrator of Anatomy
F. N. TANNAR, M.D.
Associate in Obstetrics and
Diseases of Children
F. W. HACHTEL, M.D.
Associate in Physical Diagnosis,
Demonstrator of Clinical Diagnosis
and Pathology
ELDRIDGE BASKIN, D.D.S., M.D.
Lecturer on Dental Histology
and Pathology
A. T. vonSCHULTZ, M.Sc., M.D.
Associate in Dermatology
R. V. GLANN, M.D.
Lecturer on Minor Surgery
and Bandaging

FRANKLIN SQUARE HOSPITAL

Visiting Staff

SURGEONS

PROF. J. H. BRANHAM, M.D.
PROF. J. WM. FUNCK, M.D.
PROF. F. CARUTHERS, M.D.
PROF. W. W. FRAMES, M.D.
PROF. WM. S. SMITH, M.D.
PROF. HARRY GROSS, M.D.
PROF. A. D. MC CONACHIE, M.D.
PROF. ALBERT T. CHAMBERS, M.D.

PHYSICIANS

PROF. C. URBAN SMITH, M.D.
PROF. PEARCE KINTZING, M.D.
PROF. WM. H. PEARCE, M.D.
PROF. L. H. GUNDRY, M.D.
Neurologist
PROF. GEO. B. SCHOLL, M.D.
Pathologist
PROF. MAURICE LAZENBY

Resident Physicians

HENRY B. KOLB, M.D.
Medical Superintendent
W. P. GEMMILL, M.D.
Associate Resident Physician
MILNER BORTNER, M.D.
Associate Resident Physician
A. C. BEETHAM, M.D.
Associate Resident Physician
MISS ANNA A. SIELING
Superintendent of Nurses
REV. GEORGE SCHOLL, D.D.
Business Manager

WEST END MATERNITE

PROF. B. P. MUSE, M.D., Visiting Obstetrician
F. W. TANNER, M.D., Associate in Obstetrics
L. E. BEACH, M.D., Demonstrator of Obstetrics

DISPENSARY STAFF

Dispensary Physician
MAURICE JONES, M.D.
Chief of Clinic to the Chair of Diseases of the Eye
C. L. MORTIMER, M.D.
Chief of Clinic to the Chair of Surgery
F. N. TANNAR, M.D.
Chief of Clinic to the Chairs of Proctology and Genito-Urinary Surgery
WALTER A. COX, M.D.
Chief of Clinic to the Chair of Diseases of Women
GUSTAVUS CHARLES DOHME, A.B., M.D.
Chief of Clinic to the Chair of Practice and Clinical Medicine
.............................., M.D.
Chief of Clinic to the Chair of Physical Diagnosis and Clinical Medicine
T. J. O'DONNELL, M.D.
Chief of Clinic to the Chair of Operative Surgery

SESSION OF 1910-11

WILLIAM HERBERT PEARCE, M.D.
Emeritus Professor of Diseases of Children and Clinical Medicine
C. URBAN SMITH, Ph.G., M.D.
Emeritus Professor of Theory and Practice of Medicine and Gastro-Enterology
BERNARD PURCELL MUSE, M.D.
Professor of Obstetrics
J. WILLIAM FUNCK, M.D.
Professor of Diseases of the Eye
JOSEPH H. BRANHAM, M.D.
Professor of Principles and Practice of Surgery and Abdominal Surgery
FRED. CARUTHERS, M.D.
Professor of Genito-Urinary Surgery
WILLIAM S. SMITH, M.D., Dean
Professor of Diseases of Women
LEWIS H. GUNDRY, M.D.
Professor of Diseases of the Nervous System and of the Mind
A. D. MC CONACHIE, D.D.S., M.D.
Professor of Diseases of the Ear, Nose and Throat
PEARCE KINTZING, B.Sc., M.D.
Professor of Theory and Practice of Medicine and Physical Diagnosis

ALBERT T. CHAMBERS, M.D.
Professor of Operative and Clinical Surgery
GEORGE B. SCHOLL, A.B., M.D.
Professor of Pathology, Bacteriology and Clinical Microscopy
GUSTAVUS CHARLES DOHME, A.B., M.D.
Professor of Chemistry and Associate in Medicine
WILLIAM S. LOVE, M.D.
Professor of Gastro-Enterology and Clinical Medicine
HENRY M. BAXLEY, Ph.G., M.D.
Professor of Hygiene
E. MILLER REID, M.D.
Professor of Medical Jurisprudence
J. HARRY ULLRICH, Ph.G., M.D.
Professor of Physiology and Proctology
H. C. HESS, M.D.
Professor of Dermatology
IRVIN EBAUGH, M.D.
Professor of Therapeutics and Clinical Medicine
HENRY W. KENNARD, M.D.
Professor of Orthopedic Surgery

F. N. TANNAR, A.B., LL.B., M.D.
Professor of Diseases of Children
and Instructor in
Gynecological Pathology
HOWARD D. LEWIS, M.D.
Professor of Anatomy and
Clinical Surgery
WILBUR P. STUBBS, M.D.
Professor of Materia Medica and
Associate in Clinical Medicine
MAURICE LAZENBY, A.B., M.D.
Clinical Professor of Female
Genito-Urinary Diseases
EDWARD GREMPLER, M.D.
Associate Professor of Surgery
LEONARD E. BEACH, M.D.
Associate in Electro Therapeutics
and Radiography
JOSIAH S. BOWEN, M.D.
Associate in Diseases of the Ear,
Nose and Throat
FRANK J. POWERS, M.D.
Associate in Diseases of the Ear,
Nose and Throat
HENRY G. BRANHAM, M.D.
Associate in Physiological Chemistry
and Clinical Diagnosis
ROBERT L. MORTIMER, M.D.
Associate in Operative Surgery

GEORGE A. BUNTING, A.M., Ph.G.
Associate Professor of Practical Pharmacy
A. T. vonSCHULZ, M.Sc., M.C.
Associate in Dermatology
ALFRED L. LEVY, M.D.
Associate in Physiology
H. P. HILL, A.B., Ph.G., M.D.
Associate Professor of Histology
Embryology and Biology
CHARLES H. BEETEM, Ph.G., M.D.
Associate in Obstetrics
HENRY B. KOLB, M.D.
Associate in Gynecology
ALLEN C. BEETHAM, M.D.
Associate in Osteology and Syndesmology
and Demonstrator of Obstetrics
J. GILBERT SELBY, M.D.
Demonstrator of Anatomy
WALTER A. COX, M.D.
Assistant Demonstrator of Anatomy
JAMES A. DUFF, M.D.
Assistant Demonstrator of Anatomy
ELDRIDGE BASKIN, D.D.S., M.D.
Lecturer on Dental Histology
and Pathology
R. V. GLANN, M.D.
Lecturer on Minor Surgery
and Bandaging

FRANKLIN SQUARE HOSPITAL

Visiting Staff

SURGEONS

PROF. J. H. BRANHAM, M.D.
PROF. J. WM. FUNCK, M.D.
PROF. FRED. CARUTHERS, M.D.
PROF. WM. S. SMITH, M.D.
PROF. A. D. MC CONACHIE, M.D.
PROF. ALBERT T. CHAMBERS, M.D.
PROF. J. HARRY ULLRICH, M.D.
PROF. HOWARD D. LEWIS, M.D.
PROF. EDWARD GREMPLER, M.D.
PROF. MAURICE LAZENBY, M.D.

PHYSICIANS

PROF. C. U. SMITH, M.D.
PROF. PEARCE KINTZING, M.D.
PROF. WM. H. PEARCE, M.D.
PROF. LEWIS H. GUNDRY, M.D.
Neurologist
PROF. WM. S. LOVE, M.D.
PROF. H. C. HESS, M.D.
PROF. IRVIN EBAUGH, M.D.
PROF. F. N. TANNAR, M.D.
PROF. WILBUR P. STUBBS, M.D.
PROF. GEORGE B. SCHOLL, M.D.
Pathologist

Resident Staff

JAMES A. DUFF, M.D.
Medical Superintendent
JOHN A. MILLER, M.D.
Resident Physician
OMER V. BROOKS, M.D.
Associate Resident Physician

JOSEPH L. MC LAUGHLIN, M.D.
Associate Resident Physician
MISS ANNA A. SIELING
Superintendent of Nurses
REV. GEORGE SCHOLL, D.D.
Business Manager

WEST END MATERNITY

PROF. B. P. MUSE, M.D., Visiting Obstetrician
CHARLES H. BEETEM, M.D., Associate in Obstetrics
ALLEN C. BEETHAM, M.D., Demonstrator of Obstetrics

DISPENSARY STAFF

HENRY B. KOLB, M.D.
Dispensary Physician
E. L. MORTIMER, M.D.
Chief of Clinic to the Chair of Operative Surgery
HENRY B. KOLB, M.D.
Chief of Clinic to the Chair of Diseases of Women
J. S. BOWEN, M.D.
FRANK J. POWERS, M.D.
Chiefs of Clinic to the Chair of Diseases of the
Ear, Nose and Throat
ALLEN C. BEETHAM, M.D.
Chief of Clinic to the Chair of Practice of Medicine
HENRY G. BRANHAM, M.D.
Chief of Clinic to the Chair of Surgery
E. A. DICKEY, M.D.
Chief of Clinic to the Chair of Diseases of the Eye

BOARD OF DIRECTORS OF THE MARYLAND MEDICAL COLLEGE

J. H. BRANHAM, M.D., President
F. CARUTHERS, M.D., Vice President
J. WILLIAM FUNCK, M.D., Treasurer
J. C. LINTHICUM, LL.B., Counsellor
ALBERT T. CHAMBERS, M.D., Secretary

B. P. MUSE, M.D.
C. URBAN SMITH, M.D.
WM. S. SMITH, M.D.
PEARCE KINTZING, M.D.
A. D. MC CONACHIE, D.D.S., M.D.

OFFICERS OF THE FACULTY

A. D. MC CONACHIE, D.D.S., M.D., President
J. WM. FUNCK, M.D., Vice-President
WM. S. SMITH, M.D., Dean

BOARD OF DIRECTORS OF THE FRANKLIN SQUARE HOSPITAL

J. H. BRANHAM, M.D., President
J. WM. FUNCK, M.D., Vice-President
W. S. SMITH, M.D., Secretary-Treasurer
C. URBAN SMITH, M.D.
PEARCE KINTZING, M.D.

FRED. CARUTHERS, M.D.
B. P. MUSE, M.D.
A. D. MC CONACHIE, D.D.S., M.D.
ALBERT T. CHAMBERS, M.D.
HON. J. CHAS. LINTHICUM

SESSION OF 1911-1912

Same as that of 1910-11, with the following exceptions:

Drs. Reid, Stubbs, Beach, vonSchultz, Levy and Hill were no longer on the Faculty. Dr. Allen C. Beetham became associate professor of histology and associate in clinical obstetrics. Dr. F. N. Tannar taught medical jurisprudence and diseases of children. Dr. Arthur G. Barrett was clinical professor of surgery, George H. Stuart, Ph.G., associate professor of pharmacy, Dr. J. P. Strong associate in gynecology. Dr. Glann became lecturer in osteology, Leonard E. Beach, M.D., lecturer on minor surgery and bandaging, and Dr. Cox became demonstrator in anatomy, his assistants being Charles W. Hoffman, M.D., G. J. France, M.D., and Morris Wirtshafter, M.D.

The hospital staffs were as follows:

FRANKLIN SQUARE HOSPITAL

Visiting Staff

SURGEONS

JOS. H. BRANHAM, M.D.
ALBERT T. CHAMBERS, M.D.
HOWARD D. LEWIS, M.D.

ASSOCIATES

EGBERT L. MORTIMER, M.D.

EDWARD GREMPLER, M.D.

PHYSICIANS

PEARCE KINTZING, B.Sc., M.D.

IRVIN EBAUGH, M.D.

WM. S. LOVE, M.D.

GYNECOLOGISTS

WM. S. SMITH, M.D.

MAURICE LAZENBY, A.B., M.D.

ASSOCIATES

HENRY B. KOLB, M.D.

JAS. P. STRONG, M.D.

OPHTHALMOLOGIST

J. WM. FUNCK, M.D.

LARYNGOLOGIST AND OTOLOGIST

A. D. MC CONACHIE, D.D.S., M.D.

ASSOCIATES

JOSIAH S. BOWEN, M.D.

FRANK J. POWERS, M.D.

GASTRO-ENTEROLOGIST

WM. S. LOVE, M.D.

NEUROLOGIST

LEWIS H. GUNDRY, M.D.

GENITO-URINARY SURGEON

FRED. CARUTHERS, M.D.

PROCTOLOGIST

J. HARRY ULLRICH, Ph.G., M.D.

DERMATOLOGIST

H. C. HESS, M.D.

PEDIATRIST

F. N. TANNAR, A.B., LL.B., M.D.

PATHOLOGISTS

HENRY G. BRANHAM, M.D.

MARY F. VOEGLEIN, M.D., Ass't.

RADIOGRAPHER

JOHN T. J. HARNEY, ESQ.

RESIDENT STAFF

M. L. DILLON, M.D., Medical Superintendent
CHAS. E. SCHULTZ, M.D., Associate Resident Physician
F. O. BARRETT, M.D., Associate Resident Physician
W. B. WILSON, M.D., Associate Resident Physician
W. C. DEIXEL, M.D., Associate Resident Physician
MISS FLORENCE GARNER, Superintendent of Nurses
MISS NINA GRAHAM, Assistant Superintendent of Nurses
MISS SCHUMACHER, Business Manager

WEST END MATERNITE

PROF. B. P. MUSE, M.D.
Obstetrician-in-Chief

ASSOCIATES

CHAS. H. BEETEM, M.D.

ALLEN C. BEETHAM, M.D.

DISPENSARY STAFF

HENRY B. KOLB, M.D.
Dispensary Physician

CHIEFS OF CLINICS

EGBERT L. MORTIMER, M.D.
Operative Surgery
HENRY B. KOLB, M.D.
Diseases of Women

J. S. BOWEN, M.D.

FRANK J. POWERS, M.D.

Diseases of Ear, Nose and Throat
ALLEN C. BEETHAM, M.D.
Practice of Medicine
HENRY G. BRANHAM, M.D.
Surgery
E. A. DICKEY, M.D.
Diseases of the Eye

SESSION OF 1912-13

FACULTY

EMERITUS PROFESSORS

WILLIAM HERBERT PEARCE, M.D.
Diseases of Children and Clinical Medicine
C. URBAN SMITH, Ph.G., M.D.
Theory and Practice of Medicine and Gastro-Enterology

PROFESSORS

BERNARD PURCELL MUSE, M.D.
Obstetrics
J. WILLIAM FUNCK, M.D.
Diseases of the Eye
JOSEPH H. BRANHAM, M.D.
Principles and Practice of
Surgery and Abdominal Surgery
FRED. CARUTHERS, M.D.
Genito-Urinary Surgery
WILLIAM S. SMITH, M.D., Dean
Diseases of Women
LEWIS H. GUNDRY, M.D.
Diseases of the Nervous System
and of the Mind
A. D. MC CONACHIE, D.D.S., M.D.
Diseases of the Ear,
Nose and Throat
PEARCE KINTZING, B.Sc., M.D.
Theory and Practice of Medicine
and Physical Diagnosis
ALBERT T. CHAMBERS, M.D.
Operative and Clinical Surgery
GUSTAVUS CHARLES DOHME, A.B., M.D.
Chemistry and Associate in Medicine

WILLIAM S. LOVE, M.D.
Gastro-Enterology and Clinical Medicine
J. HARRY ULLRICH, Ph.G., M.D.
Physiology and Proctology
IRVIN EBAUGH, M.D.
Therapeutics and Clinical Medicine
HOWARD D. LEWIS, M.D.
Anatomy and Clinical Surgery
F. N. TANNAR, A.B., LL.B., M.D.
Diseases of Children and
Medical Jurisprudence
HENRY M. BAXLEY, Ph.G., M.D.
Hygiene and Dietetics
H. C. HESS, M.D.
Dermatology
HENRY W. KENNARD, M.D.
Orthopoedic Surgery
E. A. DICKEY, M.D.
Materia Medica
W. MILTON LEWIS, M.D.
Pathology and Bacteriology

CLINICAL PROFESSORS

MAURICE LAZENBY, A.B., M.D.
Gynecology

ARTHUR G. BARRETT, M.D.
Comparative Surgery

ASSOCIATE PROFESSORS

EDWARD GREMPLER, M.D.
Surgery
GEO. H. STUART, Ph.G.
Pharmacy

ALLEN C. BEETHAM, M.D.
Histology
H. LEE FRANKS, M.D.
Comparative Surgery

EGBERT L. MORTIMER, M.D.
Operative Surgery
JOSIAH S. BOWEN, M.D.
Diseases of Ear, Nose
and Throat
FRANK J. POWERS, M.D.
Diseases of Ear,
Nose and Throat
HENRY G. BRANHAM, M.D.
Physiological Chemistry and
Clinical Diagnosis

HENRY B. KOLB, M.D.
Gynecology
ALLEN C. BEETHAM, M.D.
Clinical Obstetrics
CHAS. H. BEETEM, M.D.
Obstetrics
J. P. STRONG, M.D.
Gynecology
G. H. MOHR, M.D.
Comparative Surgery

LECTURERS

J. P. STRONG, M.D.
Osteology
GEORGE W. JONES, M.D.

LEONARD E. BEACH, M.D.
Minor Surgery and Bandaging
GERMANUS J. FRANCE, M.D.

Clinical Medicine

DEMONSTRATORS

ANATOMY
WALTER A. COX, M.D.

ASSISTANT
CHARLES W. HOFFMAN, M.D.

PHYSIOLOGY
GEO W. HEMMETER, M.D.

OBSTETRICS
D. H. MOHR, M.D. – E. T. BOUCHELLE, M.D.

FRANKLIN SQUARE HOSPITAL

Visiting Staff

SURGEONS

JOS. H. BRANHAM, M.D.
ALBERT T. CHAMBERS, M.D.
HOWARD D. LEWIS, M.D.

ASSOCIATES

EGBERT L. MORTIMER, M.D.
EDWARD GREMPLER, M.D.
ARTHUR G. BARRETT, M.D.

PHYSICIANS

PIERCE KINTZING, B.Sc., M.D.
WM. S. LOVE, M.D.
IRVIN EBAUGH, M.D.

GYNECOLOGISTS

WM. S. SMITH, M.D.
MAURICE LAZENBY, A.B., M.D.

ASSOCIATES

HENRY B. KOLB, M.D.
JAS. P. STRONG, M.D.

OPHTHALMOLOGIST
J. WM. FUNCK, M.D.

LARYNGOLOGIST AND OTOLOGIST
A. D. MC CONACHIE, D.D.S., M.D.

ASSOCIATES

JAMES S. BOWEN, M.D.
FRANK J. POWERS, A.B., M.D.

GASTRO-ENTEROLOGIST
WM. S. LOVE, M.D.

NEUROLOGIST
LEWIS H. GUNDRY, M.D.

GENITO-URINARY SURGEON
FRED CARUTHERS, M.D.

PROCTOLOGIST
J. HARRY ULLRICH, Ph.G., M.D.

DERMATOLOGIST
H. C. HESS, M.D.

PEDIATRIST
F. N. TANNAR, A.B., LL.B., M.D.

PATHOLOGIST
HENRY G. BRANHAM, M.D.

RONTGENOLOGIST
JAMES B. HARNEY, ESQ.

RESIDENT STAFF
W. B. WILSON, Medical Superintendent
G. S. LAWALL, M.D., Associate Resident Physician
E. V. HUNT, M.D., Associate Resident Physician
C. M. KIMBLE, M.D., Associate Resident Physician
H. J. TANKIN, M.D., Associate Resident Physician
MRS. IRMA HOCHSCHILD, Superintendent of Nurses
W. D. WEAVER, Business Manager

WEST END MATERNITE
PROF. B. P. MUSE, M.D.
Obstetrician-in-Chief

ASSOCIATES
CHAS. H. BEETEM, M.D.
D. H. MOHR, M.D.
ALLEN C. BEETHAM, M.D.
E. T. BOUCHELLE, M.D.

DISPENSARY STAFF
HENRY B. KOLB, M.D.
Dispensary Physician

CHIEFS OF CLINICS
EGBERT L. MORTIMER, M.D.
Operative Surgery
HENRY B. KOLB, M.D.
Diseases of Women
J. S. BOWEN, M.D.
FRANK J. POWERS, M.D.
Diseases of Ear, Nose and Throat
ALLEN C. BEETHAM, M.D.
Practice of Medicine
HENRY G. BRANHAM, M.D.
Surgery
E. A. DICKEY, M.D.
Diseases of the Eye
GERMANUS J. FRANCE, M.D.
Gastro-Enterology and Diseases of Children

III (B) ALPHABETIZED LIST OF MEMBERS OF THE FACULTY

(For Faculty grouped by year, see previous pages.)

The names of the members of the hospital staff do not appear in this alphabetical list.

Baker, James H., D.D.S., M.D.
Barnet, Joel J., Ph.G.
Barrett, Arthur G., M.D.
Baskin, Eldridge, D.D.S., M.D.
Baxley, Haughton, M.D.
Baxley, Henry M., Ph.G., M.D.
Beach, Leonard E., M.D.
Beetham, Allen C., M.D.
Beetem, Charles H., Ph.G., M.D.
Bell, W. K.
Bouchelle, E. T., M.D.
Bowen, Josiah S., M.D.
Branham, Henry G., M.D.
Branham, Joseph H., M.D.
Branin, Charles T. (N.), M.D.
Brayshaw, Thomas H., M.D.
Bubert, Charles H., M.D.
Bunting, George A., A.M., Ph.G.
Burkhalter, J. W., A.B., M.D.
Caruthers, Frederick, M.D.
Chambers, Albert T., M.D.
Cox, Walter A., M.D.
Craig, P. Eugene, M.D.
Davis, Charles R., M.D.
Davis, S. Griffith, M.D.
Deetjen, Christian, M.D.
Dickey, E. A., M.D.
Dohme, Gustavus Charles, A.B., M.D.
Duff, James A., M.D.
Ebaugh, Irvin, M.D.
Engel, Paul
Erkenbrack, C. P., M.D.
Evans, Gilman P., M.D.
Frames, W. Wayland, Ph.D., M.D.
France, Germanus J., M.D.
Franks, H. Lee, M.D.
Funck, J. William, M.D.
Glann, R. V., M.D.
Goff, Josiah J., M.D.
Grempler, Edward, M.D.
Gross, Harry, M.D.
Gundry, Lewis H., M.D.
Hachtel, F. W., M.D.
Hancock, Frank A., A.B.
Harley, Charles F., A.M., LL.B.
Hemmeter, George W., M.D.
Hess, H. C., M.D.
Hill, H. P., A.B., Ph.G., M.D.
Hodgdon, A. L., M.D.
Hoechst, H. B., M.D.
Hoffman, Charles W., M.D.
Hudson, Charles H., Phar.D.
Hutchins, E. H., A.B., M.D.
Jones, George W., M.D.
Jones, Howard W., M.D.
Kennard, Henry W., M.D.
Kintzing, Pearce, B.Sc., M.D.
Knorr, B. A., M.D.
Kolb, Henry B., M.D.
Lazenby, Maurice, A.B., M.D.
Lehnert, E. C.
Leitch, J. W., M.D.
Levy, Alfred L., M.D.
Lewis, Howard D., M.D.
Lewis, W. Milton, M.D.
Linthicum, G. Milton, A.B., M.D.
Linthicum, J. Charles, LL.B., M.D.
Love, William S., M.D.
McConachie, A.D., M.D., D.D.S.
McKee, Alexander, A.B., M.D.
McNe(a,e)r, Richard, M.D.
Meyer, Charles L., Ph.G.
Mohr, D. (G). H., M.D.
Mortimer, Egbert L., M.D.
Munoz, Edmund A., Ph.G., M.D.
Muse, Bernard Purcell, M.D.
O'Donnell, Thomas J., M.D.
Palmer, Harry
Parr, Jacob S., Ph.G.
Pearce, Wilbur M., A.M., M.D.
Pearce, William Herbert, M.D.
Powers, Frank J., M.D.
Quandt, Ernest E., Ph.G.
Reid, E. Miller, M.D.
Russell, Elijah J., M.D.
Scholl, George B., A.B., M.D.
Schwatka, J. B., M.D.
Selby, J. Gilbert, M.D.
Sheppe, Joseph Luther, A.B., M.D.
Smink, A. C., M.D.
Smith, Alan W., M.D.
Smith, C. Urban, A.B., Ph.G., M.D.
Smith, O. C., Ph.G.
Smith, William S., M.D.
Strong, J. P., M.D.
Stuart, George H., Ph.G.
Stubbs, Wilbur P., M.D.
Stumberg, B. K., A.B., M.D.
Talbott, Thomas J., M.D.
Tannar, F. N., M.D.
Tarr, R. F.
Ullrich, J. Harry, Ph.G., M.D.
Vermillion, J. R.
vonSchultz, A. T., M.Sc., M.D.
Wilson, H. A., D.D.S.
Wirtshafter, Morris, M.D.
Yost, W. McLean, M.D.

IV. TEXTBOOKS USED

1898

ANATOMY – Gray, Holden.
SURGERY – Park.
CHEMISTRY – Simon.
OBSTETRICS – Lusk, American Textbook; Winckel, Galabin.
PRINCIPLES AND PRACTICE OF MEDICINES – Tyson, Woods and Fitz.
MATERIA MEDICA AND THERAPEUTICS – Bartholow, Hare.
PHYSIOLOGY – Stewart's Manual of Physiology, Foster.
DISEASES OF WOMEN –
DISEASES OF CHILDREN – Holt.
DISEASES OF THE EYE – Noyes, Swanzy, Nettleship, Fick.
DISEASES OF THE EAR – Barr, Bishop, Deuch.
DISEASES OF THE NOSE, THROAT AND CHEST – Bishop, Bosworth.
PATHOLOGY – Ziegler's.
MEDICAL JURISPRUDENCE – Taylor, Clark, Bell.
HYGIENE – Wilson's Hygiene and Sanitary Science, Parkes' Practical Hygiene.
MEDICAL DICTIONARY – Gould, 3rd edition; Dunglison.
WORKS ON SPECIAL SUBJECTS – Keyes' on Genito-Urinary Diseases, Duhring's Skin Diseases, Simon's Clinical Diagnosis, Physical Diagnosis, Lyson, Page, DaCosta, Surgery of Rectum and Pelvis, Kelsey.

1899

ANATOMY – Gray, Holden.
BACTERIOLOGY – McFarland, Abbott.
CHEMISTRY – Simon, Fownes, Atfield.
CHILDREN – Holt.
DERMATOLOGY – Shoemaker, Piffard, Duhring.
DICTIONARY – Gould, latest edition; Dunglison.
EAR – Bacon and Blake, Dench.
EYE – Noyes, Nettleship, Swanzy.
GYNECOLOGY – Penrose, Garrigues, Thomas and Munde, Dudley.
HISTOLOGY – Schafer.
HYGIENE – Wilson, Parkes.
JURISPRUDENCE – Taylor, Clark Bell's Edition.
MATERIA MEDICA AND THERAPEUTICS – Culbreth, Bartholow, Wood.
NERVOUS SYSTEM AND MIND – Gray, Dana, Mills, Hammond, Chapin.
NOSE, THROAT AND CHEST – Bishop, Bosworth.
OBSTETRICS – Hirst, Playfair, Winckel, Grandin and Jarman, American Textbook.
PATHOLOGY – Green, Zeigler, Stengel.
PHYSICAL DIAGNOSIS – Tyson, Page, DaCosta.
PHYSIOLOGY – Stewart's Manual, Kirke, American Textbook.
PRINCIPLES AND PRACTICE OF MEDICINE – Tyson, Woods and Fitz, Osler.
SURGERY – Park, DaCosta.
SURGERY OF RECTUM – Gantt, Kelsey.
WORKS ON SPECIAL SUBJECTS – Keyes on Genito-Urinary Diseases; Simons' Clinical Diagnosis.

1900 – Same as in 1899, with the following exceptions:

BACTERIOLOGY – Novy added.
EYE – Jackson added.
MATERIA MEDICA – Wood replaced by Hare.
NERVOUS SYSTEM AND MIND – Hammond replaced by Potts and Gallandet.
PHYSIOLOGY – (1st year), Collins and Rockwell. (2nd year), Stewart's Manual, Kirke, Foster, American Textbook.
PRINCIPLES AND PRACTICE OF MEDICINE – Anders abandoned.

1901

ANATOMY – Gray, Morris, Holden.
BACTERIOLOGY – McFarland, Novy, Abbott.
CHEMISTRY – Simon, Fownes, Atfield.
CHILDREN – Holt.
DERMATOLOGY – Shoemaker, Piffard, Duhring.
DICTIONARY – Gould, latest edition; Dunglison.

EAR – Bacon and Blake, Dench.
EYE – Nettleship, Swanzy, Jackson.
GENITO-URINARY DISEASES – Taylor, Lydston, Sturgis and Cabot.
GYNECOLOGY – Penrose, Garrigues, Byford, Dudley.
HISTOLOGY – Schafer.
HYGIENE – Wilson, Parkes.
JURISPRUDENCE – Taylor, Clark Bell's Edition.
MATERIA MEDICA AND THERAPEUTICS – Wood's Therapeutics; Cushing's Pharmacology and Therapeutics; Culbreth's Materia; Hare's Therapeutics.
NERVOUS SYSTEM AND MIND – Gray, Dana, Mills, Potts and Galludet, Chapin.
NOSE AND THROAT – Kyle, Coakley, Bishop.
OBSTETRICS – Hirst, Playfair, Schaeffer, Grandin and Jarman, American Text Book.
PATHOLOGY – Green, Zeigler, Stengel.
PHYSICAL DIAGNOSIS – Tyson, Musser.
PHYSIOLOGY – (1st year), Collins and Rockwell. (2nd year), Stewart's Manual, Kirke, Foster, American Text Book.
PRINCIPLES AND PRACTICE OF MEDICINE – Anders, Tyson, Woods and Fitz, Osler.
SURGERY – Park, Senn.
SURGERY OF RECTUM – Gantt, Kelsey.
WORKS ON SPECIAL SUBJECTS – Jennings' Color Vision and Color Blindness; Simons' Clinical Diagnosis.

1902 – Same as in 1901, with the following exceptions:
EAR – Gradle added.
GYNECOLOGY – Davenport added.
JURISPRUDENCE – Reese replaced Taylor, Clark Bell's edition.
MATERIA MEDICA AND THERAPEUTICS – All texts earlier used replaced by Cushny's Pharmacology; Sollman's Pharmacology.
NOSE AND THROAT – Gradle added.
OBSTETRICS – Hirst, Grandin and Jarman abandoned. Jewett, Dorland added.
OPERATIVE SURGERY – Zukenkahlin, Whartona.

1903
ANATOMY – Gray, Morris, Holden.
BACTERIOLOGY – McFarland, Novy, Abbott.
CHEMISTRY – Simon, Fownes, Atfield.
CHILDREN – Holt, Koplik, Williams, Rotch.
DERMATOLOGY – Shoemaker, Jackson.
DICTIONARY – Gould, latest edition; Dunglison.
EAR – Bacon and Blake, Dench, Burnett.
EYE – Nettleship, Swanzy, Jackson.
GENITO-URINARY DISEASES – Taylor, Lydston, Sturgis and Cabot.
GYNECOLOGY – Penrose, Davenport, Garrigues, Byford, Dudley.
HISTOLOGY – Schafer.
HYGIENE – Wilson, Parkes.
JURISPRUDENCE – Reese's Medical Jurisprudence.
MATERIA MEDICA AND THERAPEUTICS – Cushny's Pharmacology; Sollman's Pharmacology; Butler.
NERVOUS SYSTEM AND MIND – Dana, Oppenheim, Church & Peterson, Berkley.
NOSE AND THROAT – Grayson, Coakley, Knight, Ingals & Newcomb.
OBSTETRICS – Hirst, Jewett, Garrigues.
OPERATIVE SURGERY – Zukenkahlin, Whartona.
PATHOLOGY – Green, Ziegler, Stengel.
PHYSICAL DIAGNOSIS – Tyson, Musser.
PHYSIOLOGY (1st year) – Collins and Rockwell. (2nd year) – Stewart's Manual, Kirke, Foster, American Text Book.
PRINCIPLES AND PRACTICE OF MEDICINE – Anders, Tyson, Thompson, Osler.
SURGERY – Park, American Textbook Surgery, International Text Book of Surgery, DaCosta.
SURGERY OF RECTUM – Gantt, Kelsey.
WORKS ON SPECIAL SUBJECTS – Jennings' Color Vision and Color Blindness, Simon's Clinical Diagnosis.

1905 – Same as in 1903, with the following exceptions:
DERMATOLOGY – Stelwagen, Crocker added; Shoemaker abandoned.
DICTIONARY – Dorland added.

EYE – Ball, Hansell and Sweet, Jackson, May. (All texts earlier used were abandoned.)
OBSTETRICS – Garrigues replaced Edgar.
PHYSICAL DIAGNOSIS – Kintzing added.
PHYSIOLOGY – (2nd year) Ott replaced American Text Book.

1907
ANATOMY – Gray, Morris, Holden.
BACTERIOLOGY – McFarland, Movy, Abbott.
CHEMISTRY – Simon, Fownes, Atfield.
CHILDREN – Holt, Koplik, Williams, Rotch.
DERMATOLOGY – Stellwagen, Crocker, Jackson, Hyde & Montgomery, Hardaway, Mracek.
DICTIONARY – Gould (latest edition), Dunglison, Dorlands.
EAR – Bacon & Blake, Dench, Burnett.
EYE – Ball, Hansell & Sweet, Jackson, May.
GENITO-URINARY DISEASES – Taylor, Lydston, Sturgis & Cabot.
GYNECOLOGY – Ashton, Hirst, Penrose, Dudley.
HISTOLOGY – Schafer.
HYGIENE – Wilson, Parkes.
JURISPRUDENCE – Reese's Medical Jurisprudence.
MATERIA MEDICA AND THERAPEUTICS – Cushny's Pharmacology, Butler.
NERVOUS SYSTEM AND MIND – Dana, Oppenheim, Church & Peterson, Berkley.
NOSE AND THROAT – Grayson, Coakley, Knight, Ingals & Newcomb.
OBSTETRICS – Hirst, Edgar, Jewett.
OPERATIVE SURGERY – Bryant, McGrath, Kocher, McNeer.
PATHOLOGY – Green, Ziegler, Stengel.
PHARMACY – Caspari.
PHYSICAL DIAGNOSIS – Kintzing's Signs of Internal Disease, Sahli's Diagnostic Methods, Tyson, Musser.
PHYSIOLOGY (first year) – Collins & Rockwell. (Second year) – Stewart's Manual, Kirke, Foster, Ott.
PRINCIPLES AND PRACTICE OF MEDICINE – Anders, Tyson, Kintzing, Thompson, Osler.
SURGERY – Park, International Textbook of Surgery, American Textbook Surgery, Da-Costa and Vaughan.
SURGERY OF RECTUM – Gantt, Kelsey.
WORKS ON SPECIAL SUBJECTS – Jennings' Color Vision and Color Blindness, Simon's Clinical Diagnosis.

1908 – Same as in 1907, with the following exceptions:
EAR, NOSE, THROAT – Grayson, Bacon, Ballenger, Coakley, Dench.
HYGIENE – Kintzing's Long Life added.
NOSE AND THROAT – All texts on Nose and Throat used in 1907 abandoned.

1909 – Same as in 1908, with the following exceptions:
MATERIA MEDICA – Butler, Wood.
OBSTETRICS – Jewett replaced by Williams.
OPERATIVE SURGERY – McNeer abandoned.
THERAPEUTICS – Cushny, Sollman, Hare.

1910
ANATOMY – Gray, Morris, Holden.
BACTERIOLOGY – Muir and Ritchie, McFarland, Williams.
CHEMISTRY – Holland, Simon.
CHILDREN – Holt, Koplik, Williams, Rotch.
DERMATOLOGY – Stellwagen, Crocker, Jackson, Hyde & Montgomery, Hardaway, Mracek.
DICTIONARIES – Gould (latest edition). Dunglison, Dorland.
EAR, NOSE AND THROAT – Grayson, Bacon, Ballenger, Coakley, Dench.
EYE – Ball, Hansell & Sweet, Jackson, May, DeSchweinitz.
GENITO-URINARY DISEASES – Taylor, Lydston, Sturgis & Cabot.
GYNECOLOGY – Ashton, Hirst, Penrose, Dudley, Gilliam.
HISTOLOGY – Bohn, Davidhoff & Huber, Schafer.
HYGIENE – Rohe & Robins, Bergey.
JURISPRUDENCE – Draper, Reese.
MATERIA MEDICA – Butler, Culbreth.

MEDICAL DIAGNOSIS – Kintzing, DaCosta, Wilson.
NERVOUS SYSTEM AND MIND – Dana, Oppenheim, Church & Peterson, Berkley.
OBSTETRICS – Hirst, Edgar, Williams.
OPERATIVE SURGERY – Bryant, McGrath, Kocher.
PATHOLOGY – Ziegler, Delafield & Prudden, Stengel, McFarland, Durck, Cattell (Post Mortem), Mallory & Wright (Technique).
PHARMACY – Caspari.
PHYSICAL DIAGNOSIS – Kintzing's Signs of Internal Disease, Sahli's Diagnostic Methods, Tyson, Musser.
PHYSIOLOGY – Ott, Howell.
PRINCIPLES AND PRACTICE OF MEDICINE – Tyson, Kintzing, Osler.
SURGERY – Park, International Textbook of Surgery, American Textbook Surgery, DaCosta and Vaughan.
SURGERY OF RECTUM – Gantt, Kelsey.
THERAPEUTICS – Cushny, Sollman, Hare.
WORKS ON SPECIAL SUBJECTS – Simon's Clinical Diagnosis.

1911-1912
ANATOMY Piersol, Gray, Morris.
BACTERIOLOGY – Muir and Ritchie, McFarland, Williams.
CHEMISTRY – Holland, Simon.
CHILDREN – Ruhrah, Tulley, Koplik.
DERMATOLOGY – Jackson, Stellwagen, Shoemaker.
DICTIONARIES – Gould (latest edition), Dunglison, Dorland.
EAR, NOSE AND THROAT – Ballenger, Gleason, Barhill and Wales, Packard, Coakley.
EYE – Ball, Hansell & Sweet, Jackson, May, DeSchweinitz.
GASTRO-ENTEROLOGY – Kemp, Fulton's Translation of Connheim.
GENITO-URINARY DISEASES – Taylor, Lydston, Sturgis & Cabot.
GYNECOLOGY – Ashton, Hirst, Penrose, Dudley, Gilliam.
HISTOLOGY – Schafer, Ferguson and Piersoll.
HYGIENE – Rohe & Robins, Bergey.
JURISPRUDENCE – Draper, Reese.
MATERIA MEDICA – Butler, Sollman, Stevens.
MEDICAL DIAGNOSIS – Kintzing, DaCosta, Wilson.
NERVOUS SYSTEM AND MIND – Dana, Church & Peterson, Stoddard, Burr on Mental Diseases.
OBSTETRICS – Hirst, Edgar, Williams.
OPERATIVE SURGERY – Bryant, McGrath, Kocher.
PATHOLOGY – Ziegler, Delafield & Prudden, Stengel, McFarland, Durck, Cattell (Post Mortem), Mallory & Wright (Technique).
PHARMACY – Caspari.
PHYSICAL DIAGNOSIS – Kintzing's Signs of Internal Disease, Sahli's Diagnostic Methods, DaCosta, Kabot, Anders and Boston.
PHYSIOLOGY – Ott, Howell.
PRINCIPLES AND PRACTICE OF MEDICINE – Tyson, Osler, Anders.
SURGERY – Park, International Textbook of Surgery, American Textbook Surgery, DaCosta and Vaughan.
SURGERY OF RECTUM – Tuttle.
THERAPEUTICS – Cushny, Sollman, Hare.

PRIZES AND HONORS

1899

HONOR MEN

First Prize, Gold Medal . . . . Jno. T. Burkhalter, A.B.
Second Prize, Gold Medal . . . . Irvin Hardy
Third Prize, Gold Medal . . . . J. Will. Palmer, A.B.
Haughton Baxley Prize . . . . J. Will. Palmer, A.B.

HONORABLE MENTION

Heber Arden Ward   John James Reason   Alex. McKee
Jno. T. Burkhalter, A.B., M.D. – Valedictorian

1900

HONOR MEN

First College Prize .... Bernhardt Kurt Stumberg
Second College Prize .... Louis Broter
Third College Prize .... William Knox Bell
Gynecological Prize .... Louis Broter
Physical Diagnosis Prize .... Charles H. Beetem

ENTITLED TO HONORABLE MENTION

S. J. Herman
Chas. L. Boyers
A. A. MacDonald
H. B. Hoechst
H. W. Palmer
J. C. Rudolph
P. B. Hanna
Nicholas Lowrey

1901

HONOR MEN

First College Prize .... E. W. Parkins
Second College Prize .... Jas. W. Barton
Third College Prize .... Paul Engle
Smith Gynecological Prize .... Alex. Eugene Wrensch
Gross Surgical Prize .... Victor Hugo Dye

ENTITLED TO HONORABLE MENTION

Clarence P. Erkenbrack
Wm. Henry Jordan
Alex. E. Wrensch
Victor Hugo Dye

1902

HONOR MEN

First College Prize .... E. F. Peters
Second College Prize .... J. M. Graham
Third College Prize .... J. H. Cahoon
Smith Gynecological Prize .... E. F. Peters
Gross Surgical Prize .... J. M. Graham
Muse Obstetrical Prize .... Sherwood Dix

ENTITLED TO HONORABLE MENTION

A. B. Russell, M.D. D. Q. Will T. L. Young

1903

HONOR MEN

First College Prize .... Walter D. Bullington
Second College Prize .... Harry T. Hopewell
Third College Prize .... Robert W. Shermantine
Willard C. Haynes
W. S. Smith Gynecological Prize .... Walter D. Bullington
Robert W. Shermantine
Muse Obstetrical Prize .... Edwin L. Naret
Gross Surgical Prize .... O. H. McNemar

ENTITLED TO HONORABLE MENTION

H. C. Johnson
B. E. Calhoun
E. Long
E. C. J. Miller
E. D. Towle
J. C. Cunningham
E. L. Naret
J. C. Hodges

1904

First College Prize .... Frank W. Hachtel
Second College Prize .... George W. Shriver
Prof. W. S. Smith Gynecological Prize .... J. A. Baker
Prof. B. A. Muse Obstetrical Prize .... J. H. Russell
Prof. Harry Gross Surgical Prize .... M. Abi Massoud
O. O. Eackle

ENTITLED TO HONORABLE MENTION

J. A. Baker
R. V. Glann
O. S. Hare
M. Abi Massoud
J. H. Russell
J. A. Gilmer
F. F. Farnsworth
J. A. Rusmisell
E. E. Jones
Clarence Drew

1910
Gold Medal . . . . Joseph L. McLaughlin

HONORABLE MENTION

Edward Eli Sollers
Omer Victor Brooks
Edward Herman Meyer
Leslie Clyde Burton
Joseph Edward Clagett

1913
Gold Medal . . . . Arthur Lee Hichew

V. LIST OF MATRICULATES AND GRADUATES of the MARYLAND MEDICAL COLLEGE OF BALTIMORE

The letters M.D. indicate that the degree of Doctor of Medicine was conferred by this school in the year stated immediately following the degree.

The absence of M.D. after a name means that available records show only that the person named was a matriculate in the year or years given.

Parentheses around M.D., i.e., (M.D.) mean that neither the date nor the school which conferred the degree is evident from the available records alone.

Parentheses around a letter, name or State indicate that the existing records show variations.

Preceptors' names and honorary degrees are given, when available.

The names of graduates of the year 1906 are missing. (The names of graduates of the year 1913 were located in the Baltimore Sun.)

Most of the Announcements from which the data for this study are drawn are among the holdings of the College of Physicians of Philadelphia, The New York Academy of Medicine, The National Library of Medicine, The Health Sciences Library of the University of Maryland, The Welch Medical Library of Johns Hopkins University and the Historical Library of the School of Medicine of Yale University.

Abbott, William Walter, M.D., '05
Maryland, (Pennsylvania)
Dr. Joseph H. Abbott
Abernathy, George W., '03
West Virginia
Dr. Z. T. Kalbaugh
Abramovitz, Morris, '03, '04
Russia
Dr. Joseph H. Scharf and
Professor C. U. Smith
Abramson, Max J., '06, '07
New York
Dr. C. A. Mitchell
Abshire, David, '10, '11
West Virginia
Adams, Edward Clarkson Leverett, M.D., '03
South Carolina
Maryland Medical College
Adams, George Brinton McClellan, M.D., '99
New Jersey
Dr. Eugene Way
Adams, Samuel H., M.D., '12
Pennsylvania
Adler, Henry I., M.D., '04
Russia
Dr. Joseph H. Scharf
Adler, Max, '11
Connecticut
Aguilar, Vespaciano B., '09
Central America
Aimar, (Mrs.) L. A., '10, '11
South Carolina
Albertson, Charles K., (R.), M.D., '07
Pennsylvania
Maryland Medical College

Aldrich, Lewis C., M.D., '03
New Hampshire
Dr. George Morrison
Alexander, James W., '08
Georgia
Alleigro, A., '11
Cuba
Allen, Henry Willard, '06
Massachusetts
Dr. F. B. Baker
Allen, Ira A. B., M.D., '05
Delaware
Dr. Charles H. Carter
Allen, Myron L., '01
Maine
Maryland Medical College
Allen, William Gadson, M.D., '05
Georgia
Dr. C. D. McRae
Anders, McTyeire Gallant, M.D., '01
North Carolina
Dr. George Doughton
Anderson, Charles R., '04
Mississippi
Maryland Medical College
Angle, Walter L., M.D., '03
Pennsylvania
Archer, L. S., M.D., '08
Georgia
Dr. H. E. Archer
Arevelo, Gilberto, '09, '10, '11
Central America
Armistead, Ernest King, M.D., '11
Alabama
Armistead, J. R., M.D., '08
Mississippi (Alabama)
Dr. L. L. Armistead
Arnold, Clement M., M.D., '12
Ohio
Ashley, F. E., '00
Maryland
Professor Schwatka
Ashmann, Jesse, '06
Massachusetts
Maryland Medical College
Bailard, C. C., '03
West Virginia
Dr. W. E. Cook
Bailey, Charles W., (Ph.G.), '98
Maryland
Professor Linthicum
Bailey, C. B., '07
West Virginia
Dr. J. E. Browning
Baker, James A., M.D., '04
West Virginia
Dr. O. B. Campbell
Baker, James H., (D.D.S.), M.D., '00
North Carolina
Maryland Medical College
Baker, Lawrence A., M.D., '05
West Virginia
Dr. Paul Engle
Baldwin, Lyles, '03
Maryland
Professor Muse
Ball, Ernest Heber, M.D., '09
Kentucky (West Virginia)
Dr. Thomas J. Casto
Ballard, Clem Campbell, M.D., '05
West Virginia
Dr. W. E. Cook
Barber, Oscar T., '04
New York
Maryland Medical College
Barenburg, Jacob W., M.D., '12
Pennsylvania
Barrett, Francis Oliver, (Ph.G.), M.D., '11
Maryland
Dr. J. H. Branham
Barrett, James Aloysius, M.D., '10
Connecticut
Barrett, William J., (Ph.G.), M.D., '04
New York
Dr. T. B. Ackerly
Barsamion, H., '00
Armenia
Professor Muse
Barton, Blaine Berthold, M.D., '05
Maryland
Dr. H. J. Hahn
Barton, James Warren, M.D., '01
Canada
Professor Muse
Baskin, Eldridge
(D.D.S.), M.D., '03, '03
Baylin, Morris J., M.D., '09
Maryland
Bays, A. E., '10, '11
West Virginia
Beach, Leonard Edward, M.D., '99
New York
Professor Muse
Bean, Frederick Warren, M.D., '00
New Hampshire
Dr. John C. Tanner
Beauparlant, Joseph David, M.D., '04
Massachusetts
Beckett, C. E., '98
Maryland
Professor Muse
Beckley, G. Herbert (Ph.G.), M.D., '00, '00
Maryland
Professor Schwatka
Beckner, William Forrest, M.D., '11
West Virginia
Beckner, M. F., '07
West Virginia
Dr. D. M. Ryan
Bedingfield, Walter Eli, M.D., '04
Georgia
Beeman, J. Mc., '98
North Carolina
Dr. P. T. Beeman
Beer, Oscar Burnham, M.D., '05
West Virginia
Maryland Medical College
Beetem, Charles H., (Ph.G.), M.D., '00
Maryland
Professor Haughton Baxley

Beetham, Allen Covert, M.D., '09
Maryland
Professor Frederick Caruthers
Bell, A. Marvin, (D.D.S.), M.D., '05
Canada
Maryland Medical College
Bell, William Knox, M.D., '00
Arkansas
Professor Caruthers
Bendick, John J., '10, '11
Pennsylvania
Benj(k)amin(e), Price M. (W.), '07, '08, '09
Maryland
Dr. H. Everhart
Benoit, J. S., '02
Massachusetts
Father Prevost and Dr. Trudeau
Benoit, S. J., '03
Massachusetts
Dr. Trudeau
Benson, Charles Edgar, M.D., '04
Maryland
Professor G. M. Linthicum
Bereston, Arthur (D.D.S.), '10, '11
Maryland
Berube, David T., M.D., '12
New Hampshire
Bevins, Oscar Emory, M.D., '09
Virginia
Bickle, H. L., (Ph.G.), '09
New Jersey
Bierstein A., '08
Russia
Bippus, Edward Samuel, '04
Ohio
Dr. J. A. Dixon
Bird, Benjamin W., M.D., '04
West Virginia
Dr. H. Thorton
Bird, John Henry, M.D., '05
West Virginia
Dr. J. R. Vermillion
Bishop, James W., M.D., '05
Florida
Dr. J. C. Bishop
Blades, George Clinton,
(Ph.G.), M.D., '00 Maryland
Blake, Grover Cleveland, '06
West Virginia
Dr. A. A. Wingrove
Blodgett, John Moody, '06
New Hampshire
Dr. C. L. Aldrich
Bloom, Arthur, '03
New York
Bockman, J., '00
Maryland
Maryland Medical College
Boenig, George C., '09
New Jersey
Boivin, Omer F., M.D., '12
Massachusetts
Bond, J. E., '03
Maryland
Professor Schwatka
Bookstaber, Harry, M.D., '07
New York
Maryland Medical College
Bordeaux, George W., B.S., M.D., '04
Georgia
Bordenski, Nathen, '04
Maryland
Dr. A. George Hubbard
Born, Frank J., (A.M.), M.D., '04
Maryland
Dr. B. K. Stumberg
Bortner, Milner, M.D., '09
Maryland
Dr. N. I. Parr
Bouchelle, Elizabeth Taylor, M.D., '12
Maryland
Bowers, Stewart Cole, M.D., '09
Maryland
Dr. J. B. Schwatka
Bowers, William, '06
Massachusetts
Maryland Medical College
Boyers, Charles Lesley, M.D., '00, '00
West Virginia
Dr. F. C. Boyers
Boyers, J. W., '08, '09
West Virginia
Boyers, Lee Bernard, M.D., '00
West Virginia
Boyers, L. L., '08
West Virginia
Boylan, Lawrence B., M.D., '13
New Jersey
Bradford, Lester Belmont, M.D., '05
New Hampshire
Maryland Medical College
Bradley, J. L., '11
New Jersey
Branham, Henry Gwynn, M.D., '05
Maryland
Professor J. H. Branham
Braswell, Benjamin Darius, B.S., M.D., '04
Georgia
Breeden, Thomas Evans, '06
Maryland
Professor J. B. Schwatka
Brickman, A. O., (Ph.G.), '98
Maryland
Professor Schwatka
Brister, S., '98
Maryland
Professor Muse
Brooks, Donald Dickinson, M.D., '10
Pennsylvania
Brooks, Omer Victor, M.D., '10
Pennsylvania
Dr. A. J. Colbourn
Broter, Louis, M.D., '00
New York

Brown, Charles F., M.D., '12
New Hampshire
Brown, C. Milton, M.D., '02
West Virginia
Brown, Hugh, '08, '09, '10, '11
Maryland
Brown, John Franklin
(D.D.S.), M.D., '03, '03
Maryland
Dr. J. C. Brown
Brown, V. L., '01
Georgia
Dr. H. M. Branham
Bruce, Francis Marion, M.D., '04
Georgia
Brunault, Oliver, '10 (see Bruneau)
Rhode Island
Bruneau, Olivier A., M.D., '12
Rhode Island
Brunier, G. F., (Ph.G.), M.D., '03, '03
Maryland
Dr. Joseph Claggett
Brunner, C. C., '04
Alabama
Maryland Medical College
Bryant, Roscoe Floyd, M.D., '11
North Carolina
Buchannan, D. J., '10, '11
Virginia
Buck, Floyd, '08
West Virginia
Bull, Stephen W., M.D., '03, '03
West Virginia
Dr. N. W. Kidd
Bullington, Walter David, M.D., '03, '03
Georgia
Dr. H. A. Mobley
Bullock, Jesse B., '04
South Carolina
Maryland Medical College
Bunner, Rowe Randolph, M.D., '09
West Virginia
Dr. L. A. Kootz
Burch, Julius Caesar, M.D., '11
Georgia
Burgess, Muss Schmucker, M.D., '07
West Virginia
Maryland Medical College
Burke, William Joseph, M.D., '11
New Jersey
Burkhalter, John Thomas, (A.B.), M.D., '99
Georgia
Dr. M. R. Hall
Burleson, Emmett, M.D., '03, '03
Texas
Dr. J. M. Burleson
Burleson, Sidney J., M.D., '05
Texas
Maryland Medical College
Burns, J. R., '11
Pennsylvania
Burroughs, James Leonard, M.D., '03, '03
Mississippi
Dr. A. S. Kirk
Burton, Leslie Clyde, M.D., '10
Virginia
Burton, R. E., '10
Virginia
Bush, A. P., '10
West Virginia
Bush, S. W., '01
West Virginia
Buss, W. J., '11
New Jersey
Bustillo, Vincenti C., (A.B.), '09, '10
Cuba
Byrn, James Finley, '09, '10, '11
Tennessee
Cahoon, Joseph Henry,
(Ph.G.), M.D., '02, '02
New York
Dr. J. H. Marshall
Calhoun, Charles Edward, M.D., '03, '03
I. T.
Dr. W. B. Miller
Callahan, T. Edward, M.D., '04
New Hampshire
Maryland Medical College
Callahan, Timothy A., M.D., '99
Maryland
Dr. William S. Archel
Campiano, E., '11
Puerto Rico
Canon, Thomas C., M.D., '03, '03
Pennsylvania
Dr. D. J. Grace
Cannon, T. Harris, '98, '00
Maryland
Maryland Medical College
Dr. E. Deichmann
Caparros, Ricardo M., M.D., '13

Cardamone, Phillip J., M.D., '13

Carey, R. S., '00
Virginia
Professor Schwatka
Carleton, Benjamin Leo, M.D., '10
Virginia
Carper, James Calvin, '06
West Virginia
Dr. J. R. Hughart
Carson, William J., M.D., '13
Pennsylvania
Carter, Wade Hampton, M.D., '05
Virginia
Dr. W. D. Carter
Carter, Wade M., M.D., '04
Virginia
Casto, J. J., M.D., '02
West Virginia

Casto, Okey J., M.D., '02
West Virginia
Casto, T. J., (M.D.), '02
West Virginia
Maryland Medical College
Chaims, Edward, '98
Maryland
Dr. George S. Chaims
Champe, Nile G., M.D., '12
West Virginia
Chaney, George P., M.D., '13

Chaney, J. P., '11
Maryland
Chedel, Lewis Julian, M.D., '04
Georgia
Chester, Hyman, M.D., '00, '00
New York
Dr. H. Strayffer
Chester, Jacob W., '08, '09
New York
Chester, Samuel W., '09
New York
Choate, Alton J., M.D., '04
Massachusetts
Choquette, Hormidas, M.D., '04
Massachusetts
Dr. J. H. Choquette
Chramoy, David H., '04
New York
Maryland Medical College
Christian, George Franklin, M.D., '03, '03
West Virginia
Drs. S. A. Daniel and W. R. Jaeger
Cion, B. B., '04
West Virginia
Maryland Medical College
Clagett, Joseph Edward, M.D., '10
Virginia
Dr. W. S. Love
Clark, Frank G., '03
New Jersey
Dr. C. M. Gray
Clark, P. J., '07
New Jersey
Dr. E. J. Fitzpatrick
Clarke, William J., '03
Maryland
Professor Schwatka
Claxton, Edward Burton, M.D., '05
Georgia
Dr. C. R. Josey
Cobian, Joseph, '09
Puerto Rico
Coffey, J. B., (Ph.G.), '10, '11
Rhode Island
Coffey, M. J., '02
New Jersey
Dr. E. J. Dowell
Coffman, Lafayette, M.D., '05
Virginia
Dr. W. E. Farhney
Cohan, A., '07
New York
Dr. W. T. Owens
Cohen, Frank Israel, M.D., '10
Pennsylvania
Colborn, A. J., M.D., '02, '02
Pennsylvania
Maryland Medical College
Coleman, H. N., (B.Sc.), M.D., '00, '02
Alabama
Maryland Medical College
Dr. A. D. Coleman
Coll, V., M.D., '08
Puerto Rico
Dr. Cayetano Coll y Foste
Compton, J. W., '11
West Virginia
Conaway, B. F., M.D., '08
West Virginia
Conaway, Robert G., '08, '09, '10, '11
West Virginia
Cone, Rufus Lester, M.D., '04
Georgia
Conn, I. C., M.D., '04
Virginia
Connolly, Ira, '11
West Virginia
Connor, George J., M.D., '09
Massachusetts
Constantine, George, '10, '11
South America
Conti, Giacomo, M.D., '11
Sicily, Italy
Converse, Ralph Dent, M.D., '01, '01
New York
Maryland Medical College
Cook, Harry, '04
Maryland
Maryland Medical College
Cooper, J. L., '03
South Carolina
Dr. J. L. Culpepper
Copelan, I. C., '11
West Virginia
Corbett, H. W., '10, '11
South Carolina
Core, Amanda Raymond, (B.S.), M.D., '04
Pennsylvania
Cornish, P. D., '04, '06
Massachusetts
Maryland Medical College
Dr. E. H. Cornish
Costello, Edmund A., M.D., '12
Pennsylvania
Costello, William John, M.D., '11
Maryland
Cottrell, John L., M.D., '00 (Special, '01)
North Carolina
Dr. George Doughton
Cox, Robert Nathaniel, '10, '11
Virginia
Cox, Walter Abner, M.D., '03, '03
New Jersey
Dr. H. A. Keenan
Cox, Wilmer E., '04
Massachusetts
Dr. W. A. Cox

Coyne, Frank M., M.D., '07
Pennsylvania
Dr. W. S. Appel
Cranston, E. A., '02, '03
Maine
Drs. H. C. Todd and B. K. Stumberg
Crescioni, D. A., '11
Puerto Rico
Crossland, Harry Mark, M.D., '04
Massachusetts (Maine)
Dr. W. A. Bumps
Crowley, William J., M.D., '13

Crowley, W. H., '11
Pennsylvania
Crumrine, L. B., '11
Pennsylvania
Cubbage, Elizabeth, '11
Pennsylvania
Cue, Isaac G., '04
Cuba
Maryland Medical College
Culbertson, Walter Leon, M.D., '11
Pennsylvania
Cunniff, Robert J., M.D., '09
Pennsylvania
Cunningham, James Cluade, M.D., '03
West Virginia
Dr. George S. Laidley
Curran, J. M., M.D., '00, '00
Pennsylvania
Dr. T. M. Curran
Currinder, Alva Batton, '04, '06
Delaware
Dr. B. B. Peters
Dailey, J. Seward, '08
Maryland
Dailey, Robert W., '11
West Virginia
Daisey, Willard Orville, M.D., '11
Delaware
Dr. H. J. Hocker
Dalton, James T., M.D., '12
Canada
Darby, Francis Oliver, M.D., '05
Louisiana
Maryland Medical College
Darby, Virgil Lee, M.D., '05
Georgia
Maryland Medical College
Darlington, Emerson E., M.D., '00
Pennsylvania
Maryland Medical College
Darrah, Robert H., '03
Delaware
Dr. Luther Truax
David, F., '98
New York
Davis, Norman R., M.D., '13
Pennsylvania
Davis, Robert E., '10, '11
West Virginia
Dean, William Arthur, '04
New York
Dr. H. Gilbert
Deemer, Roscoe Paul, M.D., '07
Pennsylvania
Maryland Medical College
Deemer, William Roger, '06
Pennsylvania
Maryland Medical College
Deery, Joseph P., M.D., '13
Maryland
Dees, John Hilton, M.D., '03
Georgia
Dr. G. T. Gray
DeFord, Harry T., '03
Maryland
Dr. B. S. French
Deibel, Henry, '09
Maryland
Deixel, Walter C., M.D., '11
New Jersey
Delaney, Thomas B., M.D., '13
Massachusetts
DeLeonardis, James Vincent, M.D., '11
New Jersey
Demely, Louis Alvin, '09, '10, '11
Maryland
Dempsey, Walter Garland, M.D., '05
Mississippi
Dr. J. L. Burroughs
Denholtz, Emanuel, M.D., '12
New Jersey
Dent, John Allston, M.D., '04, '04
Maryland
Dr. Henry Richardson
Derdiger, Louis B., M.D., '09
New York
Dessen, Louis, M.D., '98

Dr. George S. Chaims
Devers, Neil J., M.D., '12
Pennsylvania
Devitt, Ellis K., M.D., '07
New York
Dr. F. W. Devitt
Devoti, Jill J., M.D., '05
Texas
Dr. T. P. Lloyd
Dey, Walter Pettus, M.D., '04
Alabama
Dichter, Charles L., M.D., '05
New York
Professor J. B. Schwatka
Dickey, Ezra A., M.D., '04, '05
Maryland (Pennsylvania)
Dr. A. Burrall
Dickinson, H. S., '07
Pennsylvania
Dr. J. Hearn
Dickman, Herman, M.D., '11
Pennsylvania
Diebel, Harry, L08
Maryland
Dietrich, W. A., '04
New Jersey
Professor J. B. Schwatka

Dillon, Marcus Dunsford, M.D., '08
West Virginia
Maryland Medical College
Diodati, Vinenzo Maria (A.B.), M.D., '11
Pennsylvania
Dix, Sherwood W., M.D., '02
Virginia
Dr. J. M. Dix and Professor Muse
Dixon, Charles Warren, M.D., '10
Pennsylvania
Dobbs, Robert J., '11
Pennsylvania
Doherty, James M., M.D., '00
Rhode Island
Dr. J. D. O'Doherty
Dolan, James H., '04
Massachusetts
Maryland Medical College
Donnolly, J. D., '10, '11
New Jersey
Doster, W. J., '04
South Carolina
Maryland Medical College
Dovey, Howard LeRoy, M.D., '11
Pennsylvania
Dowell, Elmer J., (Ph.G.), M.D., '00
New Jersey
Dr. J. G. L. Borgmyer
Drain, Sheppard G., '04
Maryland
Professor J. H. Branham
Drew, Clarence, M.D., '04
Georgia
Dr. J. F. Lunsford
Drummond, Augustus B., M.D., '99
Maine
Dr. H. A. King
DuBose, David O'Quinn, M.D., '09
South Carolina
Maryland Medical College
Duff, James A., M.D., '09
Maryland
Dr. W. A. Cox
Duvall, Eugene N., '03
Maryland
Dr. William H. Feddeman
Dye, Victor Hugo, M.D., '01
Ohio
Dr. H. G. Meek
Eakle, (Eackel) Oscar Otis, M.D., '04
West Virginia
Dr. L. A. Koontz
Ealy, David B., Jr., M.D., '12
Pennsylvania
Eaman, Howard Kemp, M.D., '10
New York
Eames, David Wendall, '06
Virginia
Professor J. B. Schwatka
Eames, M. H., '10, '11
Virginia
Easton, J. F., '09
West Virginia
Ebey, J. C., Ph.G., '11
Maryland
Edgett, Frank J., M.D., '12
New York
Edinger, J. W., '04
Pennsylvania
Maryland Medical College
Edwards, Henry Hicks, M.D., '03, '03
North Carolina
Dr. A. M. Edwards
Edwards, W. N., '04
Virginia
Maryland Medical College
Ehlers, Edmond A., M.D., '02, '02
New York
Dr. Philantha Harris
Ellen, John C., '10
South Carolina
Ellingwood, William A., '04
Maine
Dr. E. C. Newcomb
Elliott, H. A., '02
Maine
Dr. H. C. Taggart
Ellison, William A., M.D., '04
Georgia
Ellison, H. H., '04
West Virginia
Maryland Medical College
Engle, Paul, M.D., '01
West Virginia
Dr. A. B. Campbell
English, Eugene R., M.D., '12
West Virginia
Ephraim, Harry L., '01, '02
Russia
Maryland Medical College
Ephraim, Hyman S., M.D., '09
Maryland
Dr. L. H. Ephraim
Erkenbrack, Clarence Phillip, M.D., '01
New York
Professor Muse
Escanaverino, Gines P., M.D., '12
Cuba
Espin, Louis J. C., M.D., '99
Cuba
Professor Muse
Etchison, Carlton Neal, M.D., '08
Maryland
Dr. E. C. Etchison
Evans, William Burd, (A.B.), M.D., '02, '02
Pennsylvania
Dr. S. Solis Cohen
Everets, E. M., '11
West Virginia
Ewing, Charles Henry, M.D,, '07
Delaware
Dr. E. B. Bradford
Ewing, Samuel R., M.D., '07
Delaware
Dr. E. B. Bradford
Fadely, John Melvin, M.D., '05
West Virginia
Dr. E. J. Mossman
Fairchild, Solomon Lincoln, M.D., '10
Pennsylvania
Dr. J. M. Gemmill

Faircloth, (R.) G. Ransom, M.D., '09
North Carolina
Fargo, Bunnel, (Ph.G.), M.D., '13
Maryland
Dr. E. T. Morris
Farnsworth, Floyd F., M.D., '04
West Virginia
Farres, S., '08
Syria
Faulkner, William Henry, M.D., '05
Texas
Maryland Medical College
Fearn, John W., M.D., '11
New Jersey
Fellers, W. B., '09
Virginia
Fendler, David, '06
Maryland
Professor J. B. Schwatka
Fifield, Henry Eugene, M.D., '07
Maine
Dr. A. N. French
Fineman, Harry E., M.D., '11
Pennsylvania
Finnegan, John H., M.D., '12
Rhode Island
Fischer, H. F., M.D., '08
Pennsylvania
Dr. W. T. Hall
Fisher, Otto, '07, '08
Virginia (New Jersey)
Dr. H. J. Hopewell
Fisher, W. H., '02
Maryland
Dr. Paul Jones
Fitts, S. B., '03
Georgia
Dr. C. B. Walling
Fitts, Thomas Bayard, M.D., '04
South Carolina
Fitzgerald, Daniel D., '06, '07, '08, '09
Connecticut
Maryland Medical College
Fitzmaurice, E. Vincent, '07, '08, '10
New Jersey
Dr. G. J. Koch
Flamm, L. Francis (D.D.S.), M.D., '02, '02
Missouri
Dr. A. G. Hubbard
Fleger, Chester Arthur, M.D., '05
West Virginia
Dr. J. G. McCutchen
Flickinger, William, '09, '10, '11
Pennsylvania
Floyd, John L., M.D., '02
Delaware
Maryland Medical College
Foard, Frank O., '11
North Carolina
Font, Agapito C., '04, '06
Puerto Rico
Dr. A. C. Fox
Fooks, John W., '08, '09
Delaware

Ford, Edward Francis, M.D., '01, '01
Pennsylvania
Dr. S. R. Crothers
Ford, William Edwin, M.D., '09
West Virginia
Fortney, Clark S., M.D., '05
West Virginia
Drs. Fansler and McDowell
Foster, LeRoy E., M.D., '11
Indiana
Foster, R. A., '03
Texas
Forston, Keene R., M.D., '13

Fox, Arthur Samuel, M.D., '10
Pennsylvania
Fox, J. A., '02
West Virginia
Dr. J. F. Bigony
Fox, John (M.), William, M.D., '11
West Virginia
Dr. R. J. Hughes
France, Germanus J., (Ph.G.), M.D., '11
Maryland
Dr. F. Caruthers
Fraser, L. H., '00
Massachusetts
Dr. Parker
Freeman, (Miss.), Maysville, '11
Maryland
French, Bernard S., M.D., '02
New Hampshire
Professor Muse
Freund, E. M., '10, '11
New York
Fuller, Charles F. A., '09
New York
Funderburk, David H., M.D., '04
North Carolina
Furbee(l), Gilbert David, M.D., '05
West Virginia
Maryland Medical College
Gabbe(a)ert, Forrest, (B.S.), M.D., '03, '03
Kentucky
Dr. Calder Erhman
Gallemore, G. B., (D.O.), M.D., '02, '02
Missouri
Dr. J. M. Gallemore
Gannon, Charles H., M.D., '13
Rhode Island
Garces, Lorenzo, '11
Puerto Rico
Garcia, Esteban S., '06
Puerto Rico
Dr. I. Daussa
Garcia de la Torre, Felix, M.D., '03
Puerto Rico
Maryland Medical College
Garcia, Stephen S., '04
Cuba
Maryland Medical College
Gardner, Elliot, (A.B.), M.D., '00
Pennsylvania
Drs. Krecker and Archibald

Garrett, Richard H. L., M.D., '02, '02
Alabama
Dr. F. Shackelford
Gautier, Wilson I. (J.), M.D., '04
West Virginia
Dr. D. H. Thorton
Gayle, John Head, M.D., '05
Louisiana
Dr. E. E. Simpson
Gemmill, James R., '08, '09
Pennsylvania
Gemmill, John Michael, '04
Pennsylvania
Dr. G. G. Groff
Gemmill, William Porter, M.D., '09
Pennsylvania
Dr. John M. Gemmill
George, Leslie Handlin, M.D., '05
Massachusetts
Maryland Medical College
Gerstell, F. Shaw, M.D., '02, '02
West Virginia
Dr. G. L. Pierce
Gessler, Harry Horner, M.D., '05
Pennsylvania
Professor J. B. Schwatka
Gewin, William C., Jr., M.D., '02, '02
Alabama
Dr. W. C. Gewin
Giffin, Adolph Mauger, M.D., '03, '04
New York
Giganti, D., '11
Puerto Rico
Gilette, John M., (M.D.), '09
New York
Gillette, L. L., (M.D.), '09
New York
Gilmer, J. Axley, M.D., '04
Virginia
Dr. G. B. Mabe
Gimpel, Arthur P., (Ph.G.), M.D., '04
Maryland
Dr. A. George Hubbard
Giro, Juan B., (A.B.), '09, '10
Cuba
Giro, Luis, '11
Cuba
Gladstone, Charles F., M.D., '13

Glann, Raymond Vernon, M.D., '04
New York
Dr. A. J. Brown
Glennan, Kenneth R., M.D., '12
Maryland
Godb(e)y, John Q., '09, '10
West Virginia
Godbey, Martin Van Buren, M.D., '05
West Virginia
Dr. A. J. Hatfield
Godfrey, M. A., '04
Massachusetts
Maryland Medical College
Goldberg, Harry, M.D., '07
Maryland
Dr. A. George Hubbard
Goldsmith, Chester L., (Ph.G.), M.D., '12
Massachusetts
Dr. R. M. White
Goldstein, Jacob S., M.D., '12
Pennsylvania
Goldstein, M., (L.), (W.), '09, '10
New Jersey
Goodall, Edwin B., M.D., '05
New Hampshire
Dr. E. G. Annable
Grace, Benjamin L., M.D., '12
Maryland
Gracey, Charles S., M.D., '12
Pennsylvania
Grady, J. Joseph, M.D., '10
New York
Graham, J. M., M.D., '02, '02
Virginia
Dr. J. M. Harman
Graham, Rufus Elliot, M.D., '04
Georgia
Graham, Samuel George, M.D., '10
Alabama
Gramling, Arthur Burt, M.D., '04
Alabama
Grant, Hugh D., M.D., '04
Massachusetts
Gray, Charles M., M.D., '02, '02
New Jersey
Dr. J. C. Applegate
Gray, Courtland P., M.D., '04
Louisiana
Dr. W. W. Thawer
Gray, H. C., '07, '09
West Virginia
Gray, Paris Leonard, M.D., '11
West Virginia
Gregory, Guerney A., M.D., '09
Pennsylvania
Greisser, W. R., '08, '09, '10
New York
Gridley, A. A., '03
Massachusetts
Gridley, L. A., '02, '03
Massachusetts
Dr. A. C. Cobb
Grier, Joseph T., '11
Pennsylvania
Grier, M. F., '11
Pennsylvania
Griffin, Adolph M., '03
New York
Dr. T. O. Burleson
Griffiths, Llewellyn Derwin, M.D., '10
Pennsylvania
Grisinger, George Floyd, '06
West Virginia
Dr. A. A. Wingrove
Grobman, L. E., '07
New Jersey
Groetch, George William,
(Ph.G.), M.D., '03, '03
Louisiana
Dr. J. M. Soniat

Gross, Samuel, M.D., '12
Pennsylvania
Grunberg, Abraham, (D.D.S.), '01
Maryland
Maryland Medical College
Gum, Andrew Thompson, M.D., '07
Delaware
Dr. F. M. Gum
Gurley, Lycurgus Martin, M.D., '05
Maryland
Maryland Medical College
Gwynn, Matthew K., '04
Maryland
Professor Joseph H. Branham
Hachtel, Frank W., M.D., '04, '04
Maryland
Professor Joseph H. Branham
Hackney, Urban Philo, M.D., '05
Texas
Maryland Medical College
Haddock, Horace P., '04, '06
Maryland
Dr. E. L. Mortimer
Haddock, P. P., '07
Maryland
Dr. E. R. Mortiner
Haefner, Charles Augustus, (Ph.G.), M.D., '03, '03
Ohio
Dr. H. L. Root
Haegele, Edward A., M.D., '13

Haffner, A. F., '09, '10
Maryland
Hahn, Joseph G., '03
Georgia
Hairston, William George, M.D., '04
Alabama
Hale, Stephen F., (Ph.G.), M.D., '04
Alabama
Haley, Mark Joseph, M.D., '11
Pennsylvania
Hall, Alice Louise, M.D., '11
Pennsylvania
Hammett, Walter Mitchell, M.D., '05
Maryland
Dr. J. D. Norris
Hammond, Charles Issac, M.D., '05
Maryland
Dr. C. W. Didenhover
Hamrick, John A., M.D., '04
North Carolina
Dr. T. G. Hamrick
Hand, Jesse (B.) Donald, M.D., '11
New York
Hanna, Perry B., M.D., '00, '00
Maryland
Maryland Medical College
Harbordt, Cecil de J., M.D., '05
Virginia
Maryland Medical College
Hardy, Irvin, M.D., '99
West Virginia
Maryland Medical College
Hare, John Hampton, M.D., '05
West Virginia
Dr. J. H. Hare
Hare, Oaka Sheridan, M.D., '04
West Virginia
Dr. J. H. Hare
Harmon, William C., M.D., '13
Virginia
Harnett, John J., M.D., '11
Connecticut
Harney, Joseph B., '11
Louisiana
Harris, E. A., (M.D.), '08
West Virginia
Harrison, William S., '06
Maryland
Dr. B. W. Hazell
Hart, T. H. E., '04
New Hampshire
Dr. A. P. Phichette
Hartnett, John J., '10
Connecticut
Hartzell, G. H., '04
Maryland
Maryland Medical College
Hartzell, Grant Frederick, '06
Illinois
Maryland Medical College
Haselden, Joseph Fleetwood, M. D., '04
South Carolina
Dr. J. H. Chapman
Haynes, Willare Calvin, M.D., '03
Texas
Dr. B. H. Haynes
Hazard, Elmer C., (Ph.G.), M.D., '04
New Jersey
Dr. Edward C. Hazard
Hazell, Benjamin Woodward, M.D., '05
Maryland
Professor Mc Conachie
Hearn, Thomas Oscar, M.D., '04
Alabama
Hearn, Funston Lucado, '06, '08, '09
West Virginia
Dr. J. R. Vermillion
Healey, N. S., '03
Maryland
Professor Muse
Heath, Joseph F., '10
Massachusetts
Heiskell, (Mrs.), S. O., (M.D.), '10
Maryland
Helfgott, Max A., M.D., '12
District of Columbia
Helfgott, Nathan J., M.D., '12
District of Columbia
Helm, F. L. C., '10, '11
Maryland
Herman, Samuel J., M.D., '00
New York (Maryland)
Maryland Medical College
Hess, Harry Clyde, M.D., '01
West Virginia
Drs. J. W. Hartigan and S. T. Hall

Hichew, Arthur L., M.D., '13
Maryland
Hicks, Charles Franklin, M.D., '01, '01
West Virginia
Dr. I. C. Hicks
Hicks, Wesley D., M.D., '02, '02
West Virginia
Maryland Medical College
Higgenbotham (Highinbothem), R.R., M.D., '04
Bermuda
Dr. Eldon Harvey
Hill, H. F., '03, '04
North Carolina
Dr. McClain Rogers
Hill, N. Philip, Jr., (A.B.), M.D., '07
New York
Dr. H. H. Tinker
Hine, Harry Kingsley, M.D., '08
Connecticut
Dr. J. H. Kane
Hipsh, Jacob F., M.D., '04
Tennessee
Hodges, Jesse Clarence, M.D., '03, '03
Virginia
Dr. J. M. Hodges
Hoechst, Harleigh B., M.D., '00
Pennsylvania
Dr. F. C. Wolf
Hoeler, E. R., '07
West Virginia
Hoeler, W. F., M.D., '08
West Virginia
Hoeler, William Francis, M.D., '05
New Jersey
Holland, Claude L., M.D., '01
West Virginia
Drs. C. F. Boyers and Sons
Holland, Carlton A., '08, '09, '10
District of Columbia
Hollander, Bernard Morris, '06
Pennsylvania
Dr. J. A. Rusmisell
Holley, Oliver Cromwell, M.D., '05
South Carolina
Maryland Medical College
Holloway, Donald B., (Ph.G.), M.D., '00, '00
District of Columbia
Dr. Taliefero Clark
Holmes, Noel S., M.D., '03, '03
Louisiana
Dr. R. A. Hail
Hoopes, W. W., '02
Maryland
Dr. J. W. Barton
Hopewell, Harry T., M.D., '03, '03
Virginia
Maryland Medical College
Horka, Leon S., M.D., '13
Pennsylvania
Horn, Byrom R., '04, '07
Maryland
Maryland Medical College
Dr. W. T. Watson
Hornstein, Harry H., M.D., '12
Pennsylvania
Horwitz, Morris T., M.D., '13

Hosmer, Cuthbert Lynn, M.D., '07
Maryland
Professor J. B. Schwatka
Houser, Burton C., M.D., '04, '04
Pennsylvania
Maryland Medical College
Howard, Foster C., M.D., '12
Maryland
Hubbard, A. George, (Ph.G.), M.D., '00, '00
District of Columbia
Dr. J. L. Brayshaw
Huff, Ford W., M.D., '04
West Virginia
Dr. J. C. Huff
Huffman, Frank B., M.D., '09
Virginia
Hughart, Joseph Robert, M.D., '04
West Virginia
Hughes, Reese W., '03, '04
West Virginia
Dr. Thomas M. Haskins
Hughes, David E., '07, '08
West Virginia
Dr. R. W. Hughes
Hunt, Elwood V., M.D., '12
Indiana
Hunt, James Edgar, M.D., '09
Indiana
Dr. J. A. Colborn
Hunter, I. H., '01
Georgia
Dr. W. E. Hunter
Hunter, James Richard, M.D., '05
New York
Drs. Trotten and Weekes
Hunter, John Oscar, M.D., '05
West Virginia
Maryland Medical College
Hurley, William Henry, M.D,, '03, '03
Vermont
Dr. W. B. Mayl
Hutchinson, David W., Jr., M.D., '12
New Jersey
Imber, Aaron, '98
Pennsylvania
Maryland Medical College
Ingalls, James H., '02, '03
Connecticut
University of Vermont
Inge, Francis Marion, M.D., '10
Alabama
Ireland, Dewitt F., M.D., '00
West Virginia
Dr. J. W. Jarvis
Irving, Joseph, '03
New York
Irwin, Robert Sloan, M.D., '04
Pennsylvania
Jacobson, Nathan L., M.D., '10
New Jersey
Jackson, H. S., '07
Pennsylvania
Dr. W. W. Stonestreet

Jaffe, Samuel, M.D., '12
Pennsylvania
James, Emory E., '03
West Virginia
Dr. C. M. Brown
Janisch, Frederick William, M.D., '04
Pennsylvania
Janu(sze)ski, Frank A., M.D., '12
Pennsylvania
Jarrell, Dennis B., '09
West Virginia
Jarrell, George Ernest, M.D., '04
Alabama
Dr. W. D. Gaines
Jelks, James T., '03
Arkansas
Johnson, George D., M.D., '13

Johnson, Harry C., M.D., '03
Virginia
Dr. D. V. Willard
Johnson, T. B., '03
West Virginia
Jones, Albert Bates, (Ph.G.), M.D., '04
Rhode Island
Jones, David R., '09
West Virginia
Jones, Emory E., M.D., '04
West Virginia
Jones, Maurice, M.D., '05, M.D., '09
Maryland
Professor Gross
Jones, William D., M.D., '05
Maryland
Jones, N. W., '00
Delaware
Maryland Medical College
Jones, William D., '98, '04
Maryland
Maryland Medical College
Dr. William Burke
Jordan, William Henry, M.D., '01
Rhode Island
Dr. William F. Baney
Joyner, Albert S., M.D., '04
Georgia
Juliano, Anthony, M.D., '12
New Jersey
Kahan, Joseph Carl, M.D., '11
Pennsylvania
Kahn, Maurice, '00
Maryland
Dr. D. M. Hirschman
Kaiser, A. J., '07
Connecticut
Dr.McNeil
Kaiser, Louis A., M.D., '09
New York
Kalmutz, Gustave G., M.D., '09
Pennsylvania
Kane, James Hugh, M.D., '04
Connecticut
Dr. T. G. O'Connell
Kanofsky, Peter, M.D., '10
New York
Kapeghian, Ervant, M.D., '11
Armenia
Karp, Julius P., M.D., '13
Pennsylvania
Katar, Felix Max, M.D., '10
Washington
Kay, William Eli, M.D., '05
Louisiana
Maryland Medical College
Kealy, T. I., '07
Pennsylvania
Maryland Medical College
Keatley, Harry Wronkow, M.D., '03, '03
Iowa
Dr. William P. Reeves
Keifer, Bruce, '98
West Virginia
Dr. J. D. Schmeid
Kelley, H. M., '02
Mississippi
Dr. S. M. Catchings
Kelley, R. F., '02
Mississippi
Dr. H. H. Harrison
Kelly, John I., '98
Maryland
Professor Muse
Kelsey, Ernest Russell, M.D., '01
Connecticut
Dr. H. W. Murless
Kenney, Frank J., (A.B.), M.D., '11
Maryland
Kenney, T. J., '07
West Virginia
Dr. G. E. Kenney
Kern, Harrison Benjamin, M.D., '11
Pennsylvania
Kerr, John Jonas, M.D., '05
Pennsylvania
Maryland Medical College
Kershner, Warren Edglie, M.D., '03, '03
Maine
Dr. J. G. Townes
Kibler, Clarence LeRoy, M.D.,'07
South Carolina
Dr. F. D. Kendall
Kiefer, Bruce, M.D., '00, '00
West Virginia
Dr. J. D. Schmied
Kiles, Harry Albert, M.D., '05
Ohio
Dr. C. N. Warren
Kimble, C. Marvin, M.D., '12
West Virginia
Kimble, Joseph Uriah, M.D., '05
West Virginia
Dr. H. G. Meek
Kinard, Drayton Duncan, M.D., '04
South Carolina
Maryland Medical College
Kirk, Joseph Raymond, M.D., '01
West Virginia
Dr. W. V. Kirk
Kirk, William Tilden,M.D., '01
West Virginia
Dr. W. T. Kirk

Kneeland, Wellington E., M.D., '00, '00
Maine
Dr. J. A. Twaddle
Klupt, Abram, '11
Maryland
Koch, George W., '06
New York
Dr. L. O. Nutt
Kolb, Henry Burkhart, M.D., '08
Maryland
Professor Harry Gross
Koldewey, Theodore William, M.D., '05
Maryland
Dr. A. George Hubbard
Koontz, Leonidas Allen, M.D., '01, '01
West Virginia
Dr. C. E. Copeland
Knickman, W. E., '03
Maryland
Koppleman, Max S., M.D., '08
Maryland
Dr. A. H. A. Mayer
Krum, Francis G., M.D., '08
Pennsylvania
Dr. A. G. Krum
Lacailaide, J. O., '00
Massachusetts
Dr. V. Migdeault
Lamberton, H., (D.D.S.), '02
Connecticut
Maryland Medical College
Lancaster, George E., '10, '11
Maryland
Lancaster, L. T., '03
West Virginia
Dr. S. L. Lawson
Langlois, Charles Joseph, M.D., '11
Massachusetts
Law, McIvor E., Jr., (B.S.), (C.E.),
M.D., '03, '03
Florida
Maryland Medical College
Lawall, Griffith S., M.D., '12
Pennsylvania
Lawson, Esley, E., M.D., '02, '02
West Virginia
Maryland Medical College
Lawton, R. J., M.D., '08
Connecticut
Dr. R. E. Harrington
Ledebur, Wilbur T., '10, '11
Pennsylvania
Lee, S. P. J., '03
North Carolina
Dr. L. E. Beach
Lee, Walter Evon, (Ph.D.), M.D., '05
New Jersey
Dr. J. M. Slaughter
Lee, Sanders P. J., (D.D.S.), M.D., '04
North Carolina
Leonard, B. F., (M.S.), (Special, '00)
New Jersey
Maryland Medical College
Leonard, George A., M.D., '05
Connecticut
Dr. H. J. De Ver
Levyn, I. Lester, M.D., '09
New York
Lewis, C. S., '02
Virginia
Dr. H. M. Clarkson
Lewis, Harry Ephraim, M.D., '02
Russia
Lickle, Harry Roland, M.D., '09
Maryland
Dr. E. Miller Reid
Liddon, Robert C., M.D., '00, '00
Mississippi
Professor Muse
Liesenfeld, Abraham Isack, '04
New York
Maryland Medical College
Light, J. Ray, M.D., '09
Pennsylvania
Lilly, Milton J.,M.D., '04
West Virginia
Drs. W. S. Macgill and W. A. Caldwell
Lindenbaum, Samuel M., M.D., '11
Pennsylvania
Lingo, W. B., '02
Virginia
Maryland Medical College
Link, Amelia Elizabeth, M.D., '11
Maryland
Linthicum, J. Charles, (L.L.B.),
Honorary M.D., '02
Maryland
Litsinger, Vernon L., M.D., '12
Maryland
Littlefield, John J., '01
Maine
Maryland Medical College
Longsdorf, J. P., '11
Pennsylvania
Longshore, Howard Kimball, M.D., '11
Pennsylvania
Lotterer, C. G. (Ph.G.), '98
Maryland
Professor Hodgdon
Lowr(e)y, Nicholas, M.D., '00, '00
New York
Maryland Medical College
Love, S. W. E., '98
District of Columbia
Dr. W. S. Love
Lovejoy, Edward F., '01
Massachusetts
Dr. Charles E. Eastman
Long, Eustace, M.D., '03, '03
Florida
Dr. L. C. Ruter
Long, F. Y., '03
North Carolina
Long, James Andrew, M.D., '03, '03
Virginia
Maryland Medical College
Long, W. A., '03
Florida
Dr. L. C. Ruter
Lucas, M. C., '07
South Carolina
Dr. A. E. Baker

Lyon, George R. (E.), M.D. '12
Pennsylvania
Lyon, Samuel E., M.D., '12
Pennsylvania
MacAulay, John D., M.D., '12
Massachusetts
Mac Crowe, A. E., '04
New Jersey
Maryland Medical College
MacDonald, A. A., M.D., '00, '00
Nova Scotia
Tuft's College
MacFeeters, Richard Bruce, M.D., '01, '01
Pennsylvania
Dr. D. G. Metheny
Mack, Toni F., '04
New York
Maryland Medical College
MacSorley, Harriet E., M.D., '12
Pennsylvania
Mackel, Charles F., M.D., '12
Pennsylvania
MacKimmie, Charles Richard, (Ph.G), M.D., '03, '03
Virginia
Dr. H. A. Ward
Mac Whinnie, Herbert C., '04
Massachusetts
Dr. Mac Whinnie
Maguire, T. E., '03
Virginia
Mahaney, John D., '10, '11
Connecticut
Mendelbaum, Abraham, M.D., '01, '01
New York
Dr. E. H. Schlessinger
Mankin, J. Ward, M.D., '03
West Virginia
Dr. A. W. Curry
Maneely, Raymond S., M.D., '04
Florida
Mann, Louis, M.D., '11
Pennsylvania
Mannich, W. A., '08
Pennsylvania
Marantz, Benjamin, '10
New Jersey
Marantz, Bernard D., M.D., '12
New York
March, John O., '11
Virginia
Marrett, M. C., '07
South Carolina
Dr. W. J. Carter
Marsh, John Otho, '10
Virginia
Marsh, Stanley Nay, M.D., '03
Massachusetts (Maine)
Dr. R. H. Marsh
Marsh, Walter Goldsborough, '06
New York
Maryland Medical College
Martin, Charles Burrell, M.D., '10
Maryland
Dr. Harry Gross
Martin, Claude, M.D., '11
West Virginia
Martinez, Victoriano R., (B.Sc.), M.D., '10
Central America
Mason, Claude Hutchinson, M.D., '11
West Virginia
Mason, David A., M.D., '04
Alabama
Massuod, Mittry Abi, M.D., '04
Syria
Mastin, Morrell N., M.D., '12
Pennsylvania
Matheny, B. F., '03
West Virginia
Dr. C. L. Boyers
Mattox, Edgar E., M.D., '12
Pennsylvania
Mayer, Maxwell L., M.D., '13

Maynard, Arthur, M.D., '04
Massachusetts
Maryland Medical College
Dr. B. Schofield
Maynes, Joseph Vincent, M.D., '10
Pennsylvania
McAvay, Hugh Vensin, '06
Connecticut
Dr. J. B. Boucher
McCandless, Everett LeRoy, M.D., '10
Pennsylvania
McCarthy, Charles C., '04
New Jersey
Dr. A. K. McDonald
McCarthy, John Alexander, M.D., '11
New Brunswick (Canada)
McCollum, Luther G., (Ph.G.), M.D., '04
Alabama
McComas, E. C., M.D., '04
West Virginia
McCooey, J. F., '02
Massachusetts
Maryland Medical College
McCord, Clara L., M.D., '13

McCoy, John C., M.D., '05
West Virginia
Dr. J. A. Rusmisell
McCurry, Albert Vandiver, M.D., '08
Georgia (Florida)
Dr. E. Mc Ivor Law
McDaniel, E. (C.E.), (E.C.), '98, '00
Arkansas
Dr. James McClister
McDaniel, (S.), (L.) E., '07, '08
South Carolina
McDermott, N. J., '11
Pennsylvania
McDonald, E. R., '07
Pennsylvania
Dr. F. Gillispie
McDonald, Richard L., M.D., '12
Pennsylvania
McEachen, A. D., '03
Canada
Dr. D. J. McMaster

McFaddin, A. D., '11
Alabama
McKee, Alexander, (A.B.), M.D., '99
New York
Drs. W. B. Melick and W. C. Cuthbert
McGuffin, L. L., '08
Ohio
McGuffin, Robert Kenton, M.D., '11
Ohio
McGuire, Thomas Edward, M.D., '04
West Virginia
Maryland Medical College
McGrath, J. Frank, M.D., '02, '02
Massachusetts
Maryland Medical College
McKnight, Vernon Hastings, '06
Maryland
Dr. Joseph I. France
McLaughlin, J. G., '03
South Carolina
Maryland Medical College
McLaughlin, Joseph L., M.D., '10
New Hampshire
Dr. F. W. McLaughlin
McLain, M. Mackey, M.D., '13
Pennsylvania
McLarney, J. L., '10
Connecticut
McLarney, J. J., '11
Connecticut
McMahon, William F., M.D., '13

McMillan, A., '02
Massachusetts
Dr. Albert Evans
McMillan,Henry, M.D., '05
Georgia
Maryland Medical College
McMurray, William Stewart, '03, '04, '07
South Carolina
Dr. D. G. Thompson
McNeer, Frank Luther, M.D., '11
West Virginia
McNeer, Lewis C., Jr., M.D., '04
Maryland (West Virginia)
Dr. E. W. Cook
McNeer, N. C., '03
Maryland
Professor McNeer
McNeer, Richard L., M.D.,
Honorary M.D., '99
West Virginia
McNeer, T. L., '07
West Virginia
McNemar, Oscar Harrison, M.D., '03
Maryland
Dr. T. H. Brayshaw
Meador, Hugh G., '10
West Virginia
Meason, James M., M.D., '05
Texas
Dr. J. P. Lowery
Mecluskey, John Franklin, M.D., '11
Pennsylvania
Meeks, Charles G., '10, '11
Maryland

Melvin, J. T., (A.M.), '00, '01
Pennsylvania
Dr. Guthrie and Professor Muse
Mendelsohn, Jacob E., M.D., '12
Pennsylvania
Mendelson, Joseph A., '11
New York
Menville, Leon J., M.D., '04
Louisiana
Mercer, Clarence H., M.D., '05
Connecticut
Maryland Medical College
Messon, James M., '04
Texas
Maryland Medical College
Mestre, R., '11
Puerto Rico
Metzger, G. C., '98
Maryland
Professor Schwatka
Meylackson, Saul, '10
New Jersey
Michael, Nelson B., M.D., '04
West Virginia
Drs. J. F. and W. S. Michael
Mitchell, Ralph C., M.D., '02
West Virginia
Mieckowski, Stanislaus C., M.D., '12
Connecticut
Miller, Clarence Haldeman, M.D., '07
Pennsylvania
Dr. H. P. Dickerson
Miller, Edward C. J., M.D., '03
Maryland
Dr. William M. Barnes
Miller, Edwin S., M.D., '00, '00
Maryland
Maryland Medical College
Miller, John A., M.D., '09
Maryland
Dr. T. Cooke, Jr.
Miller, John Henry, M.D., '07
Rhode Island
Dr. W. S. A. Gillan
Miller, J. R., '11
South Carolina
Miller, Lester, M.D., '04
West Virginia
Dr. W. R. Curtis
Miller, Richard T., '01
New York
Dr. Moore
Miller, Thomas C., M.D., '03, '03
Virginia
Maryland Medical College
Mitchell, R. C., '02
West Virginia
Dr. H. R. Mitchell
Mohr, Dwight H., M.D., '09
Connecticut
Moledezky, M.D., '09, '10
New Jersey
Money, E. N., '98
England
Dr. A. Money

Monohan, George F., M.D., '00, '00
Rhode Island
Dr. William F. Barrey
Montealegre, Issac J., M.D., '09
Central America
Montgomery, J. Lida, (S.), (T.), M.D., '08
West Virginia
Maryland Medical College
Dr. E. L. Koontz
Moore, Anthony J., M.D., '00, '00
Connecticut
Dr. J. M. Dix
Moore, E. A., '04
Alabama
Maryland Medical College
Moore, Ernest Henry, M.D., '99
Delaware
Dr. Luce
Moore, Gilmore H., M.D., '04
Alabama
Moore, Thomas H., M.D., '12
Massachusetts (Connecticut)
Morgan, A. D., '03
Texas
Morgan, G. E., '10
District of Columbia
Morgan, Robert Dalby, M.D., '10
Pennsylvania
Morrill, Martelle Flint, M.D., '04
Maine
Dr. W. G. Sawyer
Morris E. Frederic, M.D., '05
New York
Dr. A. J. Radick
Morris, M. W., '04
Virginia
Maryland Medical College
Morris, Samuel J., M.D., '10
Pennsylvania
Morris, Samuel H., M.D., '12
Pennsylvania
Morris, Samuel M., '11
Pennsylvania
Morrissey, John Joseph, M.D., '10
Maryland
Mortimer, Egbert Laird, M.D., '03, '03
Virginia
Dr. F. M. Sharp
Moulton, A. T., '07
Massachusetts
Mowery, J. J., (B.S.), '03
Rhode Island
Dr. W. T. Hammill
Moye, Leon Grayville, M.D., '04
Georgia
Mudgett, William Chase, M.D., '03
New Hampshire
Dr. J. B. Erskine
Munster, James A. (H.), M.D., '12
Pennsylvania
Murray, David Francis, M.D., '99
New York
Murray, James A., '11
Maryland
Murray, James H., Jr., M.D., '12
Maryland
Muse, Alexander E., (Ph.G.), M.D., '04
California
Dr. Joseph E. Muse
Muse, William S., '11
Maryland
Myer, Edward Herman, M.D., '10
New York
Dr. Mance Gillette
Myers, I. T., '02
Mississippi
Dr. H. L. Crook
Naret, Edward Linden, M.D., '03
West Virginia
Dr. J. N. Hartigan
Navarro, Salvador A., '07, '08, '09, '10, '11
Cuba
Dr. J. B. Schwatka
Nawrath, Charles Joseph, M.D., '11
New Jersey
Nealon, W. J., '01
Pennsylvania
Dr. J. J. Kelly
Neeley, G. D., '02
Texas
Dr. W. C. Haynes
Neergaard, Frederick A., M.D., '08
Tennessee
Dr. J. B. Goodwin
Newton, John Joseph, M.D., '02, '02
Pennsylvania
Dr. W. F. Paul
Newitt, Kenneth, Jr., '03
Maryland
Maryland Medical College
Nicholson, John C., M.D., '04
South Carolina
Nolt, Verlin, '04
Pennsylvania
Dr. J. E. Lawrence
Nottingham, Carlisle L., M.D., '05
Virginia
Dr. G. P. Moore
Nuber, A. C., Jr., (Ph.G.), '08, '09, '10, '11
New Jersey
Nugent, A. J., M.D., '08
Massachusetts
Nurkin, J. Joseph, M.D., '11
Pennsylvania
Offner, John E. W., M.D., '04
Virginia
Offner, J. E., '02
West Virginia
Drs. Z. T. Kalbaugh and W. W. Dear
O'Malley, Francis C., M.D., '12
Pennsylvania
O'Malley, Frank E., '10
Pennsylvania
O'Malley, William J., M.D., '12
Pennsylvania
O'Neill, Andrew, M.D., '04
Pennsylvania
Dr. P. A. Larkin

Orr, W. L., '03
Georgia
Dr. J. R. Nisbet
O'Toole, Bernard Francis, M.D., '01, '01
Pennsylvania
Dr. R. W. Jones
Ott, F. Spencer, '00
Maryland
Professor H. M. Baxley
Ott, Howard, M.D., '09
Pennsylvania
Owen, Benjamin Alexander, M.D., '05
West Virginia
Maryland Medical College
Paetzel, August F. G., M.D., '07
Germany
Drs. Ermentraunt and Currie
Page, J. E., '04
Ohio
Dr. J. Charles Beck
Page, Rollin Brock, M.D., '05
Ohio
Dr. J. Charles Beck
Paglin, Meyer David, M.D., '10
New York
Palmer, Harry W., M.D., '00
Delaware
Dr. D. D. Palmer
Palmer, Jarrett William, (A.B.), M.D., '99
Georgia
Dr. W. T. Palmer
Parker, Edward M., M.D., '00, '00
Virginia
Dr. G. B. Ward
Parkins, Edward William, M.D., '01
Virginia
Dr. T. M. Parkins
Parkins, Nathan, '02
Virginia
Dr. E. W. Parkins
Parr, Newton Isaac, M.D., '05
Maryland
Dr. H. C. Hess
Parran, James Carry, M.D., '12
Maryland
Parrish, Clifford C., M.D., '07
Texas
Professor J. B. Schwatka
Parrish, E. M., '04
Texas
Dr. H. L. McNew
Parsonnet, Aaron, M.D., '11
New Jersey
Parry, Evan Jenkins, M.D., '11
Pennsylvania
Parry, Leo D., M.D., '12
Pennsylvania
Patton, J. Hampton, M.D., '02, '02
Alabama
Dr. J. H. Donohoo
Paul, William Fletcher, M.D., '00, '00
Pennsylvania
Dr. A. H. Hulshizer
Payne, James Wallace, M.D., '03, '05
South Carolina
Maryland Medical College
Peck, Benjamin William, M.D., '05
West Virginia
Drs. Hobroyd and Hobroyd
Pemberton, Edward Milton, M.D., '02, '02
West Virginia
Dr. William S. Magill
Pentz, S. P., '02
Maryland
Maryland Medical College
Percival, Winston G., (D.D.S.), M.D., '01, '01
Pennsylvania
Maryland Medical College
Periera, Louis, '06, '07
Puerto Rico
Maryland Medical College
Perkins, Elmer Case, '06
Maryland
Professor L. H. Gundry
Perkins, E. W., Jr., '01
Virginia
Dr. E. W. Perkins
Perry, Argo Hilliard, M.D., '07
North Carolina
Dr. L. B. Young
Peters, A. J. W., '03
Maine
Peters, C. C., '04
West Virginia
Dr. E. F. Peters
Peters, E. F., M.D., '02
West Virginia
Dr. L. L. Lilly
Pettry, B. L., '04
West Virginia
Dr. H. H. Pettry
Pettry, Harvey Hinchman, M.D., '05
West Virginia
Dr. W. H. Whitson
Phillips, E. L., '98, '00
Maryland
Professor Branham
Phillips, John C., M.D., '12
Georgia
Piasecki, Joseph L., M.D., '12
Pennsylvania
Pickering, Alfred J., M.D., '10
West Virginia
Pierce, B. E., '02
Virginia
Dr. W. J. Best
Pierson, William H., '06
Maryland
Professor H. C. Hess
Pitts, B. G., '98
South Carolina
Dr. Watson
Pitchford, L. C., '02
Mississippi
Dr. V. S. McLellan
Platou, Carl A., Jr., M.D., '12
New York

Plone, Bertha, '11
Pennsylvania
Porch, Charles Lee, M.D., '05
Pennsylvania
Maryland Medical College
Porembski, Joseph, M.D., '11
Maryland
Dr. S. J. Szuwalski
Posey, C. R., '11
Pennsylvania
Posey, H. W., M.D., '00, '00
Pennsylvania
Dr. M. A. Posey
Poulson, W. W., '11
Pennsylvania
Powell, Lawson Otwood, M.D., '03
Virginia
Dr. J. W. Hope
Price, Norman Randolph, M.D., '03, '03
West Virginia
Pringle, Frederick A., M.D., '12
Pennsylvania
Quandt, E. E., (Ph.G.), '03
Maryland
Maryland Medical College
Quimby, Charles Morris, M.D., '04
Massachusetts
Quinlivan, William Francis, M.D., '07
Pennsylvania
Dr. J. M. Newton
Quinn, Frederick W. C., M.D., '05
Maryland
Dr. S. S. Quinn
Quinn, James B., M.D., '13
Connecticut
Raelkey, F. D., '03
Maryland
Ragui, Kahlil T., M.D., '13
Egypt
Maryland Medical College
Rahn, Ernest H., M.D., '12
Maryland
Ramsey, B. M., '07
West Virginia
Dr. W. A. Wykel
Rankin, Charles P., '11
Pennsylvania
Rankin, James Ballantine, M.D., '05
West Virginia
Dr. J. D. Long
Ravenscroft, J. H., M.D., '02, '02
Maryland
Dr. W. A. Shuey
Rawitz, Samuel B., M.D., '12
New Jersey
Raymond, Mark, '06
Massachusetts
Maryland Medical College
Reason, John James, (Ph.G.), M.D., '99
New Jersey
Professor Muse
Reese, Charles B., M.D., '12
Pennsylvania
Reeves, L. A., '98
New Jersey
Dr. E. L. Reeves
Reichman, Adolph, M.D., '11
Rumania
Reinhart, Maurice, M.D., '09
Illinois
Remsburg, John J., (Ph.G.), M.D., '01
Maryland
Dr. C. W. Goldsborough
Renney, F. J., '06
West Virginia
Maryland Medical College
Repilado, Diego, '09
Cuba
Rhodes, T. A., M.D., '02, '02
Kentucky
Dr. O. R. Kidd
Rhodes, W. H., M.D., '02
Kentucky
Rice, Roy, M.D., '08
Texas
Maryland Medical College
Richards, Albert Morse, M.D., '04
Alabama
Ricker, Charles D., M.D., '02
Massachusetts
Dr. H. S. Pratt
Riendeau, J. H., '03
Massachusetts
Dr. B. F. Schofield
Rigdon, Franklin Eli, M.D., '07
Maryland
Maryland Medical College
Riggin, George H., '03
Delaware
Riggin, H. S., '03
Delaware
Riland, Chester, M.D., '12
New Jersey
Rinckwitz, R. L., '10
Maryland
Ritter, H. W., '11
Maryland
Roach, James Edward, M.D., '12
Rhode Island
Roba(c)k, J. L., '10, '11
Pennsylvania
Roberts, C. W., '03
Pennsylvania
Dr. A. J. Colborn
Robertson, F. S., M.D., '08
Virginia
Dr. L. McNeer
Rodriguez, Cirilo Leonardo, M.D., '05
Cuba
Maryland Medical College
Rodriguez, Juan Ramos, '09, '10
Puerto Rico
Roelkey, Francis Daniel, M.D., '05
Maryland
Dr. F. B. Smith
Rohr, Clyde Carroll, '06
Maryland
Dr. S. Howell Gardner
Rosenstein, Eli, '06
New York
Maryland Medical College

Rosenstein, Jacob L., M.D., '04
Maryland
Dr. A. G. Hubbard
Roses, Y. Artan M., (A.B.), (B.S.), M.D., '04
Spain
Rosse, Samuel Alexander, M.D., '12
Maryland
Round, Solomon, '04
Maryland
Maryland Medical College
Rucker, Moses P., Jr., M.D., '04
Virginia
Dr. S. L. Rucker
Rudolph, John C., (A.B.), M.D., '00
Maryland
Professor Munoz
Rusmisell, Charles C., M.D., '05
West Virginia
Dr. S. C. Rusmisell
Rusmisell, James Adam, M.D., '04
West Virginia
Drs. P. V. Phillips and O. B. Beer
Russell, A. B., (M.D.), '02, '02
New Jersey
Maryland Medical College
Russell, Jesse Harris, M.D., '04
Maine
Dr. W. G. Sawyer
Rutrough, Joseph C., '09
Tennessee
Ryan, D. J., '07
Connecticut
Dr. T. M. Ryan
Rysanek, William James, M.D., '05
Maryland
Drs. Lehnert and Singewald
Salinko, Stephen, M.D., '01, '01
New York
Maryland Medical College
Salley, G. W., '02
Alabama
Dr. W. B. Crum
Sanders, J. E., '98
Virginia
Professor Muse
Sanders, James Oscar, M.D., '00, '00
South Carolina
Dr. J. O. Wilhite
Sandler, David Lewis, '06
Maryland
Professor M. Lazenby
Santaella, Alvaro, M.D., '09
Puerto Rico
Saunders, J. E. S., '00
Virginia
Professor Muse
Sanders, Thomas Henry, M.D., '04
Massachusetts
*Schroeder, Charles T., '98, '00
Maryland
Professor Schwatka
Died during session
Seabury, William Thomas, '04, '06
Connecticut
Maryland Medical College

Seale, M. Edward, M.D., '05
Texas
Maryland Medical College
Sibold, Albert L., M.D., 09
Virginia
Silverstein, Samuel, M.D., '09
Rumania
Simkims, James J., M.D., '13

Simmerman, J. Walter, (A.B.), M.D., '11
Virginia
Simmons, George W., M.D., '03, '03
West Virginia
Dr. F. S. Casto
Simmons, Oliver D., '04
Maryland
Professor J. B. Schwatka
Simpson, Furman T., '06
South Carolina
Dr. W. J. Carter
Sipes, Chester Howard, '06
West Virginia
Dr. Irvin Hardy
Sisler, G. W., '04
Mississippi
Maryland Medical College
Skladowsky, John A., '08, '09
Maryland
Skversky, Frank Benjamin, M.D., '11
Pennsylvania
Schadewald, C. A., '07
Maryland
Dr. J. B. Schwatka
Schaefer, Charles A., (Ph.G.), M.D., '04
Maryland
Maryland Medical College
Schaefer, Theodore A., '04
Maryland
Dr. Charles A. Schaefer
Schall, R. H., '00
Pennsylvania
Dr. D. H. Schall
Scharf, Joseph, M.D., '00, '00
Pennsylvania
Maryland Medical College
Schaub, George, '04
Maryland
Maryland Medical College
Scheidenbach, A. J. M., M.D., '01
New York
Schieck, F. W., Jr., '01, '04
Maryland
Maryland Medical College
Schireson, Benjamin Franklin, '06
Massachusetts
Maryland Medical College
Schlieder, J. W., M.D., '05
New York
Dr. O. G. Harrington
Schloer, Charles A., M.D., '13

Schneidenbach, A. J.M., '01
New York
Maryland Medical College
Schott, E. H., '10
Connecticut

Schultz, A. T. von, (B.S.), '04
Maryland
Professor J. B. Schwatka
Schwatka, J. B., Jr., '07
Maryland
Dr. J. B. Schwatka
Schweinsberg. John G., '06
Maryland
Dr. E. A. Muse
Schweitzer, William A., '11
Pennsylvania
Shafer, F. C., '04
West Virginia
Maryland Medical College
Schaffer, Hurst McDowell, '04, '06, '07
Maryland
Maryland Medical College
Dr. J. B. Schwatka
Shannon, J. Benjamin, M.D., '05
Texas
Maryland Medical College
Shapira, Abraham, M.D., '12
Pennsylvania
Sharp, George Tarplit, M.D., '11
District of Columbia
Shaw, H. William, M.D., '05
Georgia
Dr. A. B. McNaughton
Sheehan, J. W., (W.J.),, (A.B.), '10, '11
Connecticut
Shepler, D. R., '00
Pennsylvania
Dr. George E. Nickel
Sheppard, Alfred G., M.D., '07
New Jersey
Dr. J. H. Russell
Sheppard, Thomas S., M.D., '13

Shepherd, Walter Franklin, M.D., '05
Texas
Maryland Medical College
Sheppe, Joseph Luther, M.D., '07
Maryland
Maryland Medical College
Sherman, L. F., '04
Maryland
Professor J. B. Schwatka
Shermantine, Robert Wilbur, M.D., '03
Maryland
Professor A. L. Hodgdon
Shohan, Joseph, M.D., '01, '01
Massachusetts
Maryland Medical College
Shorts, William Francis, M.D., '11
Maryland
Shriver, George W., M.D., '04
West Virginia
Dr. H. G. Meek
Shultz, Charles Elmer, M.D., '11
Pennsylvania
Smith, A. W., '01, '02
Pennsylvania
Dr. D. J. Reese
Smith, Bart James, M.D., '02
Pennsylvania
Dr. Reese
Smith, Charles Wray, '06, '07
Pennsylvania
Dr. Robert F. Tarr
Smith, David A., M.D., '12
Pennsylvania
Smith, Eugene R., M.D., '04
Alabama
Smith, F. Edward, M.D., '02
Maryland
Professor W. S. Smith
Smith, F. R., '04
Maryland
Maryland Medical College
Smith, Frank Albert, M.D., '02
New York
Smith, J. A., Jr., '02, '03
Virginia
Dr. E. W. P. Downing
Smith, J. Almer, '04
Virginia
Dr. George W. Fischer
Smith, James Edward, M.D., '07
Pennsylvania
Maryland Medical College
Smith, I. M., '07
Virginia
Smith, Temple Joshua, M.D., '03
Louisiana
Dr. Weedon Smith
Smyser. John D., M.D., '12
New Jersey
Snarr, George G., '10, '11
Virginia
Snarr, Samuel, M.D., '09
Virginia
Snarr, Samuel Stewart, '06
Virginia
Dr. H. T. Hopewell
Snyder, Frederick, '04
New Jersey
Maryland Medical College
Snyder, H. F. R., (A.M., D.D.S.) '03
Maryland
Sollars, Edward Eli, M.D., '10
Maryland
Maryland Medical College
Solomon, Harry, '11
New York
Sosa, C., '11
Puerto Rico
Spangler, J. Latimer, '06
West Virginia
Professor R. L. McNeer
Spangler, Paul C., '08, '09
West Virginia
Sparks, Walter, '04
West Virginia
Maryland Medical College
Stadder, J. M., '07
New Jersey
Dr. J. E. McMannus
Stainbock, Frederick, William
(D.D.S.), M.D., '04
Pennsylvania
Stallings, John A., '08
Maryland

Stallings, J. Willis, '06, '07
Maryland
Maryland Medical College
Stalvey, Edgar A., M.D., '02, '02
South Carolina
Maryland Medical College
Starnes, Crawford W., (M.D.), M.D., '01
Tennessee
Dr. D. D. Britton
Steele, Manning Roe, '06
Delaware
Dr. E. R. Steele
Steele, M. L., '10, '11
West Virginia
Sterner, Burton L., M.D., '13

Stevens, Wilkin B., M.D., '04
Alabama
Dr. J. P. Lile (Siles)
Stickley, Charles V., M.D., '04
Virginia
Dr. P. C. Haushberger
Stiff, William Clifton, M.D., '03
Pennsylvania
Dr. E. S. Hayes
Stone, General Jackson, M.D., '12
Virginia
Stone, F. F., Jr., '01
Ohio
Dr. E. W. Ludlow
Stone, James Elmer, '09
West Virginia
Stoneham, H. Graham, '09
Virginia
Stoumen, Samuel, M.D., '11
Pennsylvania
Strachan, Hugh, M.D., '03
West Virginia
Dr. J. J. Kennedy
Straub, Peter, M.D., '12
Pennsylvania
Strong, J. Page, M.D., '07
Maryland
Dr. W. O. Selby
Strother, W. L., '98
West Virginia
Dr. Strother
Stuart, Alexander M., Jr., M.D., '03
Tennessee
Dr. J. S. Stuart
Stuart, F. B., '02
Tennessee
Dr. J. S. Stuart
Stumberg, Bernhardt K.,
(A.B.), M.D., '00, '00
Missouri
Dr. J. H. Stumberg
Sturdivant, Burton B., M.D., '12
North Carolina
Stutzman, Raymond H., M.D., '12
Pennsylvania
Sudler, J. Ralston, M.D., '05
Delaware
Dr. W. T. Sudler
Sullivan, Charles M., M.D., '10
Massachusetts
Sullivan, John T., M.D., '05
Canada
Dr. A. Sullivan
Sullivan, Joseph Vincent, M.D., '03
Massachusetts
Dr. J. G. Gunning
Sullivan, Michael Francis, M.D., '11
Pennsylvania
Sullivan, William Joseph, M.D., '01, '01
Maryland
Dr. J. D. Bacon
Sullivay, Rosa L., M.D., '12
Maryland
Summers, E. J., '04
West Virginia
Maryland Medical College
Sutphin, Mark, '09, '10, '11
West Virginia (Virginia)
Swain, Clement, '04
New York
Maryland Medical College
Swope, Opie William, M.D., '05
West Virginia
Dr. L. A. Koontz
Sylcurk, John Henry, M.D., '99
Maryland
Dr. S. S. Maynard
Tabler, Homer Edwin, M.D., '04
West Virginia
Professor McConachie
Tait, H. F. S., '02, '03
New Jersey (New York)
Dr. E. L. Draper
Takashima, Tamhji, (D.D.S.) M.D., '00, '00
Japan
Professor Frames
Talkin, Joseph D., M.D., '05
Maryland
Dr. F. N. Tannar
Talkin, Morris M., M.D., '08
Maryland
Dr. M. Flinder
Tankin, Harry J., M.D., '12
New York
Tannar, Frank, '09
Maryland
Tanner, Frederick N., M.D., '00
Pennsylvania
Dr. G. T. Rodman
Tapie, J. J., (Special), '01
Maryland
Maryland Medical College
Tarr, Robert F., M.D., '00, '00
Pennsylvania
Dr. J. E. Stute
Taveira, Arthur Joaquin, M.D., '10
Portugal
Taylor, Rowland E. S., '09, '10
West Virginia
Tetz, Walter J., '10
Maryland
Theel, M.F., '02
Pennsylvania
Dr. J. J. Siggins
Theide, Gustave Adolph, M.D., '01
Maryland
Professor Muse

Thomas, Claude A., M.D., '12
West Virginia
Thome, Arthur J., M.D., '07
Pennsylvania
Dr. W. B. Thome
Thompson, Edward Herbert, M.D., '05
West Virginia
Dr. J. R. Vermillion
Thompson, J. McK., '04
New Jersey
Professor J. P. Arnold
Thompson, Neill A., M.D., '05
North Carolina
Professor J. B. Schwatka
Thompson, William P., M.D., '05
New Jersey
Dr. J. P. Arnold
Thomson, Lewis B., M.D., '05
Maryland
Maryland Medical College
Thor(n)ton, Vaiden Aubrey, M.D., '10
Virginia
Thrower, W. W., '04
Alabama
Maryland Medical College
Thursby, H. E., '98
Maryland
Professor Muse
Toms, V. L., '03, '04
North Carolina
Dr. T. C. McBrayer
Toney, Mosley Johnston, M.D., '05
West Virginia
Dr. George R. Ramsey
Tonsky, Bernard, M.D., '11
Pennsylvania
Torre, Louis de la, M.D., '10
Cuba
Maryland Medical College
Torre, Teodoro de la, '04
Cuba
Maryland Medical College
Towle, Edwin Dudley, M.D., '03, '03
Massachusetts
Dr. Albert Evans
Towler, Philip Brooke, '06
Canada
Professor J. Schwatka
Travers, Charles Elias, M.D., '10
Maryland
Treadway, Moses H., M.D., '11
Virginia
Trenton, Walter D., '11
West Virginia
Truax, James Luther, (Ph.G.), M.D., '99
Maryland
Professor Caruthers
Trucks, J. F., '04
Alabama
Maryland Medical College
Truitt, James H., (Ph.G.), '03
Maryland
Dr. C. R. Truitt
Turner, Seneca S., M.D., '05
Mississippi
Maryland Medical College
Uffelman, H. W., '04
Pennsylvania
Dr. W. H. Minnich
Umsto(a)t, Samuel Wilson, M.D., '03, '03
Maryland
Usher, John Arte, M.D., '04
Georgia
Uzzell, Joseph H., '09, '10, '11
North Carolina
Van de Grift, H. F., '01
New Jersey
Dr. E. V. Buck
VanNort, J. S., '00
New York
Dr. Roberts
Vass, Finly Kyle, M.D., '07
West Virginia
Maryland Medical College
Vergne, R. V., '10, '11
Puerto Rico
Vermillion, B. T., '00
West Virginia
Dr. D. H. Thornton
Vermillion, Elbert, M.D., '04
West Virginia
Dr. J. R. Vermillion
Vermillion, James R., M.D., '00
West Virginia
Dr. D. H. Thornton
Vermillion, Uriah, M.D., '09
West Virginia
Dr. J. R. Vermillion
Vermillion, Vane A., M.D., '00, '00
West Virginia
Dr. L. W. Vermillion
Vick, Clyde W., M.D., '99
Virginia
Professor Muse
Villafranca, Leland, '09
Costa Rica
Vogel, L., '07
Maryland
Dr. J. B. Schwatka
Vogt, Morton J., M.D., '12
New York
Von Flattern, E. F., '02
Massachusetts
Dr. Thomas Roach
Von Schulz, A. T. M., (B.S.), (M.S.), M.D., '04
Maryland
Maryland Medical College
Von Sonneberg, A., '01, '02
New York
Dr. S. Martus
Wagner, Harry, '06
Maryland
Dr. Edward Grempler
Walker, Everett, M.D., '04
West Virginia
Walker, Scioto Pierce, M.D., '11
West Virginia
Dr. J. D. Burgess
Wall, Charles I., M.D., '03
West Virginia

Wall, Ira, '02, '03
West Virginia
Drs. William H. McClung and D. N. Wall
Wallace, Louis O. S., M.D., '12
New Hampshire
Wallenstrin, S., '07
New York
Walsh, Thomas M., M.D., '03, '03
New Hampshire
Dr. F. W. Bean
Walter, L. D., M.D., '00
District of Columbia
Maryland Medical College
Ward, Heber Arden, M.D., '99
North Carolina
Dr. E. H. Horton
Warner, C. S., '11
Pennsylvania
Warren, D. H., '04
Ohio
Maryland Medical College
Warriner, Harry B., M.D., '12
Pennsylvania
Watlington, F. W., (D.D.S.), M.D., '04
Bermuda
Watman, A., '02
New Jersey
Maryland Medical College
Webb, G. Clarke, M.D., '12
Maryland
Webb, Oscar Clinton, M.D., '04
Georgia
Webb, R. J., (Deceased), '03
Georgia
Dr. J. D. McCollum
Weddigen, Ferdinand E., M.D., '00, '00
Pennsylvania
Dr. H. C. McCormick
Weed, Walter Alva, M.D., '05
Alabama
Maryland Medical College
Weil, John H., (Ph.G.), M.D., '05
New York
Dr. R. H. Theyson
Weissman, Nathan F., M.D., '11
Pennsylvania
Welch, F. M., '09
Georgia
Weldon, Frank D., M.D., '12
Pennsylvania
Weldon, E. J., '10
Connecticut
Wells, Charles J., '04
Maryland
Maryland Medical College
Welsh, John E., '98, '00
Maryland
Professor Schwatka
Wenger, Morris, M.D., '11
Pennsylvania
West, Earle Clifton, M.D., '12
Delaware
Whaland, Charles Thomas, M.D., '04
Maryland
Dr. C. W. Whaland
Whims, F. G., '07
West Virginia
Whitaker, Ferdinand Cary, M.D., '11
North Carolina
Whitaker, Frederick S., M.D., '13

Whitehead, Wiley Leon, M.D., '04
South Carolina
Dr. J. D. Whitehead
Whiting, Leonard C., M.D., '12
Connecticut
Whittaker, George F., M.D., '07
Pennsylvania
Widdowson, Ord K., M.D., '07
Pennsylvania
Maryland Medical College
Wilkinson, J. E., (D.D.S.), M.D., '02, '02
Canada
Maryland Medical College
Wilkinson, W. Emmet, M.D., '10
Louisiana
Will, David Q., M.D., '02
Virginia
Dr. E. J. Will
Williams, B., (Special), '01
England
Maryland Medical College
Williams, Leslie L., M.D., '13

Williams, P. D., '07
Maryland
Dr. J. B. Schwatka
Williamson, C. E., '98, '00
Maryland
Maryland Medical College
Dr. R. J. Price
Williamson, E. C., '01
Maryland
Dr. J. C. Holdsworth
Williamson, C. G., '11
New York
Willse, Raymond G., '04
New York
Dr. H. R. Willse
Wilson, Thomas Luther, M.D., '03
West Virginia
Drs. A. R. Warden and J. W. Stother
Wilson, Wirt B., M.D., '11
West Virginia
Wilton, L. J., '11
New York
Wingert, H. Shindle, (M.S., D.O.,
M.D., '03, '03
Michigan
Dr. J. M. Magee
Windle, Okey N., M.D., '05
West Virginia
Drs. V. L. and O. J. Casto
Wingrove, Arch. H., M.D., '05
West Virginia
Wingrove, A. A., '04
West Virginia
Dr. H. H. Pettry
Winstead, John A., '09
North Carolina

Wirtshafter, Morris F., (B.S.), M.D., '11
Ohio
Wither(s), Worthy F., M.D., '11
West Virginia
Wolfe, Robert Milton, M.D., '01, '01
New York
Maryland Medical College
Wood, C. M., '03
Pennsylvania
Dr. Charles F. Palmer
Wood, Harold A., M.D., '09
Maine
Dr. B. P. Muse
Woodall, Thomas, '10
Maryland
Woods, Harvey Wharton, (M.D.), M.D., '99
Pennsylvania
Woodward, Chester Pearce, M.D., '11
Maryland
Woodward, M. P., '07
Maryland
Dr. E. Douglas
Wrensch, Alexander Eugene,
(A.B., Ph.G.), M.D., '01, '01
New Jersey
Dr. J. A. Allis
Wykel, William A. Alexander, M.D., '04
West Virginia
Yarbrough, Henry Edward, M.D., '03, '03
Texas
Dr. W. P. Connelly
York, Hugh B., '03
North Carolina
Maryland Medical College
Young, Clarence L., M.D., '11
Pennsylvania
Young, J. Lee, M.D., '02, '02
South Carolina
Dr. John W. Young
Young, John Z., M.D., '07
Texas
Dr. R. K. Ferguson
Young, William Branch, M.D., '11
West Virginia
Young, Z. T., '04
Louisiana (Maryland)
Dr. Z. T. Young, Sr.
Young, Albert T., M.D., '05
Pennsylvania
Dr. J. A. Kelley
Younger, Robert N., M.D., '04
Virginia
Zauderer, Louis J., (Ph.G.), '10
Rhode Island
Zimmerman, William Koontz, M.D., '05
Maryland
Dr. M. T. Zimmerman
Zink, C. E., '98
Connecticut
Dr. W. H. Zink
Zink, William Peter, '06
Maryland
Dr. N. I. Parr
Zwinglas, M. A., '11
New Jersey

BIBLIOGRAPHY

1. Annual Announcements of the Maryland Medical College for the years 1898-99 to 1912-13, inclusive, except those for 1904-05, and 1906-07.
2. BALTIMORE SUN, May 31, 1910 and May 27, 1913.
3. Howard A. Kelly and Walter L. Burrage: *Dictionary of American Medical Biography*. D. Appleton Co., New York, 1928.
4. The Medical Observer, Maryland Medical College, December 1898 to June 1899.

ACKNOWLEDGMENTS

Thanks are expressed to Dr. Wyndham D. Miles, Historian, National Institutes of Health, Miss Marion B. Savin, of Philadelphia, Dr. W. B. McDaniel, 2d, Dr. Elliott H. Morse, and Staff of the College of Physicians of Philadelphia, and to the following persons, who have rendered valuable help:

Miss Gertrude L. Annan and Miss Mary E. Feeney, of the New York Academy of Medicine, Miss Hilda E. Moore, of the Health Sciences Library, University of Maryland, Mr. Charles Roos and Staff of the National Library of Medicine, Mrs. Karl M. Koudelka, of the Welch Medical Library, Johns Hopkins University, Miss Madeline Stanton of the Historical Library, School of Medicine, Yale University, Miss Dorothy Baker, of the Boston Medical Library, and Miss Ruth D. Burton, of the Maryland Historical Society Library.

FOOTNOTES TO CHAPTER THREE

(1) Not to be confounded with the College of Medicine of Maryland, later known as the School of Medicine of the University of Maryland.

(2) However, the College did not maintain a three year curriculum for very long, changing instead to one of four years duration. See Section II, Curriculum.

(3) As to reasons for studying medicine in Baltimore, a later Announcement of the Maryland Medical College (1907-08), points to the following:

> Baltimore, because of its geographical location, unsurpassed climate, and natural advantages is the metropolis of the South, and one of the leading cities of America. It is easy of access because of the great trunk lines which radiate from her center, and because of the waterways which bring numerous coastwise and ocean-going steamers to her wharves.
>
> The supremacy of Baltimore as a medical center is conceded throughout our country and acknowledged abroad.
>
> There is a great advantage to a student in studying and living in an atmosphere, surrounded by thousands of other persons with similar aims, for this circumstance stimulates a student to persevere in his endeavors and to put forth his best efforts to reap the advantages of the opportunity presented to him. A College located in an isolated place, and stultified by a fancied sense of security, is likely to be unprogressive, but one which is in close contact with similar institutions, all of them subject to the strong light of comparison with each other, must remain progressive, or retire from the field.
>
> The clinical advantages of Baltimore are obvious: there are many hospitals and dispensaries, which attract both residents and thousands of patients from great distances. Railroads, car lines and shipping lines "supply innumerable cases of accidents, while intercourse with the tropics and distant countries bring to the clinics cases of rare and unusual diseases that seldom find their way to less accessible medical clinics".
>
> Living in Baltimore is proverbially good, and there are within easy reach of the College, hospitable homes which accept students at reasonable rates, and provide for the moral and physical well-being of students, amid refined surroundings.

(4) "The National Temperance Hospital . . . was succeeded by the Franklin Square Hospital in 1901 through the changing of the name and an amendment to the charter." (Personal communication from Mr. Sanford Kotzen, Administrator of the Franklin Square Hospital, November 24, 1964.)

(5) The first class graduated in May, 1899.

BALTIMORE UNIVERSITY SCHOOL OF MEDICINE

At the time when the Baltimore University was called into existence in 1884,(1) under the laws of the State of Maryland, it was the intention of the charter members to establish a complex,(2) in which all of the sciences would some day be taught. The first fruition of the idea was the immediate organizing of a Faculty of medicine, and the opening of the Baltimore University School of Medicine, the first dean being Dr. Thomas B. Evans. To obtain the M.D. degree, it was necessary to attend for but two years. By 1892 the College announced that in the future it would require attendance upon three sessions.

Successive Announcements before the turn of the century laid claim to each session as having been more successful than the previous one. The Faculty therefore felt encouraged to contemplate the erection of new college and hospital buildings, and justified in feeling that it was offering a course comprising didactic, clinical and laboratory instruction "second to none in the country". The years of its existence from 1884 to 1897 had seen expansion of the curriculum (not only in the number of years of attendance required, but in the length of the session, as will be seen below), and in Faculty and plant. The school enrollment reached its highest level at about this time (1898), after which it declined.

The school laid very great stress upon its unusual facilities for clinical experience, and the advantages of learning about the peculiarities of each case, listening to the explanation, seeing the appropriate treatment prescribed, the requisite surgical operation performed.

Associated with the University's hospital was a training school for nurses. Instruction extended over a period of three years, and included lectures by the various members of the medical school Faculty, on all subjects connected with general and special nursing, all under the direction of the superintendent.

The Baltimore University School of Medicine declared itself to be a co-educational institution, "women being admitted on the same terms as men", (Announcement for 1899-1900), but the names of matriculates and graduates include few names of women.

The ratio of graduates to matriculates was very high, most matriculates succeeding in winning the M.D. degree. The enrolment reached its highest level in the late 1890s, with the largest class graduating in 1898, and a decline in numbers setting in after that year. Names of preceptors continue to appear in the Announcements, down to the last ones available despite the decline in the preceptorial system, elsewhere, by that date.

Late in its life the University acknowledged its dedication to the principle of "mens sana in corpore sano", and announced its encouragement of outdoor sports, and the formation of clubs for football and baseball.

A branch of the city Y.M.C.A. was maintained at the school. (An intercollegiate secretary was employed to devote time to the welfare of all the students of the city.) The Y.M.C.A. directed the religious activity of students, ran classes for Bible study and regular devotional meetings, welcomed new students at the beginning of the term, listed suitable boarding-houses, and published a handbook of useful information for students. It also extended a cordial welcome to them, at its central property.

An alumni association of the medical department of the Baltimore University was early organized (1885) and the Faculty expressed its desire that the graduates "retain as close a connection and . . . lively interest in their Alma Mater" as possible, inviting the cooperation of alumni, "in the form of charity patients for the clinics" and "suggestions for the advancement of medical instruction". The members met on the first Tuesday of each month for the discussion of medical subjects. All papers read or discussed at the meetings were later published in the College paper, *The Medical Gleaner*, which appeared monthly, and gave all the College and Hospital news and items of interest. Dues in the Association were one dollar per year, which included a free subscription to the Medical Gleaner. The purpose of the Association was:

> " . . . to advance the interests, and extend the influence of the Baltimore University School of Medicine; to encourage a high standard of medical education and perpetuate college friendship . . ."

A gold medal was awarded to the member who presented the best essay.

The last class of the Baltimore University School of Medicine graduated in 1907, the school becoming extinct in that year. Among the reasons for its demise were the lack of sufficient funds to maintain the work of the school (see Appendix E), and the facts that the Faculty was weak, and the management was poor. We may also suspect the presence of the other usual disadvantages under which so many of the independent schools had to labor.

THE MEDICAL GLEANER

The *Gleaner* was a soft-cover journal, measuring about 7-1/2 by 10-1/2 inches, consisting of four sheets, 15 by 10-1/2, fastened together and folded once into eight pages, each of which was printed on both sides, resulting in a sixteen page paper, plus a cover. The inner sides of both front and back covers bore advertisements. The text included introductory addresses, medical articles by members of the Faculty; editorials; "university happenings"; notes on Faculty, alumni, Ladies' Auxiliary Association, Baltimore University Medical and Surgical Association, undergraduates, Commencement orations, and the like. The *Gleaner* was at first published under the supervision of a Faculty committee, (and welcomed contributions form all sources). Albert L. Levy, M.D., a member of the Faculty, was editor in the last years. In 1900 the price was ten cents a copy or one dollar and twenty cents per year by mail.

The issue of January, 1906 (Volume VII, number I), reproduces the Introductory Address to the Session of 1904-05, delivered by Theodore Cooke, Jr., A.B., M.D., secretary of the board of directors, dean, and professor of ophthalmology and otology.

After referring to "dark clouds (which) lowered over (the) University the past summer", he expressed the thought that the best way to begin a course of lectures in medicine was to review the history of the healing art, and note the changes which had taken place:

Whether we study the doings of man in the state of barbarism, or in that of a civilized society, we always encounter the physician, be it under that name, or any other. No matter how far back we go we find him, combining in one person, the duties of priest and poet, as well as healer, having communication with both the spiritual and the material world, hence the designation "seer". He wielded great influence in tribal and national councils, and was a potent factor for good or evil. Homer in the Odessey, Book 8, says of Demodocus:

"Whom the Muse loved and gave the good and ill."

The seer is similarly endowed by Virgil, Ovid, Herodotus, Xenephon and Tacitus. We find the same as far back as Egyptian times, and as recently as the era of the American Indian, in the writings of Cooper, Longfellow, and many others. The healer knew of poisons and of certain nostrums, but his chief stock-in-trade was the ability to play upon human superstition, via religious impulse. Hindus, Arabs, Egyptians and Greeks believed that knowledge of healing was a gift to the priests, from the Gods, and later spread by tradition.

Our first recorded medical book is "Agur Vida", (Book of Life), in Sanskrit, by Sucrutus, probably dating from the era of Augustus. At that time surgery was more advanced than medicine. Many operations and instruments were known, as were most "surgical injuries". The treatment of wounds given in the book is "simple and proper".

Among the Greeks the God of medicine was Aesculapius, a son of Apollo. He is honored by the many temples built to his glory. The knowledge of the healing art descends from him via the priests, who were sworn, upon entering the temple service, to teach the art to their successors. This oath has come down to our time, and gives evidence that there were specialists, even in that era: "Furthermore, I will never cut foristone, but will leave this operation to men of that occupation".

The historical founder of the science and art of medicine is Hippocrates, who was born on the island of Cos, in 460 B.C., lived now in Athens, now in Thessalonian towns, and died at Larissa, in 377 B.C. Some of his contemporaries were Pythagoras, Plato and Aristotle. We hold his works in high regard because of their advanced thought, clear, classical description, arrangement of material, love of the healing art, and keen, critical observations. Easily visible in his writings is the emergence, from superstition, of the study of medicine, and the scientific elaboration of medical knowledge. In the Hippocratic schools, medicine and surgery were united, forming one work. In his time, besides the Aesculapian priests, there were the educated physicians, as well as the mechanically instructed medical assistants, gymnasts, quacks and miracle workers. Xenophon, in "Anabasis", says:

" . . . in the Persian army they, (the special army physicians), together with the soothsayer and flute player, had their places near the royal tent."

Fractures and sprains were very well understood in Hippocritic times, the Greek being zealous for his bodily beauty. Greeks preferred death, rather than a life with a mutilated body, hence they avoided amputations, except after gangrene had set in, but other non-amputative operations were performed.

Dr. Anagnostakis, professor at the University of Athens, says that Greek physicians not only knew sepsis and antisepsis, but also the role of the decomposition of the blood in the prevention of the healing of wounds and suppuration. Hipprocrates knew that moisture favored putrefaction, and urged that wounds be kept dry. The antiseptic properties of alcohol and tar were known, as were the virtues of aromatics and resins, and the great advantage of clean dressing.

Further progress in medicine became impossible, for lack of better knowledge of anatomy and physiology. In Alexandria the schools made a slight effort in that direction. Greek learning spread over a part of the Orient, after Alexander's conquests, (at least for a time), but attention was devoted to philosophical systems by the physicians of the time, and little advance in scientific medicine, except for a few anatomical discoveries, resulted. Alexandrian schools divided the healing art into three separate parts: dietetics, internal medicine, surgery.

Greek slaves, their freedom acquired, were the first to carry medical knowledge to Rome. Barbers and bathers became practitioners, and to this day the barber applies the leech. Gradually the philosophers took possession of medical literature and practiced medicine without doing credit to the profession. Little original research was done by them, and they were content with writing compendia, such as the *DeArtibus* of Aulus Cornelius Celsus (30 B.C.-50 A.D.). Such compendia, having value as relics, show us that medicine had made no great progesss since the day of Hippocrates and the Alexandrian schools. ("Celsus speaks of plastic operation of hernia, and gives a method of amputation, which is still employed", and Cladius Galen (131-201 A.D.) was a "phenomenon" among Roman physicians. We have eighty-three genuine medical writings of his. As the human dead were regarded sacred, Galenus rarely dissected human cadavers, confining himself to quadrupeds. Like Hippocrates, he thought of observation as the foundation of medicine. Galen's work stood for more than a thousand years.)

A period of retrogression then set in. Byzantium did not favor the advancement of medicine. True, there was a brief flicker in the Alexandrian school, but such greatly celebrated physicians of later Roman times, as Antyllus (third century), Oribasius (326-403 A.D.), Alexander of Tralles (525-605 A.D.), and Paulus of Aegina (660), did little for medicine. There were, however, some gains in the position and scholarly attainments of the physician – under Nero there was a gymnasium; under Hadrian, an anthenaeum, a scientific institution where medicine, too, was taught; under Trajan a special medical school.

The Arabs must be credited with preventing the total degeneration of the healing art after 608 A.D. They preserved Hippocratic medicine, and the additions made to it by Alexandrians and Nestorians, until Charles Martel broke their power, and medical knowledge returned to Europe by way of Spain. Rhazes (850-932), Avicenna (980-1037), Albucasis (1106) and Avenzoar (1162) are among the best known Arab medical writers. The Arabs feared blood, and operative surgery therefore did not develop under them. When the era of Spain and western Europe arrived, medicine was not confined to the monastaries, most students being compelled to complete their education at a scientific institution. Under the Arabs there was a celebrated school at Cordova. At Salerno Charles the Great founded a school in 802, which reached its finest hour in the twelfth century. Women of a literary turn were trained in medicine at this school, Trotula being its best known personage. There was little research, but the ancient literature was closely studied. Salerno was the first corporation with the right to bestow the titles "Doctor" and "Magister". It was followed by the founding of universities in Naples (1224), Pavia and Padua (1250), Paris (1348), Salamanca (1243) and Prague (1348), each having the right to confer academic honors.

Medicine remained at a standstill, being either of the Galenic, the Arab, or the later Medico-Philosophical systems. DeLuzzi differs very little from Galen even though he based his work on anatomy (1314), upon his dissection of some human bodies.

The sixteenth century brought great changes in almost all of the sciences. Observation of nature began to resume its rightful place, and slowly free itself from "the schools", and research won its claim as the only way to knowledge. Modern anatomy developed from the work of Vesal, (Vesalius) (1513-64), Fallopio (1532-62) and Eustachio (1579). Paracelsus (1493-1554) was an early critic of the prevailing Galenical and Arabic systems, claiming, instead, that observation was the true source of medical knowledge. The old anatomy and physiology received final blows from Harvey's discovery of the circulation of the blood and Aselli's discovery of the lymphatic vessels, and were replaced by modern scientific thought. Practical medicine, however, remained enslaved in philosophical thraldom of one variety after another, corresponding to the particular system in vogue at any given time.

Not until the great advances of the nineteenth Century, made by pathological anatomy, did practical medicine find its present firm foundation.

Leeuwenhoeck demonstrated the presence of infusoria in saliva (in 1615) and out of his work with crude microscopes there grew the theory of "contagium vivum". The improvement in microscopes led to the discovery of the changes brought about in tissues by disease, and even the causative agents of these. We recall the names of contributors to our present knowledge: Virchow, Koch, Cohnheim, Pasteur and others. To them we owe our present ability to eradicate certain germ-produced diseases. Jenner removed the horror of small pox, Reed and associates did great work on yellow fever, Koch in tuberculosis, Loeffler on diphtheria, Pasteur in rabies, Weeks in pink eye, and Lister in antiseptic surgery, making possible the modern era in that field.

Man has always tried to reduce or eradicate the pain involved in surgery. In the thirteenth century Theodoric recommended that a "spongia somnifera", moistened with spiritous extracts of various narcotic substances should be held to the nostrils until sleep was induced. Nothing very important was discovered, however, until the early nineteenth century, when Sir Humphry Davy discovered the anaesthetic effects of nitrous oxide. Compression of the nerves of the limb was recommended, by Moore, to produce anaesthesia, as was excessive venesection, by Wardrop, and mesmerism by Esdaile. Then came Dr. Wells' anaesthesia upon himself, by nitrous oxide (1844), the use of ether by his student, Dr. Morton (1846), chloroform by Prof. Simpson, of Edinburgh (1847), and cocaine by Koller (1882).

Helmholtz's ophthalmoscope (1851), was a great medical achievement. Electricity, x-ray and radium have proved useful and will become more so.

The ancients founded their medicine upon superstition, while we work from known facts, based upon observation. We know what normal anatomy and physiology are, and what changes in structure and function occur when disease strikes. We know that certain diseases are caused by certain micro-organisms and their products, and we know how to cope with these. Medicine has become scientific. It is a far more complex study than it was twenty years ago, because a physician must understand the causes of diseases. A short time ago two years were considered long enough to become acquainted with the various diseases, and laboratory work was not required. Today the student is first grounded in the knowledge of the healthy body, and only after that is he given clinical training, being taught what changes occur in the body during diseases, what microorganisms destroy the body, their actions, functions and peculiarities. Only after he has mastered his anatomy, physiology, chemistry, pathology and bacteriology is he initiated into the mysteries of the practice of medicine and surgery.

The Medical Gleaner for May, 1906, reproduced the speech made by the Hon. Chauncey M. Depew, at the Commencement of the Baltimore University School of Medicine, on April 19, 1904. It was a typical Depew speech – humorous, witty and entertaining. In order that readers may sample of the temper of the times, a few excerpts are given below:

> " . . ,Certainly the way in which the world treats the medical profession is usually the test of the civilization of the country or of the world. Many among savage tribes have a medicine man, but he proceeds by mysterious processes and occult art, and claims to be the direct representative, if he is not himself, the God. When civilization gets a little further on and there comes barbarism and autocracy, then there is stripped from him the halo of divinity and he becomes little better than a slave, and is judged by the supreme power, by the success of his art. If the case is not successful, off goes the head of the doctor. (Laughter).
>
> But, as civilization progresses, as art and literature become more perfect, so it is the profession advances to the front ranks."

Urging the young graduates to use the free time of their early years in exhausting the circulating library, and thus in discovering the directions in which their minds turn with most interest, he suggested that they become thorough in some area of learning while they still have time for doing so, without neglecting their professional duties:

> " . . . The worst thing in this world is idleness. Everything decays unless it is actively worked or is actively working, and nothing decays like a man in idleness. The first years of a profession are hard, because clients are not seeking lawyers and patients are not looking for a doctor; the young man must be looking hard for the patient and looking hard for the client. In those years there is an abundance of time, and many a young man fails in his profession and blames it on luck, or blames it on the times, or blames it on the neighborhood, when he himself is to blame, because, instead of utilizing the treasures of his library, he is keeping down a dry-goods box at the corner or a chair in the grocery store. (Applause). There is nothing like the utilization of odd moments in these days when there is such universal education; in these days when the requirements of every vocation are so great that the man is superior in his calling who is most broadly cultured in other directions. (Applause).
>
> . . . See what the largest exercise of this faculty has done. I will name two instances: A glorious contribution to American literature, as well as an ornament to the medical profession was Dr. Oliver Wendell Holmes, (applause), and how superbly has that other physician filled the highest requirements of his art and risen to the highest ideals of his times, while at the same time in literature he is contributing to the pleasure of the reading public – Dr. Weir Mitchell, of Philadelphia." (Applause).
>
> " . . . Wherever you are, remember that the educated man is the power in his community. There is nothing like cultivated brain, with science added, to give to the young man a constantly increasing influence. Let that influence always be upon the side of the right. Belong to some political party; any party rather than none. Belong to some church; any creed rather than none. Take

part in its activities, as far as possible, without interfering with the practice and due attention to your profession. If there is corruption in your community, be in the reform party and not afraid to be there . . ."

The gathering dusk, and approach of night in the life of the Baltimore University School of Medicine is to be sensed in the January, 1906 number of the *Gleaner*, page 11. It was admitted that classes were now not as large as in previous years, but that was due to the fact that admission requirements had been raised, and therefore students were entering with better preparation. The University was at present being well conducted, and if it continued in this vein, success would certainly follow. In the past the University had been deficient in laboratory work, but lately that phase of its activities had become a bright spot. Dr. Albert L. Levy, recently elected Associate Professor of Pathology, Histology and Bacteriology, had had the laboratories cleaned and stocked with supplies, with the result that the University was at present giving good laboratory instruction in those subjects. Dr. J. Walker Thomas, recently elected Associate Professor of Anatomy, did not leave instruction entirely to didactic lectures, but instead personally supervised and demonstrated all work upon the cadaver in the dissecting room, (which had been moved to the College building, where the space, heat and light added much to the comfort of the students). Dr. Thomas required each senior to perform all the major operations of abdominal surgery upon dogs. The chemical laboratory, likewise, was now fully equipped. The Board of Directors had decreed that hereafter the session would open on September 1, that a preliminary course be given during the entire month, and that the regular session run for eight months, from October 1 until June 1. A medical association and a ladies' auxiliary had been organized for the purpose of interesting "outsiders" in the school, and attracting the desperately-needed funds, upon which depended the future existence of the school. The Alumni Association was also being asked for financial assistance. Presumably, however, adequate funds could not be raised in time to save the school, and it became extinct in 1907, a victim of lack of support from independent sources, or those of a "mother institution". In addition, the Faculty was weak, and the management of the school poor.

I. BUILDINGS AND EQUIPMENT

The first home of the College and Hospital was at 233 East Baltimore Street, in a part of the city which was rich in clinical material for Dispensary and Hospital. No adequate description of these facilities is given in the Announcements. Beginning with the session of 1887-88 the College and Hospital were located at 21-29 N. Bond Street. The Announcement for 1891-92 tells us that in order to meet "increasing demands" upon existing facilities, vast and desirable improvements were made. The hospital was entirely reconstructed, many new wards and private rooms added, operating rooms were set up, as were chemical, physiological and pathological laboratories, affording every facility for study. Lecture rooms were "admirably arranged", and furnished with folding chairs and all other conveniences. The entire building was steam heated.

The Announcement for 1897-98 states that additional laboratory facilities had been added earlier in 1897, and the corp of instructors enlarged. The dissecting room was large, well lighted and ventilated.

The following statements appeared in the Announcements for 1901-02 and after:

> "Although the Baltimore University School of Medicine was founded less than a score of years ago, it has outgrown its present buildings, and new ones have become a positive necessity. Twice, during its history, has its College and Hospital room been increased in size and number, and now, by its rapid growth, entirely new accommodations are imperatively demanded. Arrangements have been perfected for the erection of a new College and Hospital, which will be completed during the year. The accompanying cut will give an idea of its vast extent. The buildings will contain ample Hospital quarters, while the lecture halls and rooms for laboratory instruction will be large and complete in every detail. With the completion and occupancy of these new structures the Baltimore University School of Medicine, will stand among the best in this country."
>
> "The Baltimore University Hospital.
>
> The Faculty has secured control of a large and commodious building for the reception and treatment of private patients. The rates per week, including board, medicines, etc. will be from $8.00 to $15.00, according to the location of the room and nature of the case . . ."

(The promise of the construction of a new College and Hospital, "to be completed during the year" as well as past expansions of the plant facilities and Faculty, continued to be unabashedly made, in precisely the same language, from year to year, for many years, as though for the first time.)

There were plates and diagrams in anatomy and in surgery; microscopes "and all the modern appliances" for teaching physiology; drawings and models for teaching the various diseases and displacements of the uterus; plates, diagrams, models in wax and a "superb" manikin for teaching obstetrics; drawings and plates of every variety of skin disease.

In 1891-92 there was established the requirement that students furnish their own "test-tubes, glasses and (other) apparatus". (The College furnished all the necessary chemicals for a fee of $5.00.)

II. CURRICULUM

In the early years (1884-1890), the session ran from the first of October until about the fifteenth of March. The session of 1891-92 ran from the first of October until about the first of April following. This continued to be the practice until the session of 1897-98, in which there were two sessions, the first of which ran from the first of October until the first of April, and the second, from the eleventh of April to the first of July. In the years which followed, i.e., from 1898 until 1903, the session ran from the first of October until the fifteenth of April. The last Announcement thus far available (that for 1904-05) shows the session for that year as having run from the first of October until the first of May following. Preliminary lectures, free to all medical students, were delivered daily from the first part of September until the opening of the regular session. These were given for the purpose of preparing the students "for the duties of the regular term". (Throughout the life of the school no classes were held on Thanksgiving day, on the days from December 23 or 24 until January 2, and, beginning with 1893, on Washington's birthday.) Thus in the years from 1884 to 1906 we note a lenghtening of the annual session from that of five and a half months to one of seven months.

In the early years there was a full series of didactic lectures on each of the following subjects: practice of medicine, anatomy, surgery, physiology, chemistry, materia medica and therapeutics, obstetrics, diseases of eye and ear, diseases of women and children, dermatology, microscopy and diseases of the nervous system. These lectures were fully illustrated by daily clinics.

The Free Dispensary was open daily, except Sunday, from 12 to 2 o'clock, large numbers of out-door patients being prescribed for and treated in the presence of the students, who were expected to visit patients at their homes, under direction of the chiefs of clinics, that they might study the progress and changes in treatment of their cases. This mode of teaching the art of diagnosis and the use of remedies was believed to have advantages which could hardly be overestimated.

The Bay View Asylum and Hospital was accessible to all medical students, free of charge, and offered opportunity to see almost every form and variety of disease and accident. This 1,000 bed hospital was located more conveniently, in distance, to the Baltimore University than to any other of the Baltimore colleges, trolleys which went to Bay View passing the doors of the College.

The Lying-In and Gynecological Department of the Baltimore University Hospital was under the immediate charge of the professors of those studies, thus guaranteeing that students would have advantages in attending them. It adjoined the general hospital. Students had access to it at all times, and in cases of labor, were called upon to assist.

Thus instruction was both didactic and clinical, resulting in a thoroughly practical and progressive medical education in all departments, with laboratory instruction and manipulation constituting a prominent feature of the curriculum. There was training in the use of the instruments and appliances employed in modern medical practice.

PRINCIPLES AND PRACTICE OF MEDICINE

The professor aimed to condense and simplify his lectures so as to adapt them to the easy comprehension of the student, and ground him thoroughly in the practical details of the subject. Daily clinics and hospitals supplied ample means for practical instruction in this department.

ANATOMY

The aim was to give the student an accurate acquaintance with this branch "in keeping with its central and commanding importance as an exact science", because it was now considered "indispensable to a fit preparation for the duties of the profession". The cadaver was freely used, as were plates and diagrams, when lectures so required, rendering all matters easily understood. "Students (were) expected to give due diligence to the dissecting rooms during the session."

SURGERY

The professor made his didactic lectures "attractive and useful", by drawings, diagrams, and operations, before the class, upon the living subject, as well as upon the cadaver. There were ample opportunities to see surgical operations and manipulations upon patients at the clinics and hospitals. Students were instructed in, and required to apply, every surgical dressing and appliance in modern surgery. Operations were slowly performed upon the cadaver, and carefully explained.

CHEMISTRY

The instruction was suited to the special requirements of the future practitioner. Emphasis was upon an understanding of the principles of chemistry, as a basis for the rational study of physiology, pathology and therapeutics. Mere technical considerations, not related to this aim, were omitted from the course. Chemistry, as applied to toxicology, was given careful attention.

PHYSIOLOGY

The didactic lectures were claimed to be up-to-date in both content and method of presentation. There were experiments, and the microscope, as well as all the modern appliances for this subject, were employed in giving this course.

DISEASES OF THE EYE AND EAR

The anatomy and physiology of the eye and ear were taught in order that students might appreciate, more fully, the modes of examining these organs, and their therapeutic and surgical treatments. This was followed by thorough instruction in the surgery of these organs. There was abundant material for demonstration upon patients in the Dispensary.

DISEASES OF WOMEN

The course began with a study of the surgical anatomy of the generative organs, and the methods of uterine diagnosis. The various diseases and displacements of the uterus were illustrated by the use of accurate drawings and models, and the recent operations in uterine surgery were demonstrated. Students were privileged to see operations performed in the private operating room of the hospital without extra charge.

MATERIA MEDICA AND THERAPEUTICS

The student acquired a thorough knowledge of these both from the didactic lectures, in which the physiological action of remedies, as applied to the treatment of disease, was discussed, and from practical experience with drugs in the Dispensary. He thus became familiar with the action, composition and doses of remedies.

DISEASES OF THE NERVOUS SYSTEM

The course consisted of lectures upon the diseases of the nervous system, illustrated, in the lecture room, by such cases, as well as in the clinical course in the Hospital.

PATHOLOGY

This course was made as practical as possible. Post mortem examinations were made in the presence of the class. The professor being post-mortem surgeon of the city, he was able to make material easily available for the study of pathology.

OBSTETRICS

The course was taught in as practical a manner as was possible, and was illustrated by plates, diagrams, models in wax and an excellent manikin. Advanced students were afforded an opportunity to see cases of actual labor. The use of forceps and other obstetrical instruments were taught. (Announcement of 1888-89).

DISEASES OF CHILDREN

There were didactic lectures, as well as an opportunity to acquire practical knowledge in diagnosis and treatment by attending the clinic.

DERMATOLOGY

This consisted of didactic lectures, where "admirable" drawings and plates, representing every variety of skin disease were shown, and of clinics on the subject.

MICROSCOPY

There was practical instruction in the mechanism of the microscope and training in its use. Injecting, staining, section-cutting and mounting were taught, as was microscopic examination of urine.

Students were admitted, free of charge, to the weekly lectures and practical demonstrations of the State Microscopical Society, in Baltimore. (In 1885, and again in 1886 and 1887, Lewis M. Eastman, A.M., M.D., was scheduled to deliver a series of lectures on microscopical technology, with physiological and pathological studies.)

THROAT AND LUNGS

This subject was taught as a clinical branch only, up to 1887.

DENTISTRY

Instruction in theory and practice of dentistry was given "by a skillful dentist to students who design practicing this specialty".

MEDICAL JURISPRUDENCE

This was a series of lectures "by a prominent member of the Bar of Baltimore", the series having been "warmly endorsed by the Faculty of another Medical Institution", where the lectures had been given for several sessions.

PRACTICAL ANATOMY

The work was under the supervision of the demonstrators, who directed the dissections, and spent much of their time in helping and guiding the students in their work. The dissecting room was open every day (until 10 P.M.), except on Sundays. There was an abundance of dissecting material, free of charge.

CLINICAL INSTRUCTION

This eminently practical instruction was carried on in classes limited to small size, and under the supervision of the various professors.

During the session clinical lectures were delivered in the amphitheatre of Baltimore University as follows:

1885:

> "Monday – Surgical Clinic, Prof. Biedler; Tuesday – Medical Clinic, Profs. Linthicum and Roseberry; Wednesday – Throat and Chest Clinic, Prof. Cockey; Thursday – Clinic on Eye and Ear Diseases, Prof. Reuling; Friday – Clinic on Diseases of Women and Children, Profs. Sellman and Whitehead; Saturday – Clinic on Diseases of the Nervous System, Prof. Hoopman."

As we have already seen, the Baltimore University Hospital, a part of the school, supplied students with all clinical advantages. Every variety of disease and injury was treated in the wards, thus providing ample opportunity for students to have bedside instruction, making this school "one of the most practical . . . of the country".

> "The Faculty desire to particularly call the attention of students to the superior advantages they have in hospital practice. They are invited and are expected to attend with the physician in charge, during his visit through the

wards, thereby practically making diagnoses of diseases at the commencement of their studies. In surgery, they act as assistants, acquiring the knowledge and use of instruments, applying bandages, and administering anaesthetics, as well as becoming experienced in surgical operations, which are varied, and probably more extensive than in any other hospital in the country." (Announcement of 1887-88.)

A resident physician was elected each year from the graduating class.

1885

"The Dispensary for eye and ear patients was held every Monday and Thursday, at one o'clock, by Prof. Reuling, and any cases requiring constant treatment or serious operations were entered as Hospital patients, so that students would have ample opportunity to follow the various phases of each case."
(In 1887 Prof. Evans replaced Prof. Reuling.)

From the Announcement for 1885-86:

"THE MARYLAND EYE AND EAR INFIRMARY.
Extract from Annual Report.

The Maryland Eye and Ear Infirmary owes its origin to the pressing necessity for an Infirmary especially devoted to the treatment of Eye and Ear Diseases, at a time when there was no provision made for the special treatment of such sufferers in the city of Baltimore. It is therefore the pioneer of its kind, not only in Baltimore, but south of Philadelphia, having been opened to the public on October 1, 1868. The solicitations of Dr. Reuling, the surgeon in charge, to a number of our prominent and charitable citizens, were echoed by a spirit of liberality which gradually aided him in placing the Institution on a permanent footing.

Already, at the end of the first year, the Institution had been visited by 1225 patients, who had come from almost every part of the Union for their relief. In the second year the city authorities, recognizing its value to the city, granted an annual appropriation for the maintenance of eight free beds for city patients suffering from Eye and Ear Diseases.

During the period of the last fifteen years nearly 40,000 eye and ear patients have received treatment, and over one thousand cases of cataract-operations alone have been performed, showing the most favorable statistics of results.

Lately the Infirmary has been divided into two departments. The MARYLAND EYE AND EAR INFIRMARY, which is now located at No. 233 East Baltimore Street, in the College Building of the Baltimore University, and the MARYLAND EYE AND EAR INSTITUTE for PRIVATE PATIENTS, located at No. 79 West Monument Street (Mount Vernon Place), which latter location has the advantage that it is the permanent residence of the surgeon in charge.

The management of the Institution has been during the fifteen years of its existence in the hands of a board of trustees, the names of whom were as follows: William Chesnut, Johns Hopkins, B. F. Newcomer, Christian Ax, G. W. Gail, William Wilkins, Jacob Trust, J. A. Nichols, J. J. Stewart, H. H. Graue, Frederick Raine, John B. Morris, Hon. G. W. Dobbin, Samuel M. Shoemaker, W. F. Frick, J. Harmanus Fisher, Hon John H. B. Latrobe, W. Prescott Smith, Hon. Chas. G. Kerr, C. Morton Stewart, Dr. W. Chew Van Bibber, Dr. James Cary Thomas, Dr. John Morris, Dr. J. L. Warfield, Dr. G. Reuling, Rev. John McElroy, S. J.; Rev. John Early, President Georgetown College; Admiral W. B. Shubrik, Hon. W. W. Corcoran, of Washington; John Donnan, Petersburg, Va.; E. O. Noelting, Richmond, Va.; Hon. W. H. Battle, Raleigh, N. C.; R. R. Bridges, Wilmington, N. C.; Hon. Carl Schurz, Missouri; Hon. Geo. P. Pendleton, Ohio; Frexerick Hecker, Illinois; and others.

The list of lady patronesses contains the names of our first and most influential ladies, who kindly took charge and control of the household of the Infirmary, viz., Mrs. W. H. Brune, Mrs. R. Brown, Mrs. A. F. Murdoch, Miss Eliza Berry, Mrs. Joel Gutman, Mrs. C. Ax, Mrs. Oden Bowie, Mrs. Rob. Barry, Mrs. J. C. Boyd, Mrs. Dr. Brooks, Miss K. Belt, Miss E. K. Bradford, Mrs. Geo. Coates, Miss R. Davis, Mrs. Fred Gibson, Mrs. Dr. Henkle, Mrs. John Hunter, Mrs. Spaulding, Mrs. H. Janes, Mrs. Ed. Johnston, Mrs. H. James, Mrs. Rob. Lehr, Mrs. Thos. Murdoch, Mrs. Aug. McLaughlin, Mrs. B. F. Newcomer, Mrs. Enoch Pratt, Mrs. W. H. Perot, Mrs. Oliver Parker, Mrs. Chas. Ridgely, of Hampton, Mrs. Lawrason Riggs, Mrs. A. T. Shriver, Mrs. Skipwith Gordon, Mrs. J. P. Thom, Mrs. J. J. Taylor, Mrs. G. P. Thomas, Mrs. Sam Wyman, and others.

The incorporation of this well-established institution into our Medical School is undoubtedly of very great importance and everlasting advantage to our students, in giving to them the most thorough training in acquiring knowledge of those two highly important branches of surgery, the Diseases of the Eye and Ear."

DAILY ORDER OF LECTURES – 1885-86

MONDAY

Hours		
9 to 1	*Clinics* at Bay View	
4	Anatomy	Prof. Wiley
5	Materia Medica	Prof. Roseberry

TUESDAY

9	Diseases of the Nervous System	Prof. Hoopman
10	Surgery	Prof. Biedler
11	Chemistry	Prof. Coffroth
12	Practice of Medicine	Prof. Linthicum
1	*Diseases of Women*	Prof. Sellman
4	Physiology	Prof. Blake
5	Diseases of Children	Prof. Whitehead

WEDNESDAY

9	Anatomy	Prof. Wiley
10	Obstetrics	Prof. Jones
11	Materia Medica	Prof. Roseberry
12	Diseases of Women	Prof. Sellman
1	Surgery	Prof. Biedler
4	*Diseases of Eye and Ear*	Prof. Reuling
5	Microscopy	Prof. Cockey

THURSDAY

9	Diseases of the Nervous System	Prof. Hoopman
10	Chemistry	Prof. Coffroth
11	Physiology	Prof. Blake
12	Practice of Medicine	Prof. Linthicum
1	Diseases of the Skin	Prof. Whitehead

FRIDAY

9	Anatomy	Prof. Wiley
10	Surgery	Prof. Biedler
11	Materia Medica	Prof. Roseberry
12	*Clinical Medicine*	Prof. Linthicum
1	*Diseases of Nervous System*	Prof. Hoopman
4	Diseases of the Eye and Ear	Prof. Reuling
5	Quiz	

SATURDAY

10	Microscopy	Prof. Cockey
11	Obstetrics	Prof. Jones
12	Physiology	Prof. Blake
1	*Surgery*	Prof. Biedler
4	Diseases of Women	Prof. Sellman
5	Quiz	

Clinics in Italics. Microscopic Instructions and Quizzes free.

THE CHANGING CURRICULUM

1887

A course in hygiene was introduced, it being felt that a knowledge of this branch was necessary to the practicing physician, in addition to which it was required by many of the State Boards of Health in their examinations. The course was fully taught and illustrated.

THROAT AND CHEST

This was a thorough course, both didactic and clinical, on all diseases of throat and chest. Students were taught the use of laryngoscope, stethoscope, sphygmograph, etc., and "made familiar with all the exploratory procedures necessary for a complete understanding" of the pathological changes in diseases of the throat and chest, as well as the treatment of these diseases. Students were required to examine patients and make diagnoses.

DAILY ORDER OF LECTURES. (1887-88)

MONDAY

Hours		
9		Quiz
10	Diseases of Nervous System	Prof. Hoopman
11	Materia Medica	Prof. Roseberry
12	*Diseases of Skin*	Prof. Whitehead
4	Hygiene	Prof. Parker
5	Anatomy	Prof. Wiley

TUESDAY

9	Chemistry and Toxicology	Prof. Wilson
10	Surgery	Prof. Biedler
11	Histology	Prof. Eastman
12	Practice of Medicine	Prof. Linthicum
1	*Diseases of Women*	Prof. Sellman
4	Physiology	Prof. Parker
5	Diseases of Eye and Ear	Prof. Evans

WEDNESDAY

9		Quiz
10	Obstetrics	Prof. Hartman
11	Materia Medica	Prof. Roseberry
12	*Diseases of Children*	Prof. Whitehead
1	*Diseases of Nervous System*	Prof. Hoopman
4	Anatomy	Prof. Wiley
5	Microscopy	Prof. Cockey

THURSDAY

9	Diseases of Nervous System	Prof. Hoopman
10	Surgery	Prof. Biedler
11	Physiology	Prof. Parker
12	*Practice of Medicine*	Prof. Linthicum
1	Diseases of Women	Prof. Sellman
4	Medical Jurisprudence	S. S. Pleasants, Esq.

FRIDAY

9	Chemistry and Toxicology	Prof. Wilson
10	Surgery	Prof. Biedler
11	Materia Medica	Prof. Roseberry
12	Practice of Medicine	Prof. Linthicum
1	*Diseases of Eye and Ear*	Prof. Evans
4	Diseases of Women	Prof. Sellman
5	Diseases of Children	Prof. Whitehead

SATURDAY

9	Anatomy	Prof. Wiley
10	Obstetrics	Prof. Hartman
11	Physiology	Prof. Parker
12	*Surgery*	Prof. Biedler

1	*Diseases of Throat and Chest*	Prof. Cockey
5	Chemistry and Toxicology . . . (Quiz)	Prof. Wilson

Clinics in Italics.

Dissecting Rooms opened daily.
Clinical instructions at Bay View.
The class will be shown cases of labor during the winter.
All Quizzes free.

GRADED COURSE

1888

"To better prepare students for a final examination, and to elevate the standard of medical studies, the Faculty have determined to adopt a *Graded Course* for those who desire to take advantage of a more prolonged and complete Study of Medicine. To this end they suggest that *such students as may elect* take the first course in Anatomy, Physiology, Materia Medica, and Chemistry. For the second, Gynaecology, Diseases of the Eye and Ear, Nervous and Mental Diseases, Hygiene, Surgery and Diseases of the Throat and Chest. And the third, Principles and Practice of Medicine, Obstetrics, Diseases of Children, Dermatology, Pathology, and Microscopy. *They desire students to attend all lectures* as far as possible. At the end of each year the student will be examined on the branches taken, *and should he fail, must repeat these studies during the succeeding course, and be examined.* Such studies as he shall pass will be *credited to him at the examination of the last course.*"

From this statement, quoted in full, from the Announcement for 1888-89, it is clear that the school had begun to move toward a three year graded curriculum. (See Section V.: F. Dobyns and Charles E. Grauel.)

The Announcement for 1889-90 had the following to say on the subject:

"GRADED COURSE

To better prepare students for a final examination and to elevate the standard of medical studies, the Faculty have determined to adopt a *Graded Course* for those who desire to take advantage of a more prolonged and complete Study of Medicine. To this end they suggest that *such students as may elect* take the first course in Anatomy, Physiology, Materia Medica, and Chemistry. For the second, Gynaecology, Diseases of the Eye and Ear, Nervous and Mental Diseases, Hygiene, Surgery and Diseases of the Throat and Chest. And the third, Principles and Practice of Medicine, Obstetrics, Diseases of Children, Dermatology, Pathology, and Microscopy. *They desire students to attend all lectures* as far as possible. At the end of each year the student will be examined on the branches taken, *and should he fail, must repeat these studies during the succeeding course, and be examined.* Such studies as he shall pass will be *credited to him at the examination of the last course.*"

Accompanying this change, the price of tickets was reduced, (see section on Fees).

A "Special Notice" in the Announcement for 1889-90 reads that there would be a quiz every Tuesday and Thursday evening, by a member of the Faculty, during the entire session, at which attendance was compulsory, (in Italics).

PATHOLOGY AND CLINICAL MEDICINE

1891

The professor treated of the pathology of disease in general – the nature, origin, cause and course of the body changes which mark a deviation from the normal, and of the functional disturbances and alterations in structure which occur in many special forms of disease. The course was made as practical as possible. There were post-mortems in the presence of the class.

(Clinical medicine was taught at the bedside and in the dispensary clinics, where almost every disease could be seen.)

DISEASES OF THE EYE AND EAR

Especial attention was given to "adjusting glasses for correction of errors of refraction of the eye". The weekly clinic on eye and ear provided an opportunity for full illustration. The rest of the course is described above, under that title. (A few years later students could attend two clinics, one at the Hospital, and the other at the Presbyterian Eye and Ear Hospital.)

MEDICAL CLASSICS

This was a course of instruction in Latin and Greek, to enable students to comprehend scientific terms and their derivatives, as well as to acquire a correct grammatical style in writing prescriptions. The school claimed that it was the only medical school in the country where provision had been made for giving such training. No examination was required in this subject.

There was a Spring course in that year, from April 1, until June 30 (1892). The fee was $15.00, that sum being credited toward the student's account for the following Winter session. This course was not only complete, covering every branch taught during the Winter session, but had the advantage of allowing the student to study diseases "clinically not possible during the regular Winter session." (No reference is again made to the two-term plan, in the Announcements, until that for 1897-98, and not again, thereafter.) Indeed, the Announcements for most years placed very heavy emphasis upon the great opportunities for acquiring a practical knowledge of medicine and surgery in the Hospital, where surgical operations were "varied, and probably more extensive than in any other hospital in the country."

1892:

The three-year graded course was now required.

"For the three years' Graded Course the system of instruction is as follows:

1. During the first year attendance is required upon the lectures in Anatomy, Physiology, Chemistry and Materia Medica and Therapeutics, and upon the Laboratories of Chemistry and Normal Histology. Dissection is also required.
2. During the second year the studies of the first year are continued, and in addition the courses in General Medicine, General Surgery, Obstetrics, Gynecology and Diseases of Children and Diseases of the Eye and Ear must be taken.* Dissections and laboratory work in normal and pathological histology are also required, and attendance upon the general and special clinics is obligatory.

   At the end of the second term the student, before being admitted to the third years' class, must stand final examinations in Anatomy, Physiology, Chemistry and Materia Medica and Therapeutics. He must also produce evidence that his work in dissecting room and laboratories has been satisfactory. Should he fail to pass a successful examination in any of these branches, a second opportunity will be afforded him before the opening of the regular session in the autumn; failing in this, the studies for the second year must be repeated.
3. The studies for the third year embrace Practice of Medicine, General Surgery, Obstetrics, Diseases of Women and Children and Diseases of the Eye and Ear and Pathology (gross and microscopic).* Attendance upon the various clinics is obligatory.

   At the end of the third session the student is admitted to the final examinations in Practice of Medicine, Surgery, Obstetrics, Diseases of Women and Children and Diseases of the Eye and Ear, and upon passing successfully in these branches, will be admitted to the degree of Doctor of Medicine."

****Beginning in 1893 the second and third year studies included diseases of the nervous system, throat and chest.***

DAILY ORDER OF LECTURES (1893)

MONDAY

Hours		
9	Chemistry	Prof. ....
10	Physiology	Prof. Eilau
11	Obstetrics	Prof. Wiley
12	*Clinical Medicine*	Prof. Cuddy
1	*Diseases of the Skin*	Prof. Horn
4	Diseases of Eye and Ear	Prof. Harlan
5	Anatomy	Prof. Whitehead

TUESDAY

9	Chemistry and Toxicology	Prof. ....
10	Physiology	Prof. Eilau
11	Surgery	Prof. Biedler
12	Principles and Practice of Medicine	Prof. Linthicum
1	*Diseases of Women*	Prof. Sellman
4	Eye and Ear	Prof. Harlan
5	Diseases of the Skin	Prof. A. Horn

WEDNESDAY

9	Pathology	Prof. Eilau
10	Obstetrics	Prof. Wiley
11	Materia Medica	Prof. Cuddy
12	*Diseases of Nervous System*	Prof. Reid
1	*Diseases of Children*	Prof. Horn
4	Anatomy	Prof. Whitehead
5	Diseases of Women	Prof. Sellman

THURSDAY

9	Physiology	Prof. Eilau
10	Diseases of Nervous System	Prof. Reid
11	Surgery	Prof. Biedler
12	Diseases of Women	Prof. Sellman
1	*Clinical Medicine*	Prof. Whitehead
4	Laboratory Work	

FRIDAY

9	Chemistry and Toxicology	Prof. ....
10	Materia Medica	Prof. Cuddy
11	Surgery	Prof. Biedler
12	Principles and Practice of Medicine	Prof. Linthicum
1	*Diseases of Eye and Ear*	Prof. Harlan
4	Medical Jurisprudence	H. Bryant, Esq.
5	Diseases of Children	Prof. Horn

SATURDAY

10	Obstetrics	Prof. Wiley
11	Anatomy	Prof. Whitehead
12	*Surgery*	Prof. Biedler
1	*Diseases of Throat and Chest*	Prof. Reid

Obstetric Clinics at the Lying-in Hospital when cases of labor occur.
Clinics in Italics.
Demonstrations in Anatomy daily.
The class will be shown cases of labor during the winter.

"CLINICS

During the session Clinical Lectures are delivered in the amphitheatre of the Baltimore University Hospital as follows:

MONDAY – Clinic on Diseases of Skin, Prof. Horn;
Clinical Medicine, Prof. Cuddy.
TUESDAY – Clinic on Diseases of Women, Prof. Sellman.
WEDNESDAY – Clinic on Diseases of Children, Prof. Horn;
Clinic on Diseases of Nervous System, Prof. Reid.
THURSDAY – Clinic on Practice of Medicine, Prof. Whitehead.
FRIDAY – Clinic on Diseases of Eye and Ear, Prof. Harlan.
SATURDAY – Clinic on Surgery, Prof. Biedler;
Clinic on Diseases of Throat and Chest, Prof. Reid."

HISTOLOGY

1896:

There were lectures and laboratory work in this subject. It was necessary to pass an examination in histology, before undertaking the work in physiology.

OPERATIVE, ORTHOPEDIC AND RECTAL SURGERY

Operative surgery was a complete course of operations upon the cadaver by the advanced students, under the direction of the professor; there were also lectures, as well as operations on patients in the hospital. Orthopedic and rectal surgery were taught by both didactic lectures and clinics. (Construction and application of apparatus for correcting deformities were demonstrated, and applied in the clinic – 1904-05.)

1897:

The Announcement for that year speaks of a second session from April 11 until July 1. This was optional, and consisted of a regular course of didactic, clinical and laboratory instruction by the full Faculty. It did not count as a course for graduation, although there was a regular examination for the degree of doctor of medicine at its termination for those who had previously completed three full courses at this or other regular medical schools and had complied with all requirements for graduation. Laboratory work completed during this session was credited on the ensuing winter course. Two obvious advantages of such a course were that a student had the opportunity of benefiting from one more "exposure" before taking the final examination, and, that by completing the laboratory course in advance, a student had that much free time, for whatever purpose he desired, during the session of the following winter. The fees for the second session were smaller than for the first session – (matriculation $5.00, tickets for lectures $40.00).

The same Announcement stipulates that at the end of the first year students would be expected to pass an examination on osteology, histology, inorganic chemistry and materia medica. (Such a requirement, at the end of the *first* year, had not previously been specified.) Other changes were the addition, to the third year curriculum, of a course in diseases of the skin and the addition of diseases of the nervous system, throat and chest, and pathology, to the list of examination subjects at the end of the third year, for the degree of doctor of medicine.

Other announcements in 1897 were that, beginning in 1898 matriculates in this school would hereafter have to attend at least four courses, each of not less than six months duration, no two courses of which shall have been in the same calendar year; further, the Faculty had decided, after careful consideration "to conduct the Hospital along *strictly temperance lines*, discarding the use of alcoholic beverages entirely, in the treatment and management of patients; at the Lying-In Hospital members of the graduating class were being taken, in groups of three or four, after being notified promptly whenever labor occurred, to observe the process. These groups were assigned, in rotation, to attend labor cases in the hospital, under the immediate supervision of the professor of obstetrics, and were thoroughly instructed in vaginal examinations (and the antiseptic precautions to be taken in making such examinations), abdominal palpation, diagnosis of presentation, and in treatment of the case preparatory to, during and after labor.

1898:

The session was of longest duration to date (October 1 to April 15, with final examinations beginning on April 1). The curriculum included a full series of didactic lectures on each of the following subjects: Practice of Medicine, Obstetrics, Surgery, Diseases of Women, Chemistry, Toxicology and Microscopy, Diseases of the Eye and Ear, Diseases of Children and Diseases of the Skin, Materia Medica and Therapeutics, Diseases of the Nervous System and Diseases of the Throat and Chest, Anatomy, Physiology, Pathology, Bacteriology, Histology, Hygiene and Medical Jurisprudence. The didactic lectures were fully illustrated by clinics, given every day of the session. These studies were distributed as follows:

> "1. During the first year attendance is required upon the lectures on Anatomy, Physiology, Chemistry, and Materia Medica and Therapeutics, and upon the Laboratories of Chemistry and Normal Histology. Dissection is also required.
>
> 2. At the end of the first year the student will be expected to pass an examination in Osteology, Histology, Inorganic Chemistry and Materia Medica. During the second year the studies of the first year are continued, and, in addition, the courses in General Medicine, General Surgery, Obstetrics, Gynecology, and Diseases of Children, and Diseases of the Eye and Ear, Diseases of the Nervous System and Throat and Chest must be taken. Dissections and laboratory work in Normal and Pathological Histology are also required,

and attendance upon the general and special clinics is obligatory.

At the end of the second term the student, before being admitted to the third year's class, must stand final examinations in Anatomy, Physiology, Chemistry, and Materia Medica and Therapeutics. He must also produce evidence that his work in the dissecting room and laboratories has been satisfactory. Should he fail to pass a successful examination in any of these branches, a second opportunity will be afforded him before the opening of the regular session in the autumn; failing in this, the studies for the second year must be repeated.

3. The studies for the third year embrace Practice of Medicine, General Surgery, Obstetrics, Diseases of Women and Children, and Diseases of the Eye and Ear, and Pathology (gross and microscopic), Diseases of the Nervous System and Throat and Chest, and Diseases of the Skin. Attendance upon the various clinics is obligatory.

At the end of the third session the student is admitted to the final examinations in Pathology, Therapeutics, Medical Jurisprudence and Hygiene.

At the end of the fourth session final examinations will be held upon Practice of Medicine, General Surgery, Clinical Surgery, Diseases of Women, Diseases of Children, Diseases of Eye and Ear, Obstetrics, Diseases of the Nervous System; and upon passing successfully in these branches will be admitted to the degree of Doctor of Medicine." (1898)

1900:

A special course in Psycho-Therapeutics was announced. It was given by Dr. Nathan Herman "an expert hypnotist and psycho-therapeutist". There were ten lectures, with demonstrations, along with dispensary and hospital clinics, the latter intended to give every participant in the course

> "abundant opportunity to apply the instructions obtained, on cases selected from our numerous clinics, under the careful guidance of the instructor".

The course was optional, but students were encouraged to take it, as it was believed to give practitioners a practical knowledge of the most efficient treatment for insomnia, functional nervous derangements and psycho-pathological states, a safe and sure means of curing alcoholism, addiction to morphine and other drugs and other "vicious bodily habits" and enable doctors, "on occasions where drug anaesthetics are counter-indicated, to produce surgical anaesthesia without them". The fee, including instruction in all the various methods of producing the hypnotic state, the giving of suggestions in this as well as in the normal state, the production of surgical anaesthesia, etc. was $5.00.

The University had decided that since educational institutions were now showing greater recognition of the importance of the development of the body as well as the mind, through a program of athletics, it too would encourage and give attention to physical culture, but not to an extent which would interfere with regular medical studies. There would be outdoor sports, and, immediately upon the opening of the session football and baseball clubs should be formed. The University owned "a complete outfit for football", and it would be placed at the disposal of the clubs.

1902:

Electro-Therapeutics and its prerequisite Electrophysics, were announced. These were to be taught in a thoroughly practical manner supplemented by practical demonstrations from time to time. "Specially touched upon" were: the physiology of alternating currents and hydro-electric methods; therapeutic use of electricity in diseases of the nervous system, gynecology and surgery; physics of Roentgen rays; skiagraphy; the practical application of the Roentgen rays in medicine and surgery.

Special attention was to be given to the

> "technique and physiology of direct, alternating and static currents of electricity and Hydro-electric methods. All of the most modern and approved methods of Electricity, therapeutically applied, will be described and illustrated, with the end in view that the lack of confidence usually displayed by the general and special practitioner in applying Electricity to his patients may be dispelled and a confidence installed based on thorough knowledge of these subjects."

The Announcement for 1903-04 speaks, for the first time, of recitations, and supplies information about the number of hours being devoted to each subject in that and immediately previous years:

"COURSE OF INSTRUCTION

The course of instruction in this School embraces Lectures, Recitations and Demonstrations, with Laboratory and Clinical work, extending over four courses of six months each in four separate years.

FIRST YEAR

ANATOMY – Three hours a week throughout the session, and with dissections under the constant attention of the Demonstrator.

PHYSIOLOGY – Three hours lectures, with laboratory work.

CHEMISTRY – Two lectures each week, and laboratory work and recitations during entire session.

HISTOLOGY – Two hours recitations, with laboratory work each week.

MATERIA MEDICA AND PHARMACY – Two lectures each week, with quizzes and recitations.

SECOND YEAR

During the second year the studies of the first year are continued, to which are added the following:

THERAPEUTICS – Two lectures a week, with quizzes.

PATHOLOGY – Two hours recitations, with two hours laboratory work each week.

HYGIENE – One lecture each week.

BACTERIOLOGY – Two hours recitations, with two hours laboratory work each week.

At the end of the second year final examinations are held in Anatomy, Physiology, Chemistry and Materia Medica.

The student must also produce evidence that his work in the dissecting room and laboratories has been satisfactory. Should he fail to pass a successful examination in any of these branches, a second opportunity will be afforded him before the opening of the next regular session.

THIRD YEAR

During the third year the studies of Therapeutics, Pathology and Hygiene are continued. To these are added:

PRACTICE OF MEDICINE – Two didactic lectures each week, with two hours Clinics in the Amphitheatre and at the bedside.

SURGERY – Three hours lectures each week, with three clinics in the Amphitheatre. Ample opportunity will be given the students for observation, and for assistance at these clinics, and also in the private operating rooms.

OBSTETRICS – Two hours each week, with recitations and demonstrations.

GYNECOLOGY – Two lectures and two clinics each week.

DISEASES OF THE EYE AND EAR – Two lectures each week with clinics.

DISEASES OF THE NERVOUS SYSTEM, THROAT AND CHEST – Three lectures, with recitations and clinics.

MEDICAL JURISPRUDENCE – One lecture each week.

DERMATOLOGY – One lecture and clinic each week.

DISEASES OF CHILDREN – One lecture and one clinic each week.

At the end of the third year Students are admitted to final examinations in Pathology, Therapeutics, Medical Jurisprudence and Hygiene.

FOURTH YEAR

The studies of the fourth year are largely Clinical, there being two hours each day for this method of instruction. Constant attendance upon these clinics is positively required of the Students of this year's class and all will be afforded opportunities for close examinations, and for assistance in all departments. By this method of instruction, the Senior Students are practically trained in the use of their knowledge and senses for the diagnosis and treatment of disease. Didactic lectures, recitations and quizzes will however be maintained throughout the entire session, at the close of which final examinations will be held upon the Practice of Medicine, Surgery, Gynecology, Pediatrics, Dermatology, Otology, Ophthalmology, Obstetrics and Diseases of the Nervous System. All Students who successfully pass these examinations and who have complied with all other requirements will be admitted to the degree of Doctor of Medicine."

1904-05:

The session now ran from October 1 until May 1, following.

REQUIREMENTS FOR ADMISSION

1884-1891 (inclusive)

1. A student must be possessed of good moral character.
2. If not a matriculate of some "literary institution" or medical college, the student was required to furnish satisfactory evidence of having had a good "English" education.

1892:

A preliminary entrance examination, in accordance with the rules adopted by the Association of American Medical Colleges, was required of all persons except "students, matriculates or graduates of reputable Colleges of Literature, Sciences and the Arts or graduates of High Schools of the first grade or Normal Schools directly supported by the State (also matriculates in medicine and graduates in dentistry or pharmacy) . . . (or) students passing the entrance examination as provided by the Statute of the State of New York . . ." Students "conditioned or unable to undergo the examination in Latin" were to be afforded a course of instruction during the Freshman year in the elements of that language, stressing, as far as possible, the derivation of medical and pharmaceutical terms. (The work by Robinson, on medical derivation and terminology, was suggested as a suitable textbook for this course.) The entrance examination consisted of "writing legibly and correctly an English composition of not less than two hundred words; . . . the translation of easy Latin prose; . . . elements of algebra or higher arithmetic; . . . elementary physics". This examination must be passed before entering the Junior year. The examination was "reasonable, and . . . given to ascertain whether students (were) sufficiently educated to profit by medical study".

REQUIREMENTS FOR GRADUATION

1885

1. A candidate must have attended at least two courses of lectures at this college, or one course here, following one or more at some other medical school which was recognized by this Faculty.
2. Fitness to graduate was based upon good moral character, habits, industry, and regular attendance upon the instruction afforded by the College. (The Faculty laid strong emphasis upon the fact that complying with all the technical requirements still left the candidate subject to the right of the Faculty to make moral as well as intellectual qualifications an element in their decision. "Open irregularity of conduct, negligence, habitual and prolonged absence from lectures will always be regarded as obstacles to the attainment of a degree.")
3. A candidate must pass a final examination on the various branches of medicine taught in this school, the decision resting with the "majority of all the votes of the Faculty".
4. A candidate must write and present an original thesis on some medical topic. (In 1886, and after, the choice of either a thesis or a clinical report of not less than six cases of disease, drawn up from the student's own observations, was allowed.)
5. He must produce evidence of having attended clinical lectures on medicine and surgery and performed the required work in practical anatomy.

1891-92

Every candidate for examination for the degree must have had "one session's actual work in laboratory on microscopic examinations of urine, toxicology, and practical chemistry".

1892

1. A candidate had to be at least twenty-one years of age, ", . . and must give satisfactory evidence of possessing a good, moral character, *which includes unexceptionable conduct while at the college.** The Faculty reserves the right to terminate the connection of any student with the institution at any time on the ground of what they may deem moral or mental unfitness for the profession."

*(*Italics in the original)*

2. The candidate must have pursued the study of medicine for three years and have attended

three full courses of lectures of at least six months each, no two having been delivered in one twelvemonth. Of these, the first two could have been at other recognized medical colleges, but the last must be at this College.

3. The thesis and written examination requirements, as well as those dealing with attendance at medical and surgical clinics, practical anatomy and practical chemistry, discussed above, in force in the earlier years, remained the same.

1898

It was now obligatory to pursue the study of medicine for four years and to attend at least four courses of medical instruction, of not less than six months each, no two courses being in the same calendar year. Of these, the last year must have been at this school.

ANNUAL COMMENCEMENT
at
HARRIS' ACADEMY OF MUSIC

March 21st, *1894*

PROGRAMME

OVERTURE – "Jolly Robbers" .... Suppe
SELECTION – "Sounds from the South" .... Lax
MEDLEY – "Popular Airs" .... Moses
RUSSIAN DANCE – "La Czarine" .... Pettie

Flute Solo by PROF. FRED LAX

Prayer
REV. J. FRED. HEISSE

Announcement of the Graduates by the Secretary
PROF. H. H. BIEDLER, M.D.

WALTZ – "Thirze" .... Lenz

Conferring of Degrees
GEN'L R. H. CARR

Graduates called by the Dean
PROF. E. W. EILAU, M.D.

PATROL – "Return of the Troops" .... Eilenberg

Oration
GEORGE EDWARD REED, D.D., LL.D.
President of Dickinson College, Pa.

MARCH – "Cuirrassier Ottaque" .... Michaels

Benediction

MARCH – "Harris, Britton & Dean" .... Lax

Musical Director – PROF. FRED LAX

FEES

1884:

Matriculation Fee	$ 5.00
General Ticket (complete course of lectures)	120.00
Dissecting Ticket	10.00
Graduating Fee	30.00

Students who could satisfy the Faculty that they were without sufficient means to defray the expenses of a medical education could take a competitive examination in mathematics, elementary physics and Latin, Greek, French or German held at the College during the session. (There were only a few such scholarships. Successful candidates paid matriculation, dissecting and graduation fees.)

No fee was charged for a third course of lectures after having attended one or more at this school. Graduates were admitted upon payment of the matriculation fee and cost of materials. Persons who so desired, could take one or more special courses, upon payment of the matriculation fee and the price of each of the professors' tickets involved. All quizzes were free of charge.

Board, including heat and lights, could be had for from $3.00 to $5.00 per week.

1886:

A person who had already attended two courses in other schools and recent graduates of other schools were required to pay the matriculation fee and $60.00, (half of the regular fee).

(The matriculation ticket must be countersigned by the professors and shown, upon demand, to the janitor.)

1887:

Holders of scholarships paid $60.00 for the professors' tickets.

1888:

While there was no fee for a third course, if ungraded, a charge was made for a third, graded course, when this was introduced.

Patients from rural districts wishing to be treated at the Hospital could do so "in either the private or public wards at charges from $4.00 to $10.00 per week, depending upon such extras as they may desire".

1889:

Tickets for the full course of lectures	$50.00
Tickets for one branch	5.00
Practical Anatomy	10.00
Matriculation fee	5.00
Graduation fee	30.00

(The decline in the schedule of fees is probably related to the change to the three-year graded curriculum.) The College made the following statement about scholarships:

> "To meet the exigencies of the times, and to enable worthy young men of limited means an opportunity of acquiring a medical education, the Faculty, after due deliberation, have placed the Fees at an uniform rate. Hence all students are admitted on the same standing. Where scholarships have been granted, much dissatisfaction has been caused by their improper distribution, although care has been exercised in granting them. Some capable of paying full fees have received them. The standard of education will be fully maintained." (1889)

With the fee for the full course set at $50.00, students who had already attended two full courses in other regular schools, and recent graduates of other schools, were required to pay matriculation fee and only half of the regular fee, (which now became half of $50.00, i.e., $25.00). As was the case previously, there was no charge for a third, ungraded course, for students who had already taken one or more courses in this school.

1892-92:

There was a fee of $5.00 per session for the use of chemicals.

1892:

The practical anatomy fee and the practical chemistry materials fee must each be paid for two years. Tickets for one branch became $10.00.

Students who had already attended three full courses (raised from two full courses in earlier years) and recent graduates of other schools paid the matriculation fee and $25.00 (half of the regular fee).

Students who had taken two or more courses in this school were not required to pay a fee for a fourth course.

1897:

The fees for the second session were:
Matriculation $5.00, lecture tickets $40.00.

1898:

In addition to the fees stated for previous years, there were fees in histology ($5.00), and pathology ($5.00).

1900:

The fee for the course in psycho-therapeutics was $5.00. Tickets for the full course were now raised to $75.00.

PRIZES

1885:

FACULTY PRIZE: "As a stimulus to excellence" the Faculty offered a gold medal to the graduate who had "the best general examination".

HOOPMAN PRIZE: Professor Hoopman offered a gold medal for "the second best general examination".

BIEDLER PRIZE: Professor Biedler offered a pocket-case of surgical instruments for "the best examination in his branch", (surgery).

REULING PRIZE: Professor Reuling offered an ophthalmoscope for "the best examination in ophthalmology".

1903-04:

UNIVERSITY PRIZE: Same as the former Faculty Prize.

The THEODORE COOKE, JR. OPHTHALMIC PRIZE: An ophthalmoscope to the student most proficient in its use and in passing the best examination in ophthalmology and otology.

The J. A. MELVIN OBSTETRICAL PRIZE: To the student passing the best examination in obstetrics.

SURGERY PRIZE: To the senior making the highest mark in surgery – a pocket operating case, presented by the International Journal of Surgery Co., of New York.

PRIZE WINNERS

	Faculty	*Hoopman*	*Biedler*	*Reuling*
1885:		D. R. Rothrock		
1887:	David W. Jones	John S. Jackson	J. P. Brown	J. J. Brockbank (J. I.?)

1904:

University Prize . . . . Charles F. Wilinsky, Mass.
The Theodore Cook, Jr. Ophthalmic Prize . . . . Louis P. Knoll, N. Y.
The J. A. Melvin Obstetrical Prize . . . . Charles F. Wilinsky, Mass.
The International Journal of Surgery Prize . . . . Geo. W. Bell, N. J.
The Dean's Prize . . . . Charles L. Bates, W. Va.

HONORABLE MENTION *

C. S. Bates . . . . West Virginia
Erwin Reissman . . . . New York
George W. Bell . . . . New Jersey
James E. Lynch . . . . Connecticut
Charles T. Schwatka . . . . Maryland
Joseph MacDonald, Jr. . . . . New York
John Scott . . . . Pennsylvania
David W. Bloom . . . . Maryland
Cardinal C. McCormick . . . . Pennsylvania
Austin F. O'Mally . . . . Massachusetts

* "The ten students who pass the best general examination."

OFFICERS OF THE ALUMNI ASSOCIATION OF THE BALTIMORE UNIVERSITY SCHOOL OF MEDICINE

1885
President, DR. GEORGE W. MC ELVEEN
Vice-President, DR. N. N. WARLICK
Recording Sec'y., DR. C. T. WEEKS
Corresponding
Secretary, DR. D. R. ROTHROCK
Treasurer, DR. L. A. LAUCK

–

Executive Committee
The President and Treasurer of
the Association, and
DR. WILSON P. FULLER

1886
President, DR. W. A. B. SEELMAN
Vice-President, DR. R. C. ELLIS
Recording Sec'y., DR. D. W. JONES
Corresponding
Secretary, DR. J. P. BROWN
Treasurer, DR. C. S. PARKER

–

Executive Committee
The President and Treasurer of
the Association, and
DR. JOHN I. BROCKBANK

1888
President, DR. THOMAS J. EDWARDS
Vice-Presidents, DR. JULIAN S. PATTERSON
DR. LUDWIG HAMMER
Recording Sec'y., DR. ELWOOD HUGGINS
Corresponding
Secretary, DR. S. M. SNYDER
Treasurer, DR. FRED W. WEBER

–

Executive Committee
The President and Treasurer of
the Association, and
DR. W. O. GRIGGS

1890
President, THOS. A. MILLIMAN
1st Vice-President, R. C. RASIN
2nd Vice-President, W. H. TOLSON
Secretary, EDWARD PLUMMER
Treasurer, J. WARD WILLSON

–

Executive Committee
J. S. Pattison, M.D.
H. G. Baird, M.D.
F. W. Weber, M.D.

1894
J. C. SCHOFIELD, M.D., President
R. P. C. SCHEDIT, M.D., Vice-President
O. M. REINHARDT, M.D.,
2nd Vice-President
J. C. OHLENDORF, M.D., Secretary
P. B. WILSON, JR., M.D., Treasurer

–

Executive Committee
J. L. CROSSMORE, M.D.
JOHN ROTH, M.D.
I. J. WOODWARD, M.D.

DATA for COMPARISON and EVALUATION

The general tone of the Announcements, regarding teaching facilities and curricular offerings, was rather unpretentious. Most of the immodesty displayed was related to its clinical advantages and the new buildings which it planned to erect, (but did not, because it suffered extinction before this could be achieved). Below are a few of its claims:

> "CLINICAL INSTRUCTION
> The Clinical instruction is given under the supervision of the various Professors. The Faculty would call attention of students, that these Clinics are larger* than any other Medical Institution in the United States. And the system of forming small classes, gives each student an opportunity of seeing more cases of actual diagnosis and treatment than is usually seen in many years of practice." (Announcement for 1889-90, page 10.)

It regarded itself as "one of the most practical schools", (Announcement of 1891-92, page 12), and that in surgery the students acted as

> "assistants, acquiring the knowledge and use of instruments, applying bandages and administering anesthetics, as well as becoming experienced in

> surgical operations, which are varied, and probably more extensive than in any other hospital in the country." (Announcement of 1891-92, page 12.)

*In the Announcement for 1892-93, (page 14) this was changed to "as large as", and in 1894-95, (page 12), "as large as those of any medical school in the United States, and, by far, larger than the majority.

Great stress was placed upon clinical instruction and the special advantages which this college could offer its students because of the abundance of clinical materials and the important features of instruction which flowed therefrom: "the peculiarities of each case are explained, the approproate treatment is prescribed, and the requisite surgical operations are performed in the presence of the class".

Stress was also placed upon laboratory instructions, a feature largely missing in earlier schools. The curriculum was

> "*didactic and clinical*, and rendered *thoroughly practical and progressive* in *all* departments of a complete medical education. Thus, *Laboratory* instruction and manipulations will form a prominent feature in the curriculum, and students will be made familiar with the instruments and appliances so often called for in modern practice." (Announcement for 1892-93, page 5).

The length of the session increased from the original five-and-one-half month to the seven-month term of the last years, and the requirements for graduation changed from two sessions to three, and finally to four. The curriculum became more complex, and graded. The recitation, as a teaching method, is first stipulated very late in the life of the school (1903). The fourth year was said to be "largely clinical", but a glance at the description of the work of the fourth year shows that there were but two hours each day for this method of instruction in that year, (Announcement of 1904-05, page 15), the rest of the day being devoted to didactic lectures, recitations and quizzes. In all of these things this school differed from its predecessors, the extinct schools of Philadelphia, which had shorter sessions, a two year ungraded curriculum of less complex nature, and little experience in clinic and hospital.

The Baltimore University School of Medicine, unlike its contemporaries, maintained a system of required preceptors down to the year 1904-05, the last year for which Announcements have been located.

More emphasis than usual was placed upon the good behavior of students while attending this school, and upon good character as a test for winning the M.D. degree.

Interesting features of this school were:

(a) A course in psycho-therapeutics, which lasted but one year, (1900-01).
(b) A course in electro-therapeutics and electro-physics, including skiagraphy, (1902-04).
(c) A second session – April 11 to July 1. This was a regular (optional) course, but did not count for graduation. However, there was a regular examination for the M.D. degree at the conclusion of this course, for those who had previously completed all requirements at this or other regular medical schools. Laboratory work completed during that session was, however, credited on the next winter course (1897).

III. (A) FACULTY

SESSION OF 1885-86

JAMES G. LINTHICUM, M.D.
(President Faculty)
Professor of Principles and Practice of Medicine

ZEPHANIAH K. WILEY, M.D.
Professor of Anatomy and Dean of the Faculty

HAMPSON H. BIEDLER, M.D.
Professor of Principles and Practice of Surgery and of Clinical Surgery

H. JANNEY COFFROTH, M.D.
Professor of Chemistry and Toxicology

JOHN D. BLAKE, M.D.
Professor of Physiology

GEORGE REULING, A.M., M.D.
Professor of Diseases of the Eye and Ear

WILLIAM A. B. SELLMAN, M.D.
Professor of Diseases of Women

BENJAMIN S. ROSEBERRY, M.D.
Professor of Materia Medica and Therapeutics

SYLVESTER V. HOOPMAN, A.M., M.D.
Professor of Diseases of the Nervous System and Pathology

WILLIAM A. JONES, M.D.
Professor of Obstetrics

ALFRED WHITEHEAD, M.D., M.R.C.S.
Professor of Diseases of Children and Dermatology

CHARLES H. COCKEY, M.D.
Professor of Microscopy and
Diseases of the Nose and Throat

GEORGE C. SHANNON, M.D.
Demonstrator of Anatomy

Clinical Assistants

JOHN W. LINTHICUM, M.D.
RANDOLPH W. SMITH, M.D.
L. RIDGELEY WILSON, M.D.

SESSION OF 1886-87

JAMES G. LINTHICUM, M.D.
(President Faculty)
Professor of Principles and
Practice of Medicine
ZEPHANIAH K. WILEY, M.D.
Professor of Anatomy
HAMPSON H. BIEDLER, M.D.
Professor of Principles and Practice
of Surgery and of Clinical
Surgery
H. JANNEY COFFROTH, M.D.
Professor of Physiology
GEORGE REULING, A.M., M.D.
Professor of Diseases of the
Eye and Ear
GEORGE A. HARTMAN, M.D.
Professor of Obstetrics
WILLIAM A. B. SELLMAN, M.D.
Professor of Diseases of Women

BENJAMIN S. ROSEBERRY, M.D.
Professor of Materia Medica and
Therapeutics
SYLVESTER V. HOOPMAN, A.M., M.D.
Professor of Diseases of the
Nervous System and Pathology
ALFRED WHITEHEAD, M.D., M.R.C.S.
Professor of Diseases of Children
and Dermatology
CHARLES H. COCKEY, M.D.
Professor of Microscopy and
Diseases of the Nose and Throat
P. B. WILSON, M.D.
Professor of Chemistry and Toxicology
GEORGE E. NELSON
Lecturer Medical Jurisprudence
GEORGE C. SHANNON, M.D.
Demonstrator of Anatomy

C. S. PARKER, M.D.
Dispensary Physician

Clinical Assistants

J. W. LINTHICUM, M.D.
J. P. BROWN, M.D.
L. RIDGELEY WILSON, M.D.
J. D. KREMIEN, M.D.
J. E. WILLETT, M.D.

SESSION OF 1887-88

JAMES G. LINTHICUM, M.D.
(President Faculty)
Professor of Principles and
Practice of Medicine
ZEPHANIAH K. WILEY, M.D.
Professor of Anatomy and
Clinical Surgery
HAMPSON H. BIEDLER, M.D.
Professor of Principles and
Practice of Surgery and of
Clinical Surgery
WILLIAM A. B. SELLMAN, M.D.
Professor of Diseases of Women
BENJAMIN S. ROSEBERRY, M.D.
Professor of Materia Medica
Therapeutics, and Clinical Medicine
SYLVESTER V. HOOPMAN, A.M., M.D.
Professor of Diseases of the
Nervous System, and Pathology
ALFRED WHITEHEAD, M.R.C.S.
Professor of Diseases of
Children, and Dermatology

CHARLES H. COCKEY, M.D.
Professor of Microscopy, and
Diseases of the Throat and Chest
PIERCE B. WILSON, M.D.
Professor of Chemistry and Toxicology
GEORGE A. HARTMAN, M.D.
Professor of Obstetrics
CHARLES S. PARKER, M.D.
Professor of Physiology and Hygiene
THOMAS B. EVANS, M.D.
Professor of Ophthalmology and Otology
S. S. PLEASANTS, ESQ.
Lecturer on Medical Jurisprudence
WILLIAM T. CATHELL, M.D.
E. HALL RUTLEDGE, M.D.
Demonstrators of Anatomy
Z. K. WILEY, M.D., Dean

SESSION OF 1888-89

JAMES G. LINTHICUM, M.D.
(President of Faculty)
Professor of Principles and
Practice of Medicine
ZEPHANIAH K. WILEY, M.D.
Professor of Anatomy and
Clinical Surgery
HAMPSON H. BIEDLER, M.D.
Professor of Principles and Practice
of Surgery and of Clinical Surgery
SYLVESTER V. HOOPMAN, A.M., M.D.
Professor of Diseases of the Nervous
System and Pathology
WILLIAM A. B. SELLMAN, M.D.
Professor of Diseases of Women
CHARLES H. COCKEY, M.D.
Professor of Microscopy, and Diseases
of Throat and Chest
PIERCE B. WILSON, M.D.
Professor of Chemistry and Toxicology

GEORGE A. HARTMAN, M.D.
Professor of Obstetrics
THOMAS B. EVANS, M.D.
Professor of Ophthalmology
and Otology
LOUIS C. HORN, M.D.
Professor of Diseases of
Children and Dermatology
JOHN W. C. CUDDY, A.M., M.D.
Professor of Materia Medica,
Therapeutics and Clinical Medicine
E. MILLER REID, M.D.
Professor of Physiology and Hygiene
HOWARD BRYANT, A.B., Esq.
Lecturer on Medical Jurisprudence
WILLIAM T. CATHELL, M.D.
E. HALL RUTLEDGE, M.D.
Demonstrators of Anatomy

Z. K. WILEY, M.D., (Dean)

SESSION OF 1889-90

JAMES G. LINTHICUM, M.D.
(President Faculty)
Professor of Principles and
Practice of Medicine
ZEPHANIAH K. WILEY, M.D.
Professor of Obstetrics
HAMPSON H. BIEDLER, M.D.
Professor of Principles and Practice
of Surgery and of Clinical Surgery
SYLVESTER V. HOOPMAN, A.M., M.D.
Professor of Diseases of the
Nervous System and Pathology
WILLIAM A. B. SELLMAN, M.D.
Professor of Diseases of Women
PIERCE B. WILSON, M.D.
Professor of Chemistry,
Toxicology and Microscopy
THOMAS B. EVANS, M.D.
Professor of Ophthalmology
and Otology

LOUIS C. HORN, M.D.
Professor of Diseases of
Children and Dermatology
JOHN W. C. CUDDY, A.M., M.D.
Professor of Materia Medica,
Therapeutics and Clinical Medicine
E. MILLER REID, M.D.
Professor of Physiology, Hygiene,
and Diseases of Throat and Chest
ALFRED WHITEHEAD, M.R.C.S.
Professor of Anatomy
HOWARD BRYANT, A.B., Esq.
Lecturer on Medical Jurisprudence
WILLIAM T. CATHELL, M.D.
Demonstrator of Anatomy
J. WARD WILLSON, M.D., Prosector
Z. K. WILEY, M.D., (Dean)

SESSION OF 1890-91

The same as in 1889-90, with the following exceptions:

Dr. Hoopman was no longer on the Faculty. Emanuel W. Eilau, M.D. became professor of physiology, pathology and hygiene. Dr. Reid was now professor of diseases of the nervous system and diseases of the throat and chest. A. B. Lyman, M.D., L.M., was lecturer on medical classics. H. B. Gwynn, M.D., was an additional demonstrator of anatomy.

SESSION OF 1891-92

JAMES G. LINTHICUM, M.D.
Professor of Principles and
Practice of Medicine
ZEPHANIAH K. WILEY, M.D.
Professor of Obstetrics
HAMPSON H. BIEDLER, M.D.
Professor of Principles and
Practice of Surgery and
Clinical Surgery

WILLIAM A. B. SELLMAN, M.D.
Professor of Diseases of Women
PIERCE B. WILSON, M.D. (President)
Professor of Chemistry, Toxicology,
and Microscopy
THOMAS B. EVANS, M.D., (Dean)
Professor of Pathology and
Clinical Medicine

LOUIS C. HORN, M.D.
Professor of Diseases of
Children and Dermatology
J. W. C. CUDDY, A.M., M.D.
Professor of Materia Medica
and Therapeutics
E. MILLER REID, M.D.
Professor of Diseases of Nervous
System and Diseases of
Throat and Chest
ALFRED WHITEHEAD, M.D., M.R.C.S.
Professor of Anatomy
EMANUEL W. EILAU, M.D.
Professor of Physiology and Hygiene
HERBERT HARLAN, A.M., M.D.
Professor of Ophthalmology
and Otology

Lecturers

HOWARD BRYANT, A.B., Esq.
Lecturer on Medical Jurisprudence
A. B. LYMAN, M.D., L.M.
Lecturer on Medical Classics
J. E. WILLING, M.D.
Demonstrator of Anatomy
H. C. SILVER, M.D.
Prosector and Assistant
Demonstrator of Anatomy

SESSION OF 1892-93

JAMES C. LINTHICUM, M.D., President
Professor of Principles and
Practice of Medicine
ZEPHANIAH K. WILEY, M.D.
Professor of Obstetrics
HAMPSON H. BIEDLER, M.D.
Professor of Principles and Practices
of Surgery and Clinical Surgery
WILLIAM A. B. SELLMAN, M.D., Treas.
Professor of Diseases of Women
LOUIS C. HORN, M.D.
Professor of Diseases of
Children and Dermatology
*..........................
Professor of Chemistry, Toxicology
and Microscopy
J. W. C. CUDDY, A.M., M.D.
Professor of Materia Medica and
Therapeutics and Clinical Medicine
E. MILLER REID, M.D.
Professor of Diseases of the Nervous
System and Diseases of the
Throat and Chest
ALFRED WHITEHEAD, M.D., M.R.C.S.
Professor of Anatomy and
Clinical Surgery

EMANUEL W. EILAU, M.D., Dean
Professor of Physiology, Hygiene,
and Pathology
HERBERT HARLAN, A.M., M.D.
Professor of Ophthalmology and Otology

Lecturers

HOWARD BRYANT, A.B., Esq.
Lecturer on Medical Jurisprudence
J. E. WILLING, M.D.
Demonstrator of Anatomy and
Lecturer on Pathology
AUGUST HORN, M.D.
Lecturer on Dermatology
EUGENE L. CRUTCHFIELD, M.D., F.S.Sc.
Lecturer on Applied Therapeutics
CHARLES W. HARTWIG, M.D.
Prosector and Assistant Demonstrator
of Anatomy
JOHN W. LINTHICUM, M.D.
Lecturer on the Principles and
Practice of Medicine
WILLIAM J. CHAPPELL, M.D.
Lecturer on Diseases of the
Nervous System

*"This chair will be filled by the opening of the session."

SESSION OF 1893-94

The same as in 1892-93, with the following exceptions:

Dr. Whitehead was no longer on the Faculty. (The name of the new professor of chemistry, toxicology and microscopy, and that of anatomy and pathology are not stated in the Announcement for that year.) Dr. Willing was no longer demonstrator of anatomy and lecturer on pathology, his successor not being named in the Announcement.

SESSION OF 1894-95

The same as in 1892-93, with the following exceptions:

Dr. Wiley was once again professor of anatomy, (instead of obstetrics), Dr. Sellman became professor of obstetrics and diseases of women, Pierce B. Wilson, M.D., became professor of chemistry, toxicology and microscopy, (Dr. Whitehead had left the year previously), and the following changes were made in the Adjunct Faculty: J. C. Schofield, M.D., was demonstrator of anatomy and lecturer on pathology, (instead of Dr. Willing, who left, as did Dr. Hartwig), Pierce B. Wilson, Jr., M.D., was demonstrator of chemistry and toxicology. The name of the prosector and assistant demonstrator of anatomy is not given in the Announcement.

SESSION OF 1895-96

The same as in 1892-93, with the following exceptions:

Dr. Wiley was professor of anatomy and clinical surgery, and Dean of the Faculty, Dr. Sellman was professor of obstetrics and diseases of women, and Treasurer, Dr. Wilson was professor of chemistry, toxicology and microscopy, Drs. Whitehead and Harlan had left, and B. P. Muse, M.D., was lecturer on ophthalmology and otology. The adjunct Faculty consisted of: J. C. Schofield, M.D., demonstrator of anatomy and lecturer on pathology, Dr. Bryant (jurisprudence), Dr. Horn (dermatology), Dr. Crutchfield (applied therapeutics), Dr. John W. Linthicum (principles and practice of medicine), F. C. Jewett, M.D., lecturer on diseases of the nervous system, and Robert X. Giering, M.D., prosector and assistant demonstrator of anatomy.

SESSION OF 1896-97

JAMES G. LINTHICUM, M.D.
Emeritus Professor of Principles and Practice of Medicine
ZEPHANIAH K. WILEY, M.D.
Professor of Obstetrics
HAMPSON H. BIEDLER, M.D.
Professor of Principles and Practice of Surgery and Clinical Surgery
WILLIAM A. B. SELLMAN, M.D., Treas.
Professor of Diseases of Women
PIERCE B. WILSON, M.D.
Professor of Chemistry, Toxicology, and Microscopy
LOUIS C. HORN, M.D.
Professor of Diseases of Children and Dermatology
J. W. C. CUDDY, A.M., M.D.
Professor of Theory and Practice of Medicine and Clinical Medicine
E. MILLER REID, M.D.
Professor of Diseases of the Nervous System and Diseases of the Throat and Chest
EMANUEL W. EILAU, M.D.
Professor of Materia Medica and Therapeutics
BERNARD PURCELL MUSE, M.D.
Professor of Physiology and Hygiene
JOHN B. SCHWATKA, M.D.
Professor of Anatomy and Pathology
JOHN W. FUNCK, M.D.
Professor of Ophthalmology and Otology
JOSEPH H. BRANHAM, M.D.
Professor Operative, Orthopedic and Rectal Surgery

Adjunct Faculty

J. C. SCHOFIELD, M.D.
Demonstrator of Anatomy and Lecturer on Pathology
HOWARD BRYANT, A.B.
Lecturer on Medical Jurisprudence
AUGUST HORN, M.D.
Lecturer on Dermatology
F. C. JEWETT, M.D.
Lecturer on Diseases of the Nervous System
P. B. WILSON, JR., M.D.
Demonstrator of Chemistry
CHARLES T. HARPER, M.D.
Lecturer on Minor Surgery and Bandaging
EDMUND A. MUNOZ, M.D.
Demonstrator of Histology and Lecturer on Hygiene
EDWARD PLUMMER, JR., M.D.
Lecturer on Theory and Practice of Medicine
WM. H. SCHWATKA, M.D.
Prosector and Demonstrator of Anatomy
HAUGHTON BAXLEY, M.D.
Prosector to the Chair of Surgery and Demonstrator of Pathology
HARRY M. BAXLEY, M.D.
Lecturer on applied Therapeutics
T. SOLLERS WATERS, A.M., D.D.S.
Lecturer on Dental Surgery

SESSION OF 1897-98

JAMES G. LINTHICUM, M.D.
Emeritus Professor of Principles and Practice of Medicine
HAMPSON H. Biedler, M.D., Dean
Professor of Principles and Practice of Surgery and Clinical Surgery
WILLIAM A. B. SELLMAN, M.D., Treasurer
Professor of Diseases of Women
J. W. C. CUDDY, A.M., M.D.
Professor of Theory and Practice of Medicine and Clinical Medicine
E. MILLER REID, M.D., President
Professor of Diseases of the Nervous System and Diseases of the Throat and Chest

BERNARD PURCELL MUSE, M.D.
Professor of Physiology and Hygiene
JOHN B. SCHWATKA, M.D.
Professor of Diseases of Children
and Diseases of the Skin
J. WM. FUNCK, M.D.
Professor of Diseases of the
Eye and Ear
JOSEPH H. BRANHAM, M.D.
Professor of Obstetrics and
Clinical Gynecology

EDMUND A. MUNOZ, Ph.G., M.D.
Professor of Chemistry and Toxicology
FREDERICK CARUTHERS, M.D.
Professor of Anatomy and Pathology
HENRY M. BAXLEY, Ph.G., M.D.
Professor of Materia Medica
and Therapeutics

Adjunct Faculty

S. GRIFFITH DAVIS, M.D.
Demonstrator of Anatomy
HOWARD BRYANT, Esq.
Lecturer on Medical Jurisprudence
F. C. JEWETT, M.D.
Lec'r. on Diseases of the
Nervous System
CHARLES T. HARPER, M.D.
Lecturer on Minor Surgery and
Bandaging
HAUGHTON BAXLEY, M.D.
Lec'r. on Histology and Physical
Diagnosis
S. LEROY ROBINSON, Ph.G.
Lecturer on Practical Pharmacy

H. W. WILSON, D.D.S.
Lecturer on Dental Surgery
J. PERCY WADE, M.D.
Lecturer on Mental Diseases
MATHEW K. GWYN, M.D.
Demonstrator of Pathology
JOSEPH A. SELIGMAN, M.D.
Lecturer on Diseases of the Skin
HARRY E. KNIPP, M.D.
Lecturer on Diseases of Children
W. T. RILEY, M.D.
Lecturer on and Demonstrator
of Obstetrics

SESSION OF 1898-99

JAMES G. LINTHICUM, M.D.
Emeritus Professor of Principles
and Practice of Medicine
HAMPSON H. BIEDLER, A.M., M.D., Dean
Professor of Principles and Practice
of Surgery and Clinical Surgery
WILLIAM A. B. SELLMAN, M.D., Treasurer
Professor of Diseases of Women and
Children
J. W. C. CUDDY, A.M., M.D.
Professor of Theory and Practice
of Medicine and Clinical Medicine
E. MILLER REID, M.D., President
Professor of Diseases of the Nervous
System and Diseases of the
Throat and Chest

ZEPHANIAH K. WILEY, M.D.
Professor of Anatomy and Pathology
FRED. C. JEWETT, M.D.
Professor of Physiology and Hygiene
THEODORE COOKE, JR., A.B., M.D.
Professor of Diseases of Eye and Ear
ARTHUR G. BARRETT, Ph.G., M.D.
Professor of Chemistry and Toxicology
C. URBAN SMITH, Ph.G., M.D.
Professor of Materia Medica and
Therapeutics, and Diseases
of the Stomach
IRVIN EBAUGH, M.D.
Professor of Obstetrics

Adjunct Faculty

HENRY J. HINKEL, B.S., M.D.
Demonstrator of Anatomy
HENRY A. HYLAND, M.D.
Assistant Demonstrator of Anatomy
HOWARD BRYANT, A.B.
Lecturer on Medical Jurisprudence
SHELTON LAW, M.D.
Lecturer on Minor Surgery and
Bandaging
WILLIAM J. KASTEN, M.D.
Lecturer on Bacteriology and
Histology
S. LEROY ROBINSON, Ph.G.
Lecturer on Practical Pharmacy

M. J. KELLEY, M.D.
Demonstrator of Pathology
EDW. C. MORIARTY, M.D.
Assistant Demonstrator of Pathology
H. YOUNG WESTBROOK, M.D.
Lecturer on Diseases of Children
C. H. HUBERT, M.D.
Lecturer on Hygiene
J. T. MC CARTHY, M.D.
Lecturer on Diseases of the Skin
WILLIAM J. CHAPPELL, M.D.
Lecturer on Diseases of the
Nervous System

J. H. ULLRICH, M.D.
Demonstrator of Chemistry
GEORGE A. STRAUSS, M.D.
Lecturer on Applied Therapeutics

J. HARRY MC CORMICK, M.D.
Lecturer on Clinical Medicine

SESSION OF 1899-1900

The same as in 1898-99, with the following exceptions:

Drs. Barrett, Smith and Ebaugh were no longer on the Faculty, Dr. E. W. Eilau returned as professor of materia medica and therapeutics, J. H. Ullrich, M.D., became lecturer on chemistry and toxicology, and the name of the professor of obstetrics was not stated in the Announcement. The Adjunct Faculty lost the services of Drs. Hinkel, Hyland, Law, Kelley, Bubert and Ullrich, (who was not lecturer on chemistry and toxicology); Ferdinand H. Scholle, M.D., became demonstrator of anatomy, and Benjamin S. Hayden, M.D., lecturer on diseases of women.

SESSION OF 1900-01

JAMES G. LINTHICUM, M.D.
Emeritus Professor of Principles and Practice of Medicine
HAMPSON H. BIEDLER, A.M., M.D., Dean
Professor of Principles and Practice of Surgery and Clinical Surgery
WILLIAM A. B. SELLMAN, M.D., Treasurer
Professor of Diseases of Women and Children
J. W. C. CUDDY, A.M., M.D.
Professor of Theory and Practice of Medicine and Clinical Medicine
E. MILLER REID, M.D., President
Professor of Diseases of the Nervous System and Diseases of Throat and Chest

ZEPHANIAH K. WILEY, M.D.
Professor of Anatomy and Pathology
FRED. CLARKE JEWETT, M.D.
Professor of Physiology and Hygiene
THEODORE COOKE, JR., A.B., M.D.
Professor of Diseases of Eye and Ear
P. B. WILSON, M.D.
Professor of Chemistry and Toxicology
JAMES A. MELVIN, M.D.
Professor of Obstetrics
B. S. HAYDEN, M.D.
Professor of Materia Medica and Therapeutics

Adjunct Faculty

FERDINAND H. SCHOLLE, M.D.
Demonstrator of Anatomy
THOMAS R. CLENDINEN
Lecturer on Medical Jurisprudence
H. YOUNG WESTBROOK, M.D.
Lecturer on Diseases of Children
J. T. MC CARTHY, M.D.
Lecturer on Diseases of the Skin
WILLIAM J. CHAPPELL, M.D.
Lec. on Diseases of the Nervous System

NATHAN HERMAN, M.D.
Lec. on Bacteriology and Histology
S. LEROY ROBINSON, Ph.G.
Lecturer on Practical Pharmacy
GEORGE A. STRAUSS, M.D.
Lecturer on Applied Therapeutics
EDW. C. MORIARTY, M.D.
Demonstrator of Pathology
J. HARRY MC CORMICK, M.D.
Lecturer on Clinical Medicine

F. J. POWERS
Lecturer on Hygiene

SESSION OF 1901-02

The same as in 1900-01, except that Dr. Wiley was professor of anatomy and clinical surgery, (instead of anatomy and pathology). The Adjunct Faculty was as follows:

Adjunct Faculty

H. YOUNG WESTBROOK, M.D.
Clinical Professor Diseases of Children
FRANK J. POWERS, M.D.
Lecturer on Diseases of Children
H. DISTON BROWN, M.D.
Lecturer on Minor Surgery and Bandaging
WILLIAM J. CHAPPELL, M.D.
Lecturer on Diseases of the Nervous System

NATHAN HERMAN, M.D.
Lecturer on Bacteriology and Histology
J. T. MC CARTHY, M.D.
Lecturer on Hygiene and Sanitary Science
A. A. BURDICK, M.D.
Demonstrator of Anatomy
S. LEROY ROBINSON, Ph.G.
Lecturer on Practical Pharmacy

GEORGE A. STRAUSS, M.D.
Lecturer on Applied Therapeutics
EDW. C. MORIARTY, M.D.
Demonstrator of Pathology
J. HARRY MC CORMICK, M.D.
Lecturer on Clinical Medicine
JOHN G. JEFFERS, M.D.
Lecturer on Diseases of the Skin
JOHN PHELPS
Lecturer on Medical Jurisprudence

HENRY J. HINKEL, M.D.
Lecturer on Clinical Gynaecology
JOHN ROTH, M.D.
Demonstrator of Clinical Medicine
A. C. HEARN, M.D.
Demonstrator of Obstetrics
THOS. H. MAGNESS, M.D.
Demonstrator of Chemistry

SESSION OF 1902-03

The same as in 1900-01, with the following exceptions:

Dr. Cuddy was now professor of theory and practice of medicine and clinical dermatology, Dr. Wiley was professor of anatomy and clinical surgery, and Dr. Hayden was professor of materia medica and therapeutics and clinical medicine.

The Adjunct Faculty was the same as that of 1901-02, with the following exceptions: Drs. Herman, Phelps and McCarthy left, and Louis McKim Kines, L.L.B. became lecturer on medical jurisprudence.

SESSION OF 1903-04

The same as in 1900-01, with the following exceptions:

Dr. Cuddy was professor of theory and practice of medicine and clinical dermatology, Dr. Wiley was professor of anatomy and clinical surgery, Dr. Jewett was professor of physiology, and clinical professor of diseases of the heart and kidneys, Dr. Hayden was professor of materia medica and therapeutics, and clinical medicine, and E. A. Munoz, M.D., became professor of chemistry and toxicology, and clinical professor of diseases of the nose and throat. Dr. P. B. Wilson left the Faculty. The Adjunct Faculty was as follows:

H. YOUNG WESTBROOK, M.D.
Associate Professor Diseases of Children
H. DISSTON BROWN, M.D.
Associate Professor of Surgery
FRANK J. POWERS, M.D.
Lecturer on Diseases of Children
WILLIAM J. CHAPPELL, M.D.
Lecturer on Diseases of the Nervous System
A. A. BURDICK, M.D.
Demonstrator of Anatomy
HENRY J. HINKEL, M.D.
Associate Professor of Gynaecology

S. LEROY ROBINSON, Ph.G.
Lecturer on Practical Pharmacy
GEORGE A. STRAUSS, M.D.
Lecturer on Applied Therapeutics
EDW. C. MORIARTY, M.D.
Demonstrator of Pathology
J. HARRY MC CORMICK, M.D.
Lecturer on Clinical Medicine
WILLIAM H. LAWRENCE, LL.B.
Lecturer on Medical Jurisprudence
JOHN ROTH, M.D.
Demonstrator of Clinical Medicine

SESSION OF 1904-05

JAMES G. LINTHICUM, M.D.
Emeritus Professor of Principles and Practice of Medicine
HAMPSON H. BIEDLER, A.M., M.D., Dean
Professor of Principles and Practice of Surgery and Clinical Surgery
WILLIAM A. B. SELLMAN, M.D., Treasurer
Professor of Diseases of Women
J. W. C. CUDDY, A.M., M.D., President
Professor of Theory and Practice of Medicine and Clinical Dermatology
E. MILLER REID, M.D.
Professor of Diseases of the Nervous System and Diseases of Throat and Chest

ZEPHANIAH K. WILEY, M.D.
Professor of Anatomy and Genito-Urinary Surgery
FRED. CLARKE JEWETT, M.D.
Professor of Diseases of Children and Orthopaedic Surgery
THEODORE COOKE, JR., A.B., M.D.
Professor of Diseases of Eye and Ear
JAMES A. MELVIN, M.D.
Professor of Obstetrics
FRANK J. POWERS, M.D.
Professor of Materia Medica and Therapeutics, and Clinical Medicine
GEORGE A. STRAUSS, M.D.
Professor of Chemistry and Toxicology, Clinical Professor of Diseases of the Nose and Throat

GEORGE H. EVERHART, M.D.
Professor of Physiology and
Electro-Therapeutics

RICHARD B. NORMENT, M.D.
Professor of Hygiene and
Sanitary Science

Adjunct Faculty

H. YOUNG WESTBROOK, M.D.
Associate Professor Diseases
of Children
H. DISSTON BROWN, M.D.
Associate Professor of Surgery
HOUGHTON BAXLEY, M.D.
Associate Professor of Histology
and Bacteriology
HENRY J. HINKEL, M.D.
Associate Professor of Gynaecology
H. BURTON STEVENSON, M.D.
Associate Professor of Theory and
Practice of Medicine
ANTHONY L. RETALIATTA, M.D.
Lecturer on Anatomy of the
Pelvic Organs
WILLIAM J. CHAPPELL, M.D.
Lecturer on Diseases of the
Nervous System

S. LEROY ROBINSON, Ph.G.
Lecturer on Practical Pharmacy
A. A. BURDICK, M.D.
Demonstrator of Anatomy
JOHN T. AVERY, M.D.
Lecturer on Diseases of Children
P. A. M. ROVITTI
Lecturer on Chemistry
J. HARRY MC CORMICK, M.D.
Lecturer on Clinical Medicine
WILLIAM H. LAWRENCE, LL.B.
Lecturer on Medical Jurisprudence
JOHN ROTH, M.D.
Demonstrator of Clinical Medicine

DIRECTORS OF THE BALTIMORE UNIVERSITY SCHOOL OF MEDICINE

1887-88

Gen'l ROBERT H. CARR
President
JAMES G. LINTHICUM, M.D.
ZEPHANIAH K. WILEY, M.D.
HAMPSON H. BIEDLER, M.D.
Secretary
PIERCE B. WILSON, M.D.
FIELDER C. SLINGLUFF, A.B.
LOUIS C. HORN, M.D.

1894-96 inclusive
Hon. FRANK BROWN, Governor of
Maryland, President
JAMES G. LINTHICUM, M.D.
ZEPHANIAH K. WILEY, M.D.
HAMPSON H. BIEDLER, M.D.
Secretary
HOWARD BRYANT
LOUIS C. HORN, M.D.

1896-97
Hon. FRANK BROWN, President
JAMES G. LINTHICUM, M.D.
ZEPHANIAH K. WILEY, M.D.
HAMPSON H. BIEDLER, M.D.
Secretary
LOUIS C. HORN, M.D.
HOWARD BRYANT, A.B.
W. A. B. SELLMAN, M.D.

1899-1900
JAMES G. LINTHICUM, M.D.
President
ZEPHANIAH K. WILEY, M.D.
HAMPSON H. BIEDLER, A.M., M.D.
Secretary
HOWARD BRYANT, A.B.
W. A. B. SELLMAN, M.D.
J. W. C. CUDDY, A.M., M.D.
E. MILLER REID, M.D.

1900-1904 inclusive
JAMES G. LINTHICUM, M.D.
President
ZEPHANIAH K. WILEY, M.D.
HAMPSON H. BIEDLER, A.M., M.D.
Secretary
W. A. B. SELLMAN, M.D.
J. W. C. CUDDY, A.M., M.D.
THOMAS R. CLENDINEN, Esq.

1906
RICHARD B. NORMENT, M.D.
President
THEO. COOKE, JR., A.B., M.D.
Secretary
W. A. B. SELLMAN, M.D.
F. C. JEWITT, M.D.
LEE MAGNES, M.D.
G. H. EVERHART, M.D.
H. H. BIEDLER, M.D.
WM. H. LAW

STAFFS OF THE BALTIMORE UNIVERSITY HOSPITAL

1885-86

Surgeons

PROF. H. H. BIEDLER, M.D.
PROF. G. REULING, M.D.

Physicians

PROF. J. G. LINTHICUM, M.D.
PROF. J. D. BLAKE, M.D.
PROF. W. A. B. SELLMAN, M.D.
PROF. Z. K. WILEY, M.D.
PROF. S. W. HOOPMAN, M.D.
PROF. B. S. ROSEBERRY, M.D.
PROF. A. WHITEHEAD, M.D.

Resident Physician

CHARLES T. WEEKS, M.D.

1886-87

Surgeons

PROF. H. H. BIEDLER, M.D.
PROF. G. REULING, M.D.
PROF. Z. K. WILEY, M.D.

Physicians

PROF. J. G. LINTHICUM, M.D.
PROF. W. A. B. SELLMAN, M.D.
PROF. A. WHITEHEAD, M.D.
PROF. B. S. ROSEBERRY, M.D.
PROF. S. V. HOOPMAN, M.D.
PROF. G. A. HARTMAN, M.D.

Resident Physician

CURTH SEYFERTH, M.D.

1887-88

Surgeons

PROF. H. H. BIEDLER, M.D.
PROF. WM. A. B. SELLMAN, M.D.
PROF. Z. K. WILEY, M.D.
PROF. T. B. EVANS, M.D.

Physicians

PROF. J. G. LINTHICUM, M.D.
PROF. C. S. PARKER, M.D.
PROF. B. S. ROSEBERRY, M.D.
PROF. C. H. COCKEY, M.D.
PROF. S. V. HOOPMAN, M.D.
PROF. G. A. HARTMAN, M.D.
PROF. A. WHITEHEAD, M.R.C.S.

Resident Physician

M. L. HENRY, M.D.

1888-89

Surgeons

PROF. H. H. BIEDLER, M.D.
PROF. Z. K. WILEY, M.D.
PROF. WM. A. B. SELLMAN, M.D.
PROF. T. B. EVANS, M.D.

Physicians

PROF. J. G. LINTHICUM, M.D.
PROF. C. H. COCKEY, M.D.
PROF. S. V. HOOPMAN, M.D.
PROF. G. A. HARTMAN, M.D.
PROF. L. C. HORN, M.D.
PROF. J. W. C. CUDDY
E. MILLER REID, M.D.

Resident Physician

ARTHUR A. HOOPMAN, M.D.

The Resident Physician is elected every year from the graduating class.

Clinical Assistants

H. B. GWYNN, M.D.
W. O. GRIGGS, M.D.
ELWOOD HUGGINS, M.D.
F. W. WEBBER, M.D.

1889-90

Surgeons

PROF. H. H. BIEDLER, M.D.
PROF. WM. A. B. SELLMAN, M.D.
PROF. T. B. EVANS, M.D.
PROF. A. WHITEHEAD, M.R.C.S.

Physicians

PROF. J. G. LINTHICUM, M.D.
PROF. S. V. HOOPMAN, M.D.
PROF. L. C. HORN, M.D.
PROF. Z. K. WILEY, M.D.
PROF. J. W. C. CUDDY, M.D.
PROF. E. MILLER REID, M.D.

Resident Physicians

J. CLARK BRAWLEY, M.D.

1st Asst. JOSEPH MAYER, M.D.
2nd Asst. H. L. HILGARTNER, M.D.

Clinical Assistants

F. W. WEBBER, M.D.
JOS. J. VALENTINE, M.D.
AUGUST HORN, M.D.
FRANK BECKER, M.D.

1891-92

Surgeons

PROF. H. H. BIEDLER, M.D.
PROF. HERBERT HARLAN, M.D.
PROF. WM. A. B. SELLMAN, M.D.
PROF. ALFRED WHITEHEAD, M.D.

Physicians

PROF. J. G. LINTHICUM, M.D.
PROF. Z. K. WILEY, M.D.
PROF. T. B. EVANS, M.D.
PROF. LOUIS C. HORN, M.D.
PROF. J. W. C. CUDDY, M.D.
PROF. E. MILLER REID, M.D.
PROF. EMANUEL W. EILAU, M.D.

Resident Physician

A. R. SOMERS, M.D.

Dispensary Physician

CHAS. W. WOOD, M.D.

Clinical Assistants

F. J. CAMERON, M.D., to the Prof. of Surgery
H. K. BAIRD, M.D., to the Prof. of Diseases of Women
J. H. MC GANN, M.D., to the Prof. of Diseases of Children
J. C. SCHOFIELD, M.D., to the Prof. of Diseases of Throat and Chest
ROBERT C. RASIN, M.D., to the Prof. of Obstetrics

(The Dispensary for Eye and Ear patients was held every Monday and Friday at one o'clock, by Professor Harlan, and any cases requiring constant treatment or serious operations were entered as hospital patients, so that students would have ample opportunity to follow the various phases of each case.)

1892-93

Surgeons

PROF. H. H. BIEDLER, M.D.
PROF. HERBERT HARLAN, M.D.
PROF. WM. A. B. SELLMAN, M.D.
PROF. ALFRED WHITEHEAD, M.D.

Physicians

PROF. J. G. LINTHICUM, M.D.
PROF. Z. K. WILEY, M.D.
PROF. LOUIS C. HORN, M.D.
PROF. J. W. C. CUDDY, M.D.
PROF. E. MILLER REID, M.D.
PROF. EMANUEL W. EILAU, M.D.

Resident Physician

THOMAS L. CRAIG, M.D.

The Resident Physician is elected every year from the graduating class.

Dispensary Physician

HENRY A. HYLAND, M.D.

Clinical Assistants

Assistant to the Prof. of Surgery, ...
Chief of Clinic to the Professor of Diseases of Women
ROBERT C. RASIN, M.D.
Clinical Asst., F. C. LINK, M.D.
Assistant to the Prof. of Diseases of Children, AUGUST HORN, M.D.

Assistant to the Prof. of Diseases of Throat and Chest
J. C. SCHOFIELD, M.D.
Assistant to the Prof. of Obstetrics, F. J. CAMERON, M.D.
Assistant to the Prof. of Clinical Medicine, THOMAS A. MILLIMAN, M.D.

1893-94

Surgeons

PROF. H. H. BIEDLER, M.D.
PROF. WM. A. B. SELLMAN, M.D.
PROF. HERBERT HARLAN, M.D.

Physicians

PROF. J. G. LINTHICUM, M.D.
PROF. J. W. C. CUDDY, M.D.
PROF. Z. K. WILEY, M.D.
PROF. E. MILLER REID, M.D.
PROF. LOUIS C. HORN, M.D.
PROF. EMANUEL W. EILAU, M.D.

Resident Physician
THOMAS L. CRAIG, M.D.

Dispensary Physician
HENRY B. TREAKLE, M.D.

Clinical Assistants
Assistant to the Prof. of Surgery, THOMAS A. MILLIMAN, M.D.
Chief of Clinic to the Professor of Diseases of Women,
F. C. LINK, M.D.
J. C. OHLENDORF, JR., M.D., Clinical Assistant
Assistant to the Prof. of Diseases of Children,
OTTO M. REINHARDT, M.D.
Assistant to the Professor of Diseases of Throat and Chest
....
Assistant to the Prof. of Obstetrics, EMANUEL ISENBERG, M.D.
Assistant to the Prof. of Clinical Medicine, HENRY B. HYLAND, M.D.

1894-95

Surgeons

PROF. H. H. BIEDLER, M.D.
PROF. WM. A. B. SELLMAN, M.D.
PROF. HERBERT HARLAN, M.D.
PROF. Z. K. WILEY, M.D.

Physicians

PROF. J. G. LINTHICUM, M.D.
PROF. E. MILLER REID, M.D.
PROF. LOUIS C. HORN, M.D.
PROF. EMANUEL W. EILAU, M.D.
PROF. J. W. C. CUDDY, M.D.

Resident Physician
ISRAEL J. WOODWARD, M.D.
The Resident Physician is elected every year from the graduating class.

Dispensary Physician
MORITZ LOWENTHAL, M.D.

Clinical Assistants
Assistant to the Prof. of Surgery, ROBT. X. GIERING, M.D.
Chief of Clinic to the Professor of Diseases of Women,
FRED C. LINK, M.D.
Clinical Asst., JOHN ROTH, M.D.
Assistant to the Prof. of Diseases of Children, AUGUST HORN, M.D.
Assistant to the Prof. of Diseases of Throat and Chest,
F. C. JEWETT, M.D.
Assistant to the Prof. of Obstetrics, ..., M.D.
Assistant to the Prof. of Clinical Medicine, PERCY STANSBURY, M.D.
Assistant to the Prof. of Clinical Genito-Urinary Surgery,
ADOLPH C. EISENBERG, M.D.

1895-96

Surgeons

PROF. H. H. BIEDLER, M.D.
PROF. WM. A. B. SELLMAN, M.D.
PROF. Z. K. WILEY, M.D.

Physicians

PROF. J. G. LINTHICUM, M.D.
PROF. J. W. C. CUDDY, M.D.
PROF. LOUIS C. HORN, M.D.
PROF. E. MILLER REID, M.D.
PROF. EMANUEL W. EILAU, M.D.

Resident Physician

N. H. D. COX, M.D.
The Resident Physician is elected every year from the graduating class.

Dispensary Physician

....

Clinical Assistants

Assistant to the Prof. of Surgery, CHARLES T. HARPER, M.D.
Chief of Clinic to the Professor of Diseases of Women
EDWARD PLUMMER, M.D.
Clinical Assistant, H. H. FLOOD
Assistant to the Professor of Diseases of Children, AUGUST HORN, M.D.
Assistant to the Professor of Diseases of Throat and Chest
F. C. JEWETT, M.D.
Assistant to the Professor of Obstetrics, J. C. OHLENDORF, M.D.
Assistant to the Professor of Clinical Medicine, PERCY STANSBURY, M.D.
Assistant to the Professor of Clinical Genito-Urinary Surgery
ADOLPH C. EISENBERG, M.D.
Assistant to the Chair of Ophthalmology and Otology
E. RUSSELL ZEMP, M.D.

1896-97

Surgeons

PROF. H. H. BIEDLER, M.D.
PROF. WM. A. B. SELLMAN, M.D.
PROF. J. B. SCHWATKA, M.D.
PROF. J. WM. FUNCK, M.D.
PROF. J. H. BRANHAM, M.D.

Physicians

PROF. Z. K. WILEY, M.D.
PROF. J. W. C. CUDDY, M.D.
PROF. LOUIS C. HORN, M.D.
PROF. E. MILLER REID, M.D.
PROF. EMANUEL W. EILAU, M.D.
PROF. B. P. MUSE, M.D.

Resident Physicians

HENRY J. HINKEL, M.D.
The Resident Physician is elected every year from the graduating class.

Dispensary Physician

....

Clinical Assistants

Chief of Clinic to the Prof. of Surgery, CHARLES T. HARPER, M.D.
Clinical Assistants, C. T. SCUDDER, M.D., J. BURCH JOYCE, M.D.
Chief of Clinic to the Prof. of Diseases of Women, H. H. FLOOD, M.D.
Assistant to the Professor of Diseases of Children
ADOLPH C. EISENBERG, M.D.
Assistant to the Professor of Diseases of Throat and Chest
F. C. JEWETT, M.D.
Assistant to the Professor of Obstetrics, EDWARD EISLINGER, M.D.
Assistant to the Professor of Clinical Medicine, EDWARD PLUMMER, JR., M.D.

1897-98

Surgeons

PROF. H. H. BIEDLER, M.D.
PROF. J. WILLIAM FUNCK, M.D.
PROF. WILLIAM W. B. SELLMAN, M.D.
PROF. J. H. BRANHAM, M.D.

Physicians

PROF. J. W. C. CUDDY, M.D.
PROF. E. MILLER REID, M.D.
PROF. B. P. MUSE, M.D.
PROF. J. B. SCHWATKA, M.D.

Resident Physician
HENRY J. HINKEL, M.D.

Asst. Resident and Asst. Dispensary Physician
FERDINAND H. SCHOLLE, M.D.
The Resident Physicians are elected every year from the graduates of the School.

Dispensary Physician
CHARLES T. HARPER, M.D.

Clinical Assistants
CHARLES T. HARPER, M.D., Chief of Clinic to the Professor of Surgery
C. T. SCUDDER, M.D., SHELTON LAW, M.D.
Clinical Assistants to the Professor of Surgery
F. C. JEWETT, M.D., Assistant to the Professor
of Diseases of Throat and Chest
MATHEW K. GWYN, M.D., Chief of Clinic to the Professor
of Diseases of Women
GEORGE ROSENTHAL, M.D., G. S. CHAIMS, M.D.
Clinical Assistants to the Professor of Diseases of Women

1898-99

Surgeons

PROF. H. H. BIEDLER, M.D.
PROF. W. A. B. SELLMAN, M.D.
PROF. Z. K. WILEY, M.D.
PROF. THEODORE COOKE, JR., M.D.
PROF. IRVIN EBAUGH, M.D.

Physicians

PROF. J. W. C. CUDDY, M.D.
PROF. E. MILLER REID, M.D.
PROF. J. C. JEWETT, M.D.
PROF. A. G. BARRETT, M.D.
PROF. C. URBAN SMITH, M.D.

Resident Physician
FERDINAND H. SCHOLLE, M.D.

Assistant Resident Physicians
M. M. DOLAN, M.D.
J. W. WHITESCARVER, M.D.

Dispensary Physician
CHAUNCEY T. SCUDDER, M.D.

Assistant Dispensary Physician
C. IRVING WOOLFORD, M.D.

Clinical Assistants
SHELTON LAW, M.D.
ROBERT S. KIRK, M.D.
AUSTIN A. LAMAR, M.D.
To the Professor of Surgery

BENJ. S. HAYDEN, M.D., Chief, C. M. G. ENGLAR, M.D., S. KAHN, M.D.
To the Professor of Gynecology
FRANK T. POWERS, M.D., PERCY STANSBURY, M.D., FRED C. LINK, M.D.
To the Professor of Practice of Medicine
GEORGE W. LAUTENBACH, M.D., To the Chair of Nose, Throat and Chest
THOS. A. POOLE, M.D., To the Chair of Diseases of Eye and Ear

The Baltimore University Hospital
Training School of Nurses

The pupils in this School were instructed in all branches that pertain to scientific nursing. They were constantly under the direction of the Superintendent. Lectures were delivered to them by the various members of the Faculty on all subjects connected with general and special nursing, etc. Mrs. Doralynn Bryan was Superintendent.

1899-1900

Surgeons

PROF. H. H. BIEDLER, M.D.
PROF. W. A. B. SELLMAN, M.D.
PROF. Z. K. WILEY, M.D.
PROF. THEODORE COOKE, JR., M.D.

Physicians

PROF. J. W. C. CUDDY, M.D.
PROF. E. MILLER REID, M.D.
PROF. F. C. JEWETT, M.D.
PROF. E. W. EILAU, M.D.

Resident Physician
JOSEPH F. WARD, M.D.

Assistant Resident Physicians
JOHN HENRY RILEY, M.D.

Dispensary Physician
FRANK J. POWERS, M.D.

Clinical Assistants
To the Professor of Surgery
H. DISSTON BROWN, M.D., ROBERT S. KIRK, M.D.
To the Professor of Gynecology, JOHN F. MANGER, M.D., Chief
To the Professor of Practice of Medicine
JOHN H. MC GANN, M.D., Chief
PERCY STANSBURY, M.D., FRED C. LINK, M.D.
To the Chair of Nose, Throat and Chest, GEORGE W. LAUTENBACH, M.D.
To the Chair of Diseases of Eye and Ear, THOS. A. POOLE, M.D.

1900-1901

Surgeons

PROF. H. H. BIEDLER, M.D.
PROF. W. A. B. SELLMAN, M.D.
PROF. Z. K. WILEY, M.D.
PROF. THEODORE COOKE, JR., M.D.

Physicians

PROF. J. W. C. CUDDY, M.D.
PROF. E. MILLER REID, M.D.
PROF. F. C. JEWETT, M.D.
PROF. B. S. HAYDEN, M.D.

Resident Physician
W. R. STOVER, M.D.

Assistant Resident Physician
WILLIAM D. BACON, M.D.

Dispensary Physician
A. A. BURDICK, M.D.

Clinical Assistants
To the Professor of Surgery
H. DISSTON BROWN, M.D., W. S. HOWARD, M.D.
To the Professor of Gynecology, JOHN F. MANGER, M.D., Chief
To the Professor of Practice of Medicine
JOHN H. MC GANN, M.D., Chief
PERCY STANSBURY, M.D., FRED C. LINK, M.D.
To the Chair of Nose, Throat and Chest
GEORGE W. LAUTENBACH, M.D.
To the Chair of Diseases of Eye and Ear, THOS. A. POOLE, M.D.

1901-02

Surgeons

PROF. H. H. BIEDLER, M.D.
PROF. W. A. B. SELLMAN, M.D.
PROF. Z. K. WILEY, M.D.
PROF. THEODORE COOKE, JR., M.D.

Physicians

PROF. J. W. C. CUDDY, M.D.
PROF. E. MILLER REID, M.D.
PROF. F. C. JEWETT, M.D.
PROF. B. S. HAYDEN, M.D.

Resident Physician
THOS. H. MAGNESS, M.D.

Asst. Resident Physician
EDW. C. MORIARTY, M.D.

Dispensary Physician
A. A. BURDICK, M.D.

Clinical Assistants
To the Professor of Surgery
H. DISSTON BROWN, M.D., N. VAN WIRT WRIGHT, M.D.
To the Professor of Gynaecology
JOHN F. MANGER, M.D., Chief, ANTHONY L. RETTALIATA, M.D.
To the Professor of Practice of Medicine
JOHN H. MC GANN, M.D., Chief, PERCY STANSBURY, M.D., T. S. HUMPHREYS, M.D.
To the Chair of Nose, Throat and Chest, C. H. MEDDERS, M.D.

1902-03

Surgeons

PROF. H. H. BIEDLER, M.D.
PROF. W. A. B. SELLMAN, M.D.
PROF. Z. K. WILEY, M.D.
PROF. THEODORE COOKE, JR., M.D.

Physicians

PROF. J. W. C. CUDDY, M.D.
PROF. E. MILLER REID, M.D.
PROF. F. C. JEWETT, M.D.
PROF. B. S. HAYDEN, M.D.

Resident Physician
EDWARD C. MORIARTY, M.D.

Assistant Resident Physician
CHARLES H. BLAKE, M.D.

Dispensary Physician
A. D. BURDICK, M.D.

Clinical Assistants
To the Professor of Surgery
H. DISSTON BROWN, M.D., N. VAN WIRT WRIGHT, M.D.,
To the Professor of Gynaecology
HENRY J. HINKEL, M.D., Chief, KARL KLAESIUS, M.D.
To the Professor of Practice of Medicine
JOHN H. MC GANN, M.D., Chief, PERCY STANSBURY, M.D., T. S. HUMPHREYS, M.D.
To the Chair of Nose, Throat and Chest, C. H. MEDDERS, M.D.

1903-04

Surgeons

PROF. H. H. BIEDLER, M.D.
PROF. W. A. B. SELLMAN, M.D.
PROF. Z. K. WILEY, M.D.
PROF. THEODORE COOKE, JR., M.D.

Physicians

PROF. J. W. C. CUDDY, M.D.
PROF. E. MILLER REID, M.D.
PROF. F. C. JEWETT, M.D.
PROF. B. S. HAYDEN, M.D.
PROF. E. A. MUNOZ, M.D.

Resident Physician
EDWARD C. MORIARTY, M.D.

Assistant Resident Physician
IRVIN B. KELLER, M.D.

Dispensary Physician
SAMUEL J. KING, M.D.

Clinical Assistants
To the Professor of Surgery, H. DISSTON BROWN, M.D., C. H. BLAKE, M.D.
To the Professor of Gynaecology
HENRY J. HINKEL, M.D., Chief, ANDREW J. LAWRENCE, M.D.
To the Professor of Practice of Medicine
JOHN H. MC GANN, M.D., Chief, PERCY STANSBURY, M.D., T. S. HUMPHREYS, M.D.
To the Chair of Nose, Throat and Chest, C. H. MEDDERS, M.D.

1904-05

Surgeons

PROF. H. H. BIEDLER, M.D.
PROF. W. A. B. SELLMAN, M.D.
PROF. Z. K. WILEY, M.D.
PROF. THEODORE COOKE, JR., M.D.

Physicians

PROF. J. W. C. CUDDY, M.D.
PROF. E. MILLER REID, M.D.
PROF. F. C. JEWETT, M.D.
PROF. F. J. POWERS, M.D.
PROF. G. A. EVERHART, M.D.
PROF. H. B. STEVENSON, M.D.
PROF. GEORGE A. STRAUSS, M.D.

Resident Physician
KARL KLAESIUS, M.D.

Dispensary Physician
....

Clinical Assistants
To the Professor of Surgery
H. DISSTON BROWN, M.D., C. H. BLAKE, M.D.
To the Professor of Gynaecology
HENRY J. HINKEL, M.D., Chief
ANDREW J. LAWRENCE, M.D. ANTHONY L. RETALIATTA, M.D.
To the Professor of Practice of Medicine
JOHN H. MC GANN, M.D., Chief, PERCY STANSBURY, M.D., T. S. HUMPHREYS, M.D.
To the Chair of Nose, Throat and Chest, C. H. MEDDERS, M.D.

III. (B) ALPHABETIZED LIST OF MEMBERS OF THE FACULTY

(For Faculty grouped by year, see previous pages)

The names of the members of the Hospital Staff are not considered in this list.

Avery, John T., M.D. . . . . '04
Barrett, Arthur G., Ph.G., M.D. . . . . '98
Baxley, Haughton, M.D. . . . . . '96, '97, '04
Baxley, Henry, Ph.G., M.D. . . . .'96, '97
Biedler, Hampson H., A.M., M.D. . . '85-'04
Blake, John D., M.D. . . . . '85
Branham, Joseph H., M.D. . . . .'96, '97
Brown, H. Disston, M.D. . . . . '01-'04
Brown, J. P., M.D. . . . . '86
Bryant, Howard, Esq., A.B. . . . . '88-'99
Bubert, C. H., M.D. . . . . '98
Burdick, A. A., M.D. . . . . '01-'04
Caruthers, Frederick, M.D. . . . . '97
Cathell, William T., M.D. . . . . '87-'90
Chappell, William J., M.D. . .'92-'94; '98-'04
Clendinen, Thomas R. . . . . '00
Cockey, Charles H., M.D. . . . . '85-'88
Coffroth, H. Janney, M.D. . . . . '85-'86
Cooke, Theodore, Jr., A.B., M.D. . . '98-'04
Crutchfield, Eugene L., M.D., F.S.Sc. '92-'95
Cuddy, John W. C., A.M., M.D. . . . . '88-'04
Davis, S. Griffith, M.D. . . . . '97
Ebaugh, Irvin, M.D. . . . . '98
Eilau, Emanuel W., M.D. . . . . . .'90-'96; '99
Evans, Thomas B., M.D. . . . . '87-'91
Everhart, George H., M.D. . . . . '04
Funck, John W., M.D. . . . .'96, '97
Giering, Robert X., M.D. . . . . '95
Gwyn, Mathew K., M.D. . . . . '97
Gwynn, H. B., M.D. . . . . '90
Harlan, Herbert, A.M., M.D. . . . . . . '91-'94
Harper, Charles T., M.D. . . . .'96, '97

Hartman, George A., M.D. . . . . '86-'88
Hartwig, Charles W., M.D. . . . .'92, '93
Hayden, B. S., M.D. . . . . '99-'03
Hearn, A. C., M.D. . . . .'01, '02
Herman, Nathan, M.D. . . . .'00, '01
Hinkel, Henry J., B.S., M.D. . . .'98; '01-'04
Hoopman, Sylvester V., A.M., M.D. . '85-'89
Horn, August, M.D. . . . . '92-'96
Horn, Louis C., M.D. . . . . '88-'96
Hyland, Henry A., M.D. . . . . '98
Jeffers, John G., M.D. . . . .'01, '02
Jewett, Fred. Clarke, M.D. . . . . '95-'04
Jones, William A., M.D. . . . . '85
Kasten, William J., M.D. . . . .'98, '99
Kelley, M. J., M.D. . . . . '98
Kines, Louis McKim, LL.B. . . . . '02
Knipp, Harry E., M.D. . . . . '97
Kremien, J. D., M.D. . . . . '86
Law, Shelton, M.D. . . . . '98
Lawrence, William H., LL.B. . . . . . .'03; '04
Linthicum, James G., M.D. . . . . '85-'04
Linthicum, John W., M.D. . '85, '86; '92-'95
Lyman, A. B., M.D., L.M. . . . .'90, '91
Magness, Thomas H., M.D. . . . .'01, '02
McCarthy, J. T., M.D. . . . . '98-'01
McCormick, J. Harry, M.D. . . . . '98-'04
Melvin, James A., M.D. . . . . '01-'04
Moriarty, Edward C., M.D. . . . . '98-'03
Munoz, Edmund A., Ph.G., M.D.'96, '97, '03
Muse, Bernard Purcell, M.D. . . . . . . '95-'97
Nelson, George E. . . . . '86
Norment, Richard B., M.D. . . . . '04
Parker, Charles S., M.D. . . . .'86, '87
Phelps, John . . . . '01
Pleasants, S. S., Esq. . . . . '87
Plummer, Edward, Jr., M.D. . . . . '96
Powers, Frank J., M.D. . . . . '00-'04
Reid, E. Miller, M.D. . . . . '88-'04
Retaliatta, Anthony L., M.D. . . . . '04
Reuling, George, A.M., M.D. . . . '85, '86(3)
Riley, W. T., M.D. . . . . '97
Robinson, S. LeRoy, Ph.G. . . . . '97-'04
Roseberry, Benjamin S., M.D. . . . . . '85-'87
Roth, John, M.D. . . . . '01-'04
Rovitti, P. A. M. '04
Rutledge, E. Hall, M.D. . . . .'87, '88
Schofield, J. C., M.D. . . . . '94-'96
Scholle, Ferdinand H., M.D. . . . . . .'99, '00
Schwatka, John B., M.D. . . . .'96, '97
Schwatka, William H., M.D. . . . .'96
Seligman, Joseph A., M.D. . . . . '97
Sellman, William A. B., M.D. . . . . . . '85-'04
Shannon, George C., M.D. . . . . '85,'86
Silver, H. C., M.D. . . . . '91
Smith, C. Urban, Ph.G., M.D. . . . . '98
Smith, Randolph W., M.D. . . . . '85
Stevenson, H. Burton, M.D. . . . . '04
Strauss, George A., M.D. . . . . '98-'04
Ullrich, J. H., M.D. . . . .'98, '99
Wade, J. Percy, M.D. . . . . '97
Waters, T. Sollers, M.D., D.D.S. . . . . '96
Westbrook, H. Young, M.D. . . . . '98-'04
Whitehead, Alfred, M.R.C.S. '85-'87; '89-'92
Wiley, Zephaniah K., M.D. . . . . '85-'04
Willett, J. E., M.D. . . . . '86
Willing, J. E., M.D. . . . .'91, '92
Willson, J. Ward, M.D. . . . .'89, '90
Wilson, H. A., D.D.S. . . . . '97
Wilson, L. Ridgeley, M.D. . . . .'85, '86
Wilson, Pierce B.,M.D.'86-'91;'94-'96;'00-'02
Wilson, Pierce B., Jr., M.D. . . . . '94-'96

IV. TEXT BOOKS USED

1885-1886

ANATOMY – Gray, Wilson, Sharpey and Quain.
SURGERY – Ashhurst, Bryant, Holmes, Erichsen.
CHEMISTRY AND TOXICOLOGY – Attfield, Roscoe's Elementary Chemistry, Taylor on Poisons.
PHYSIOLOGY – Martin, Foster, Flint, Kirk's Handbook of Physiology.
PRINCIPLES AND PRACTICE OF MEDICINE – Bartholow, Flint, Roberts.
MATERIA MEDICA AND THERAPEUTICS – National Dispensatory, Bartholow's Materia Medica, Biddle.
DISEASES OF WOMEN – Munde, Thomas's 7th edition, Emmett: Gynaecology, Barnes.
OBSTETRICS – Leishman, Playfair, Meadow, Lusk.
DISEASES OF CHILDREN – Smith, Day, West.
EYE AND EAR – Soelberg Wells on the Eye; Adolph Alt, Pathology of the Eye; Troeltsch Diseases of the Ear; St. John Roosa on the Ear.
DISEASES OF NERVOUS SYSTEM – Hammond, Hamilton, Wilkes, Rosenthal.
DERMATOLOGY – Duhring.
MICROSCOPY – Frey, Microscopic Technology; Frey, Histo-Chemistry of Man; Cornil and Ranvier.
PATHOLOGY – Green's Pathology, Ziegler's Pathological Anatomy.
GENITO-URINARY DISEASES – Van Buren, Bumstead on Venereal Diseases, Otis on Stricture.
COHEN on Throat.

1887

ANATOMY – Gray, Wilson, Sharpey and Quain.
SURGERY – Ashhurst, Bryant, Holmes, Erichsen.

CHEMISTRY AND TOXICOLOGY – Attfield, Roscoe's Elementary Chemistry, Taylor on Poisons, Fownes.
PHYSIOLOGY – Martin, Foster, Flint, Kirkes' Handbook of Physiology, Yeo.
PRINCIPLES AND PRACTICE OF MEDICINE – Bartholow, Flint, Roberts.
MATERIA MEDICA AND THERAPEUTICS – National Dispensatory, Bartholow's Materia Medica, Biddle, H. C. Wood, Jr.
DISEASES OF WOMEN – Thomas's 7th edition, Emmett; Gynaecology, May and Parvin.
OBSTETRICS – Leishman, Playfair, Meadows, Lusk.
DISEASES OF CHILDREN – Smith, Day, West.
EYE AND EAR – Soelberg Wells on the Eye; Adolf Alt, Pathology of the Eye; Troeltsch, Diseases of the Ear; St. John Roosa on the Ear.
DISEASES OF NERVOUS SYSTEM – Hammond, Hamilton, Wilkes, Rosenthal.
DERMATOLOGY – Duhring.
MICROSCOPY – Frey, Microscopic Technology; Frey, Histo-Chemistry of Man; Cornil and Ranvier, Whitman, Freidlaender.
PATHOLOGY – Green's Pathology, Ziegler's Pathological Anatomy.
GENITO-URINARY DISEASES – Van Buren, Bumstead on Venereal Diseases, Otis on Stricture.
THROAT AND CHEST – Sajous, Mackenzie, Cohen, Flint, Loomis, DaCosta.

1888

Same as in 1877, with the following exceptions:
CHEMISTRY AND TOXICOLOGY – Woody's Essentials of Chemistry and Urinalysis was added.
DISEASES OF WOMEN – Two works were added – Byford, May and Parvin; Gynecological Operations, Doran.
MICROSCOPY – Frey's Microscopic Technology and Frey's Histo-Chemistry of Man were added. Miller was abandoned.
THROAT AND CHEST – Browne was added.

1889

Same as in 1887, with the following exceptions:
ANATOMY – Sharpey and Quain was abandoned.
CHEMISTRY AND TOXICOLOGY – Woody's Essentials added (in 1888).
DISEASES OF WOMEN – Thomas's 5th edition; Doran; A. J. C. Skene and Winckel were used, and the works used in previous years abandoned.
MICROSCOPY – One of the two works by Frey was abandoned. (It is not clear which one was retained.)
THROAT AND CHEST – Browne was added (1888).

1890

ANATOMY – Gray, Wilson, Holden's Anatomy, Holden's Osteology.
SURGERY – Ashhurst, Bryant, Holmes, Erichsen.
CHEMISTRY AND TOXICOLOGY – Attfield, Taylor on Poisons, Fownes, Woody's Essentials of Chemistry and Urinalysis, Wormley and Taylor on Poisons.
PHYSIOLOGY – Foster, Kirkes' Handbook of Physiology, Yeo, Martin, Flint.
PRINCIPLES AND PRACTICE OF MEDICINE – Bartholow, Flint, Roberts.
MATERIA MEDICA AND THERAPEUTICS – National Dispensatory, Bartholow's Materia Medica, Biddle, H. C. Wood, Jr.
DISEASES OF WOMEN – Thomas's 5th edition. Gynaecological Operations, Doran, A. J. C. Skene, Winckel and Tait.
OBSTETRICS – Leishman, Playfair, Meadows, Lusk.
DISEASES OF CHILDREN – Smith, Day, West.
EYE AND EAR – Soelberg Wells on the Eye; Adolf Alt, Pathology of the Eye; Troeltsch, Diseases of the Ear; St. John Roosa on the Ear.
DISEASES OF NERVOUS SYSTEM – Hammond, Hamilton, Wilkes, Rosenthal.
DERMATOLOGY – Duhring.
MICROSCOPY – Frey, Cornil and Ranvier, Whitman, Friedlaendler, Miller.
PATHOLOGY – Green's Pathology, Ziegler's Pathological Anatomy, Chapman.
GENITO-URINARY DISEASES - Van Buren, Bumstead on Venereal Diseases, Otis on Stricture.
THROAT AND CHEST – Browne, Sajous, Mackenzie, Cohen, Flint, Loomis, DaCosta.

1891

Same as in 1890, with the following exceptions:

DISEASES OF CHILDREN – J. Lewis Smith, Louis Starr, Eustace Smith were used. (Others abandoned.)
EYE AND EAR – Noyes' Diseases of the Eye, Nettleship's Diseases of the Eye, Roosa's Diseases of the Ear were used. (Others abandoned.)
DISEASES OF NERVOUS SYSTEM – Spitzka was added.
DERMATOLOGY – Anderson, VanHarlingan were added.

1892

Same as in 1891, with the following exceptions:
ANATOMY – Wilson was replaced by Weise, and the work by Ellis and Ford was added.
DISEASES OF NERVOUS SYSTEM – Gowers; Ormerod were added; Hammond was abandoned.

1893

Same as in 1892, with the following exceptions:
PHYSIOLOGY – Chapman was added and Yeo, Martin, Flint abandoned.
PRINCIPLES AND PRACTICE OF MEDICINE – Pepper, Loomis, Page, Fagge were used. All 1892 texts were abandoned.
MATERIA MEDICA AND THERAPEUTICS – Hare was added.
DISEASES OF NERVOUS SYSTEM – Dana was used. The texts of 1892 were abandoned.
PATHOLOGY – Chapman was abandoned.
THROAT AND CHEST – Ingals was used. The texts of 1892 were abandoned.

1894

ANATOMY – Gray, Weisse, Holden's Anatomy, Ellis and Ford, Holden's Osteology.
SURGERY – Ashhurst, Bryant, Holmes, Erichsen, Moullins.
CHEMISTRY AND TOXICOLOGY – Fownes, Woody's Essentials of Chemistry and Urinalysis, Wormley and Taylor on Poisons.
PHYSIOLOGY – Foster, Kirke's Handbook of Physiology, Chapman.
PRINCIPLES AND PRACTICE OF MEDICINE – Pepper, Loomis, Page, Fagge.
MATERIA MEDICA AND THERAPEUTICS – H. C. Wood, Bartholow, Hare, National Dispensatory.
OBSTETRICS – E. P. Davis (Cazeaux and Tarnier) (last edition).
DISEASES OF WOMEN – Carrigues.
DISEASES OF CHILDREN – J. Lewis Smith, Louis Starr, Eustace Smith.
EYE AND EAR – Noyes' Diseases of the Eye, Nettleship's Diseases of the Eye, Roosa's Diseases of the Ear.
DISEASE OF NERVOUS SYSTEM – Gowers, Dana, Hirt, Ormerod.
DERMATOLOGY – Duhring, Anderson, Van Harlingan.
MICROSCOPY – Cornil and Ranvier, Carpenter.
PATHOLOGY – Green's Pathology, Zeigler's Pathological Anatomy.
GENITO-URINARY DISEASES – Van Buren, Bumstead on Venereal Diseases, Otis on Stricture, Keyes.
THROAT AND CHEST – Ingals, McBride.

1895

Same as in 1894, with the following exceptions:
SURGERY – Senn's Principles of Surgery was added.
CHEMISTRY AND TOXICOLOGY – Sadtler and Trimble's Pharmaceutical and Medical Chemistry; Fownes; Purdy's Urinalysis and Urinary Diagnosis; Vaughn and Novy's Ptomaines and Leucomaines; Attfield; Wormley and Taylor on Poisons. (Woody abandoned.)
DISEASES OF CHILDREN – Starr replaced by Goodhart.
DERMATOLOGY – Kaposi, Shoemaker; Crocker were used. The texts of 1894 were abandoned.
MICROSCOPY – Abbott's Principles of Bacteriology; F. L. James' Elementary Microscopical Technology; Carpenter. (Cornil and Ranvier was abandoned.)

1896

Same as in 1895, with the following exceptions:
PHYSIOLOGY – Flint was added.
PRINCIPLES AND PRACTICE OF MEDICINE – Flint was added; Page, Fagge were abandoned.
DISEASES OF NERVOUS SYSTEM – Dercum, Jacob were added; Ormerod was abandoned.

1897

ANATOMY – Gray, Holden's Osteology.

SURGERY – Ashhurst, Bryant, Holmes, Erichsen, Moullins, Senn's Principles of Surgery.

CHEMISTRY AND TOXICOLOGY – Chemistry – Simon, Attfield, Fownes. Toxicology – Taylor and Reese. Urinalysis – Piffard, Canfield.

PHYSIOLOGY – Kirke's Handbook of Physiology, Foster, American Textbook.

PRINCIPLES AND PRACTICE OF MEDICINE – Wood and Fitz, Tyson, Loomis, Flint.

MATERIA MEDICA AND THERAPEUTICS – H. C. Wood, Bartholow, Hare, National Dispensatory.

OBSTETRICS – Galabin, Lusk, Winckel.

DISEASES OF WOMEN – Carrigues.

DISEASES OF CHILDREN – J. Lewis Smith, Goodhart, Eustace Smith.

EYE AND EAR – Diseases of the Eye – Noyes, Nettleship. Diseases of the Ear – Roosa, Buck.

DISEASES OF THE NERVOUS SYSTEM – Dercum, Gray, Jakob, Gowers, Danna, Hirt.

DERMATOLOGY – Kaposi, Shoemaker.

HISTOLOGY – Shafer, Marden.

PATHOLOGY – Green's Pathology, Zeigler's Pathological Anatomy, Abbott's Bacteriology.

GENITO-URINARY DISEASES – Van Buren, Bumstead on Venereal Diseases, Otis on Stricture, Keyes.

THROAT AND CHEST – Ingal's, McBride.

LEXICON – Lippincott's Medical Dictionary.

1898

Same as in 1897, with the following exceptions:

ANATOMY – Wilson was restored.

SURGERY – The following were added: American Textbook; Surgical Diagnosis Treatment – Macdonald; Modern Surgery – DaCosta; The Practice of Surgery – Wharton and Curtis; Orthopedic Surgery – Moore. Holmes, Ericksen were abandoned.

PHYSIOLOGY – Flint was added; Kirk, Foster abandoned.

PRINCIPLES AND PRACTICE OF MEDICINE – Anders was added, Loomis abandoned.

MATERIA MEDICA AND THERAPEUTICS – Potter, (5th edition), was added.

EYE AND EAR – Fuchs was added.

DISEASES OF THE STOMACH – Ewald.

CLINICAL DIAGNOSIS – Simon.

1899

Same as in 1898, with the following exceptions:

ANATOMY – Gray (last edition), Morris, Holden's Osteology, Weisse's Practical Human Anatomy, (4th edition). Wilson abandoned.

PHYSIOLOGY – Kirke was restored.

PRINCIPLES AND PRACTICE OF MEDICINE – Tyson, Anders, Flint, Hare's Practical Diagnosis were used.

DISEASES OF WOMEN – Dudley, Penrose were added.

DISEASES OF THE NERVOUS SYSTEM – Chapin's Compendium of Insanity was added; Dercum, Jakob, Gowers were abandoned.

THROAT AND CHEST – Grunwald was added.

1900

ANATOMY – Gray, last edition. Morris, Holden's Osteology, Weisse's Practical Human Anatomy, 4th edition. Wilson. Anatomy of Nervous System – Barker, Edinger.

SURGERY – Ashhurst, Bryant, Moullin's, Senn's Principles of Surgery. American Textbook. Surgical Diagnosis and Treatment – Macdonald. Modern Surgery – DaCosta. The Practice of Surgery – Wharton and Curtis. Orthopedic Surgery – Moore. International Textbook of Surgery.

CHEMISTRY AND TOXICOLOGY – Chemistry – Simon, Attfield, Fownes. Toxicology – Taylor and Reese. Urinalysis – Piffard, Canfield.

PHYSIOLOGY – American Textbook. Sterling, Flint, Kirke's.

PRINCIPLES AND PRACTICE OF MEDICINE – Tyson, Anders, Flint, Hare's Practical Diagnosis.

MATERIA MEDICA AND THERAPEUTICS – H. C. Wood, Bartholow, Hare, National Dispensatory, Potter's 5th edition.

OBSTETRICS – Galabin, Lusk, Winckel.

DISEASES OF WOMEN – Carrigues, Dudley, Penrose.

DISEASES OF CHILDREN – J. Lewis Smith, Goodhart, Eustace Smith.

EYE AND EAR – Diseases of the Eye – Noyes, Nettleship. Diseases of the Ear – Roosa, Buck, Fuchs.

DISEASES OF THE NERVOUS SYSTEM – Gray, Danna, Hirt, Chapin's Compendium of Insanity. Potts.
DERMATOLOGY – Kaposi, Shoemaker.
HISTOLOGY – Schafer, Marden.
PATHOLOGY – Green's Pathology, Zeigler's Pathological Anatomy, Abbott's Bacteriology.
GENITO-URINARY DISEASES – Van Buren, Bumstead on Venereal Diseases, Otis on Stricture, Keyes and Chetwood.
THROAT AND CHEST – Ingals, McBride, Grunwald, Coakley, Bishop.
DISEASES OF THE STOMACH – Ewald.
LEXICON – Lippincott's Medical Dictionary. Duane.
SIMON'S CLINICAL DIAGNOSIS.

1901-1902

Same as in 1900, with the following exceptions:
OPERATIVE SURGERY – J. D. Bryant.
CHEMISTRY – Simon was abandoned.
PRINCIPLES AND PRACTICE OF MEDICINE – Flint was replaced by Thompson.
DISEASES OF WOMEN – Montgomery was added; Carrigues, Dudley abandoned.
DISEASES OF THE NERVOUS SYSTEM – Sanders' Hand Atlas of the Nervous System – Jakob.
DERMATOLOGY – Hyde, Van Harlingen added, and Kaposi abandoned.
THROAT AND CHEST – Diseases of the Ear, Nose and Throat, by Burnett, Ingals and Newcomb was added.

1903

Same as in 1902, with the following exceptions:
OBSTETRICS – Carrigues, Darland, Jewett were added; Winckel abandoned.
EYE – Fuchs, DeSchweinitz, May were added.
EAR – Bishop replaced Fuchs.

1904

Same as in 1903, with the following exceptions:
ANATOMY – Cunningham was added and Wilson abandoned.
DISEASES OF CHILDREN – Taylor and Wells, the texts of 1903 being abandoned.
DISEASES OF THE EAR – Fuchs replaced Bishop.

V. LIST OF MATRICULATES AND GRADUATES OF THE BALTIMORE UNIVERSITY SCHOOL OF MEDICINE

The Letters M.D. indicate that the degree of Doctor of Medicine was conferred by this school in the year stated immediately following the degree.

The absence of M.D. after a name means that available records show only that the person named was a matriculate in the year or years given.

Parentheses around M.D., i.e. (M.D.), mean that neither the date nor the school which conferred the degree is evident from the available records alone.

Parentheses around a letter, name or State indicate that the existing records show variations.

Preceptors' names and honorary degrees are given, when available.

The names of graduates of the years 1905, 1906 and 1907 are missing, as are those of the matriculates for 1904, 1905 and 1906.

Most of the Announcements from which the data for this study are drawn are among the holdings of the Library of the College of Physicians of Philadelphia, the Library of the New York Academy of Medicine, the National Library of Medicine and the Health Sciences Library of the University of Maryland.

Abel, T. E., M.D., '98
Massachusetts
Dr. Frank Lougee

Abel(l), J. F. (T.), M.D., '92
North Carolina
Drs. J. M. Mease and Ellis

Abrahamson, J., M.D., '91
Pennsylvania
Baltimore University

Adler, J., M.D., '98
New York
Baltimore University

Aichner, Otto C., M.D., '94
Pennsylvania
Dr. Oscar Aichner

Allee, Katharine Wave, M.D., '99
Pennsylvania
Dr. William N. Young

Allen, William J., M.D., '86
Pennsylvania
Drs. Sahm and Gutshall

Alexander, Hugh S., M.D., '91
Pennsylvania
Dr. V. J. McKim
Allison, Thomas Judson, M.D., '97
Ohio
Dr. R. D. Jacobs
Altman, Max, M.D., '99
New York
Baltimore University and University
Medical College of New York
Altman, Morris R., M.D., '99
New York
Dr. E. Brown
Amy, J. M., '97
Pennsylvania
Baltimore University
Anderson, George, M.D., '98
New York
Baltimore University
Anderson, R. L., '97
South Carolina
Dr. I. A. Bigger
Angel, Annie E., '02
Maryland
Baltimore University
Armstrong, Herbert T., M.D., '97
Canada
Dr. T. R. Wren
Avery, John T., M.D., '01
Maryland (Baltimore)
Baltimore University
Professor J. B. Schwatka and Dr. Gilroy
Ayers, Franklin, (M.D.), M.D., '93
New York
Dr. C. B. Trafford
Bacon, J. A., Jr., M.D., '91
Rhode Island
Professor A. Whitehead
Bacon, Walter A., M.D., '98
Rhode Island
Dr. J. A. Bacon
Bacon, William D., M.D., '00
Central Falls, Rhode Island
Drs. Joseph A. and W. A. Bacon
Bahan, George M., '92
Massachusetts
Baltimore University
Bair, F. Marion, M.D., '99
Ohio
Dr. L. P. Lisle
Baird, H. G., M.D., '90
Kansas (Pennsylvania)
Dr. E. J. (I.) Lutz
Baird, H. K., M.D., '91
Pennsylvania
Baltimore University
Professor A. Whitehead
Ball, Charles H., A.B., M.D., '00
Hoboken, New Jersey
Baltimore University
Professor A. G. Barrett
Banks, Edward, M.D., '94
North Carolina
Dr. Thomas L. Banks
Banks, J. E., '87
Maryland
Dr. E. Hall Rutledge
Bannan, James, '94, '96, '97, '98
Rhode Island (Maryland)
Baltimore University
Barasz, Samuel, M.D., '00
New York City
Baltimore University
Barney, Lemuel S., M.D., '98
New York
Baltimore University
Professor B. Muse
Barrett, Arthur G., M.D., '96
Delaware (Maryland)
Professor B. P. Muse
Barry, John J., M.D., '98
Rhode Island
Dr. T. F. Smith
Bassow, G. J., M.D., '99
Connecticut
Baltimore University
Bates, Charles L., M.D., '04
Clarksburg, West Virginia
Dr. S. A. Cavalier
Bauman, William J., M.D., '01
Brooklyn, New York
Baltimore University
Ba(u)mgarner, Albert L., D.D.S., M.D., '98
Maryland
Dr. S. Ashbrook
Beach, L. E., '97
New York
Baltimore University
Bean, Leonard B., M.D., '04
Florida
Baltimore University, Maryland
Bechtold, August W., '97
Illinois
Dr. L. J. Bechtold
Becket, C. E., '97
Maryland
Professor B. P. Muse
Becker, Allen B., M.D., '90
New York
Dr. C. A. Becker
Becker, William, M.D., '95
Maryland
Baltimore University
Beckley, George H., M.D., '96
Connecticut
Dr. T. D. Griswold
Bell, Ellis C., M.D., '92
West Virginia
Baltimore University
Bell, George W., M.D., '04
New Egypt, New Jersey
Dr. C. P. Woodward
Bell, W. K., '97
Texas
Professor Caruthers
Belmore, Adolor O., '02, '03
Massachusetts
Dr. G. D. Small
Bennett, W. C., '95
Maryland
Professor J. G. Linthicum

Bennett, W. H., M.D., '92
Maine
Drs. Turner and Turner
Benoit, S. J., M.D., '04
Massachusetts
Dr. Troudane
Benson, James John, M.D., '99
New York
Dr. J. D. Featherstonhaugh
Benson, Vivian Lionel, M.D., '97
Maine
Millenmaine Medical School
Berger, Maurice M., Ph.G., M.D., '97
New York
Dr. Nathan Friedman
Bern(h)ard, William Ph; B.S., M.D., '01
Watervliet, New York
Drs. Van Vranken and Van Denberg
Berkowitz, Bernard, M.D., '99
New York
Dr. J. I. Bluestone
Berth, William Henry, '03
Rhode Island
Dr. J. T. Griffin
Beydler, Benjamin H., M.D., '97
Virginia
Dr. Robert T. Grove
Bianchi, Angelo R., M.D., '98
New York
Professor H. H. Biedler
Biener, George, '85
Louisiana
Dr. S. V. Hoopman
Blake, Charles Henry, M.D., '02
Maryland
Dr. Theodore Cooke
Blass, B., M.D., '00
New York City
Dr. M. Fishberg
Blitzer, Nathaniel, '98
New York
Baltimore University
Block, B., '97
New York
Dr. J. Block
Block, Michael, '97, '98
New York
Dr. John Block
Bloom, David N., M.D., '04
Springfield, Massachusetts (Maryland)
Drs. N. Gordon and H. H. Biedler
Bl(oo)(u)mberg, Abraham, M.D., '02
Pennsylvania (New York)
Baltimore University
Boggs, W. H., M.D., '92
Pennsylvania
Dr. S. M. Brown
Bond, J. M., '96
Maryland
Professor J. B. Schwatka
Bootay, Frederick Starr, M.D., '04
New Jersey
Dr. C. LeKerr
Booth, Charles L. (M.), M.D., '98
Colorado
Dr. E. W. F. Shipman
Born, Charles Edward, M.D., '02
Pennsylvania
Dr. Thomas E. Kelley
Boush, Charles W., M.D., '93
Pennsylvania
Dr. William Baker
Bowen, Andrew J., M.D., '04
Georgia
Dr. W. K. Kennedy
Bowen, William H., Jr., '00
Providence, Rhode Island
Dr. W. S. Bowen
Boyd, C. Lavergne, M.D., '03
Maryland (Illinois)
Dr. C. M. Bowcock
Boyd, W. J., M.D., '98
New York
Baltimore University
Boyers, C. L. (B.), '97
West Virginia
Dr. C. F. Boyers
Boyles, A. C., M.D., '98
North Carolina
P. & S. Baltimore
Bradley, W. M., M.D., '00
Mayesville, South Carolina
Dr. C. E. King
Bra(u)ecklein, Alfred H., M.D., '03
Baltimore, Maryland
Baltimore University School of Medicine, Dr. J. C. Hummer
Brawley, J. Clarke, M.D., '89
South Carolina
Dr. A. F. Andrews (Anderson)
Bray, Edward Van Dusen, M.D., '94
New York
Dr. C. L. Lodge
Breckenridge, H. E., M.D., '92
Vermont
Drs. Baker and Green
Brennan, James A., '95
New York
Dr. J. S. Gilbert
Brennan, T. J. C., M.D., '04
Woodhaven, Long Island
Baltimore University School of Medicine, Dr. F. Burke
Brewer, Robert W., '98
Tennessee
Dr. Brewer
Bridgham, Paul Chester, M.D., '04
Massachusetts
Dr. C. B. Bridgham
Brister, Samuel S., M.D., '99
Pennsylvania (New York)
Baltimore University
Brockbank, John I., M.D., '86
Pennsylvania
Dr. S. V. Hoopman
Brophy, Edwin E., '01, '02, '03
New York
Dr. A. B. Becker
Broter, Louis, '99
Baltimore University
Brown, H. Disston, M.D., '99
Maryland
Dr. H. Young Westbrook

Brown, John P., M.D., '66
Maryland
Dr. J. G. Linthicum
Brown, Ralph G., '02
Maryland
Dr. H. D. Brown
Brown, S. Marion, M.D., '88
Pennsylvania
Dr. Roswell Rothrock
Bru(ur)st, Emil W., M.D., '97
Maryland
Professors B. P. Muse and
Z. K. Wiley and A. C. Eisinburg
Bryan, Mrs. Doralynn (Doraylan), M.D., '01
Baltimore, Maryland
Baltimore University
Buchelle, Theodore W., B.S., '97
Maryland
Dr. T. A. Worrall
Buckley, D. J., M.D., '90
New York
Dr. J. T. Buckley
Buckman, I. J., M.D., '03
Maryland
Dr. D. Grumberg
Buckmyer, Evangeline, '98
New York
Dr. C. F. Blake
Budeker, William, '91
Maryland
Maryland University
Bunkhalter, John T., A.B., '97
Georgia
Dr. W. W. Pilcher
Bush, S. Warren, M.D., '01
New England (West Virginia)
Dr. Allan Bush
Bushey, Harry Frederick, M.D., '04
New Jersey
Dr. S. G. Bushey
Burdick, Alfred A., M.D., '00
New London, Connecticut
Baltimore University
Burgess, G. H., '93
West Virginia
Baltimore University
Burkholder, Alexander Joseph, M.D., '02
Virginia
Dr. J. B. Catlett
Burr, James G., M.D., '93
New York
Dr. A. B. Burr
Burritt, G. L., M.D., '01
Vermont
Burroughs, H. H., M.D., '00
Conway, South Carolina
Dr. E. Norton
Burson, Harry C., M.D., '96
Kansas
Dr. G. S. Robinson
Butcher, James A., '93
West Virginia
Dr. R. H. Felty
Butler, Samuel, M.D., '04
New Jersey
Dr. M. F. Squir(v)es

Butman, William A., M.D., '98
Maine
Baltimore University
P. and S., Boston
Buttman, W. A., '96
Maine
Baltimore University
Byrkit, G. E., M.D., '99
Ohio
Dr. W. W. Grube
Calvert, Thomas M., M.D., '92
West Virginia
Baltimore University
Cameron, Frederick J., M.D., '90
New York
Dr. G. W. Whitney
Carter, Charles H., M.D., '95
Maryland
Baltimore University
Carter, W. B., M.D., '86
Georgia
Dr. M. H. Rogers
Cassel, Wilbur F., M.D., '03
Pennsylvania
Dr. J. C. Mewhinney
Cathrall, Walter J., M.D., '01
Philadelphia, Pennsylvania
Baltimore University
Cavalier, J. P. (V.), M.D., '00
Wallace, West Virginia
Dr. S. A. Cavalier
Cavalier, Silas (T.) A., M.D., '94
West Virginia
Baltimore University
Caveness, Alfred H., M.D., '01
North (South) Carolina
Baltimore University
Dr. R. L. Caveness
Caveness, R. L., M.D., '92
North Carolina
Drs. J. E. Caveness and Kirkman
Caviness, J. E., M.D., '90
North Carolina
Dr. V. N. Seawell
Cawood, J. H. Maclane, '98
Maryland
Dr. B. B. Hayden
Cecil, Charles L., M.D., '95
Maryland
Baltimore University
Drs. Richardson and Eilau
Cecil, Ned, '01
Vermont
Baltimore University
Chahill, J. H., M.D., '92
Nova Scotia
Dr. E. S. Gaudet
Chaims, Edward, '97
Maryland
Dr. Chaims
Chaim(e)s, G. E., M.D., '91
Maryland (District of Columbia)
Dr. Franks
Chase, Edwin L., M.D., '98
Maine
Dr. T. J. Fitzmaurice

Chavalier, Morris J., '99
West Virginia
Baltimore University
Chestnutwood, August, M.D., '89
Pennsylvania
Dr. A. S. Chestnutwood
Chiles, George E., M.D., '87
Virginia
Dr. L. R. Chiles
Chisholm, Archibald Ambrose, '97
Canada
Dr. A. A. McDonald
Chisolm, James W., '98
Nova Scotia
Baltimore University
Choate, Horace H., M.D., '99
Maine
Dartmouth Medical College
Citron, G. B., M.D., '00
New York City
Baltimore University
Clair, J. B., Jr., M.D., '00
Waterville, Maine
Dr. J. L. Fortier
Clark, Albert D., '95
Maryland
Baltimore University
Clayton, J. E., M.D., '87
West Virginia
Dr. J. E. Clayton
Cleland, Charles S., M.D., '87
New York
Dr. A. A. Stevens
Clements, D. Oscar, M.D., '97
Virginia
Professor B. P. Muse
Cleveland, Theodore P., M.D., '99
Massachusetts
Dr. W. G. Potter
Clough, Osgood Flint, M.D., '97
New York
Baltimore Medical College
Colburn, A. J., '96, '97
Pennsylvania
Baltimore University
Dr. J. F. Cogan
Cole, D. W., M.D., '92
Pennsylvania
Drs. John and Kimbell
Collins, Stephen, D.D.S., M.D., '01
Schenectady, New York
Dr. J. H. Collins
Collins, Thomas H., M.D., '03
Massachusetts
Dr. Bacon
Connolly, Commodore, M.D., '93
West Virginia
Dr. J. F. White
Conradi, Adolph (F.) W., M.D., '93
Maryland
Baltimore University
Professors T. B. Evans and Eilau
Cook, Earl H., M.D., '97
Maryland
Dr. J. C. Smith
Cook, George E., M.D., '96
Pennsylvania
Professor B. P. Muse
Cooper, H. Westwood, M.D., '89
Australia
Baltimore University
Cooper, H. F., (M.D.), M.D., '93
Australia
Baltimore University
Copelan, Miss A. R., M.D., '03
Virginia
Dr. H. H. Biedler
Copeland, John C., M.D., '96
Mississippi
Dr. H. A. Hughes
Corns, Charles H., '00
Baltimore, Maryland
Baltimore University
Cornelius, George C., '95
Maryland
Dr. Charles Wegefarth
Cousins, J. C., M.D., '91
Alabama
Dr. J. A. Goggans
Cox, John R., '87
Maryland
Professor C. H. Cockey
Cox, Newman H. D., M.D., '95
Nova Scotia
Dr. Dowkouth(kontt)
Cox, Walter, M.D., '98
Maryland
Johns Hopkins University
Craig, H. F. (S.), M.D., '88
West Virginia
Dr. A. B. Denly
Craig, Thomas L., M.D., '92, M.D., '93
New York
Dr. H. P. Hubbell
Craven, William O., M.D., '94
Pennsylvania
Dr. L. M. Archey
Creason, J. A., '89
Kentucky
Dr. R. A. Moore
Crone, Albert Loring, M.D., '97
New Jersey
Drs. D. W. Longstreet and
G. B. Curtis
Cronin, Thomas J., M.D., '98
Massachusetts
Dr. H. W. Cronin
Crossmore, James L., M.D., '94
Delaware
Dr. L. B. Chapman
Crouse, Henry J., M.D., '99
New Jersey
Dr. J. H. Putnam
Crouse, Sheridan A., B.S., M.D., '98
Ohio
Baltimore University
Dr. A. L. Cope
Crowell, Victor Lee, M.D., '97
Texas
Dr. Walverton

Crutchfield, Eugene L., '84, '85
Maryland
Drs. J. W. C. Cuddy and
Harvey C. Byrd
Cuddy, Clarence E., '88
Maryland
Professor I. W. C. Cuddy
Cudworth, Linn M., M.D., '96
New York
Drs. P. A. Gleason and
E. E. Norwood
Culbertson, William R., M.D., '04
Virginia
Baltimore University School
of Medicine
Cummings, M. A., '93
West Virginia
Dr. Ralph Fetty
Cunningham, John C., D.D.S., '85
Maryland
Baltimore University
Cunningham, J. L. (S.), M.D., '91
West Virginia
Dr. John T. Huff
Curran, James (M.) Joseph,
M.D., '04
Pennsylvania
Dr. W. F. Doyle
Curran, Oram G., M.D., '00
Cross Roads, Pennsylvania
Baltimore University
Dr. Thomas M. Curran
Curtiss, William M., M.D., '93
Connecticut
Baltimore University
Curtis, W. R., M.D., '87
West Virginia
Baltimore University
D'Amours, Z. A., M.D., '02
Quebec, Canada
Dr. G. Garon
Damm, W. G., M.D., '90
Maryland
Professor James G. Linthicum
Davies, James G. A., '91
New York
Baltimore University
Davis, I. D., '88
Idaho Territory
Dr. I. H. Hevern
Davis, Samuel C., '94
Indian Territory
Dr. C. B. Ingram
Davis, W. C., M.D., '96
North Carolina
Dr. E. N. Allred
Davis, William N., M.D., '03
Pennsylvania
Dr. T. E. Davis
Day, Richard, '98
Baltimore University
Dean, Joseph A. (S.), M.D., '01
New York City
Baltimore University
Deemer, Walter L., M.D., '95
Indiana
Baltimore University
Dent, George B., M.D., '98
Maryland
Dr. E. D. Huett
Denton, George B., '96
Maryland
Dr. E. D. Hurt
Dermody, Christopher J.,
M.D., '98
Connecticut
Dr. T. J. O'Sullivan
Devine, Joseph F.,
D.V.S., M.D., '01
New York City
Baltimore University
Dichter, Charles L., '02, '03
New York
Dr. L. Weber
Dickinson, J. T., M.D., '87
Pennsylvania
Dr. H. M. Moody
Dietrich, William A., '00, '01, '03
West Hoboken, New Jersey
Drs. W. Meyer and
Charles L. DeMerritt
Dinsmore, Philip C., '87
Pennsylvania
Dr. G. B. Wood
Dix, J. Morgan, M.D., '98
Maryland
Professor B. P. Muse
Dobyns, F., '89
Maryland (Graded Course)
Baltimore University
Dodd, Harry Hall, M.D., '97
Delaware
University of Pennsylvania
Dodson, Porter F., M.D., '89
West Virginia
Dr. E. H. Dodson
Doege, Herman E., M.D., '01
Van West, New York
Dr. Hugo Meyer
Doehring, C. F. W., Ph.G., '97
Baltimore University
Dolan, M. M., M.D., '98
New York
Professor B. P. Muse
Donovan, Timothy Stephen,
M.D., '02
Massachusetts
Dr. J. A. Bacon
Doran, P. J., M.D., '91
Maryland
Professor A. Whitehead
Dorfman, S. A., M.D., '98
New York
Baltimore University
Dorris, S. M., M.D., '86
Tennessee
Dr. W. T. Allen
Dougher, E. J., M.E., M.D., '98
Pennsylvania
Dr. W. W. Berge

Dougherty, J. C., M.D., '98
Pennsylvania
Dr. Henry Smith
Dougherty, John T., M.D., '96
Pennsylvania
Dr. William H. Birge
Down, Howard C., M.D., '93
Pennsylvania
Dr. G. (T.) F. Rodman
Downey, Frederick C., M.D., '98
Virginia
Dr. F. M. Hisey
Drexler, Herman, M.D., '00
New York City (Maryland)
Baltimore University
Drouin, John A., M.D., '02
Vermont
Dr. C. A. Privost
Drum, G. (C.) F., M.D., '00
Coningham, Pennsylvania
Dr. H. V. Hower
Druskin, Louis, M.D., '00
New York City
Baltimore University
Dubler, W. J., M.D., '98
Pennsylvania
Dr. W. J. Shoemaker
Dudley, George J., M.D., '98
North Carolina
Dr. W. G. Sutler
Duff, Edmund L., (M.D.), M.D., '98
Pennsylvania
Jefferson Medical College
Duff(e)y, Harry E., M.D., '04
Pennsylvania
Dr. William Denny
Duffy, J. J., M.D., '91
West Virginia
Dr. W. S. Howard
Duhaim, J. L., '95
Ohio
Baltimore University
Dulin, Thomas B., M.D., '92
North Carolina
Baltimore University
Duncan, Grey Franklin, M.D., '02
North Carolina
Dr. Robert Thompson
Duncan, J. P., M.D., '98
Vermont
Dr. Duncan
Dunham, W. Logan, '84
Pennsylvania
Dr. S. A. Bell
Dunlap, John M. A., M.D., '99
New Jersey
Dr. F. F. Root
Duvall, John M., M.D., '94
Maryland
Baltimore University
Eagen, P. E., '95
Baltimore University
Eastman, Charles A., (M.D.), M.D., '93
Massachusetts
Baltimore University
Eddy, Isaac P., M.D., '97
Ohio
Dr. George T. Gale
Edwards, Thomas J., M.D., '87
Maryland
Professor C. H. Cockey
Edwards, William F., '88
Maryland
Professor S. V. Hoopman
Eisenberg, Adolph C., M.D., '94
Maryland, Baltimore University
Professors T. B. Evans and Eilau
Ei(s)slinger, Edward C., M.D., '96
Maryland
Professor E. W. Eilau
Ellis, Charles W., M.D., '93
Maryland
Dr. W. G. I. Ellis
Ellis, R. C., M.D., '86
North Carolina
Dr. H. McClean
England, Aaron S., '98
Baltimore University
Englar, Curtin M. G., M.D., '98
Maryland
Dr. C. W. Benson
Engle, Paul, '97
West Virginia
Dr. A. B. Campbell
Ernay, C. A., '90
New York
Dr. W. Gillmore
Espin, L. J. C., '97
New York
Baltimore University
Essenson, Oscar S., M.D., '99
New York
Baltimore University
Dr. S. J. Essenson
Evans, Daniel, M.D., '92
Pennsylvania
Dr. Kingsberry
Evelin, Arthur C., M.D., '98
New York
Baltimore University
Dr. H. P. Vosburg
Everhart, David L., M.D., '94
Pennsylvania
Dr. J. A. Kelly
Ewart, A. Carlyle, '91
New York
Baltimore University
Ewing, George W., M.D., '99
New York
Dr. C. H. Travell
Ewing, Joseph P., M.D., '92
North Carolina
Dr. J. W. Ewing
Falk, Samuel, M.D., '98
New York
Dr. Julius Stein
Farlow, E. H. (F.), M.D., '91
Maryland
Dr. G. W. Freeny
Faulkner, Carson Charles, M.D., '97
New York
Dr. R. L. O'Dell

Feigenbaum, George, M.D., '00
Baltimore, Maryland
Dr. H. Horse
Fendler, H. S., M.D., '98
New York
Baltimore University
Fenerstein, Jacob, M.D., '92
Russia
Dr. Moses Stearns
Fenstermaker, E. H., M.D., '98
Pennsylvania
Baltimore University
Ferguson, John D., M.D., '96
New Hampshire
Dr. John Ferguson
Ferrell, Grant, M.D., '93
West Virginia
Dr. S. P. Hartman
Fetty, Ralph H., M.D., '88
West Virginia
Dr. William Lairfield
Field, Frederick G., M.D., '04
Maine
Dr. Brenant
Filippino, Hugo F., '92
Maryland
Baltimore University
Finch, F. A., M.D., '99
New York
Dr. Edward Osborne
Finnessey, J. H., M.D., '90
New York
Dr. J. E. Earl
Fiscus, Harry L., M.D., '97
Pennsylvania
Drs. Charles T. Harper and
N. H. Debendarfer
Fleetwood, A. J., M.D., '96
Delaware
Dr. S. F. Jones
Fleischman, Jerome C., '01
Maryland
Dr. S. Halfern
Fleischman, O., '97
Maryland
Baltimore University
Fletcher, Frederick W., Ph.G., M.D., '00
Babylon, New York
Dr. W. A. Hulse
Flinder, Harris Haim, M.D., '02
Maryland
Dr. H. H. Biedler
Flood, Henry H., M.D., '96
New York
Dr. William Chappell(e)
Flood, Thomas Wilfrid, M.D., '02
New Hampshire
Dr. T. A. McCarthy
Follweiler, R. D. E., M.D., '98
Pennsylvania
Dr. D. W. W. Follweiler
Fore, J. D., '91, '92, '93
Maryland
Drs. Cameron and T. L. Craig
Fore, Rolla B., M.D., '98
Pennsylvania
Drs. H. H. Mothersbaugh
and E. M. Reid
Fox, Alfred J., '00
New York
Baltimore University
Fox, Fabius, M.D., '98
Maryland
Baltimore University
Frazier, Louis G., M.D., '95
North Carolina
Baltimore University
Dr. W. A. Cable
Freedom, A. G., '96

Fricke, Richard, Reverend, M.D., '91
Maryland
Baltimore University
Professor A. Whitehead
Friedland, Elias J., D.D.S., M.D., '98
New York
University of Maryland
Fuller, Wilson P., M.D., '85
New York
Dr. O. M. Allaben
Funk, William A., M.D., '00
New York City
Dr. W. E. Bailey
Gabbert, Forrest, '02
Kentucky
Dr. C. Clorman
Gaddess, Harry (Henry) W., M.D., '00
Baltimore, Maryland
Baltimore University
Gaffney, J. A., '97
Connecticut
Dr. S. Garlick
Gallagher, Frank M., Ph.G., M.D., '00
Racine, Ohio
Dr. C. K. Gardner, A.M.
Galvin, (J.) (G.), Edward, M.D., '95
West Virginia
Dr. Muse
Gardner, Edward W. (N.), '02, '03
New York
Dr. Philip E(m)be(u)rg
Garee, Ellis C., '89
Pennsylvania
Dr. C. B. McMullin
Garrison, R. F., B.A., M.D., '01
Bridgeport, New Jersey
Dr. H. H. Biedler
Gauline, C. E., '93
Maryland
Baltimore University
Gei(ie)ring, Herman J., M.D., '98
Maryland
Baltimore University
Geisregen, William Edmund, M.D., '04
New Jersey
Dr. Edmund Kolb
Ge(i)nsimore, Charles W., M.D., '98
Pennsylvania
Drs. S. M. Singer and Snyder

Geoghegan, J. R., Jr., M.D., '92
Maryland
Professor L. C. Horn
Getzendanner, Harvey E. (F.), M.D., '94
Maryland
Baltimore University
Giering, Mrs. Mary W., '98
Dr. Robert Giering
Giering, Robert X., M.D., '94
Maryland
Baltimore University
Gilmer, Frank Kernan, M.D., '03
Virginia
Dr. O. S. Burns
Ginsburg, Samuel A., M.D., '03
New York
Baltimore University
Glasscock, W. E., '86
West Virginia
Dr. J. A. Jamison
Glicksberg, Barnet E., '01
New York
Dr. E. Falk
Glover, Charles Henry, M.D., '04
Connecticut
Dr. D. Hitchcoch
Gluck, Samuel A., M.D., '99
New York
Dr. H. H. Hellenstein
Goddard, G. C., '96
Maryland
Dr. T. M. Turner
Goldberg, Henry, M.D., '98
New York
Dr. L. Friedman
Goldberg, Max, '87
Maryland
Professor H. H. Biedler
Goldwag, Joseph, '03
New York
Dr. M. Junger
Goodfriend, Ignatius L., M.D., '98
New York
Dr. Tobias Berger
Goodrich, Edson E., M.D., '00
Waterville, Maine
Dr. M. S. Goodrich
Grabenstein, James, M.D., '98
New York
Dr. J. S. Frieder
Grady, James C., M.D., '87
North Carolina
Dr. James C. Grady
Graetzel, Henry F., M.D., '92
Maryland
Baltimore University
Professor T. B. Evans
Graham, James A., '95
Scotland
Dr. J. Naion, M.R.C.S.
Graham, T. H., '90
Maryland
Professor J. G. Linthicum
Grauel, Charles., '88, '89, '95
Maryland (Graded Course)
Professor L. C. Horn
Green, Charles H., '84
South Carolina
Dr. Charles H. Green, Sr.
Green, Charles E., M.D., '01
New York City
Dr. H. H. Biedler
Greenwood, Nathaniel S., M.D., '96
Maryland
Baltimore University
Grieu(n)mard, Charles A., M.D., '94
Louisiana
Baltimore University
Griggs, W. O., M.D., '88
Maryland
Dr. W. T. Cathell
Groginsky, Philip H., M.D., '00
New York City
Dr. B. Gordon
Gurney, R. B., '90
Maryland
Baltimore University
Professor E. W. Eilau
Guthrie, Daniel W., M.D., '93
Pennsylvania
Dr. S. H. Pettigrew
Guy, A. A., '90
New York
Dr. E. Guy
Gwyn(n), Henry B., M.D., '87
Maryland
Dr. Charles H. Cockey
Gwyn, Mathew K., M.D., '97
Maryland
Professor J. H. Branham
Hagerthy, A. R., '02
New York
Baltimore University
Hahn, A. L., M.D., '91
Pennsylvania
Baltimore University
Haire, E. A., M.D., '98
Connecticut
Baltimore University
Haines, J. C., M.D., '98
New Jersey
Drs. Sharpe and Richards
Hajjar Fall Alla Khelil, M.D., '94
Syria
Baltimore University
Hall, B. H., M.D., '98
Pennsylvania
Drs. Benninghoff and Stuart
Halper, Charles J., '96
Connecticut
Dr. L. D. Labonte
Hamilton, Ira E. (L.), M.D., '94
Maryland
Baltimore University
Hamilton, William H., M.D., '92
Pennsylvania
Dr. A. T. Hamilton
Hammer, E. W. Ludwig, M.D., '87
Maryland
Professor Whitehead
Hammon, Louis V., '95
Maryland

Professor E. M. Reid
Hancock, Frank L., '94
Connecticut
Baltimore University
Hannum, W. H., '96, '97
Virginia (West Virginia)
Baltimore University
Harcourt, Grace Mae, M.D., '01
Baltimore, Maryland
Baltimore University
Dr. H. H. Biedler
Harmon, George Lucas, M.D., '97
Georgia
Dr. H. B. Stanley
Harrer, William J., M.D., '86
New York
Dr. William Roessel
Harris, William, M.D., '03
New Jersey
Dr. A. E. Roussell
Harrison, William F., M.D., '04
Pennsylvania
Dr. E. L. Wilkinson
Hart, E. W., M.D., '91
Alabama
Dr. Goggans
Hartman, S. P., M.D., '88
West Virginia
Dr. J. F. Hartman
Hasson, Joseph A., '92
Maryland
Dr. J. E. Willing
Hatfield, Asa, '00
Baltimore, Maryland (Kentucky
Baltimore University
Haven, Allison M., M.D., '90
New York
Dr. A. W. Green
Hawkins, Vallee, '91
Pennsylvania
Dr. John A. Hawkins
Hayden, Benjamin S., M.D., '97
Maryland
Professor E. M. Reid
Heiligenstadt, G. C., '94
Maryland
Dr. Howard
Heimer, William Henry, M.D., '95
Pennsylvania
Dr. Ingram
Henderson, John (H.) E., M.D., '95
Jamaica
Dr. G. D. Gowkou(n)th
Henry, Thomas (Thompson) W., '94, '95
Maryland
Dr. Hodgdon
Henry, H. L., '86
West Virginia
Dr. M. A. Blair
Hess, Samuel, '98
Maryland
Baltimore University
Higdon, Thomas L., M.D., '97
Maryland
Dr. L. R. Towles
Higginbotham, R. R., '95, '96
Bermuda
Dr. E. E. Brown
Hilde(r)brand, J. H., '96, '97
Pennsylvania
Baltimore University
Hill, Warren B., M.D., '92
Iowa
Drs. F. W. Daubney and F. N. Danbury
Hinkel, H. J., M.D., '96
Ohio
Professor B. P. Muse
Hintlian, Michael, M.D., '98
Turkey
Baltimore University
Hirsch, Samuel, M.D., '98
New York
Baltimore University
Dr. L. Kohn
Hirschmann, David, M.D., '98
New York
Dr. D. Robinson
Hirschmann, Herman, M.D., '03
New York (Baltimore, Maryland)
Dr. D. (M.) Hirschmann
Hirschman, Moses, M.D., '98
Maryland
Baltimore University
Hitch, Joseph Martin, M.D., '97
Delaware
Professor H. H. Biedler
Hocker, K. L., M.D., '98
Baltimore University
Hodes, Zoesman, '94
Ireland
Baltimore University
Hoechst, H. B., '97
Pennsylvania
Baltimore University
Hogan, W. P., M.D., '91
New Foundland, Nova Scotia
Baltimore University
Dr. W. H. McDonald
Hohman, Charles A., M.D., '86
Pennsylvania
Dr. S. V. Hoopman
Holdren, C. W., M.D., '92
West Virginia
Dr. (S.) L. W. Thompson
Holdridge, Henry L., M.D., '87
West Virginia
Holland, George C., M.D., '90
North Carolina
Dr. E. B. Holland
Holton, E., '95
New Hampshire
Baltimore University
Hook, George A., '97
Massachusetts
Dr. W. S. Hoyt
Hook, Lawrence M., M.D., '93
South Carolina
Baltimore University
Hoopman, Arthur A., M.D., '88
Maryland
Dr. S. V. Hoopman
Hordes, Zorsman, '96

Ireland (Maryland)
Baltimore University
Horton, T. B., M.D., '91
North Carolina
Dr. E. S. Foster
Houston, E. E., '95

Houser, Emanuel Alvin, M.D., '02
North Carolina
Dr. W. A. Bess
Howard, William S., M.D., '00
Pennsylvania (Wales, England)
Baltimore University
Dr. L. J. Enders
Huddle, Garland E., M.D., '92
Virginia
Drs. J. B. Pierce and R. W. Jones
Huebner, R. E. L., '97
Pennsylvania
Dr. D. A. Huebner
Huggins, Elwood, M.D., '88
Maryland
Professor H. H. Biedler
Humphrey, Thomas Stanton, M.D., '97
Pennsylvania
Dr. W. J. Humphrey
Hunter, George Braden, M.D., '97
New York
Baltimore University
Dr. H. J. Hunter
Hunter, H. J., M.D., '90
New York
Dr. Robert W. Warner
Hurley, William H., '02
Vermont
Dr. W. B. Mayo
Hutchason, Clark I., M.D., '99
Massachusetts
Dr. C. E. Mathis
Huyck, Emory, Burr, M.D., '95
New York
Dr. Huyck
Hyland, Henry A., M.D., '92
Maryland
Baltimore University
Hynard, Eugene R., M.D., '03
New York
Baltimore University
Imhofe, Henry H., M.D., '93
Maryland
Baltimore University
Professor Z. K. Wiley
Ing, William M., M.D., '99
Maryland
Baltimore University
Drs. A. W. McDonald and Silver
Ingalls, Joseph H., '02
Connecticut
Baltimore University
Ireland, D. F., '97
West Virginia
Dr. J. W. P. Jarvis
Irvin, Samuel J., '94
Texas
Dr. W. P. Irvin
Irving, Levin M., M.D., '96
Virginia
University of Virginia
Isenberg, Emanuel, M.D., '93
New York
Dr. Russell
Jackson, John S., M.D., '86
Pennsylvania
Dr. D. Cunningham
Jacobs, Simon M., M.D., '00
New York City
Dr. D. N. Booth
Jacobson, Matthew M., '96
New York
Baltimore University
Jamison, W. C., M.D., '88
West Virginia
Dr. W. H. W. Brock
Janko, N., M.D., '98
New York
Baltimore University
Jarvis, Josiah W. P., M.D., '95
West Virginia
Baltimore University
Jenkins, John C., '85
North Carolina
Dr. Thomas M. Jordan
Jennings, Charles R., M.D., '90
New York
Baltimore University
Jennings, Curtis Herman, M.D., '02
Massachusetts
Dr. L. Paradise
Jewett, Bert G., M.D., '96
Maine
Dr. L. J. Crook(er)
Jewett, F. C., M.D., '93
Maine
Drs. Turner and Turner
Johnson, I. B., M.D., '03
Texas
Baltimore University
Johnson, Irving J., M.D., '97
Vermont
Dartmouth Medical College
Jolliffe, Charles C., '91
Maryland
Dr. Hugh McGuire
Jones, David W., M.D., '86
Pennsylvania
Baltimore University
Jones, Frederick Elmer, M.D., '97
Maine
Dr. M. B. Rayner
Jones, George E., '86, '87
Maryland
Baltimore University
Jones, J. W., '96
Pennsylvania
Dr. E. Evans
Jones, Pius Henry, Ph.G., M.D., '02
Pennsylvania
Dr. H. H. Biedler
Jordy, G. H., M.D., '98
Pennsylvania
Baltimore University
Joyce, William A., M.D., '00

Brooklyn, New York
Dr. Joseph F. Ward
Joynson, H. Bromelow, M.D., '97
England
Dr. G. T. Johnson
Kaessman, F. D. J., '90
Maryland
Dr. H. B. Gwynn
Kahn, Maurice, M.D., '03
Baltimore, Maryland
Dr. M. Hirschman
Kahn, Paul, M.D., '96
New York (Maryland)
College of P. and S.
Kahn, Samuel, M.D., '98
Maryland
Baltimore University
Kahn, Wulf, M.D., '96
New York
College of P. and S.
Kavanaugh, W. J., B.S., M.D., '01
Brooklyn, New York
Dr. J. Ward
Keefer, Clarence G., M.D., '92
Maryland
Professor J. G. Linthicum
Keilm, John I., '01
Maryland
Dr. M. D. Brown
Keishner, Warren E., '00
Waterville, Maine
Drs. Goodrich and Goodrich
Keller, Irwin B., M.D., '03
Tiffin, Ohio
Drs. C. F. Magers and
W. K. Chamberlain
Kelley, Edward, M.D., '87
New Jersey
Dr. P. J. Gallagher
Kelly, A. O. (D.), M.D., '03
West Virginia (Maryland)
Baltimore University
Dr. S. A. Cavalier
Kelly, A. V., M.D., '92
Connecticut
Dr. G. O. Robbins
Kelly, G. W., '90
West Virginia
Dr. W. E. Hill
Kelly, Thomas Marlin, M.D., '04
Pennsylvania
Dr. William S. Highbee
Kendell, William A., M.D., '89
West Virginia
Dr. I. E. Kendell
Kenna, R. J., M.D., '01
Brooklyn, New York
Dr. Robert Wylie
Kennedy, James E. O. (C.), M.D., '03
Connecticut
Dr. J. E. Martin
Kern, W. W., M.D., '98
Pennsylvania
Dr. William M. Kern
Ketchum, Frank T. (I.), M.D., '95
Arkansas
Dr. J. G. Eberle
Keyser, Robert L., '03
Virginia
Dr. H. H. Biedler
Kibler, C. L., A. B., '97
South Carolina
Dr. F. D. Kendall
Kidd, James William, M.D., '97
Scotland
University of Vermont
Kiefer, Bruce, '97
West Virginia
Dr. J. D. Smied
King, Claude E., M.D., '93
South Carolina
Dr. L. (J.) Y. (W.) King
King, J. O., M.D., '95
Maryland
Baltimore University
King, James R., M.D., '93
Ohio
Dr. J. Frank Piper
Kipp, Jeremiah G., M.D., '97
New York
Dr. George B. Lewis
Kipp, William F., M.D., '93
Ohio
University of Maryland
Kirchhoff, William F., M.D., '98
New Jersey
Medico Chirurgical College
of Philadelphia
Koch, George J. P., M.D., '04
New Jersey
Dr. J. E. Ward
Klaesius, Karl, M.D., '02
Baltimore, Maryland
Baltimore University
Dr. H. H. Biedler
Klein, Herman, M.D., '01
New York City
Baltimore University
Dr. F. Borsody
Klein, Morris (Maurice) I., M.D., '02
Baltimore, Maryland (New York)
Professor H. H. Biedler
Klingstine, Walter H., '00
Baltimore, Maryland
Dr. Percy Stansbery
Knickman, Walter E., M.D., '04
Maryland
Baltimore University School of Medicine
Knoll, Louis P., M.D., '04
New York
Dr. John G. W. Kno(e)ll
Kraker, David Aaron, M.D., '02
New York
Dr. L. Adams
Kramer, J. G., M.D., '98
Pennsylvania
Dr. E. L. Dickenson
Kremia(e)n, John D., M.D., '86
Maryland
Dr. W. M. Sauerhering
Krem(m)er, Reverend Isaac, '99
Maryland

Baltimore University
Kritchevsky, Benedict, D.D.S., M.D., '98
Russia
University of Virginia
Kriz, G. H., M.D., '98
Pennsylvania
Baltimore University
Kromer, Mrs. Ida B., '98, '99
Baltimore
Professor E. M. Reid
Kuhn, John L. Ignatius, M.D., '04
Baltimore, Maryland
Dr. H. (W.) D. Brown
Kumpf, John E., M.D., '00
New York City
Baltimore University
Kyle, Edward Vance, M.D., '96
Pennsylvania
Dr. (N.) H. E. Holden
Lamb, G. W., '97
Pennsylvania
Jefferson Medical College
Lamb, T., '97
Pennsylvania
Baltimore University
Lambert, C. C., M.D., '01
Baltimore, Maryland
Jefferson Medical College
Lancaster, Lloyd Thomas, M.D., '04
West Virginia
Baltimore University School of Medicine
Langdon, Marie Geraldine, M.D., '04
Maryland
Dr. R. M. Langdon
Langelier, F. X., M.D., '93
Canada
Baltimore University
Lansdale, Howard, '86
Maryland
Baltimore University
Lanterman, Roy A., M.D., '93
California
Baltimore University
Lapman, Charles, '98
New York
Baltimore University
LaPraik, John, M.D., '92
Maine (Massachusetts)
Dr. Hummell
Lauck, L. A., M.D., '85
Pennsylvania
Dr. Thomas J. Stevens
Laurin, Theophilus, M.D., '95
New York
Baltimore University
Lavin, Edward Joseph, M.D., '04
Rhode Island
Baltimore University School of Medicine
Lavoie, Zenon, '98
Massachusetts
Dr. A. St. George
Law, Shelton, M.D., '97
Maryland
Professor J. H. Branham
Lawrence, Andrew C. (J.), M.D., '03
Maryland
Dr. F. C. Jewett
Lawrence, W. H., '94
North Carolina
Dr. J. O. Wilcox
Lawson, La Fayette, M.D., '94
West Virginia
Dr. G. W. Lawson
Layton, Samuel M. (H.), M.D., '02
Maryland
Dr. Feurst (Feurslein)
Lazarus, Bernard, M.D., '99
New York
Dr. Leon Cherung
Lebelson, Isidore, M.D., '00
New York City
Dr. B. Mulberg
Le Blanc, Hilarion, M.D., '91
Nova Scotia
Dr. E. T. Gaudet
Leeson, Dor(a)(e), M.D., '94
West Virginia
Baltimore University
Dr. G. F. Perry
Lehman, John H., '98, '99
Boiling Springs, Pennsylvania
Dr. Kasten(w)
Leibman, Samuel J., '99
New York City
Dr. D. N. Booth
Lenney, J. B., M.D., '90
Illinois
Dr. C. W. McKee
Lene(t)zky, N., '96, '97
Maryland
Baltimore University
Dr. Dobrutzky
Lentz, Nathan, M.D., '99
Maryland
Professor H. H. Biedler
Leonard, A. M., A.B., M.D., '01
Lawrence, Massachusetts
Dr. J. A. Bacon
Lesage, Joseph Arthur, M.D., '99
Canada
Dr. St. Germain
Levin, M. Irving, M.D., '96
Virginia
Levine, Louis J., M.D., '98
New York
University of New York
Dr. J. W. Winner
Levitt, Marcus J., M.D., '00
New York
Dr. M. Bur(n)stein
Levy, Joseph R., '98
New York
Drs. G. B. Grady and Houston
Lewis, Allard D., M.D., '97
South Carolina
Dr. C. T. Ford
Lewis, Harvey (Harry) E., M.D., '94
New York
Baltimore University
Libby, Augustine B., M.D., '94
Maine
Dr. Charles B. Porter

Lickle, John D., M.D., '87
Maryland
Dr. C. H. Cockey
Linde(n)mann, Adolph D., '02, '03
New York
Drs. D. M. Neustaldter and
K. M. Necestoedler
Lindridge, Edwin B., M.D., '01
Brooklyn, New York
Dr. E. F. Lindridge
Lingo, W. B., M.D., '03
Maryland
Dr. G. L. Hines
Link, Ferdinand C., M.D., '92
Maryland
Professor J. G. Linthicum
Lloyd, Edwin (Edward) T., M.D., '00
Baltimore, Maryland
Baltimore University
Drs. B. F. Muse and Z. K. Wiley
Locklear, G. W., M.D., '93
North Carolina
Dr. W. (I.) J. Gilbert
Loftin, W. R., '90
North Carolina
Dr. A. Butler
Long, B. F., M.D., '00
McCoysville, Pennsylvania
Dr. B. H. Ritter
Longstreet, Delavan, M.D., '89
Drs. Longstreet and Keller
Loomis, Loring R., M.D., '94, '98
New York
Baltimore University
Dr. L. A. Whitehorn
Lord, Herbert, M.D., '97
Maine
Dr. C. (L.) E. Grant
Louden, Edward T., M.D., '00
Amityville, Long Island, New York
Baltimore University
Louden, John F., M.D., '00
Amityville, Long Island, New York
Baltimore University
Loughnan, A. J., Ph.G., '98
Baltimore University
Love, Robert W., '95
Scotland
Dr. J. Naion, M.R.C.S.
Love, S. W. E., '91
Delaware
Baltimore University
Lowenthal, Moritz, M.D., '94
Germany
Baltimore University
Lowry, J. W., '92
Ohio
Baltimore University
Lutz, Edgar J., M.D., '86
Pennsylvania
Drs. Fleming and Shope
Lybrand, W. E., '97, '98
South Carolina
Dr. P. W. Hite
Lynch, James Edward, M.D., '04
Connecticut
Dr. J. Cassidy
Lyon, C. S., '97
Baltimore University
MacAllister, J. F., M.D., '91
District of Columbia
Dr. V. F. Graham
Mackenzie, R. H. M., B.A., M.D., '98
Pennsylvania
Baltimore University
MacDonald, Joseph Jr., M.D., '04
Newark, New Jersey
Drs. G. O. Welchman and A. H. Gollet
MacMaster, D. J., B.A., M.D., '98
Nova Scotia
Dr. J. J. Cameron
Magness, Thomas H., M.D., '01
Baltimore, Maryland
Drs. H. B. Jones and J. W. C. Cuddy
Makepeace, Frank C., '03
New Jersey
Dr. J. Tattersall
Maloney, Michael L. (J.), M.D., '97
Pennsylvania
University of Pennsylvania
Manahan, William J., '01
Maryland
Dr. Harry Shipley
Manger, John F., M.D., '97
Maryland
Professor B. P. Muse
Mann, Lewis Litchfield, M.D., '97
Maine
Dr. W. H. Hainer
Manning, John B., Jr., M.D., '99
Illinois
Dr. Sanford
Marsh, W. H., M.D., '98
Pennsylvania
Dr. S. P. Hakes
Martin, L. O., M.D., '99
West Virginia
Dr. S. A. Cavalier
Martin, William Peter, M.D., '02
New Jersey
Dr. H. H. Biedler
Matteson, Charles D., '98
New York
Dr. H. P. Wilcox
Matthews, A. A., '95
Maryland
Professor A. B. Sellman
May, George W., '93
Connecticut
Dr. Thomas H. Weldon
Mays, Harry N., '94
Utah
Dr. A. C. Ewing
Mayer, Joseph, M.D., '89
West Virginia
Dr. D. Mayer
McElveen, George W., M.D., '85
South Carolina
Dr. Harvey L. Byrd
McCabe, Arthur, M.D., '97
Nova Scotia
Dr. C. T. Weeks

McCabe, Henry C., '93
Maryland
Dr. John Roth
McCormick, Cardinal Claude, M.D., '04
Pennsylvania
Dr. H. C. McCormick
McCormick, John A.(H.), M.D., '93
Pennsylvania
Drs. Allison and Schaefer
McClellan, Henry J., M.D., '98
Pennsylvania
Dr. H. T. Ziebart(h)
McCollough, Frank A., M.D., '97
New York
Dr. B. S. Beach
McCuaig, James W., '94
Vermont
Dr. Gibson
McDonald, A. A., '97
Canada
Tufts College, Boston
McGann, J. H., M.D., '91
Maryland
Dr. J. F. Lang
McGeary, Thomas James, M.D., '04
New Jersey
Dr. T. C. Smith
McGinness, Robert F., M.D., '98
New York
Dr. E. Miller
McLaughlin, Frank W., M.D., '94
Maine
Dr. V. M. Newton
McMahon, Frank M., M.D., '95
Pennsylvania
Dr. C. B. Stratten
McMaster, J. R., Jr., M.D., '86
South Carolina
Dr. J. C. McMaster
Meadows, L. B., M.D., '92
West Virginia
Dr. J. E. Clayton
Meek, Henry G., M.D., '93
Ohio
Dr. J. Frank Piper
Melvin, J. T., '96, '97
Pennsylvania
Dr. Guthrie
Mercier, J. E., M.D., '99
Massachusetts
Dr. E. D. Laforce
Mershimer, J. M., M.D., '99
Illinois
Drs. J. W. Maguire and H. D. Hockenberg
Metzger, George C., '97
Maryland
Baltimore University
Meyer, William A. B., Ph.G., M.D., '00
West Hoboken, New Jersey
Dr. Hecht
Mickel, J. O., '96

Miller, John A., '97, '98
North Carolina (New Jersey)
Dr. A. A. Kent
Miller, Richard T., Ph.G., M.D., '01
New York City
Dr. E. B. Moore
Milliman, Thomas A., M.D., '90
Maryland
Professor J. W. C. Cuddy
Mills, Abner W. D. (S.), M.D., '04
New York
Dr. J. A. Mearg
Mills, James, '86
Maryland
Professor Reuling
Minor, Ward A., M.D., '94
New York
Baltimore University
Mohn, Charles L., '84
Pennsylvania
Dr. J. F. Kanawell
Money, Ernest N., '97, '98
Florida
Professor H. H. Biedler
Moriarty, Edward C., M.D., '98
Connecticut
Dr. M. S. Bradley
Moore, C. L., M.D., '98
Pennsylvania
Dr. J. P. McCord
Moore, John H., M.D., '88
Virginia
Medical College of Virginia
Morrison, Josiah C., M.D., '96
Pennsylvania
Dr. J. E. (Be(u)ck
Morrissey, Michael J., '94
Connecticut
Dr. E. M. Ripley
Morrow, James A., M.D., '89
Pennsylvania
Professor H. H. Biedler
Morse, R. S., M.D., '88
Massachusetts (Canada)
Dr. C. J. Morse
Mount, Louis B., '98
New York
Baltimore University
Mowry, John J., M.D., '04
Rhode Island
Dr. W. T. Hamill
Moyer, C. C., M.D., '93
Pennsylvania
Dr. D. R. Rothrock
Moyer, J. H., '02
Maryland
Dr. E. A. Grove
Mueller, (Miller), C.A.A.J., M.D., '92
Maryland
Professor A. Whitehead
Mulvey, John (M.), M.D., '03
Massachusetts
Dr. Butmore
Munk, Eric (M.D.), M.D., '91
Pennsylvania
Baltimore University
Munson, William R., M.D., '92
Connecticut
Dr. O. C. Smith
Murray, John T., M.D., '98

Rhode Island
Dr. H. Baxley
Murtha, A. L., M.D., '01
New York
Muse, W. C., '87
Maryland
Dr. J. P. Brown
Nalitsky, David I., '97
New Jersey
Dr. D. Bondy
Nance, James W., M.D., '94
Alabama
Dr. J. M. Clark
Nelson, Joseph T. (P.), M.D., '00
Waverly, Maryland
Baltimore University
Drs. J. B. Schwatka and A.G. Barrett
Nichols, Bernard H., '98
Ohio
Dr. A. M. Douthitt
Nolte, H. S., M.D., '98
Pennsylvania
Dr. H. W. Sweigart
Normandine, Alphonse, M.D., '95
Massachusetts
Dr. L. Z. Normandine
Northwood, W. H., '91
Connecticut
Dr. C. A. Hamilton
Norton, Elbert Arthur, M.D., '04
New Jersey (New York)
Dr. William F. Donovan
Norwood, Edwin E., M.D., M.D., '93
New York
Dr. J. E. Norwood
Nowland, George D., M.D., '96
Maine
Dr. G. C. Upham
Noyes, G. K., M.D., '98
Wisconsin
Dr. G. D. Ladd
Nutt, Walter E., M.D., '99
New Hampshire
Tufts Medical College
Nutter, Harry M., M.D., '03
Delaware
Dr. Neely Rhoade
Nutting, James D., Jr., M.D., '03
Maine
Dr. J. D. Nutting
O'Brien, John F., M.D., '98
Connecticut
Dr. T. J. C. (O.) Sullivan
O'Brien, Robert Lee, M.D., '04
West Virginia
Dr. W. E. Perry
Octon, Ignomar F., '88
Maryland
Dr. C. F. Parker
Ohlendorf, J. C., Jr., M.D., '93
Maryland
Baltimore University
Oliveros, Clifford J., M.D., '90
South Carolina
Dr. A. S. Hydrick
O'Mally, Austin F., M.D., '04
Massachusetts
Dr. P. A. S. Grady
O'Neill, John H. Walsh, M.D., '02
Rhode Island
Dr. William D. Bacon
O'Neil, Thomas J., '98
New York
Dr. James D. Featherstonhaugh
Orr, William Lucius, M.D., '04
Georgia
Dr. J. R. Nishett
Ostro, M., M.D., '99
Delaware
Dr. B. Downes
Ostrowsky, M., '96, '97
Delaware
Dr. B. Downs
Owens, R. Hamilton, '95
Maryland
Dr. R. P. S. Scheidt
Padgett, James B., M.D., '87
South Carolina
Dr. J. E. Kinsey
Page, R. B., '02
Ohio
Baltimore University
Palmer, Harry, '97
Delaware
Dr. D. D. Palmer
Panetti, Philip A. (W.), '87, '90, '91
Maryland
Baltimore University
Dr. J. J. Valentine
Paradis, A. H., M.D., '01
Connecticut
Dr. J. Mac Intosh
Parker, E. E., M.D., '00
Freehold, New Jersey
Dr. J. S. Long
Parker, E. M., '98
Virginia
Dr. G. B. Wood
Patterson, Julian S., M.D., '88
Pennsylvania
Drs. Mackey and Clark
Patton, Horace Melville, M.D., '97
Maryland
Dr. Z. K. Wiley
Paulman, George P., M.D., '02
New York
Dr. O. S. Williamson
Peirce, William, M.D., '86
Virginia
Dr. C. C. Campbell
Peggs, H. M., M.D., '00
Boston, Massachusetts
Dr. H. H. Brown
Pen(n)ington, D. F., D.D.S., '85
Maryland
Drs. J. G. Linthicum and Harvey L. Byrd
Perilli, John William, M.D., '98
New York
Drs. A. Burkleman and R. Guiberas
Peters, William H., M.D., '95
Pennsylvania
Dr. W. H. Siebert

Pfeiffer, C. A., M.D., '93
Maryland
Professor Linthicum
Phelan, Nicholas J. P., M.D., '04
New Jersey
Dr. J. J. Benson
Phillips, Albert J., M.D., '95
Maryland
Baltimore University
Phillips, C. H., M.D., '92
North Carolina
Baltimore University
Dr. A. Fuller
Phillips, William S. P., '96, '97, '98
Delaware
Baltimore University
Professor H. H. Biedler
Pillsbury, Ernest D., '93
Massachusetts
Dr. Charles E. Eastman
Piper, J. Frank, M.D., '88
Ohio
Dr. William Piper
Piper, W. O. S., M.D., '93
Ohio
Dr. J. Frank Piper
Pippin, W. H. (M.), M.D., '92
Maryland
Dr. J. M. Mease and
Professor W. A. B. Sellman
Pitt, Thomas S., M.D., '87
New Brunswick
Drs. D. J. Brown and D. E. Boozman
Plummer, Edward, Jr., M.D., '90
Maryland
Baltimore University
Plunkett, John L., M.D., '94
Maryland
Baltimore University
Poole, Thomas A., M.D., '98
Maryland
Baltimore University
Powell, Henry B., M.D., '95
Texas
Dr. L. A. Cook
Powell, L. M., M.D., '87
New York
Dr. H. Morley
Powers, Francis J., M.D., '98
Maryland
Professor E. M. Reid
Prentiss, Charles C., M.D., '95
Connecticut
Dr. Pomeroy
Price, J. M., '01
Florida
Dr. J. A. Townsend
Prior, James E., M.D., '96
Connecticut
Dr. T. F. Kane
Pritchard, Hugh J., M.D., '95
Maryland
Dr. J. E. Pritchard
Pruett, D. M., '90
North Carolina
Baltimore University
Pullen, A. J., '97
Vermont
Dr. D. P. Webster
Rab(i)nowitz, Solomon, M.D., '02
New Jersey (Pennsylvania and Maryland)
Dr. N. S. Greenwood
Raisin, Robert C., M.D., '90
Maryland
Baltimore University
Professor P. B. Wilson
Ramos, Nicholas I., M.D., '90
Maryland
Professor H. H. Biedler
Randall, W. F., M.D., '90
Pennsylvania
Dr. F. Choffee
Rangely, Walter W., M.D., '96
Virginia
Dr. R. S. Martin
Rappaport, David Nathan, M.D., '04
New Jersey
Dr. N. S. Greenwood
Rappoport, Armin, M.D., '00
New York City
Dr. Joseph Baitin
Rastatter, Paul F., M.D., '02
Maryland
Dr. George A. Garries
Ratnoff, N. O., M.D., '99
New York
Baltimore University
Rawdin, N. S., M.D., '00
New York City
Dr. Ladmsky
Reason, John J., '97
New Jersey
New York College of Pharmacy
Reed, Elliott A., M.D., '97
Pennsylvania
Lebanon N.N.U.
Reeves, James Truman, M.D., '04
Louisiana
Dr. M. C. Reeves
Reeves, Leon A., '97
New Jersey
Dr. E. L. Reeves
Reeves, Marcus Clifford, M.D., '97
Georgia
University of Georgia
Reines, Joseph, '94
Baltimore University
Reinesz, Joseph Charles, M.D., '97
Maryland
Baltimore University
Dr. J. Kratz
Reinhardt, Otto M., M.D., '93
Maryland
Professor L. C. Horn
Reiss(i)man, (I.) Erwin, M.D., '04
New York
Dr. A. H. Goelet
Reistman, Irwin, Ph.G., '01
New York
Dr. A. H. Goelet
Reiter, Henry, M.D., '00
New York City

Drs. Stein and Bruder
Rhodes, Frank Edson. M.D., '95
Massachusetts
Dr. F. Frutchey
Richards, J. W., M.D., '98
Pennsylvania
Drs. Williams and Davis
Richard(s)on, E. H., Jr., '88
Maryland
Dr. E. Hall Richardson
Richardson, F. A., A.B., B.S., M.D., '01
Cambridge, Massachusetts
Baltimore University
Richardson, W. B., '92
Virginia
Dr. J. J. Duck
Riddel, S. W., '01, '02, '03
West Virginia
Dr. (N.) (W.) S. G. Ferrell
Riley, John H., M.D., '99
New York
Professor H. H. Biedler
Ritter, D. Edward (C.), '01, '02, '03
Maryland (West Virginia)
Dr. C. T. A(m)wrett
Ritter, Samuel H., '02
West Virginia
Dr. Whitescarver
Roberts, Frank, M.D., '95
North Carolina
Baltimore University
Robinson, C. R., M.D., '92
Virginia
Dr. William Pierce
Robinson, J. H., '97
Canada
Dr. D. A. Rose, M.R.C.S.
Robinson, W. L., '86
Maryland
Dr. Hawkins
Roche, Michael W., M.D., '95
Rhode Island
Dr. M. W. Kelliher
Rogers, Charles T. G., M.D., '99
New York
Dr. Robert Ormsby
Romm, Abraham, M.D., '02
Baltimore, Maryland
Baltimore University
Dr. J. H. McCormick
Rosenthal, George W., M.D., '97
Maryland
Dr. Oscar Hoffman
Ross, C. H., M.D., '91
Virginia
Dr. R. S. Martin
Ross, William T., M.D., '89
Virginia (Ohio)
Dr. W. F. B. Taylor
Roth, A. B., M.D., '92
California
Roth, John, M.D., M.D., '94
Maryland
Baltimore University
Dr. Daush
Roth, John C. (E.), M.D., '90
Maryland
Professor Z. K. Wiley
Roth, Julius F., '91
California
Baltimore University
Rothrock, D. R., M.D., '85
Pennsylvania
Dr. R. Rothrock
Rotto, John C., '84
Maryland
Baltimore University
Rovitti, Peter, A.M., Ph.G., M.D., '02
New York
Dr. D. Saladino(us)
Roy, Joseph Napoleon, M.D., '02
Rhode Island
Laral University
Rubinsohn, L. S., '91
Pennsylvania
Baltimore University
Rudolph, John C. (J.), M.D., '98
New Jersey (Maryland)
Baltimore University
Dr. G. A. Strauss
Ruhl, Frank, M.D., '92
Maryland
Professor Z. K. Wiley
Russell, A. B., '01
Virginia
Baltimore University
Russell, C. H., '98
Pennsylvania
Dr. Harry Neafie
Ruzicka, O. J., Ph.G., '97
New York
Dr. D. J. Ruzicka
Sacks, Robert, M.D., '91
Maryland
Professor A. Whitehead
Salinkewitz, S. Salinko, '97
Russia
Baltimore University
Samuel(s), Gail, M.D., '97
West Virginia
Dr. W. N. Burn(w)ell
Sanders, Walton J., M.D., '91
Pennsylvania
Dr. W. E. Lloyd
Sands, George M., M.D., '96
Maryland
Dr. Chappell
Sanford, James B., M.D., '00
San Antonio, Texas
Dr. D. C. Rodenhurst
Sanford, W. W., '99
New York
Baltimore University
Sanor, Daniel Grant, M.D., '94
Ohio
Dr. J. M. Ernst
Santosuosso, Joseph, M.D., '99
Massachusetts
Dr. John C. Tanner
Saunders, James E., M.D., '02
White Stone, Virginia
Dr. H. H. Biedler

Saunders, R. C., '95
Florida
Baltimore University
Savage, C. Grant, M.D., '98
Connecticut
Dr. John D. Kenyon
Seftenberg, Benjamin F., M.D., '99
New York
Dr. Alexander Hadden
Seyferth, Curth, M.D., '86
Germany
Baltimore University
Scharf, Joseph, '94
Pennsylvania (Austria)
Scheidt, Robert P. C., M.D., '93
Maryland
Professor Z. K. Wiley
Schekkin, M. L., '00
Baltimore, Maryland
Baltimore University
Schelkshorn, Otto W., M.D., '94
Pennsylvania
Dr. X. O. Werder
Schell, S. W., M.D., '99
North Carolina
University Medical College of Richmond
Schenthal, Alexander, M.D., '97
Maryland
Baltimore University
Drs. B. F. Leonard and W. T. Cathell
Schimmel, M. J. (S.), M.D., '95
New York City
Baltimore University
Professor Eilau
Schloegel, William E., A.B., '00, '01
Baltimore, Maryland
Dr. A. A. Bo(u)rdick
Schneider, John, '95, '96
Pennsylvania
Dr. John Morrow
Schneider, Oscar, '97
New York
Dr. B. W. Vanderpoelder
Schofield, J. F., M.D., '93
Pennsylvania
Dr. L. M. Snyder
Schofield, John C., M.D., '91
Pennsylvania
Dr. S. M. Snyder
Schofield, Robert K., M.D., '98
Pennsylvania
Dr. J. F. (T.) Schofield
S(c)holle(r), Ferdinand, M.D., '97
Maryland
Professor J. (F.) G. Linthicum
Schultz(e), August W., M.D., '93
Maryland
Dr. C. M. Schultz
Schwartz, Charles, M.D., '98
New York (Maryland)
Dr. Solow
Schwatka, Charles A., '00
Govanstown, Maryland
Baltimore University
Schwatka, Charles Taylor, M.D., '04
Maryland
Baltimore University
Dr. A. A. Burdick
Scott, John, M.D., '04
Pennsylvania
Dr. E. F. Apeldorn
Shammo, G. C., M.D., '98
Pennsylvania
Baltimore University
Shanks, Morris, M.D., '91
Maryland
Professor E. M. Reid
Shannon, Thomas I., Ph.G., M.D., '99
Connecticut
Dr. Joseph J. Higgins
Shannon, Walter Roland, M.D., '97
Pennsylvania
Dr. D. W. Longstreet
Shapira, Frederick I., '92
Pennsylvania
Baltimore University
Shapira, Israel J. E., M.D., '97
Massachusetts
M. Medical U. M. H., Rus.
Shapiro(a), Victor, '01, '02, '03
Massachusetts
Dr. I. J. E. Shapiro(a)
Sharer, J. V., '85
North Carolina
Dr. L. M. Archey
Shaw, W. E., '95
Maryland
Dr. J. B. Schwatka
Shay, Daniel A., M.D., '01
Brooklyn, New York
Dr. Seth Scott Bishop
Sheedy, John F., M.D., '98
Massachusetts
Dr. J. A. Mc(a)gee(s)
Shepherd, C. W., M.D., '91
West Virginia
Baltimore University
Shepler, D. W. (R.), M.D., '03
Pennsylvania
Dr. George E. (F.) Mickel (Mitchell)
She(a)r, Philip, M.D., '02
Reading, Pennsylvania (Maryland)
Baltimore University
Shine, John P., M.D., '99
Massachusetts
Dr. S. A. Mahoney
Shipley, Harry F., M.D., '98
Maryland
Dr. B. F. Shipley
Shipper, James H., M.D., '97
West Virginia
Dr. L. E. Cincindiver
Shook, J. H., M.D., '98
Pennsylvania
Dr. E. C. Miller
Short, B. P., M.D., '92
Georgia
Dr. W. Jefferson
Sieverts, L. Bernard, '02
Pennsylvania
Dr. S. P. Knoll
Silberstein, Samuel, M.D., '00

Passaic, New Jersey
Dr. Van Vere Runken (Wuvanken)
Silverman, Herman, M.D., '96
Louisiana (New York)
Baltimore University
Simms, Joseph S., '96, '97
Delaware
University of Pennsylvania
Dr. J. H. Simms
Skeew, Marion P., '94
North Carolina
Dr. C. H. Lewis
Slavin, M. M., A.B., '00
Baltimore, Maryland
Baltimore University
Sloan, R. T., M.D., '86
South Carolina
Dr. C. M. Littlejohn
Slutzski (Slutskin), Morris L., '98, '01
Maryland
Drs. H. H. Biedler and J. H. McCormick
Smith, C. D., '86
Texas
Dr. W. H. Park
Smith, F. C., M.D., '98
Pennsylvania
Dr. J. H. Horne
Small, Guy Darwin, M.D., '02
Massachusetts
Dr. L. A. Merritt
Smith, H. A., M.D., '98
Canada
Dr. T. H. Smith
Smith, H. R., '90
Ohio
Dr. G. P. Campbell
Smith, J. Carl, M.D., '88
Pennsylvania
Dr. August Chestnutwood
Smith, J. James, M.D., '97
Nova Scotia
Dr. J. P. Smith
Smith, J. Thornton, M.D., '90
Pennsylvania
Dr. J. T. Rollins
Smith, Samuel Easton, M.D., '89
Pennsylvania
Dr. I. H. Smith
Smith, Dr. William F., M.D., '04
Tennessee
University of Washington
Smithline, Jacob, M.D., '00
New York City
Dr. E. H. Reidel
Snyder, Henry F. R., '95
Maryland
Dr. E. L. Crutchfield
Snyder, S. M., M.D., '88
Pennsylvania
Drs. R. M. Quig and W. J. Allen
Sobernheimer, Harry B., M.D., '03
Pennsylvania
Dr. H. H. Biedler
Somers, Arthur R., M.D., '91
Maryland
Professor A. Whitehead
Somers, Ira C., '97, '98
Maryland
Baltimore University
Dr. J. F. Somers
Sossnitz, Isaac, M.D., '98
New York
Dr. I. J. Bluestone
Soule, William O., '91
Connecticut
Dr. W. Soule
Southgard, E., '96
Maryland
Dr. J. C. Schofield
Spooner, W. R., M.D., '98, M.D., '99
Ohio
Dr. H. K. Spooner
Stansbury, Percy, M.D., '94
Maryland
Baltimore University
Professors Z. K. Wiley and T. B. Evans
Stapp, Frederick Starr, M.D., '04
Pennsylvania
Dr. H. W. Soul(e)
Starr, Gron(tt)an (Grattan), F., M.D., '89
Ohio
Dr. M. Starr
St. Clair, Emma N., M.D., '00
Canisteo, New York
Dr. Henry P. Jack
St. Dennis, N. J., M.D., '92
Massachusetts
Dr. A. G. Gironard
Stearn(s), Isaac, M.D., '93
Pennsylvania (Maryland)
Dr. Moses Stearn(s)
Stearn(e)s, Moses, M.D., '89
Pennsylvania
Baltimore University
Steele, William S., M.D., '93
West Virginia
Drs. Holden, Woods and S. V. Thompson
Steeves, J. W., M.D., '92
New Brunswick
Dr. Melvin
Steifer, Homer M., M.D., '95
Georgia
Baltimore University
Dr. W. C. Burns
Stein, Max, D.D.S., M.D., '98
Russia
University of Maryland
Sterner, H. W., M.D., '99
Pennsylvania
Dr. G. C. Shammo
Stevens, Frank A., M.D., '97
Vermont
Dr. Charles N. Cox
Stewart, J. D., '96
New York
Dr. A. B. Becker
St. George, Wilfred, M.D., '93
Massachusetts
Dr. Carpenter
St. Germain, J. A., M.D., '98
Massachusetts
Dr. Archie St. George

Stilson, Jesse M., M.D., '95
New York
Dr. B. P. Muse
Stoerger, Charles, '98
Baltimore University
Stoerger, H. A., Jr., '98
Baltimore University
Stone, G. H., M.D., '98
Massachusetts
Dr. C. W. Jackson
Stoner, D. C., M.D., '99
Pennsylvania
Dr. J. A. Bierer
Stout, John L., '98
West Virginia
Dr. S. A. Cavalier
Stover, William R., M.D., '00
Luray, Virginia
Professor H. H. Biedler
Strasser, Robert E., M.D., '94
Pennsylvania
Dr. Thomas A. Strasser
Strauss, George (Gerson), '92, '93, '94
Connecticut
Dr. H. Fleishner
Striebich, Joseph A., M.D., '99
Pennsylvania
Dr. M. J. Miller
Stuart, James, M.D., '99
New York
Dr. A. B. Becker
Stumbaugh, W. D., M.D., '97
Iowa
Dr. Moore
Stumberg, B. Kurt, A. B., '97
Missouri
Dr. J. H. Stumberg
Stump, E. H., M.D., '94
West Virginia
Baltimore University
Sturgis, Leigh F., '99
New York City
Baltimore University
Sullivan, Daniel T., '93
Massachusetts
Dr. J. A. Bacon
Sweeny, L. D., '95
Illinois
Dr. Cole
Sweeney, John L., M.D., '98
New York
Professor H. H. Biedler
Sylcurk, John H., '96, '97
Maryland
Drs. H. F. Getzendanner and S. S. Maynard
Szuwalski, Stephen J., M.D., '96
Maryland
Baltimore University
Dr. S. S. Ulrich
Taggart, G. C., M.D., '98
Pennsylvania
Baltimore University
Tanner, Frederick N., '97
Pennsylvania
Dr. G. F. Rodman
Tanner, James F. (H.), M.D., '98
Connecticut
Drs. James Doley and T. H. Weldon
Tanner, John C. (H.), M.D., '97
Connecticut
Drs. James Doley and M. E. Bradley
Tarr, Robert F., '97
Pennsylvania
Dr. J. E. Stute
Tattersall, Joseph, M.D., '00
Paterson, New Jersey
Dr. J. M. Stewart
Taylor, Charles P., M.D., '93
West Virginia
Drs. Miller and Yeakley
Taylor, D. Grant, M.D., '97
Ohio
Dr. John McFadden
Taylor, W. A., '90
Pennsylvania
Baltimore University
Teachner, K., '96
Ohio
Dr. J. N. Hamilton
Teller, H. J., M.D., '98
New York
Dr. D. B. Kyle
Thatcher, H. D., M.D., '98
New Jersey
Dr. T. B. Tulper
Thielman, H. B., M.D., '92
Maryland
Baltimore University
Thome, Arthur J., '03
Pennsylvania
Dr. W. B. Thome
Thome, Winfield Missimer, M.D., '04
Pennsylvania
Dr. W. B. Thome
Thompson, James E., M.D., '97
Pennsylvania
Dr. John A. Burlington
Thompson, L. W. (H.), M.D., '90
West Virginia
Dr. J. C. Hughes
Thompson, Z. A., '03
West Virginia
Dr. J. W. Thompson
Thomson, C. W., '90
South Carolina
Baltimore University
Thorn, Paul D., M.D., '87
Pennsylvania
Dr. A. Thom
Tiedeman, Frederick, Jr., M.D., '99
New York
Dr. James P. Fiske
Tierkel, W. T., M.D., '91
New York
Dr. T. Flandran
Tierney, Michael Frances, M.D., '04
Massachusetts
Baltimore University
Tillapaugh, J. J., M.D., '90
New York
Dr. C. C. Histon
Ting(e)ley, Hilbert B., M.D., '89

New Brunswick, Canada
Dr. D. C. Allen
Todd, John D., '94
Tennessee
Baltimore University
Tolson, William H., M.D., '90
Maryland
Baltimore University
Professor A. Whitehead
Tomlinson, J. W., M.D., '98
Pennsylvania
Dr. John Tomlinson
Towne, J. Gerald, M.D., '00
Waterville, Maine
Dr. M. S. Goodrich
Townsend, Frank A., '97
Vermont
Dr. Foster
Townsend, J. Allen, M.D., '92
Florida
Dr. James P. Peeler
Tracey, B. A., M.D., '91
New York
Dr. G. A. Tracy
Trachman, Henry J., M.D., '00
Newark, New Jersey
Dr. (L.) Seidman
Treakle, Henry B., M.D., '93
Virginia
Baltimore University
Trexler, Jacob A., '97
Pennsylvania
Drs. T. A. and R. C. Stross
Truax, James L., '97
Maryland
Professor F. Caruthers
Tulchinsky, W., Ph.G., M.D., '00
Baltimore, Maryland
Dr. S. Tarler
Tult(s)chinsky, W., M.D., '00, M.D., '01
New York City
Dr. S. Tarler
Turner, J. D., '98
West Virginia
University Medical College, Richmond
Tyndall, Ira C., M.D., '96
Delaware
Professor B. P. Muse
Valentine, Joseph John, M.D., '98
Maryland
Drs. I. I. Gross and T. Kelly
Varner, S. W., M.D., '91
West Virginia
Dr. E. H. Dodson
Vick, Clyde, '96, '97
Virginia
Baltimore University
Vosteg, William, '86
Maryland
Professor Wiley
Voorhees, Grant S., M.D., '98
Pennsylvania
Dr. Sherman Voorhees
Wade, George B., M.D., '92
Massachusetts
Dr. C. A. Lovejoy
Walden, James C. (G.), M.D., '92
New York
Dr. S. G. Olin
Walker, J. (I.) H., M.D., '90
West Virginia
Dr. D. Mayer
Walls, H. V., D.D.S., M.D., '99
Connecticut
Dr. J. C. Lynch
Ward, Joseph F., M.D., '99
Illinois
Dr. J. J. O'Connell
Ward, W. A., '97
North Carolina
Dr. E. H. Horton
Ward, William W., M.D., '95
Maryland
Dr. H. W. Webster, Jr., and
Professor P. B. Wilson
Warlick, N. N., M.D., '85
Tennessee
Dr. J. H. Sensabaugh
Warren, Alvah A., '03
Rhode Island
Baltimore University
Warren, George W., M.D., '02
Alabama
Drs. Drennan and Drennan
Watkins, J. S., '86
Maryland
Professor Roseberry
Watson, John E. (Asbury), M.D., '02
Maryland
Baltimore University
Widby, E. J., M.D., '99
North Carolina
University Medical College, Richmond
Wilin(ni)sky, Charles Francis, M.D., '04
Springfield, Massachusetts
Dr. A. Wilinsky
Wilkinson, S. D., M.D., '93
Ohio
Dr. J. Frank Piper
Williams, C. H., '94
Maryland
Dr. B. P. Muse
Williams, Joseph (James) (Fulton), M.D., '99
Virginia
Dr. W. L. Williams
Williams, W. Eason, M.D., '97
California (Maryland)
Professor B. P. Muse
Willson, J. Ward, M.D., '89
Maryland
Dr. Alfred Whitehead
Wilson, Frederick W., M.D., '96
Maryland
Dr. P. B. Wilson, Jr., and
Professor A. Whitehead
Wilson, G. H., '86
Maryland
Professor Linthicum
Wilson, H. G., '86
Maryland
Professor Linthicum
Wilson, Louis S., '95

Maryland
Dr. P. B. Wilson, Jr.
Wilson, Pierce B., Jr., M.D., '94
Maryland
Professors P. B. Wilson and A. Whitehead
Wir(e)tz, Louis Joseph, M.D., '04
Hoboken, New Jersey
Dr. M. D. Meyer
Wittig, S. G., '98
Virginia
Dr. B. F. Moyers
Webb, J. W., '01, '02, '03
West Virginia
Drs. D. R. Iveland and W. S. G. Ferrell
Weber, Frederick W., M.D., '88
Maryland
Professor Z. K. Wiley
Weeks, Charles T., M.D., '85
Nova Scotia
Dr. C. O. Black
Weidman, John A., '97
New York
Dr. James E. Crisfield
Weiss, J. S., B.S., M.D., '03
Maryland (Illinois)
Baltimore University
Drs. H. H. Biedler and A. A. Burdick
Weitzman, Miss Frances E., M.D., '03
New York
Dr. H. H. Biedler
Welch, John L.

Weld, Charles R., '91
Maryland
Harvard University
Wells, Abner T., Ph.G., M.D., '99
Maine
Maine Medical College, P. and S., Boston,
Dr. H. B. Palmer
Wertman, A. G., M.D., '98
Pennsylvania
Dr. A. A. Wertman
Westbrook, Edward A., M.D., '02
Maryland
Dr. H. Young Westbrook
Westbrook, Horace Y., M.D., '90
Pennsylvania
Dr. John F. Goode
Whelan, William M., M.D., '97
Canada
Dr. S. R. Jenkins
White, Cummins E., M.D., '92
West Virginia
Professor H. H. Biedler and
Dr. R. H. Fel(t)ty
White, Hugh H., '93
Virginia
Dr. I. S. Stone
White, H. J., '90
Maryland
Professor Z. K. Wiley
Whitehead, Alfred, M.D., '90
England
Baltimore University
Whitehead, J. E. N., M.D., '01
Philadelphia, Pennsylvania
Medical Chirurgical College
Whitney, Samuel (F.) D., M.D., '90
New York
Dr. G. W. Whitney
Whitescarver, John S., M.D., '98
West Virginia
Professor H. H. Biedler
Whitford, A. F., M.D., '93
Massachusetts (Nova Scotia)
Dr. F. W. Keely
Wolff, Benjamin, M.D., '01
New York City
Dr. P. A. Siegelstein
Wood, Charles W. (H.), M.D., '91
Maryland
Professor Z. K. Wiley
Wood, G. N. B., '89
North Carolina
Dr. J. H. Wood
Wood, L. J., M.D., '87
South Carolina
Dr. P. B. Carwiel and
Professor S. V. Hoopman
Wood, Oscar H., '95
Bermuda
Dr. E. E. Brown
Woods, H. W., M.D., '98
Pennsylvania
Baltimore University
Woodley, J. A., M.D., '87
South Carolina
Drs. R. B. Covington and Hanna
Woodley, J. D. (L.), M.D., '91
South Carolina
Dr. J. A. Woodley
Woodward, C. P., M.D., '92
New Jersey
Dr. Woodward
Woodward, G., '96
New York
Dr. G. E. Woodford
Woodward, Israel J., M.D., '94
New Jersey
Dr. C. E. Woodward
Woolford, Charles T. (I.), M.D., '98
Maryland
Drs. A. C. Eisenberg and C. T. Scudder
Wright, Frank O., M.D., '97
Ohio
N. N. U., Lebanon, Ohio
Wright, Harper Ancel, M.D., '04
Pennsylvania
Dr. G. M. Glasgow
Wright, Nathaniel Van Virt, M.D., '01
Baltimore, Maryland
Baltimore University
Wulf, Kahn, M.D., '96
Maryland
Yeakley, H. K., M.D., '91
Virginia
Baltimore University
Yost, Robert J. (Y.), M.D., '95
Pennsylvania
Dr. M. L. Yost
Young, J. L., '98
Baltimore University

Yount, B. H., M.D., '89
Washington Territory
Dr. I. M. Little

Zanderer, Louis J., '02, '03
Maryland
Baltimore University, Dr. A. Sangree

Zellner, Charles Harvey, M.D., '04
Pennsylvania
Drs. W. P. and E. M. Kistler

Zille, Ernst, M.D., '97
New Jersey
Professor Z. K. Wiley

Zineman, William B., M.D., '96
Pennsylvania
Dr. E. B. Iangree

Zink, Charles E., Ph.G., M.D., '00
Branford, Connecticut
Dr. W. H. Zink

Zobiska, Mary, '02
Maryland
Baltimore University

ACKNOWLEDGMENTS

Deep thanks are expressed for the valuable assistance of Miss Marion B. Savin and Mr. Kenneth V. Hahn, both of Philadelphia, and for the kind help of Miss Hilda E. Moore, of the Health Sciences Library, University of Maryland, Miss Gertrude L. Annan and Miss Mary E. Feeney, of the Library of the New York Academy of Medicine, Mr. Charles Roos and Staff, of the National Library of Medicine, Dr. Margaret B. Ballard, of Union, West Virginia, and the Information Bureau, of the Baltimore Sun.

BIBLIOGRAPHY

1. Annual Announcements of the Baltimore University School of Medicine, 1885-86 to 1904-05, inclusive.
2. Howard A. Kelly and Walter L. Burrage: *Dictionary of American Medical Biography, New York,* D. Appleton and Co., 1928.
3. Maryland Medical Journal, Volume XI, August 23, 1884, pp.337-8.
4. Eugene F. Cordell: *The Medical Annals of Maryland*, Baltimore, 1903.
5. Records of the Superior Court of Baltimore City, Liber 38, Folio 570; R.O. Liber 46, Folio 59; S.C.L. Liber 58, Folio 407, Item 198; S.C.L. Liber 59, Folio 274; Charter Record Liber 21, Folio 490-93; Circuit Court records of Baltimore City, 24A, Folio 248, (1884).

FOOTNOTES TO CHAPTER FOUR

(1) *The Maryland Medical Journal*, (Volume XI, August 23, 1884, pp. 337-8), under the heading "Dissensions in the Baltimore Medical College", reported that the rumors of "inharmonious proceedings in the Faculty of Baltimore Medical College", had eventually proved to be true, and that the Faculty had split into two halves, one under Dr. Harvey L. Byrd, and the other under Dr. Monroe, each of which claimed recognition as the rightful owner of the charter. (One of the causes of contention may have been disagreement over the admission of women, Dr. Byrd being in favor, and Dr. Monroe opposed.) Dr. Byrd's faction secured a building in the eastern section of the city, and Dr. Monroe's in the northern section. Each of the two Faculties issued a catalogue, and now there loomed a legal suit, to determine which half was entitled to hold the rights and franchises granted by the charter. The *Journal* bewailed the possible chartering of the unsuccessful litigant in this suit, and the addition of the newly chartered half to the already too numerous medical schools, a development not in the best interests of "local professional reputation and ethics". (Personal communication from Margaret B. Ballard, M.D., now residing in Union, West Virginia, and the Reference Department of the Health Sciences Library, University of Maryland, December 11, 1964.)

Dr. Byrd died on November 29, 1884. (The Index Catalogue of the Library of the Surgeon General's Office, Second Series, 1897, Volume 2, p. 8, mentions, among the holdings of that library, an obituary notice of Dr. Byrd, written by the Faculty, dated December 29, 1884.)

Thus the Baltimore University School of Medicine arose by splitting from the Baltimore Medical College. (See Appendices C and D.)

(For a biographical note on Dr. Byrd, see the chapter on the Washington University School of Medicine, Second Period, footnote #6.)

(William Robert Monroe, 1821-1894, took his M.D. at Washington University School of Medicine, in 1849. He was Professor of Materia Medica, Therapeutics and Hygiene at Baltimore Medical College, of which he was a Founder, and was Dean there, 1882-1884.)

(2) Departments of veterinary science, law and dentistry were organized soon after the rise of the School of Medicine.

(3) (For a biographical note on Dr. Reuling, see the chapter on the Washington University School of Medicine, Second Period, footnote #9.)

THE SOUTHERN HOMOEOPATHIC MEDICAL COLLEGE – ATLANTIC MEDICAL COLLEGE

In the half decade preceding the year 1890 a feeling had grown among the homoeopaths of Baltimore that their system of medicine should play its part in the promotion of the general welfare, to which all the educational enterprises of the city were contributing so much. Their State society was flourishing; a medical journal, to succeed a less pretentious, local periodical, was about to be established, as was their medical examining board; "above all, the necessity of enlarging the scope of the dispensary was generally recognized". (This was the only dispensary in Baltimore where a sick, needy person could obtain homoeopathic treatment. It had a staff of from three to six physicians.) It was felt that since homoeopathy's "pre-eminence in its allotted sphere had been determined in the homes of . . . patrons, it should also be demonstrated in the wards of a hospital and proclaimed from the platform of a College".(1) It was further believed that liberal-minded citizens, who had learned, from personal experience, of the advantages of homoeopathy would help in its extension, if the agencies for doing so, i.e., a homoeopathic medical College, were once established in the city. An additional reason for setting up such a school was that doing so would make it possible for worthy young men and women of limited means to study in their native city, under more favorable circumstances, and at smaller expense than studying at a distant school, thus preventing persons who might some day adorn the profession, from being diverted to other callings in life because medical education had been lengthened and become so costly. Furthermore the number of specialists was very small. There were few surgeons and oculists, and homoeopathic physicians found this rather embarrassing.

As to reasons for studying medicine in Baltimore the Announcement for 1892-3 had the following to say:

> ". . . Baltimore is, in fact, essentially a university city, where not only the South may come in search of knowledge, but the North, East and West as well, with every assurance that the advantages offered cannot be surpassed elsewhere.
>
> Baltimore is the first city of magnitude south of Mason and Dixon's line, and it appropriately stands as the leading city of the South. Allied to the South by no ordinary attachment, it is proper that no other city should supersede Baltimore as the educational centre of the South. Endowed with great universities and hospitals, large and well-appointed libraries, galleries of painting and sculpture, etc., one could scarcely find a more delightful seat of learning, or one presenting more varied advantages.
>
> The climate is for the most part mild, being a pleasant change for those whose lives have been passed in more rigorous latitudes; while the air is sufficiently bracing to have a salutary effect upon one reared in the more enervating southern climates.
>
> The people are more closely allied to the old-fashioned Southerner than those of any city farther north, and students who may desire to pursue their studies in Baltimore, will find themselves surrounded by all that is calculated to please, improve and interest them."

Additional reasons for locating in Baltimore were: ease of access to the city, from North, South, East and West, low cost of living there, liberal City and State appropriations, enabling Hospital and College to provide ample opportunities for clinical instruction, and the abundance of every variety of clinical material in an area of large population and fame as a seat of medical and surgical learning.

The College, in its Announcements made a repeated bid for students from the South, considering it a special privilege to be the instrument of the advancement of Homoeopathy in that section of our country. By 1899 it felt that "the southern states are rapidly opening a rich field to homoeopathic physicians, and as Baltimore is essentially a southern city and closely affiliated with the South by business and social ties, the graduate who proposes to locate in the South will find it an advantage to have graduated from a southern city"

On May 15, 1890 twenty six citizens of Baltimore, fourteen of whom were physicians, received from the State, articles of incorporation for establishing the Southern Homoeopathic Medical College and Hospital of Baltimore.(2) Of those twenty six incorporators twenty five were directors during the first year. The operation of schools of medicine, dentistry, pharmacy and veterinary science for male and female students was authorized, as was the issuance of stock.

On the same day the Maryland Homoeopathic Free Dispensary and Hospital of Baltimore was authorized, no provision for capital stock being made, because it was felt that private contributions would be forthcoming. It was located at 323 North Paca Street, and opened for patients on October 9, 1890, staffed almost entirely by the physicians who next year were the members of the first Faculty of the College. The fifteen year old Dispensary was abandoned, similar service now being available in the Hospital (and, next year, also in the College Dispensary).

By May 29, 1891 the Faculty had taken 420 shares of stock and lay members of the corporation 120 shares. (By 1905, 720 shares were sold, 362 preferred and 358 common.)

Enrolments were never very high, the session of 1898-1899, when there were forty students, ten of whom were women, being the "high-water mark". (Over the years there were many women among the matriculates, the school being co-educational from its inception. The Announcement for 1900 points out that women "have always been numbered among the most zealous supporters" of homoeopathy, and that it was therefore proper that they should have equal opportunity with men for medical education, that attitude toward them having proved justified by the "elevated moral tone which pervades the Institution, promoting sentiments so conducive to the efficient discharge of the physician's duties".)

The College received some support from the City and State, but it was small – $500. in 1894, for maintenance of the Dispensary and $800. the following year, after which the sums granted varied, until the College removed to the Hospital grounds, when the amount was merged with the money granted to the Hospital.

There was disagreement among the Faculty as to policy on the relations between Hospital and College, and some Faculty resignations resulted in 1899. Peace was restored after a satisfactory adjustment of relations between the two institutions, after which additional appropriations were made for further equipment of the laboratories.

Dr. Harper Peddicord, a graduate of 1899, passed the examination for the medical service and took up his post in the Philippines.

At the turn of the century the pioneers at the College

> "began to indulge the hope that their burden might ere long be safely transferred to the more vigorous shoulders of those who had enjoyed many advantages denied to themselves in their student days. Yet they have distinctly recognized that one duty yet remains for the older members of the profession to discharge, and that to insist upon the undiminished importance of homoeopathic therapeutics, all the more earnestly as it constitutes the raison d'etre of the homoeopathic medical college."(3)

A branch of the city Y.M.C.A. was maintained at the College, which made an appropriation toward the support of an Inter-Collegiate Secretary. The College set up a well equipped reading and amusement room for the use of students, in the College building. This was under control of the Y.M.C.A. which also directed religious activities and encouraged Bible studies and devotional meetings. The "Y" also made new students welcome, set up a list of suitable boarding houses for them, and issued a handbook for their use. They were also welcome to use the gymnasium and bathing facilities at the Central branch, at a small fee and to enjoy lectures and entertainments there.

An alumni association was formed in 1892, and rendered service in promoting the general interests of the College. In 1900 the officers were: William Dulany Thomas, President, Harper Peddicord, Vice-President, and M. Alva Fair, Secretary-Treasurer.

The Announcement of 1902 hopefully stated that although the medical profession might be overcrowded, as is commonly asserted, it was well known that homoeopathic physicians were not being educated in numbers sufficient to meet the public demand for their services. The Announcement further stated that "a prominent medical register reveals the names of thousands of towns and cities, particularly in the growing South, with populations ranging from one thousand upwards, in which there are no practitioners of the homoeopathic school." It made the point, once again, that until the Southern Homoeopathic Medical College was established, even Baltimore had only a small dispensary, staffed by from three to six physicians, where the needy sick could obtain homoeopathic treatment.

The tone of the Announcements and claims of clinical superiority may be sampled from the following passage, which appeared in 1903.

> "While the ratio of the physicians of our system to the general body of practitioners is one-tenth, the attendance at our school would obviously be much less than the average among the medical institutions in this community, but as their patrons constitute one-seventh of the entire population the consequent demand for more Homoeopathic physicians should be expected to increase the number of our students proportionately.
>
> While we desire, and have always aimed to merit, as large an attendance as our facilities will accommodate, we also realize that certain advantages accrue to the student from a limited body of scholars.
>
> The classes being small the largest possible opportunity is afforded the members to familiarize themselves with the variety of cases which appear at the dispensary for treatment. They are more frequently assigned to gyneco-

logical examinations and surgical operations, thus acquiring greater dexterity in the technique of those branches.

The same advantages apply to the out-patient visits, sub-clinic work. laboratory training, and attendance at the bed side of the hospital patients.

As an illustration of the means for acquiring experience, the obstetric cases assigned during the past year averaged ten for each member of the Junior and Senior classes.

Throughout the course of instruction in its numerous details students are brought into more immediate contact with their instructors, and the influence of the old time preceptor, a recognized power in the past in certain aspects which colleges have imperfectly supplied, is thus maintained in a multiplied degree."

The College received limited financial support from the State Legislature. In 1902 it was given $2500, and in 1903 the same amount, which it used for the purchase of laboratory equipment. In 1896 the Hospital received $1,000, in later years $2,500, $3,000, and in 1905, $5,000. As a result of the great fire which did so much damage to Baltimore no further State appropriation was made to the College, and the municipality having transferred its support from Dispensary to the Hospital, the College was now left solely to its own resources after 1904. The chief element in its maintenance-capital was the spirit of hopefulness of College and alumni. The Hospital represented a monetary value double that of the original purchase price, "embracing improvements and three dwellings outside its limits, occupied by the nurses". The city, for a number of years, contributed toward the maintenance of thirty beds, the Hospital also having another thirteen free beds, and accommodations for fifteen private patients. The Hospital carried on the function of education for the nursing profession from the opening year, graduating two nurses in 1892, and continuing thereafter to send forth graduates to a total number of forty-six by 1905.

The composition of the student body during the College's first year may be of interest. Of a total of nineteen students, six were in the third year class, five being graduates of the University of Maryland, and the sixth a transfer student from another homoeopathic school. "One student, having presented the requisite credentials, was admitted" to the second year class. There were ten men and two women in the first year class.

In 1906 an athletic association was organized, and attention given, in 1907, to sparring, fencing, wrestling, tennis and basketball. Activities were under the direction of a "competent instructor in athletics", who was an alumnus of the school. In 1908 football and baseball were added to the list of activities, it being anticipated that an excellent football team would be organized, immediately following the opening of the session. Other associations at the College were the Hering Institute and Epsilon Tau, which are discussed in Section II, Curriculum.

In 1907 the name of the College became the Atlantic Medical College. (See under that year, in Section II, Curriculum.)

The school became extinct in 1910.

I. BUILDINGS AND EQUIPMENT

In mid-summer of 1891 the College purchased, for the sum of $16,000 a three-story building, ("Calvert Hall"), on Saratoga St. between Charles and Cathedral, a location easily accessible by street cars from all railway stations, and steamboat lines as well as the various parts of the city. An additional expenditure of $5,000 was required for painting, repairing, creation of a dispensary and installing a heating plant. The Announcement for 1892-93 claimed that this building "ranks as one of the most commodious structures for medical teaching in the country", and well adapted to its purposes. The building was dedicated on October 7, of that year.

The Polyclinic Dispensary of the College covered a space of fifty by seventy-five feet on the first floor of this building. The space was divided into a large waiting room and hall, opening into eight well-lighted clinic rooms, twenty by fifteen feet each, and a Pharmacy. On the right of the entrance was the Eye and Ear Department with dark room adjoining. Immediately following were rooms for Gynecology, Surgery and Surgical Diseases, Diseases of Children and Orthopedic Surgery, and Diseases of Throat and Chest. Opposite these were rooms for Diseases of the Skin, Genito-Urinary Organs, Nervous System, General Medical Diseases, and the Pharmacy. At the rear of this floor were coat rooms, lavatory, morgue and boiler room.

The Lecture Halls and Laboratories were located on the second and third floors. On the second were located the Dean's office and Alumni Hall, followed on either side by lecture halls for chemistry and anatomy. These halls were "handsomely furnished" with single theatre chairs, and had a seating capacity of 400 in the aggregate. In the rear of the chemical hall was the chemical laboratory, with table-space for twenty-four students. A Faculty room and Faculty lavatory completed this floor. The third floor had a men's dissecting room, ("one of the largest and best equipped extant", commodious, well lighted, and equipped with stationary wash-stands, coat-closets and modern tables), a physiological laboratory, obstetrical and surgical demonstration rooms, women's dissecting room, museum, pathological laboratory and women's study and wash rooms, all being commodious and fully equipped. The building was heated throughout by steam.

The Maryland Homoeopathic Hospital at 323 N. Paca St. was controlled by the Faculty and offered every requirement for hospital cases in private rooms and public wards, which were in charge of a corps of trained nurses, under supervision of a superintendent. Its wards were well filled from its opening day. A part of the building was used as a city hospital and contained "charity beds", supported by the city. This department, crowded as it always was, provided excellent opportunities for clinical teaching, and was conducted with the special purpose of furnishing material for illustrating lectures. The arrangement of the building was well suited to this purpose, and the Faculty was able to exploit this advantage for teaching purposes.

In 1894 the Hospital was moved to a building at North Mount Street and Riggs Avenue. In 1898 upwards of $10,000. were spent on improvements in the Hospital. It now had sixty-five beds and could meet every requirement of sick or injured patients, both in private rooms and public wards, which were in charge of trained nurses, under supervision of an efficinet superintendent.

In addition to the opportunities at the Hospital, the Bay View Asylum and Hospital was accessible to all medical students, free of charge.

The Library of the State Homoeopathic Medical Society was accessible to students beyond the first year, at certain hours. The Pratt and Peabody Libraries were also available to students, who were given certificates for the use of these facilities by the registrar.

The monthly *Homoeopathic Advocate* was delivered to each student, free of charge.

In May, 1900, the decision was reached that, if an offer of $25,000 could be obtained, the College building should be sold, and a new home be erected near the Hospital. Ex-Governor Frank Brown, shortly thereafter, bought the building for $22,500, and construction of a new building, on the Hospital grounds, to the north of that edifice, was begun in March, 1901. By the following July construction had progessed so far, that the College dispensary could be, and was, opened, in the basement. The rest of the structure was completed soon thereafter, and the new building was dedicated in ceremonial fashion, on September 30 of the same year. It was hoped that the proximity of Hospital and College would prove mutually advantageous, the latter profiting from improved facilities for clinical teaching, and the former from the resulting enlarged staff, and therefore, their greater usefulness.

It was claimed that the situation of the new building was one of the finest and most elevated in the city. From the upper part of the building an extended and charming view, "reaching from the harbor across the city, to the fields and woods beyond the city limits" could be had. The building had a frontage of fifty feet and a depth of sixty feet, and consisted of a basement and two stories. It was built of cherry-red brick, with brownstone base, and ornate terra-cotta trimmings to match. It was not only handsome on the outside, but arranged carefully on the inside as well, in order that the work in all departments might be performed to best advantage. The building was set about forty feet back from the street, and surrounded by a lawn. The gravelled pathways were studded with shrubbery.

In the basement were located a large dispensary, twenty-seven by twenty-nine feet, lighted from three sides, and a waiting-room, thirteen by nineteen feet, each room having a private entrance. The basement also had a bandaging room, public and private cloak and locker room for students, a photograph room and dark room attached. The floor of the entire basement was of cement, in order that this part of the building could be washed with a hose.

The approach to the first floor was by a handsome terra-cotta entrance in the Doric style, and immediately under this entrance was another entrance to the basement (in addition to the entrances to the dispensary and to the waiting-room).

On the first floor there were two large lecture rooms, each nineteen by twenty-nine feet, lighted from two sides, and separated by an eight foot corridor. On this floor were also located a chemical laboratory (the largest room in the building), twenty-eight by twenty-nine feet, and a Faculty room.

On the second floor there were a study-room and adjoining cloak-room for women students, a laboratory for microscopical studies, equipped with "excellent apparatus", a large assembly-room and a dissecting room, lighted from two sides, with a skylight for additional light. The assembly-room was used as an additional study-room, library, Y.M.C.A. room and a society-meeting room.

Great care was taken to insure adequate light and ventilation, (by both direct and indirect means), "fresh air being introduced . . with the heat", to the various rooms. The halls were wainscoted, and the building was of cypress finish, throughout its interior. The College thought it proper to congratulate its students upon having so convenient and complete a building in which to pursue their medical studies. The surrounding neighborhood was good, and could furnish the students with pleasant homes, yet the College did, after all, consist of Faculty and students, in the quality of which the institution had hopes of "holding its own", and proper housing was only secondary to this main aim.

The laboratories, located, arranged and equipped with care, were five in number, (chemical, histological, anatomical or "dissecting room", pathological, and bandaging or practical surgical). In 1906 two more laboratories were added, i.e., pharmaceutical and physiological.

The chemical laboratory was fitted with "stands" for practical work, each equipped with gas outlet, set of reagents and glassware for carrying out the usual experiments and acquiring the practical knowledge needed to understand the first and second year work in this subject, thus becoming familiar with the principles of general, medical, physiological and organic chemistry, and mastering the techniques needed for ordinary chemical analysis, and the detection of poisons.

The microscopical laboratory was large, airy, well lighted, and supplied with microscopes, apparatus for cutting sections, mounting and staining slides, and making drawings. Each student had a separate locker. First and second year students were here made familiar with the use of the microscope, and how to prepare both normal and pathological tissues for study under magnification. Special facilities for advanced work in pathological histology were available. There were facilities for practical work in bacteriology, i.e., apparatus for preparing various culture media, and propagation of micro-organisms, whose growth and life-histories were studied.

The dissecting-room was large, adequately illuminated, and equipped with washstands, tables and closets.

There were "appropriate experiments, charts, models and . . . various appliances used in professional work".

The amphitheatre of the hospital, as well as a suitable place in the College building, were used for daily clinics.

The polyclinic dispensary consisted of nine departments, each operating in its own room, and in these sub-clinics, (for general medicine, eye and ear, surgery, genito-urinary diseases, pediatrics, nose, and throat, dermatology, nervous affections and gynecology), the junior and senior students, in groups, spent two weeks per clinic. (There were also the bedside clinics in the free wards of the hospital.)

In 1904 the hospital reported that it had a capacity of fifty-five beds, and further enlargement was contemplated. It was unde; the supervision of an "efficient superintendent", and there was a corps of trained nurses. Part of the hospital was operated as a City institution, having charity beds which had the financial support of the municipality. Accident cases, as well as those of the various general medical and surgical diseases, provided the students with improved clinical advantages, and were useful additional sources for illustrating the lecture courses.

The free lying-in hospital provided invaluable clinical advantages in the study of obstetrics.

(For a strongly divergent view of the equipment of this school, see the excerpt from the Flexner report, later in this chapter.)

II. CURRICULUM

The first session of the Southern Homoeopathic Medical College opened on October 5, 1891, and continued for six months, closing with a public commencement on April 6, 1892, at which six persons received their degrees. As this was a three year curriculum, a degree-awarding convocation would have been impossible until 1894, but for the fact that five matriculates had already graduated from the University of Maryland and the sixth had previously attended a homoeopathic college elsewhere.

The College pledged itself to maintain the standards set up by the American Institute of Homoeopathy in 1890. A high order of teaching was promised. The aim was to give a course which would be thoroughly practical, clinical facilities being made as complete as the Faculty could make them, via Dispensary and Hospital, and each student having the benefit of personal clinical instruction.

The course was said to be of the four year graded type, but the first year was "to be employed in preliminary medical study, satisfactory evidence of which must be submitted to the Dean on matriculation" – in other words, three sessions of lectures, each of six months duration, plus study under a preceptor for one year preceding the college work. (This requirement was enacted by the Inter-Collegiate Committee of the American Institute of Homoeopathy, and became operative in the Fall of 1892.)

> "The attention of students is directed to the fact thai attendance upon three courses of lectures in the College does not constitute a complete period of study. The year preceding the attendance upon the first course of lectures should be spent in preparatory study, and students are requested to register with a preceptor at the commencement of this period, so that he may be able to produce the required evidence as to the time spent in medical study.

Instruction was by didactic and clinical lectures, laboratory work (including dissecting), and weekly quizzes and recitations. The purpose of the quizzes was to explain difficult or obscure points and to give a practical direction to the studies as well as an indication of the thoroughness with which students were prosecuting their work.

1891

The curriculum consisted of the following courses:

INSTITUTES OF MEDICINE

One lecture per week was devoted to this subject, the course beginning with the history of medicine extending back 3300 years and reaching down to the present day. There was instruction in the principles and practice of homoeopathy as taught by the Organon, and reliable statistics given "to show its superior merits".

GYNECOLOGY

There were lectures, elaborately illustrated by diagrams and various kinds of preparations, for the purpose of thoroughly acquainting the student with the anatomy of the parts concerned as well as with pathological conditions. Abundant material was available from the Dispensary, and was used for clinical instruction. The course was made as practical as possible.

CHEMISTRY

There were two lectures per week on physics, general chemistry and medical chemistry, illustrated by suitable experiments.

BIOLOGY, HISTOLOGY, HYGIENE

In biology, fundamental facts were taught – comparison of living and non-living matter, structure and function of typical plants and animals, principles of classification, origin of plants and animals from a single cell, and the general evolution of tissues and organs during development.

Since pathology cannot be properly understood without a knowledge of the tissues in the state of health, special effort was made to give efficient and practical instruction in histology. The tissues under consideration were studied as far as practicable, by means of charts and microscopic specimens. In addition to attending lectures the student was required to do laboratory work, thus becoming familiar with the microscope and micro-histological methods.

The work in biology and histology prepared the way "for the discussion of the practical bearings of hygiene in its relation to the condition of modern life, and the subject of bacteria and the germ theory of disease" was brought up for consideration.

CLINICAL MEDICINE AND PHYSICAL DIAGNOSIS

The professor conducted two medical clinics per week before the entire class. At these clinics the professor tried to familiarize the student with the kinds of cases met with in every day practice. The Hospital and Dispensary furnished sufficient quality material to make these clinics of first class in every particular.

Advanced students were grouped into sections for practical instruction in physical diagnosis. There were also lectures upon this subject before the entire class, as time permitted.

MATERIA MEDICA AND THERAPEUTICS

These lectures were based upon the latest scientific investigations, and included a treatment of the various "drug relationships of both physiological and pathogenic therapeutics", said the first Announcement. Chemical, mechanical and antiparasitic methods, as well as the allopathic and antipathic theories were critically examined, "and their legitimate place in therapeutics defined, so that the student will be prepared to fully appreciate the broad scope of homoeopathy".

"The homoeopathic therapeutic relationship will be taught and illustrated in accordance with the effects of drugs upon the healthy, so far as such information is attainable; the fundamental material for such instruction being the reconstructive work of the Medical Investigation Club of Baltimore.

Supplemental to this study of pure pathogenesey, and in conjunction, the most trustworthy clinical observations will be taught."

It was the hope of the professor that his lectures would result in the acquisition, by the student, of a thorough knowledge of drugs and their uses.

PATHOLOGY AND PRACTICE OF MEDICINE

The purpose of the lectures was to impart a clear and comprehensive knowledge of the diseases "met by the general practitioner in practice, and citing the old school plans of treatment en passant", to dwell upon the homoeopathic treatment, and show its superiority.

OPHTHALMOLOGY AND OTOLOGY

This was a course on the medical and surgical treatment of diseases of eye and ear, with special reference to the use of homoeopathic remedies. An important part of the course was the use of the diagnostic instruments, as was the proper selection of glasses. Students had the opportunity of observing operations and making diagnoses at the weekly clinic.

PEDOLOGY AND ORTHOPEDIC SURGERY

There were two lectures per week on medical and surgical diseases of children. There was special attention to the care and proper feeding of infants, diagnosis of children's diseases and most modern methods of treatment. The prevention and management of spinal deformities and club foot were made special features of lectures and clinics.

OPERATIVE, CLINICAL AND ORIFICIAL SURGERY

There were two lectures per week, students being instructed in the most approved methods of operating and in the latest phases of surgical pathology and treatment. Illustrative material included wet and dry preparations, models and drawings. The various operations known to modern surgery were described and shown on the cadaver.

In one general clinic per week the various surgical operations of general practice were demonstrated. Special attention was given to the application of homoeopathic treatment before and after operations. Students had the advantage of making personal examinations and were permitted to perform minor operations and apply dressings, under the supervision of the professor.

SURGERY

There were lectures upon the principles of surgery and surgical pathology. Pathological conditions necessitating operations, and modern requirements of these were minutely considered. The after-treatment and amenability of many conditions to homoeopathic remedies, avoiding surgery if possible,were given attention. The student was familiarized with the latest theories and most important methods of modern surgery.

PHYSIOLOGY

This was taught principally by didactic lectures, and avoiding discussion of abstract, undecided questions. The course was illustrated by diagrams and specimens. A reasonable amount of time was devoted to quizzing.

James W. Bright, of the Faculty of Johns Hopkins University, gave a series of lectures on the physiology of speech.

NEUROLOGY

There was one lecture per week, illustrated, as far as possible, by clinical cases.

ANATOMY

There was a thorough lectures course, illustrated by plates, and supplemented by demonstration upon the cadaver. Particular attention was paid to surgical anatomy.

OBSTETRICS

From the professor's point of view every physician should be a "thorough obstetrician" and his aim was to teach the principles and practice of obstetrics by didactic lectures and demonstrations of normal and difficult labor, upon the manikin, in such a manner that his students would be efficient in this specialty. Attention was given to the puerperal state and infancy. Every student was made familiar with the presentations and use of obstetrical instruments by the demonstrator's work upon cadaver and fetus, and were admitted, in groups, to the lying-in room of the Maternite Hospital, for purposes of observing the process of labor from the first to the last stage.

TRAINING SCHOOL FOR NURSES

This was part of the Maryland Homoeopathic Hospital. Students received instruction in the art of nursing, both in lectures by the Faculty of the College and other lecturers, and in careful instruction at the bedside.

A diploma, signed by the lecturers of the training school, was awarded after the two-year training course was completed and an examination was passed.

1892

During the week preceding the opening of the session of 1892-93, there were daily lectures on collateral medical branches, these serving as an introduction to the regular course. This became an annual series.

The Announcement emphasized the standing of Baltimore as a great seat of medical and surgical learning and the abundance of clinical material of every variety.

The Hospital provided abundant clinical material for illustrating lectures. In addition to the regular clinical lectures in the amphitheatre, much attention was devoted to strictly bedside instruction, in which third-year students, in classes, were required to accompany the physician or surgeon through the wards, thus becoming familiar in a practical way with methods of diagnosis and treatment.

Education opportunities at the Bay View Asylum and Hospital have been referred to above, in the section on Buildings. Here a wide variety of cases of diseases and accidents could be observed. There were regular clinics during the winter and spring by the visiting staff, amphitheatres were well-lighted and comfortable, and there were unusual opportunities for practical teaching. The many post-mortem examinations made here provided good opportunities to study pathological phenomena.

In a building adjacent to the hospital arrangements were made to accommodate four resident students, who were called Internes. To these were assigned hospital wards, and they attended the sick, under daily supervision of the professors of the College and the resident physician. Undergraduates were permitted constant observation of the sick and received daily bedside instruction from the members of the Faculty. There was rotation in the Ward service, in order to provide the student with experience which was as varied as possible.

One of the wards in the Hospital was devoted to midwifery, and was open during the entire year. This provided students with the opportunity to study midwifery in the clinics. These were held in the lying-in chamber, and attendance upon these by the members of the graduating class, in sections, was obligatory.

There was also an out-patient department, connected with the lying-in department, thus extending the facilities for practical instruction in obstetrics. Advanced students were given charge of special cases, under personal supervision of the professor and demonstrator of obstetrics.

Institutes of Medicine was reduced from one lecture per week to one every two weeks in 1892, gynecology was a two lecture per week subject, chemistry three, materia medica four, three in pathology and practice of medicine, two in principles and practice of surgery, two in operative and clinical surgery (with orificial surgery as a special feature of this course), one on surgical anatomy, two on pedology and orthopedic surgery, three on physiology and normal histology, with demonstrations, and a lecture on alternate weeks on neurology, one on hygiene and sanitary science, three on anatomy, with demonstrations on the cadaver, three on obstetrics (and the course in practical obstetrics being obligatory), one on ophthalmology and otology.

SKIN AND VENEREAL DISEASE

There was one lecture per week, illustrated by cases from the clinic.

NOSE AND THROAT

This was a series of lectures upon the more common diseases of these organs.

MEDICAL JURISPRUDENCE

A complete course of lectures upon this subject was given.
The lecture courses were distributed as follows:

> "THE FIRST YEAR is largely devoted to practical laboratory work in the fundamental branches. Didactic teaching and recitations are supplemented by demonstrative and practical courses.
>
> Instruction is given in Anatomy, Physiology, Chemistry, Institutes, Pharmacy and Toxicology, Histology, Practical Chemistry, Practical Anatomy.
>
> Examinations at the end of this year in Institutes, Pharmacy, Histology and Practical Chemistry.
>
> ## SECOND YEAR
>
> IN THE SECOND YEAR, Practical Anatomy is continued and also advanced laboratory work in Medical Chemistry and Pathology. The general branches of medicine, including Anatomy, Physiology, Chemistry, Materia Medica and Therapeutics, Pathology and Practice of Medicine, Surgery and Surgical Pathology, Operative Surgery, Gynecology, Pedology, Obstetrics, Hygiene and Sanitary Science, and Clinical Medicine are taken up in lectures, recitations and clinics.
>
> Examinations at the end of this year in Anatomy, Physiology, Chemistry and Sanitary Science.
>
> ## THIRD YEAR
>
> IN THE THIRD YEAR, the courses of lectures and clinics of the second year are continued and augmented by the addition of Ophthalmology and Otology, Rhinology and Laryngology, Dermatology, Physical Diagnosis, Orthopedic Surgery, Neurology and Medical Jurisprudence.
>
> Examinations at the end of this year in Materia Medica, Pathology and Practice of Medicine, Principles of Surgery, Operative Surgery, Gynecology, Pedology and Orthopedic Surgery, Obstetrics, Clinical Medicine, Ophthalmology and Otology."

THE COLLEGE POLYCLINIC DISPENSARY

The Announcement of 1892 states that the Polyclinic had been created and equipped at great expense, with the latest scientific instruments and appliances, and had been modeled after the great teaching-schools of Europe. Here the needy poor of Maryland were treated free of charge by the professors of the College, each of whom was a specialist in his department. The course in clinical training was obligatory for all third year students, in order that they graduate as thoroughly learned and practical physicians. A full dispensary staff was in attendance between 12 o'clock and 2 P.M. The clinic provided ample material for purposes of instruction.

EAR AND EYE CLINIC

The ophthalmoscope was demonstrated, all forms of diseases of eye and ear were exhibited, various necessary operations were performed, treatment explained, and students required to examine and diagnose cases. There was thorough training in the optics of fitting eye-glasses, and in the new method of massage in the treatment of catarrhal deafness.

GYNECOLOGICAL CLINIC

The student was required to introduce the speculum and make examinations necessary for diagnosis and treatment of uterine and vaginal diseases. There was a special arrangement for preventing the identification of female patients, and this attracted abundant material for illustrating the various operations in gynecology. The professor performed operations in the treatment of diseases of women, in the presence of students.

SURGERY AND SURGICAL DISEASES

Students were required to make surgical diagnoses, apply bandages and dress wounds, under direction of the professor. The class, in sections, was given instruction at the bedside, in adjustment of fractures, application of splints, and antiseptic management of wounds.

DISEASES OF CHILDREN AND ORTHOPEDIC SURGERY

(See lecture course on this subject, below.)

THROAT AND NOSE CLINIC

The class was taught how to make rhinoscopic and laryngoscopic examinations, and observed operations performed on the air passages.

DISEASES OF THE SKIN AND GENITO-URINARY ORGANS

All forms of these diseases were exhibited and treated, including surgical operations when required. Students were taught the techniques of catheter and sounds.

NEUROLOGICAL CLINIC

Students were taught the methods and use of appliances for diagnosis, and especially prophylaxis and treatment. A feature was the application of electro-therapeutics to suitable cases.

GENERAL MEDICAL CLINIC

The professor held a daily clinic on the practice of medicine, selecting cases for illustrating his didactic lectures, studying each case analytically, so that he might then show his students the different phases and peculiarities which diseases assume, and diagnose and treat patients in the presence of the students. Physical diagnosis was taught in the clinics, each third-year student being required to examine patients in the presence of the class, under guidance of the professor.

PRACTICAL ANATOMY

The dissecting room was commodious, well lighted and equipped with stationary washstands, coat closets and modern tables, and was under the immediate supervision of a demonstrator.

PRACTICAL OBSTETRICS

In addition to instruction in obstetrics, at the bedside students were trained in manipulations upon the manikin and cadaver, in order to familiarize them with the diagnosis of the presentations in labor.

PRACTICAL SURGERY

This included ligation of arteries, resections and amputations upon the cadaver, and practice in applying splints, bandages and surgical dressings, in all of which students were trained to become proficient.

PRACTICAL CHEMISTRY

The chemical laboratory was fully equipped with apparatus, was under the supervision of a chemist whose plan of teaching enabled the student to become fully acquainted with chemicals and their properties.

PRACTICAL HISTOLOGY

Simple physiological processes were demonstrated, and the student was given special instruction in the use of the microscope and how to prepare and study both normal and pathological tissues. Those who wished to pursue advanced work in this department were allowed special facilities.

POST GRADUATE COURSE

Graduates of other reputable colleges were admitted, and permitted to take out tickets for courses of their choice. A certificate of such attendance was issued to them, but to obtain a diploma of the College, they were obliged to satisfy the entire Faculty, by means of an examination, that they had fulfilled all the requirements of the College for graduation. (To obtain the diploma in 1899 and thereafter, graduates had to attend all lectures and clinics of the fourth year.)

SPECIAL COURSES

Suitable persons were allowed to take such courses as they selected, without credit for any part of the college course.

1894

In 1894 it was announced that a four-year collegiate course (i.e., four sessions, regardless of preliminary work, under a preceptor), would be introduced in 1895. Students found qualified in the first year studies of this curriculum would be accepted into the second year, even though they had not taken them at a medical school, since many academic institutions provided a course which included the elementary subjects "necessary to a full appreciation of the more technical branches of medicine".

The curriculum was organized as given below, only changes from earlier years being noted:

INSTITUTES, HYGIENE, MEDICAL JURISPRUDENCE

Professor Elias C. Price, M.D.

Lecturer C. E. Hill, A.M.

Institutes – see above.

Hygiene included food substances, their preparation and adulteration; examination of water; ventilation and heating, drainage and other topics of interest to the general practitioner.

Medical Jurisprudence covered the medico-legal relations relating to the general practitioner, the course being given by a skilled member of the Baltimore Bar.

ANATOMY

Professor – E. H. Condon, M.D., Lecturer and Demonstrator – M. G. Smith, M.D.

Lectures upon descriptive and surgical anatomy supplemented by dissections, each student being required to dissect two parts, one upper and one lower, satisfactorily.

PHYSIOLOGY, HISTOLOGY, PATHOLOGY, BACTERIOLOGY

Professors – G. T. Shower, M.D., and H. Chandlee, M.D.

Lecturer – C. L. Rumsey, M.D.

Demonstrator – W. M. Panebaker, M.D.

The didactic lectures were illustrated by suitable experiments, and the relationship of physiology to practice of medicine in the broadest sense emphasized.

Histology included the microscopical study of every tissue and organ of the body.

Pathology and Bacteriology were taught by lectures, supplemented by post-mortem and laboratory work in pathological histology. Culture media were prepared, and the more common pathogenic bacteria studied in a practical way.

MATERIA MEDICA, PHARMACY, TOXICOLOGY, CHEMISTRY

Professor – Eldridge C. Price, M.D.

Lecturers – G. T. Shower, M.D., Albert M. Reese, A.B.

There were four lectures per week upon Materia Medica. (This course is described above.)

Pharmacy and Toxicology were taught by lecture, with laboratory work in the former.

Chemistry included a study of chemical reactions of the common metals, and of alkaloids, and a study of the principles of qualitative analysis, the entire course being adapted to the particular requirements of the student of medicine. Toxicology also came in for discussion in the lectures upon chemistry.

PRACTICE OF MEDICINE

Professors –
R. W. Mifflin, M.D., O. E. Janney, M.D.
C. H. Thomas, M.D., Henry Chandlee, M.D.
Chiefs of Clinic –
L. R. Palmer, M.D.
A. S. Atkinson, M.D.
J. A. Shower, M.D.

Three lectures per week (see above under Pathology and Practice of Medicine, 1891).

In the medical clinics, students made examinations of interesting and instructive cases, and suitable out-patients were placed under the care of fourth-year students, who made visits to patients' homes, then made full reports on these cases, to the professor of clinical medicine.

Special attention was given to the care and feeding of infants and prevention and treatment of diseases of children.

There was instruction in the mechanism and application of electrical and other apparatus and in diagnosis and treatment of nervous diseases, in addition to the homoeopathic therapeutics, "particularly keeping in view the needs of the general practitioner."

There was also a complete course on dermatology, amply illustrated by photo-lithographs, and clinical cases, in this department.

SURGERY

Professors –
S. Barnard, M.D.
T. L. Macdonald, M.D.
O. E. Janney, M.D.
Demonstrators –
C. L. Rumsey, M.D.
Bartus Trew, M.D.
Chiefs of Clinic –
M. G. Smith, M.D.
J. A. Clement, M.D.

(See Surgery, and Operative, Clinical and Orificial Surgery, 1891, above.)

The principles of orificial surgery, up-to-date in conception, was a special feature of the course.

Practical work in bandaging, application of splints and surgical dressings was done, and there was full instruction in the prevention, correction and treatment of spinal curvature and other deformities in childhood.

GYNECOLOGY, OBSTETRICS

Professors –
N. W. Kneass, M.D.
J. B. G. Curtis, M.D.
Henry Chandlee, M.D.
Demonstrator–
L. R. Palmer, M.D.
Chiefs of Clinic –
Bartus Trew, M.D.
W. M. Panebaker, M.D.

There were didactic lectures, and demonstrations on manikin and cadaver, as well as bedside instruction in diagnosis of pregnancy, abdominal palpation, diagnosis of presentations and positions, and management of labor and the puerperal state.

Confinement cases were assigned to fourth year students, and arrangements made for each student to receive direct personal instruction. The homoeopathic treatment of the disorders of pregnancy and the lying-in period received full consideration.

There were two didactic lectures per week on gynecology. At the weekly Hospital clinics advanced students diagnosed and treated the diseases of women and the student was given careful training in the recognition of uterine displacements and other pelvic disorders.

OPHTHALMOLOGY, OTOLOGY, LARYNGOLOGY, RHINOLOGY

Professors –
Eldridge C. Price, M.D.
W. R. King, M.D.
Lecturers –
C. L. Rumsey, M.D.
W. D. Thomas, M.D.
Demonstrator –
Clarence Nichols, M.D.

There were weekly lectures on laryngology and rhinology, with practical work in general and sub-clinics (see below), with special attention to the homoeopathic treatment of the many chronic conditions met with in this department.

Didactic lectures on ophthalmology and otology were supplemented by weekly clinics and sub-clinics, leading to familiarization of the student with diagnosis using ophthalmoscope, otoscope, laryngoscope and rhinoscope, and treatment of the more common diseases of eye and ear. Advanced students were admitted to some operations.

(Urine analysis is specified as a third year subject, but it is not clear from the Announcement whether this was a part of the course in chemistry. The same is true of bacteriology.)

The examination for the degree included all the subjects taught. If a student wished to extend his term of study beyond the fourth year, he was permitted, at the end of that year, to take examinations in gynecology, pedology, dermatology, neurology, ophthalmology and otology, rhinology and laryngology, patholgoy, bacteriology and medical jurisprudence.

CLINICS

Sub-clinics: These were held at the Dispensary in the following fields: Eye and Ear, Surgery, Diseases of Women, Diseases of Women, Diseases of Children, Nose and Throat, Skin, Diseases of the Nervous System, General Medical Diseases. The clinical course based upon these facilities was obligatory for fourth year students (and, later, for third year students, also). The classes were small, and they were admitted, in rotation, to those special clinic rooms, where they examined patients and prescribed for them, under supervision of the professor.

General Clinics:

The clinics at the College were on: General Medicine, Diseases of Children, Dermatology, Laryngology and Rhinology, Ophthalmology and Otology, Neurology, Gynecology, General Surgery.

The clinics on general surgery, and general medicine were held at the Maryland Homoeopathic Hospital, to the medical and surgical bed-side clinics of which fourth year students were admitted.

1895

The Southern Homoeopathic Medical College was now running on the plan of a four-year graded curriculum:

"SCHEDULE OF STUDIES, FOUR YEAR COURSE

Final Examination at end of		*Year of Study*
1st Year	Normal Histology, Lectures	1
1st Year	Normal Histology, Laboratory	1
1st Year	Institutes	1
1st Year	Pharmacy	1
2nd Year	Anatomy	1, 2
2nd Year	Physiology	1, 2
2nd Year	Chemistry	1, 2
2nd Year	Practical Anatomy, Laboratory	1, 2
2nd Year	Practical Chemistry, Laboratory	2
2nd Year	Pathology and Pathological Anatomy	2
2nd Year	Pathological Histology, Laboratory	2
2nd Year	Minor Surgery	2
2nd Year	Toxicology	2

2nd Year	Hygiene and Sanitary Science	2
2nd Year	Surgical Anatomy	2
3rd Year	Obstetrics, Physiology and Embryology	2, 3
4th Year	Materia Medica	2, 3, 4
3rd Year	Physical Diagnosis	3
3rd Year	Dermatology	3
3rd Year	Nervous and Mental Diseases	3
3rd Year	Rhinology and Laryngology	3
3rd Year	Bacteriology	3
3rd Year	Urinary Analysis	3
3rd Year	Practical Surgery	3
3rd Year	Practical Obstetrics	3
4th Year	Practice of Medicine	3, 4
4th Year	Principles of Surgery	3, 4
4th Year	Operative Gynecol. and Orificial Surgery	3, 4
4th Year	Medical Diseases of Women	3, 4
4th Year	Pedology and Orthopedic Surgery	3, 4
4th Year	Clinical and Operative Surgery	3, 4
4th Year	Practice of Obstetrics	3, 4
4th Year	Ophthalmology and Otology	3, 4
4th Year	Ophthalmology and Otology, Clinical	3, 4
4th Year	Medical Jurisprudence	4
4th Year	Clinical Medicine, Out-visits	4
	General Surgical Clinic	1, 2, 3, 4
	General Medical Clinic	1, 2, 3, 4
	Gynecological Clinic	3, 4
	Neurol., Rhinol., Dermatol., Pedol., Clinic	2, 3, 4
	Sub-Clinics	4"

"SPECIAL COURSE IN ORIFICIAL SURGERY"

During the week commencing Monday, September 23, Prof. E. H. Pratt, A.M., M.D., LL.D., will hold a clinical course in Orificial and Gynecological Surgery at the Maryland Homoeopathic Hospital. The class will assemble in the new amphitheatre erected for this purpose in connection with the Maryland Homoeopathic Hospital, on Monday Morning, September 23, at nine o'clock. There will be a four hours session daily during the entire week. The course will be both clinical and didactic. Members of the class are invited to bring clinical material.

These courses have been held annually in Chicago with great success; but in order to meet the steadily increasing demand for instruction in Orificial Surgery, the additional course in Baltimore has been arranged. The course will be similar to those which have been held by Dr. Pratt in Chicago for so many years, and we have reason to believe that our eastern and southern physicians will show their appreciation of this unusual opportunity which is offered them for surgical instruction in the new and important department of the healing art, by joining the class.

The fee for this course to practitioners of medicine is twenty five dollars. Arrangements have been made, however, by which matriculates of this College who pay in advance one-half of their fees for the school year, will be presented with a ticket to Prof. Pratt's course. A rare opportunity is thus afforded matriculates of the Southern College for 1895-96."

1899

The following changes may be noted:

MATERIA MEDICA: The lectures were devoted to "a study of the pathogenic effects of drugs as developed by provings upon the healthy, and confirmed by clinical applications", while also considering the physiological action. The student was given a knowledge of the characteristics of drugs and their individualities, by frequent comparisons, in order that their choice of the law of similars for a guide might be fully vindicated.

PRACTICE OF MEDICINE:
The associate professor gave a full course of lectures on diseases of heart and lungs.

PHYSICAL DIAGNOSIS AND CLINICAL MEDICINE:

These were taught to second and third year students. Didactic lectures included the topography of all organs in the thoracic and abdominal regions, their physical exploration, signs and diagnoses; clinical, microscopy of sputum, blood, urine, illustrations being drawn from among patients of the College dispensary. The professor selected cases, from that source, and showed the relation which the general practitioner must sustain to all classes in order to detect the early signs of disease. The student was taught how to examine a patient, understand the elements of disease, predict their courses, and how to find and apply the proper remedy.

Fourth year students were taught the practical application of the several methods of physical diagnosis and remedies, in the public wards of the College dispensary, accompanying the physician through the wards. The class was divided for sub-clinic work, as pointed out above, each student being given full instructions and essential records of each case. Clinical microscopy was restored to by students, who were obliged to make written reports, to the professor of clinical medicine, on out-clinic patients. In effect each fourth year student was made a special interne during the collegiate course.

GYNECOLOGY:

There was one lecture per week upon the anatomy of the pelvis and its surgical diseases, and one lecture per week upon the principles and practice of gynecology. Illustrations showing effect of local treatment, and action of homoeopathic medicines, applied according to principles, were drawn from the College dispensary.

Members of the fourth-year class, in groups, assisted in all operations in the clinics, and made examinations of patients under anaesthesia, thus becoming familiar with uterine deviations, normal and abnormal tissues, and the preparation and application of dressings.

BIOLOGY AND EMBRYOLOGY (first year):

This was a review of the general principles of biology, and a thorough course in embryology, leading up to and including the development of the human ovum.

SURGERY:

(See earlier discussions above)

Fourth year students were taught how and permitted to assist in preparing patients aseptically for surgery, assist in administering anaesthetics, in the operation, and in post-operative care. Instruction included prevention, correction and treatment of physical deformities, and the application of fixed dressings, such as plaster of Paris. The course was intended to be so practical that graduates would be able to meet skillfully the emergencies which arise in practice.

PRACTICAL OBSTETRICS:

Third year students – see above (1892).

Fourth year students were assigned to practical obstetrical work at the bedside.

PRACTICAL SURGERY:

Third year students – practice in applying splints, bandages, and surgical dressings – see above (1892).

Fourth year students – surgery upon the cadaver, including ligation of arteries, resections, amputations, and service as clinical assistants to the professors of surgery and gynecology – see above (1892).

1900

Instructional method was now given variation by the addition of recitations from text-books, in certain branches (in addition to the customary didactic and clinical lectures, laboratory work in anatomy, histology, surgery, (bandaging), chemistry, and pathology, and quizzes "in the nature of reviews"). Teaching was strengthened, wherever possible by appropriate experiments, charts, models, and practice in using the various medical appliances.

The program of studies for the four years, distributed by year, is listed in the pages which follow (see 1902). William H. King tells us that a course in blood analysis was initiated in 1900, and that this was supplemented, in the next session, with one on diseases of the alimentary canal.

In June, 1900, the Faculty had resolved to extend the term by one month, and the school was now upon a four year basis, each of seven months.

1902

Studies were pursued in the following order, those underscored being completed in the indicated year:

FIRST YEAR

Normal Histology (Lectures and Laboratory Work)
Biology (Lectures and Laboratory)
Pharmacy Institutes and History of Medicine
Toxicology, Anatomy, Dissections, Physiology
Chemistry (Lectures and Laboratory), Materia Medica
Medical Terminology

SECOND YEAR

Anatomy, Dissections, Regional Anatomy, Physiology
Embryology, Chemistry (Lectures and Laboratory)
Pathological Histology, Toxicology
Institutes and History of Medicine
Sanitary Science, Bacteriology, Materia Medica
Medical Terminology, Minor Surgery, General Clinics

THIRD YEAR

Physical Diagnosis, Dermatology, Nervous and Mental Diseases
Rhinology and Laryngology
Pathology, Minor Surgery, Practical Obstetrics
Practice of Medicine, Materia Medica and Therapeutics
Gynecology Obstetrics Pediatrics
Ophthalmology and Otology, Surgery
Clinical Medicine, Clinics and Out-visits

FOURTH YEAR

Practice of Medicine, Surgery, Gynecology, Pediatrics
Obstetrics, Ophthalmology and Otology
Diseases of the Chest, Materia Medica and Therapeutics
Practical Surgery, Clinical Medicine
Medical Jurisprudence, Life Insurance
Genito-Urinary Diseases, General Clinics, Sub-Clinics

Students selected from the Third-year Class acted as assistants in the dissecting room, under the supervision of the Demonstrators of Anatomy.

FIRST YEAR

NORMAL HISTOLOGY

Normal histology was now six hours per week of lecture and laboratory work, the aim being to familiarize the student with the details preparatory to the scientific investigation of diseased conditions which were studied in the succeeding terms. Cell growth and the structure of normal tissues and organs of the body were studied. Microscopical specimens were prepared by the student, under supervision of instructors, and training in hardening, imbedding, sectioning, staining and mounting were included. The slides thus prepared and accumulated became the property of the students, upon payment of the cost of materials. There was an examination at the end of the year.

BIOLOGY

The general principles of the subject were taught and microscopical study carried on in illustration of the principles of the subject. Groups of the lower orders of organic life, parasitic worms, fungi and ferments were considered. There was an examination at the end of the year.

INSTITUTES AND HISTORY OF MEDICINE

The principles of homoeopathy, application of the Law of Similars, the causes of diseases, methods of proving durgs, examination of patients and observing their progress under administration of the indicated remedy were taught. Such details of the history of medicine as might be profitable to the student were included in the course.

PHARMACY

The first half of the term was devoted to instruction in the principles of homoeopathic pharmacy, the recognition and preservation of drug substances, steps in the preparation of triturations and dilutions and methods of dispending them. The course closed with an examination at the end of the year.

TOXICOLOGY

The most important poisons, their effects upon the body, methods of detection and antidotal treatment were studied. There were also lectures upon prescription writing. There was a partial examination at the close of the term.

ANATOMY

This course extended over two years. Didactic lectures were illustrated by means of charts, models and all the approved appliances. The lectures upon osseous and ligamentous systems were followed by an examination; the lectures upon the muscular, vascular and nervous systems were followed by a partial examination; supervised dissections (during the seasonable time of year), made under demonstrators, assisted by members of the third-year class, involved the required dissection of two parts, and an examination before qualifying for the work of the next year.

PHYSIOLOGY

Two years were devoted to this subject, and the lectures were illustrated with the usual aids, and references to chemical experiments. There was emphasis upon the relation between physiology, pathology, diagnosis and symptomatology. The chemical composition of the body, digestion, absorption, circulation and respiration were treated, and an end-of-the-term examination required.

CHEMISTRY

Two years were devoted to the principles of inorganic and organic chemistry, the first year and the early half of the second to the former branch of chemistry, and the final half of the second year to the latter. There were two illustrated lectures per week, in the first year, dealing with non-metals, and five hours of laboratory work. Experimentation, demonstration and observation were emphasized. There were frequent reviews. The course closed with an examination.

MATERIA MEDICA

There were two lectures per week, to students of the first and second years. The history of each drug, its toxicological and physiological effects, "prominent symptoms", and whatever else that would give a student an intelligent knowledge of its use in all schools of medical practice, was studied.

SECOND YEAR

ANATOMY

This was a review of the studies of the preceding year, followed by dissections conducted under conditions similar to that year. There were demonstrator's lectures upon regional anatomy. An examination closed the course.

PHYSIOLOGY

There were lectures upon animal heat, metabolism, muscular and nervous systems and the special senses, closing with an examination on all topics considered.

EMBRYOLOGY

There were didactic lectures, illustrated by means of charts, models and microscopic slides. Cell reproduction was studied in the successive stages. Particular consideration was given to the development of the human embryo.

CHEMISTRY

The chemistry of the metals was considered in the months preceding the Christmas recess, the general outline being similar to that of the first year and the choice of metals limited to those which enter into medicinal preparations. Five hours per week were devoted to laboratory work in qualitative analysis.

Organic chemistry was a two lecture per week study, beginning after Christmas. "The chief groups and well known representatives of each series used in medicine" were discussed. There was laboratory work on the preparation of such organic substances as alcohol, ether and chloroform. An examination concluded the work of the year.

PATHOLOGICAL HISTOLOGY

There were lectures and laboratory work on many details in manipulation similar to those of the first year, dealing with the preparation of pathological specimens for microscopical examination, with particular attention to abnormal growths, and the special pathology of human tissues.

BACTERIOLOGY

Examination and culture of bacteria, with special attention to pathogenic forms.

TOXICOLOGY

A continuation of the studies of the first year.

INSTITUTES AND HISTORY OF MEDICINE

Continuation of the work of the first year, concluding with an examination.

SANITARY SCIENCE

This was a study of the preparation and adulteration of food substances, examination of water, ventilation, heating, drainage, and such other subjects as would be of particular interest to the general practitioner.

MINOR SURGERY

There were one lecture and one demonstration per week upon the minor surgical operations which so often demand the physician's attention, the use and care of instruments, and bandaging.

MATERIA MEDICA

The course was a completion of the work of the first year, with an examination at the close.

CLINICS

Students were required to attend the various clinical lectures, whenever time permitted.

THIRD YEAR

MATERIA MEDICA

This was a continuation of the work of the second year, with special attention to the symptomatology of the homoeopathic materia medica, "based upon the most reliable provings". The value of symptoms, their origin, the tissue changes which they imply and their therapeutic uses were taught, and drugs similar in action were compared, in order to make each drug stand out in its peculiar individuality, in the mind of the student, and vindicate the choice of the law of similars for a guide.

PRACTICE

The aim was to give a clear comprehension of the etiology, pathology, symptomatology, diagnosis, prognosis and treatment of diseases beyond the pale of the specialist. Diet and hygiene were given thorough consideration, "in the belief that much of the success in daily practice depends upon a proper knowledge of the general management of disease". The remedies advised were suggestive rather than exhaustive, and were those employed by our best authorities, in accordance with law of similars. All remedies specially indicated for each disease were minutely discussed and concisely described by the professor of materia medica and therapeutics.

PHYSICAL DIAGNOSIS

A study of healthy conditions, enabling him to make diagnosis in cases of disease. The use of newer instruments of precision were taught, as were methods of examination of blood and sputum, by means of microscope and other resources. There was also treatment of urine analysis and the significance of the ingredients of abnormal urine.

PEDIATRICS

The disorders of infancy and childhood care and feeding, anatomy and physiology of infancy, disorders and accidents of early life and weeklv clinics comprised this course.

NERVOUS AND MENTAL DISEASES

Didactic lectures and clinics familiarized the student with the diseases of the nervous system and their homoeopathic treatment. There was instruction in the mechanism and use of electrical apparatus in diagnosis and treatment. Insanity and modern methods of management were considered.

DERMATOLOGY

The anatomy and physiology of the skin were discussed, and the morbid alterations in dermal tissues described. All common varieties of skin diseases were considered, and attention given to diagnosis and treatment, both local and homoeopathic.

LARYNGOLOGY AND RHINOLOGY

There were didactic lectures and clinics, and instruction in use of laryngoscope and rhinoscope. Surgical affections of nose and throat were considered, and modern methods of treatment demonstrated clinically.

OPHTHALMOLOGY AND OTOLOGY

In the third year course students were taught the normal structure of eye and ear, and their functions, diseases, and appropriate treatment. There was practical instruction in clinical lectures, sub-clinics, use of diagnostic instruments in eye affections and in prescriptions of eye-glasses. Operations on eye and ear were performed, and modern methods of treating disorders of these organs explained and illustrated.

SURGERY

Instruction in principles and pathology of surgery was begun in the third year, emphasis being upon differential diagnosis. Special attention was given to surgical therapeutics, and such conservative measures as can be relied upon for the relief and cure of many surgical conditions, instead of resorting to surgery. There was attention to surgical emergencies, especially fractures and dislocations. Minor surgery, bandaging, and the use of splints were taught in a practical way. There was an examination on the practical work of the course at the end of the term.

There was demonstration of the use of radiography in diagnosis treatment.

GYNECOLOGY

This was a combination of didactic and clinical instruction, illustrated by operative cases in the hospital clinics and supplemented by a course on the medical diseases of women and sub-clinical work in the dispensary. The anatomy and functions of pelvis and its contained organs, the medical and surgical diseases, illustrated by hospital and dispensary cases, showing the result of local treatment and the action of homoeopathically applied remedies, were taught.

OBSTETRICS

This study was begun in the third year. There were lectures on the science and art of obstetrics supplemented by a course of lectures and demonstrations by means of diagram and manikin. The plan of teaching took the student through the study of the generative organs, then through ovulation, menstruation and gestation, to the mechanism of labor, normal labor, dystocia and the puerperal state. There was also a course in practical obstetrics, in which the manikin was used, to render the student familiar with positions and presentations.

PATHOLOGY

This was a general course, and included nutritive changes (atrophy, hypertrophy and the like), and pathological diagnosis as developed through post-mortem examinations and confirmed by microscopic tests.

CLINICS

All third-year students were required to attend all clinics in the Hospitals, and sub-clinics in the dispensary groups, where they received practical instruction for two weeks in each department.

(ANATOMY

Students were selected from the third year class to act as demonstrators in the dissecting room.)

FOURTH YEAR

Materia medica, practice of medicine, pediatrics and ophthalmology and otology were continued, along lines similar to these studies in the third year, final examinations in all the branches of the fourth year being held at the end of that year. In addition the following branches were studied:

SURGERY

This was a continuation of the work begun in the third year, with special emphasis upon operative and clinical work. Each student performed operations upon the cadaver, and fourth year students assisted in operative work in the clinics. This course is discussed in the pages devoted to the earlier years.

GYNECOLOGY

This was a continuation of the work begun in the third year, with special attention to practical instruction in Hospital and dispensary clinics, including diagnosis and treatment. (See discussion, earlier years.)

OBSTETRICS

Fourth year students were assigned to cases at the homes of patients. They were notified when cases of labor were about to occur in the Hospital and were expected to be present. Students were instructed in the use of forceps, the performance of version and all other obstetric measures and operations.

CLINICAL MEDICINE

Students and patients were brought together, examinations were made in the presence of the professors, diagnoses and treatments decided upon. The professors selected cases from the dispensary for teaching purposes, and to show the relationship which the general practitioner should sustain to specialists, in order to detect the first approach of disease. Members of the fourth year class received instruction at the bedside, in the public wards of the Hospital and dispensary, in the practical application of physical diagnosis, selection of the indicated remedy and other therapeutic measures.

The class was divided into groups, each group being given careful instruction. Each fourth year student was required to make written reports on cases in the out-department, thus becoming a special interne. This method was favored by the fact that classes were small and could receive special attention from the instructors. The reputation of the College had grown by having such attention given to clinical teaching, said the Announcement of 1902.

GENITO-URINARY DISEASES

Didactic and clinical lectures, (and a final examination at the end of the year).

DISEASES OF THE CHEST

Diagnosis, etiology, pathology and treatment of all diseases of heart and lungs, the course ending with an examination.

MEDICAL JURISPRUDENCE

The legal relations of physician to patient, to community, and to other physicians, his duty with respect to mal-practice, abortion, infanticide, homicide and other crimes, post-mortems, legitimacy, the insane, and the subject of evidence in court were all discussed by the professor, who was an attorney-at-law. This was a comprehensive course planned so as to give the physician a clear understanding of this important branch.

LIFE INSURANCE

Lectures on the duties of the physician as medical examiner, and the determination of the moral and physical risk, in accordance with the rules of the leading insurance companies fully explained.

CLINICS

Requirements similar to those of the third year. These were held daily in the amphitheatre of the Hospital or in the College building on all classes of diseases, illustrating the entire range of the curriculum, all students being required to attend. Sub-clinics, bedside clinics in the free wards of the Hospital (for fourth year students), and the out-department have been discussed above.

HOSPITAL APPOINTMENTS

Each Spring a Resident Physician was appointed to the Hospital, and graduates were eligible for this post, as they were to positions in homoeopathic hospitals in Philadelphia, Washington, Pittsburgh, Wilmington, and other cities. A limited number of internes was selected for service in the Hospital, each year, from among advanced students.

"REQUIREMENTS FOR PROMOTION

> Examinations are held at the close of each College term, and at such intermediate periods as each instructor may determine. These examinations are obligatory upon all the students, and include all the branches taught during the term. No exemptions from these examinations will be permitted. The standing of students in laboratory work will be determined by the regularity and proficiency of their daily exercises, so as to avoid unnecessary final examinations.
>
> Examinations will be either oral or written, or both, as may be directed by the Faculty.
>
> A student, whose rating falls below seventy in any branch will be conditioned in that branch, and any and all conditions must be removed before he will be allowed to matriculate for the succeeding class. Failing to pass the term examination with a general average of seventy-five per cent, he will be required to repeat the studies of that term before further examination or promotion.
>
> A certificate of the result of the examinations, and notification of failure to make the required averages for promotion, or of conditions to be removed before being allowed to take the next succeeding course of lectures, will be issued to each student.
>
> Students to be admitted to the graduating class must be 21 years old on or before the next succeeding commencement."

CHEMISTRY (Second Year)

1904

No course in qualitative analysis was specified, but second year chemistry consisted of two lectures per week on organic chemistry. This included "representatives of each series used in medicine". In addition to preparation of certain organic compounds, such as alcohol, ether and chloroform, there was analysis of water, milk, morbid products of the body, and a course in physiological chemistry.

PREVENTIVE MEDICINE (Second Year)

Formerly designated as Sanitary Science, this course was devoted to personal and public hygiene, including the discussion of diet, alcohol, bathing, clothing, exercise, school sanitation, water supply, preparation and adulteration of food substances, heating, ventilation, drainage and such other topics as would enable the physician to take a leading part in the promotion of health.

RECTAL SURGERY (Second Year)

The anatomy of the parts involved were taught in preparation for the work in this field in the third year.

MEDICAL DIAGNOSIS (Third Year)

There was instruction in physical examination, including a consideration of objective and subjective symptoms, surface topography, general pathology, and pathological diagnosis as developed through post-mortem examination and confirmed by microscopic test. Exhaustive examination of blood, sputum, urine and stomach contents, by microscope and chemical reactions, were taught. There were two lectures per week, and practical illustrations through bedside clinics, dispensary, post-mortem examinations and laboratory work.

DISEASES OF THE CHEST

This course was now taught in both third and fourth years.

(Life Insurance was no longer a part of the curriculum.)

Other than the changes notes above, the curriculum was the same as in 1903.

ORGANON (First Year)

1905

This text book served as a basis for teaching the principles of homoeopathy and the application of the Law of Similars, with a discussion of the causes of disease, methods of proving drugs, examination of patients, observation of their progress under administration of the indicated remedy, and as much of the history of medicine as might be profitable to the student.

Institutes and History of Medicine and Rectal Surgery were not in the second year curriculum.

THEREAPEUTIC PHILOSOPHY (Third Year)

> "Instruction will be continued throughout the third and fourth years. This subject will be taught in accordance with facts. The character of those who have contributed significant ideas, theories, methods, principles, etc., to this great field, will be discussed; and the genetic relation of these contributions to the existing methods of practice will be considered.
>
> All effective therapeutic methods, including homoeopathy, antipathy, allopathy, hypnotism, etc., will be taught, and the sphere of application of each clearly outlined. Where it is practicable cases will be presented to the class in illustration of these various methods of therapeutics. All the fads of the day will receive consideration, and will be sifted carefully for underlying principles; the endeavor being to teach what is really effective in therapeutics, to instruct as well what to avoid as to what to adopt, and to instill into the student a practical philosophy for every day use, whereby he will be enabled to practice medicine in accordance with the facts of science."

Otherwise, the curriculum remained the same as in 1904.

1906

The Announcement of 1906 opened with a statement, the intent of which was to prepare everyone concerned for the fact that a change in philosophy (and in the name by which the College was to be henceforth known), were on the way. It was asserted that there was to be "a broadening of the course of instruction" and that future graduates would be "even better qualified to meet all medical practitioners on an equal footing than before, having been taught all that is of practical utility in all modern schools of medicine". The institution was, "in point of fact . . . non-sectarian" and graduates "will know both when and when not to apply other than homoeopathic agents, and when and when not to apply homoeopathic agents". The broadening of the course did not imply a loss of confidence in homoeopathy, but rather that a belief that the time had come when the world of science must accept the fact that homoeopathy demonstrably has a prominent place in therapeutics, that it must in a short time be recognized by all medical colleges, and be taught honestly side by side with other useful methods of healing the sick. The College would therefore from now on teach, consistently, what is practiced by all progressive practitioners of homoeopathy, (i.e., a combination of homoeopathy and allopathy). The College claimed that it "now stands as an exponent of the most progressive medical education, second to none in the City of Baltimore".

By way of reducing the embarrassment which probably attended this abandonment of homoeopathy the Announcement further said:

"A NON-SECTARIAN EDUCATOR.

While the Southern Medical College stands among the exponents of non-sectarian medical education, yet the central idea is the inculcation of that therapeutic principle from which more permanent cures are produced by drugs than by any other known method of cure. It is furthermore recognized that homoeopathy has a legitimate sphere of application, outside of which results must be obtained by other methods, and the student is also taught how and when to apply these adjuvant methods.

OLD SCHOOL GRADUATES

In this day when competition is so close in all occupations, the medical practitioner cannot escape the necessity of acquainting himself with all the effective methods in vogue for healing the sick. This applies to graduates of all schools of medicine, and in the light of this knowledge the Southern Medical College is prepared to round out the education of those physicians who have not previously had instruction in practical homoeopathy. There seems to be no doubt that in the near future a practical working knowledge of homoeopathy will be one of the necessities of all well educated progressive physicians."

Students would hereafter receive instruction in two hospitals, the Maryland Homoeopathic and St. Luke's. In addition there would be sub-clinic, laboratory and remarkable obstetrical training (some students having accouched twenty-five cases individually, during the past winter (1905-06).

Methods of teaching heretofore in use would continue to be employed, and it was further expected that the students would organize quiz classes among themselves. The Hering Institute was an organization of the students for "mutual assistance in study, through a system of quizzes": It was suggested that all students join Hering Institute.

There was an effort to swing the content of courses into line with those taught in non-homoeopathic colleges.

BACTERIOLOGY

This was a four hour per week course, and consisted of laboratory instruction in classification, differentiation, nomenclature and morphology of bacteria, as well as methods of preparing culture media and isolation of bacteria from water, air and soil. The relations between micro-organisms and diseases which they produce were taught. Preparation and use of staining solutions, and preparation of specimens for microscopic study were part of the course.

MATERIA MEDICA

In addition to what has been said above concerning instruction in this subject, it may be added that students were now being instructed in the matter of when not to prescribe a drug according to the given method or principle, and when to prescribe it. Especial attention was also given to the physiological dosage of drugs.

SURGERY

The course was so graded as to cover the principles and practice of modern surgery in all its branches. This was didactic teaching, illustrated on the cadaver, and in clinics. Asepsis and antisepsis, methods of administering anaesthetics, preparation of dressings, care of instruments, care of patient and surgeon, and a full course on minor surgery and bandaging, were taught to second and third year students. Orthopedic surgery, including every phase of spinal and chronic joint diseases, club foot and various congenital or acquired deformities, was taught to third and fourth year students. Operative surgery, with fractures and dislocations were taught in a practical manner. Seniors were allowed to administer anesthetics and assist in the surgical clinics. In the comprehensive course on genito-urinary and rectal surgery, the use of cystoscope, endoscope and proctoscope was demonstrated.

OPHTHALMOLOGY AND OTOLOGY

Colored plates were added to the illustrative aids in this year. The relations between diseases of the eye and ear to other organs were taught. (For further discussion of the work of this department, see above.)

MEDICAL TERMINOLOGY

This was a course upon the origin, roots, prefixes and suffixes of usual and unusual technical terms.

Otherwise, the curriculum remained the same as in the previous year.

(The Announcement for 1906 mentions not only the Hering Institute (see above) but also an Epsilon Tau society of women students, "organized for mutual aid in all things pertaining to College work". It met once a month.)

CHANGE OF NAME TO ATLANTIC MEDICAL COLLEGE

The Announcement for 1907 opened with a statement to alumni and friends of the College, in the following vein:

The Faculty requested the stockholders, on June 4, to adopt the new name, Atlantic Medical College, because it was convinced that the interests of all, including stockholders, Faculty and students, would thus be best served. It requested appointment of a Committee, empowered to have the College charter amended to permit this change. The stockholders adopted the resolution and the name was changed. The step had been under contemplation for more than one year, and the hope was that there would no longer be any misconception on the part of some persons that the College was a sectional, political or sectarian school, not prepared to give as liberal an education as had been claimed. The statement repeated the attitude expressed in the previous year (see above), and ended by saying that the College saw "nothing to be gained by retaining the old misleading distinction, but much to be expected in the link of liberal progress by the adoption of this new name."

The College admitted that "there are means applicable to the healing of the sick which bear no relation to the law of similars", and that to be a progressive practitioner of today it was "necessary to know more than homoeopathy alone":

"THE PURPOSE OF THE COLLEGE

> The purpose of the College is to teach men and women how to practice medicine in its broadest sense, and to satisfactorily demonstrate to the student that to be among the progesssive practitioners of the present time it is necessary to know more than homoeopathy alone, to know there are means applicable to the healing of the sick which bear no relation to the law of similars, but that both science and humanity demand of the physician not only a knowledge of these facts, but a clear understanding of how to apply them intelligently. At the same time the student is impressed by the fact that homoeopathy has a positively defined sphere of applicability. And furthermore he is not only taught the theory but is taught how to practically apply

what he has been shown in his varied clinical work. From such therapeutic training students must of necessity evolve into physicians who are liberal in their views, who are full of consideration for those with whom they cannot agree, who grasp intelligently the whole subject of therapeutics, but who are withal thorough and practical believers in homoeopathy. The purpose of the College is therefore, briefly, to give men and women a practical, all-around medical education."

1907:

CURRICULUM

FIRST YEAR

Normal Histology (Lectures and Laboratory Work), Biology (Lectures and Laboratory), Pharmacy, Toxicology, Anatomy, Dissections, Physiology, Chemistry (Lectures and Laboratory), Materia Medica, Medical Terminology.

SECOND YEAR

Anatomy, Dissections, Medical Terminology, Physiology, Embryology, Chemistry (Lectures and Laboratory), Pathological Histology, Toxicology, Preventive Medicine, Bacteriology, Materia Medica, Regional Anatomy, Minor Surgery, General Clinics.

THIRD YEAR

Physical Diagnosis, Dermatology, Surgical Anatomy, Rhinology and Laryngology, Pathology, Minor Surgery, Rectal Surgery, Practical Obstetrics, Practice of Medicine, Materia Medica and Therapeutics, Gynecology, Obstetrics, Pediatrics, Therapeutic Philosophy, Ophthalmology and Otology, Nervous and Mental Diseases, Surgery, Clinical Medicine, Medical Diagnosis, Diseases of the Chest, Clinics and Out-visits.

FOURTH YEAR

Practice of Medicine, Surgery, Gynecology, Pediatrics, Obstetrics, Ophthalmology and Otology, Diseases of the Chest, Materia Medica and Therapeutics, Practical Surgery, Clinical Medicine, Medical Jurisprudence, Therapeutic Philosophy, Genito-Urinary Diseases, Medical Diagnosis, Nervous and Mental Diseases, Electro-Therapeutics, General Clinics, Sub-Clinics.

(The curriculum given above remained nearly unchanged for the final years of the school (1907, 1908, 1909), the last session being that of 1909-10.)

ANATOMY

The professor's aim was to arouse "scientific curiosity" as to just how Nature has fitted together the human body, and hoped that each student would have an opportunity to learn about this, in the dissecting room. The student would learn by observing Nature, and not from a dependence upon textbooks. This philosophy stated, the course was otherwise the same as in earlier years.

CHEMISTRY

Organic chemistry (a second year subject), consisted of lectures and recitations upon acyclic and cyclic hydrocarbons, with special reference to physiology and medicine. There was also a brief course in physiological chemistry. Laboratory work in examination of urine, gastric fluid and milk was done, and a study made of the reactions of alkaloids, as well as a practical examination of the substances treated in the course in physiological chemistry.

PHARMACY

Attention was now given to the principles of the pharmacy of "both" of the "dominant" schools of medicine, recognition and preservation of drug substances, steps in the preparation of all drugs, including fluid extracts, tinctures, dilutions, triturations, ointments, suppositories and other medicines, and the method of dispensing them.

MATERIA MEDICA

Homoeopathic materia medica, "the relative value of symptoms, their origin, the tissue changes which they suggest, and their thorough therapeutic uses", remained a third and

CONSI)DERATION

fourth year subject, despite the change to non-sectarianism. In therapeutic philosophy consideration was given to the legitimate uses of diuretics, anodynes and purgatives, and their improper uses explained. Hahnemann's Organon was critically studied, section by section and its relation to modern thought impartially considered.

THEORY AND PRACTICE OF MEDICINE

The drugs which were suggested for use were still those "employed by our best authorities, in accordance with law of similars" – (the course in theory and practice of medicine remained unchanged).

Otherwise the course contents remained the same.

1908:

FIRST YEAR – materia medica was no longer taught.

SECOND YEAR – the term "preventive medicine" was replaced by "sanitation and dietetics".

THIRD YEAR – Diseases of the chest and medical diagnosis were no longer listed as subjects for study in the third year. Clinical diagnosis was a part of the third year curriculum (see below).

FOURTH YEAR – Diseases of the chest and medical diagnosis were no longer listed as subjects for study in the fourth year. Physical diagnosis was a part of the fourth year curriculum (see below).

CHEMISTRY

Prospective students were now advised to take an elementary course in chemistry and physics, if possible, before matriculating.

CLINICAL DIAGNOSIS

There were didactic lectures upon the blood, urine, feces, sputum, gastric juice, the various exudates and transudates, the immune sera, etc., in detail, and there were appropriate laboratory demonstrations, for which the laboratory had been recently supplied with all necessary apparatus. The purpose of the course was to enable the student to apply this knowledge to the study of hospital and dispensary cases in the practical work of the senior year.

PHYSICAL DIAGNOSIS

The diagnosis, etiology, pathology and treatment of diseases of the chest and abdomen were taught in fourth year, with clinical hospital instruction.

ELECTRO-THERAPEUTICS

There were both theoretical and practical instruction in the application of "modern forms of electricity", with sufficient training "to lay the foundation for special post-graduate work".

In other respects the curriculum of 1907 was followed in 1908.

1909:

The regular course, beginning on October 1, 1909, was preceded by an optional preliminary course, (from September 16 to September 30), intended to familiarize s'idents with laboratory methods. There was little, if any, change in the curriculum of the last session of the College.

ENTRANCE REQUIREMENTS

1891:

An applicant had to present a certificate of good moral character ("This is to certify that .... is personally known to me, and that .... moral character and personal habits are good."), and another certificate that he or she had graduated from a respectable "literary" college or high school, or had passed the entrance examination to a reputable literary college, or possessed a first grade teacher's certificate.

Failing to present one of the educational certificates named above, a candidate had to pass a preliminary entrance examination. The nature of this examination is given below:

"In conformity with the action of the American Institute of Homoeopathy at its last meeting, after 1891 students not able to present the necessary diploma or certificate will be required to pass an examination as follows:

1. English composition, by writing at the time of the examination an essay of not less than two hundred words, by which may be judged the writer's attainments in grammar, spelling and writing. 2. Arithmetic as far as square root. 3. Geography, physical and political, such as is contained in advanced school geographies. 4. History; the outlines of history of modern civilized nations, especially of American history, such as is contained in the ordinary manuals of history. 5. Latin, sufficient to read easy prose and to give a fair comprehension of scientific terms and formulae. 6. Physics, such as is comprised in Balfour Stewart's Primer of Physics. 7. Biology and physiology, as much as is comprised in the briefer course of Martin's Human Body. 8. Chemistry as comprised in Miller's Elementary Chemistry. 9. Botany as found in the elementary manual."

(Latin could be "made up" under private instruction, in the second year.)

Students who came by transfer from other accredited medical colleges could receive credit for previous medical studies, but had to complete at least the last year at this school.

Graduates in Pharmacy or Dentistry could enter as second year students. Graduates of other accredited medical colleges could matriculate as third year students upon complying with the rules governing students who had attended two terms in another college.

1896:

REQUIREMENTS FOR MATRICULATION

Each student will be expected to present, from his preceptor, a certificate of good moral character and that he is otherwise qualified for the study of medicine.

Students of medicine, who matriculated prior to the Fall of 1895 at other colleges requiring preliminary qualifications equivalent to those adopted by the American Institute of Homoeopathy, may matriculate at this College and enter the third year of a three year course, becoming a candidate for degree in April, 1897.

For all students beginning the study of medicine on or after the Fall of 1895, the required course of instruction will extend over four collegiate years, and is graded and so arranged that the studies of one year are a necessary preparation for those that follow.

Regulations governing educational requirements for admission remained the same as in earlier years.

1902:

The requirements for admission to the first year of the College, and admission with advanced standing were now as follows:

EXAMINATION FOR ADMISSION

"(1) English composition – exercise on assigned theme, not less than two hundred words. Criticised with reference to (a) thought; (b) construction; (c) orthography; (d) syntax; (e) capitalization; (f) punctuation; (g) paragraphing; (h) penmanship.

Exercise in reading, criticised with reference to (a) fluency; (b) pronunciation; (c) expression.

Exercise in correction of ungrammatical sentences.

(2) Mathematics – Arithmetical exercises in (a) vulgar fractions; (b) decimals; (c) percentage; (d) proportion; (e) square and cube root; (f) weights and measures; (g) metric system.

Mensuration – (a) definition of terms; (b) exercises under the more fundamental rules.

(3) Geography – Natural divisions, physical features, climate, topography; all with reference to North America.

(4) History – General, with particular reference to human progress in art, science and letters. (The examination to avoid exact dates and minor details of the subject.)

(5) Latin Language – (a) Grammar; (b) four books of Caesar, or its equivalent.

Students may be exempted from the above examination upon presentation of any of the following evidences of possessing the requisite qualifications: (a) The diploma or certificate of a literary or scientific college, high school, normal school or academy. (b) A "teacher's certificate" of qualification. (c) The certificate of the Examining Board of an accredited Medical Society. (d) The certificate of a legally authorized Medical Examining Board. Provided that no certificate will be accepted except in and for the branches specified therein."

ADMISSION WITH ADVANCED STANDING

"Students applying for 'advanced standing' – i.e., admission to the second year in this college – must exhibit and file documentary evidence (a) of having graduated in Arts or Science in an accredited College or University, and of having passed, in connection with the course in said institution a satisfactory examination in Biology, Botany, Zoology, Physics, Chemistry, Anatomy and Physiology, or (b) of having successfully passed the examinations of the "Preparatory Medical Course" in an accredited College or University in which course all the above-mentioned branches are taught as part of the regular curriculum.

Graduates of Colleges of Pharmacy, Dentistry, or Veterinary Medicine in good standing, in which the course of study embraces all the branches mentioned in Regulation 4, may, upon presentation of their diplomas, matriculate and enter the second year of this College.

Students who have attended one or more annual terms in other accredited Medical Colleges may, upon passing an examination in the branches taught in the corresponding term or terms in this College, matriculate and enter the following term. But they will be exempted from examination in any or all of these branches upon presentation of documentary evidence that they have already passed these examinations in the College first attended.

Graduates of old school Medical Colleges requiring four years of study, may be admitted to the fourth year class of this College on passing an examination in junior year Materia Medica and Therapeutics, and Institutes of Homoeopathy. In order to obtain the diploma of the College they must attend all the lectures and clinics of the fourth year, and satisfy the entire Faculty that they have fulfilled all the requirements of the College for graduation. Partial courses may be taken by suitable persons, for which credit will be given."

REQUIREMENTS FOR GRADUATION

Until 1898:

The candidate must:

1. Be at least twenty-one years of age.
2. Be of good moral character and professional standing.
3. Have studied medicine for four years, including attendance upon three full graded courses, the last of which must have been in this School.
4. Have had one course each in practical anatomy, chemistry, histology, obstetrics and surgery, and present evidence of satisfactory work in these practical courses, i.e., tickets signed by demonstrators.
5. Have been regular in attendance upon lectures, absenting himself only for reasons of an imperative character. Absence must not have exceeded one month in the aggregate. All tickets must be endorsed by the professors, indicating satisfactory attendance at the lectures. Attendance upon all clinical lectures was obligatory.
6. Have given notice to the Dean on or before the first of March of his desire to graduate, and exhibited his tickets or other satisfactory evidence of having complied with the rules of the College. (See under Fees and Rules of Conduct.)
7. Have paid all fees and the thirty-dollar graduation fee before the permit for examination could be issued.
8. The final examination (on the various branches taught in the school) was conducted in private by each professor, and each candidate was voted for by the ballot. If a candidate failed, the thirty dollar graduation fee was returned to the student, who then was required to attend another annual course of lectures, for which no charge was made, before applying for re-examination.
9. Candidates had to be present at Commencement exercises to receive their diplomas in person.

(The judgment of the Faculty upon the fitness of a candidate was based upon his attendance, industry, character and habits, as well as upon the result of his final examination. The Faculty reserved the right to make moral as well as intellectual qualifications an element in their decision. Open irregularity of conduct, negligence, habitual and prolonged absence from lectures were considered obstacles to attainment of the degree in medicine.)

To pass an examination, admitting the student to the next year's work or to graduation, it was necessary to attain a rating of 70% in each study, and a general average of 75% (1895).

After 1898:

1. A student must have applied himself or herself to the study of medicine for four years, and attended four full graded courses of not less than seven months each, in four separate years, the last of which must be in this college.
   A student must not be absent for more than one month in the aggregate.
2. Notice of intention to apply for graduation must be filed with the Dean by *April 1.*
   A student must exhibit tickets or other satisfactory evidence of having complied with the regulations of the College.
3. The final examination was to be *written*, or oral, *or both*, and the student must attain a general average of 75% in the senior examinations.
4. The graduation average was computed from the ratings in the branches of the preceding years and those of the final examinations in all senior year subjects.

As stated above, the Faculty reserved the right to make moral judgments about candidates for graduation – (their attendance, industry, character, habits, and so on), as well as judgments on results of final examinations.

A candidate must be present at Commencement exercises to receive the diploma in person.

RULES OF CONDUCT

I. – Students are expected to observe such rules of decorum, and such orderly conduct in the lecture rooms, laboratories and halls of the College as would be expected of gentlemen in the ordinary relations of life.

II. – All students are expected to be regular in their attendance, and to be in their seats in the lecture rooms promptly, that there may be no interruption after the entrance of the professor or lecturer.

III. – Smoking in any part of the building, except in the room provided for the same is not permitted.

IV. – Defacing the walls or furniture in any manner is strictly prohibited.

V. – All damage to College property must be made good by the individual doing the damage.

VI. – Infringement of these rules will subject the student to a private reprimand by the Dean, and in case of a repetition of the offense to a summons before the Faculty, who may publicly reprimand or dismiss from the College as the nature of the case may seem to require.

FEES

1891:

Matriculation (paid but once)	$ 5.00
General Lecture Ticket (including all courses for one year)	$100.00
For Ticket admitting to three full courses	$250.00
For graduates of other colleges (including graduation fee)	$100.00
For Partial Course, each chair	$ 10.00
Fee for Examination and Graduation	$ 30.00

Dissection material was furnished at cost.

There was no laboratory fee for students following the regular course, but a $3.00 deposit for breakage was required, any unexpended balance being returned to the student, at the end of the session.

SCHOLARSHIPS

A limited number of these were available, the candidate being required to submit a written statement from the preceptor, testifying that the student was deserving, and unable to pay the full fees.

A person holding a scholarship paid:

Matriculation Fee	$ 5.00
Lecture Fee (single course)	$ 65.00
Lecture Fee (three years, in advance)	$150.00
Demonstrator's Fee (each practical course)	$ 5.00
Anatomical material (each part)	$ 5.00

Graduates of other colleges .... $ 40.00
Fee for each partial course .... $ 10.00
Examination Fee, not returnable .... $ 30.00

Boarding in the immediate vicinity of the College could be had at from $3.50 to $5.00 per week, heat and light included (1894). The Announcement made the point that Baltimore had "the finest, most abundant and cheapest markets in the world", resulting in a lower cost of living "than any other city in the country presenting the same medical advantages". Students could live at even lower rates by clubbing together, or by living at some distance from the College.

1902:

Matriculation .... $ 5.00
General Ticket (including all departments for one year) $100.00
Ticket admitting to all four full courses, in advance) $350.00
Graduates of other colleges (including graduation fee) $100.00
Partial Course, each chair .... $ 10.00
Fee for examination and graduation .... $ 30.00

Dissection material at cost.

(There were no extra laboratory fees, if the student was following the regular course, but there was a $3.00 deposit for breakage, returnable, minus any damage done.)

1903:

It was announced that there would be a reduction in the tuition fee for worthy students, upon presentation of satisfactory credentials, and undoubted evidence that they were deserving and lacking in necessary means, and that this reduction would continue throughout the course if warranted by the diligence and progress of the student. The reduction could amount to fifty percent in a limited number of cases. Third year students who *maintained* an average of 90% in attendance and examinations were given a 25% reduction in the fourth year, and those who had such an average throughout the three preceding years were given a 50% reduction in the fourth year.

1906:

Rates declined, as follows:

Matriculation .... $ 5.00
General Course Ticket, for one year .... $ 75.00
Graduates from other colleges, including Graduation Fee .... $ 75.00
Sons and daughters of physicians, holding academical
degrees or degrees from other accredited medical colleges .... $ 60.00
Partial course (each chair) .... $ 10.00
Examination and Graduation Fee .... $ 30.00
Chemical laboratory deposit, to be refunded at
the end of the session after deducting breakage .... $ 5.00
Dissection material at cost.

1908:

The following changes in the schedule of 1906 is to be noted:

Chemical laboratory fee, each of two years $10.00
Physiological laboratory fee, each of two years .... $ 5.00
Dissection fee, each of two years .... $ 5.00
Histological laboratory fee .... $ 5.00
Pathological laboratory fee, each of two years .... $ 5.00
Clinical Diagnosis laboratory fee $10.00

1909: Same as above.

DATA for COMPARISON and EVALUATION

Compared with the other extinct schools of Philadelphia and Baltimore, the numbers of both matriculates and graduates of the Southern Homoeopathic-Atlantic Medical College were small, and, unlike the Philadelphia schools, the appeal was rather sectionalist. On the other hand, the various subjects taught constituted a formidable array, by comparison with those schools. Specialization was very noticeable, and emphasis upon laboratory and clinical instruction seems to have been a matter of the greatest pride, even though the distance between what the College said of itself and what Dr. Flexner saw, on his visit in 1909 was of the order of magnitude of that between "Dan and Beersheba". Course contents and educational methods were sufficiently in agreement with the other schools, considering that this was a sectarian institution, and separated by decades from most of those colleges. The lengthening of the school year, and the increased number of years were steps in the right direction and when added to laboratory and hospital facilities could have led to a combination resulting in a good school, assuming maintenance of the standards of education which the school claimed for itself. However, we have Dr. Flexner's report to the contrary:

> "of 21 graduates, class of 1908, almost all had failed at other schools or before the regular state board before entering the Atlantic Medical College, on graduation from which they could appear before the Homoeopathic State Board of Maryland, reputed to be a much easier board to pass".
>
> "Laboratory facilities: The School occupies a filthy building, in which are to be found an elementary chemical laboratory, a small room assigned to pathology, bacteriology and histology, equipment being scant and dirty, an ordinary dissecting room, a lecture room with half a skeleton, a small amount of imperfect physiological apparatus with a few frogs, and a few cases of books, mostly old and useless".
>
> Hospital facilities "can at best be hardly more than nominal".
> (Visited March, 1909) –
> (*Medical Education in the United States and Canada*, New York, 1910, page 238.)

The course offerings claimed by the school were much wider than those of the colleges of earlier years, particularly in the chemical and biological bases for the science of medicine, with studies being made upon body fluids of various types. Textbook selections bore some resemblance to those used elsewhere. Without counterpart were such courses as blood analysis, life insurance, electro-thereapeutics and radiography. Almost, but not quite unique were the program of student athletics and the attention given to possible ways in which to make the lives of students physically more comfortable.

III. (A) FACULTY

SESSION OF 1891-92

PROFESSORS

Institutes of Medicine
ELIAS C. PRICE, M.D.
Gynaecology
NICHOLAS W. KNEASS, M.D.
General and Medical Chemistry
E. H. HOLBROOK, M.D.
Biology, Histology and Hygiene
JOHN HOOD, M.D.
Clinical Medicine and Physical Diagnosis
CHARLES H. THOMAS, M.D.
Materia Medica and Therapeutics
ELDRIDGE C. PRICE, M.D.
Pathology and Practice of Medicine
ROBERT W. MIFFLIN, M.D.

Ophthalmology and Otology
HENRY F. GAREY, M.D.
Paedology and Orthopaedic Surgery
O. EDWARD JANNEY, M.D.
Operative, Clinical and Orificial Surgery
JAMES S. BARNARD, M.D.
Physiology and Neurology
HENRY CHANDLEE, M.D., Registrar
Anatomy
EDWARD H. CONDON, M.D.
Principles and Practice of Surgery
THOMAS L. MACDONALD, M.D.
Obstetrics
FRANK C. DRANE, M.D., Dean

LECTURERS AND DEMONSTRATORS

HAVARD LINDLEY, M.D., Lecturer on Surgical Anatomy and Demonstrator of Anatomy
C. WESLEY ROBERTS, M.D., Lecturer on Pharmacy and Toxicology
H. F. GAREY, Esq., Lecturer on Medical Jurisprudence
JAMES W. BRIGHT, Ph.D., Lecturer on Physiology of Speech
W. DULANEY THOMAS, M.D., Demonstrator of Obstetrics
BARTUS TREW, M.D., Demonstrator of Histology and Microscopy

DISPENSARY AND HOSPITAL STAFF

N. W. KNEASS, M.D., Chief of Staff
R. W. MIFFLIN, M.D., Resident Physician

GENERAL MEDICAL DEPARTMENT

C. H. THOMAS, M.D. and
R. W. MIFFLIN, M.D.
Physicians in Charge

G. D. CONSTABLE, M.D.
W. H. JOHNSON, M.D.
E. H. HOLBROOK, M.D.
C. K. JUMP, M.D.
BARTUS TREW, M.D.
CORA B. BREWSTER, M.D.
W. D. THOMAS, M.D.
P. F. DE FORD, M.D.
V. Z. HEERMANN, M.D.
THOMAS E. SEARS, M.D.

EYE AND EAR DEPARTMENT

H. F. GAREY, M.D., Surgeon in Charge
V. Z. HEERMANN, M.D., Assistant

THROAT, NOSE AND CHEST DEPARTMENT

ELDRIDGE C. PRICE, M.D., In Charge
W. D. THOMAS, M.D., Assistant

SURGICAL DEPARTMENT

JAMES S. BARNARD, M.D., In Charge
HAVARD LINDLEY, M.D.
E. H. CONDON, M.D.

CHRONIC DISEASE DEPARTMENT

WM. L. MORGAN, M.D., In Charge

CHILDREN'S DEPARTMENT

O. E. JANNEY, M.D., In Charge

OUT DOOR DEPARTMENT

O. E. JANNEY, M.D., In Charge

GYNAECOLOGICAL DEPARTMENT

N. W. KNEASS, M.D., In Charge
FLORA A. BREWSTER, M.D.
C. B. BREWSTER, M.D.
F. C. DRANE, M.D.

SKIN DEPARTMENT

ROBERT W. MIFFLIN, M.D., In Charge

NERVOUS DEPARTMENT

HENRY CHANDLEE, M.D., In Charge

OBSTETRICAL DEPARTMENT

F. C. DRANE, M.D., In Charge
Consultants – ELIAS C. PRICE, M.D.
N. W. KNEASS, M.D.
C. H. THOMAS, M.D.

CONSULTING PHYSICIANS

M. HAMMOND, M.D.
ELIAS C. PRICE, M.D.
C. H. THOMAS, M.D.
JOHN HOOD, M.D.
R. K. KNEASS, M.D.
H. W. WEBNER, M.D.
G. T. SHOWER, M.D.

ROSTER OF GENERAL MEDICAL CLINIC OF THE MARYLAND HOMOEOPATHIC FREE DISPENSARY

323 N. Paca Street
Baltimore, Md.

Hours	Mon.	Tues.	Wed.	Thurs.	Fri.	Sat.
10 to 11 A.M	Trew	Trew	Trew	Trew	Trew	Trew
11 to 12 M.	Johnson	Jump	Johnson	Jump	Johnson	Jump
12 to 1 P.M.	Heermann	Heermann	Heermann	Heermann	Heermann	Heermann
1 to 2 P.M.	Sears	Sears	Sears	Sears	Sears	Sears
2 to 3 P.M.	De Ford	Holbrook	De Ford	Holbrook	De Ford	Holbrook
3 to 4 P.M.	Constable	Holbrook	Constable	Holbrook	Constable	Holbrook
4 to 5 P.M.		Mifflin		Mifflin		Mifflin
			General Surgical			
12 to 1 P.M.	Lindley	Barnard	Lindley	Barnard	Lindley	Barnard

	Eye and Ear					
1 to 2 P.M.	Garey Heermann	Garey Heermann	Garey Heermann	Garey Heermann	Garey Heermann	Garey Heermann
	Gynaecological					
2 to 3 P.M.	Kneass	Drane	Kneass	Drane	Kneass	Drane
3 to 4 P.M.	Brewster	Brewster		Brewster	Brewster	
	Throat, Nose and Chest					
2 to 3 P.M.	Thomas	Thomas	Thomas	Thomas	E. C. Price	Thomas

12 to 1 P.M. CHILDREN'S DISEASES – Daily except Sunday – Dr. Janney
1 to 2 P.M. NERVOUS DISEASES – Tuesday, Thursday and Saturday – Dr. Henry Chandlee
4 to 5 P.M. VENEREAL AND SKIN DISEASES – Daily except Sunday – Dr. Mifflin

GYNAECOLOGICAL CLINIC – Sundays from 12 to 1 – Drs. Kneass and Drane

OFFICERS

DIRECTORS – 1890

LEVI Z. CONDON, President
AUBREY PEARRE, Vice President
JOHN T. GRAHAM, Treasurer
MARTIN LANE, Secretary
GEORGE M. LAMB
HY. F. GAREY, ESQ.
JOSHUA REGISTER
W. S. CARROLL
WOODWARD ABRAHAMS
PETER THOMPSON
SEBASTIAN BROWN
R. BRENT KEYSER
DR. ELIAS C. PRICE
DR. HENRY CHANDLEE
DR. E. H. CONDON
DR. NICHOLAS W. KNEASS
DR. JOHN HOOD
DR. CHARLES H. THOMAS
DR. ELDRIDGE C. PRICE
DR. O. E. JANNEY
DR. R. W. MIFFLIN
DR. H. F. GAREY
DR. H. W. WEBNER
DR. R. K. KNEASS
DR. F. C. DRANE

President
LEVI Z. CONDON

Vice-President
AUBREY PEARRE

Secretary
EDWIN HIGGINS, Esq.

Treasurer
F. W. SCHULTZ

TRUSTEES

Term Expires May, 1892
CHAS. H. BROWN, JR.
CHAS. P. BLACKBURN
H. W. WEBNER, M.D.
HENRY CHANDLEE, M.D.
F. C. DRANE, M.D.

Term Expires May,1893
R. BRENT KEYSER
E. H. HOLBROOK, M.D.
R. K. KNEASS, M.D.
O. E. JANNEY, M.D.

Term Expires May, 1894
G. A. DOBLER
EDWIN HIGGINS
R. W. MIFFLIN, M.D.
H. F. GAREY, M.D.
JAMES S. BARNARD, M.D.

Term Expires May, 1895
GEORGE M. LAMB
F. W. SCHULTZ
C. H. THOMAS, M.D.
ELDRIDGE C. PRICE, M.D.
E. H. CONDON, M.D.

Term Expires May, 1896
LEVI Z. CONDON
AUBREY PEARRE
ELIAS C. PRICE, M.D.
N. W. KNEASS, M.D.
JOHN HOOD, M.D.

MEMBERS OF THE CORPORATION

W. S. CARROLL
MARTIN LANE
JOHN T. GRAHAM
H. F. GAREY, Esq.
JOSHUA REGISTER
WOODWARD ABRAHAMS
PETER THOMPSON

Rev. JOHN S. GOUCHER
SAML. ECCLES, Jr.
JOS. L. FINK
S. C. MASON
JAMES CLEMENTS
SEBASTIAN BROWN
J. C. FRANCE

SESSION OF 1892-93

The professors were the same as in the session of 1891-92, except that Dr. Hood held the chair of hygiene and sanitary science, there being no professor of biology listed for this session, and histology being the responsibility of the demonstrator of the subject (see below). The lecturers and demonstrators were as follows:

LECTURERS AND DEMONSTRATORS

Lecturer on Surgical Anatomy and Demonstrator of Surgery
HAVARD LINDLEY, M.D.

Lecturer on Pharmacy and Toxicology
GEORGE T. SHOWER, M.D.

Lecturer on Rhinology and Laryngology
W. DULANY THOMAS, M.D.

Lecturer on Medical Jurisprudence
– – – –

Lecturer on Physiology
JAMES H. BRIGHT, Ph.D.

Demonstrator of Anatomy
MARSHALL G. SMITH, M.D.

Demonstrator of Histology
BARTUS TREW, M.D.

Demonstrator of Chemistry
A. G. PALMER, Ph.D.

Demonstrator of Ophthalmology and Otology
PAUL DE FORD, M.D.

Demonstrator of Obstetrics
– – – –

Pharmacist
V. Z. HEERMANN, M.D.

CLINICAL ASSISTANTS

W. DULANY THOMAS, M.D.
PAUL F. DE FORD, M.D.
CLARENCE NICHOLS, M.D.
MARSHALL G. SMITH, M.D.
PHILIP T. JOHNSON, M.D.
LEWIS R. PALMER, M.D.

DEAN

FRANK C. DRANE, M.D.

SESSION OF 1893-94

ANATOMY

E. H. CONDON, M.D., Prof. Anatomy
MARSHALL G. SMITH, M.D., Lecturer on Surgical Anatomy and Demonstrator of Anatomy

PHYSIOLOGY, HISTOLOGY, BACTERIOLOGY

GEORGE T. SHOWER, M.D., Associate Prof. Physiology
HENRY CHANDLEE, M.D., Associate Prof. Physiology
CHARLES LESLIE RUMSEY, A.M., M.D., Lecturer on Bacteriology and Demonstrator of Histology
W. M. PANEBAKER, A.B., M.D., Assistant Demonstrator of Histology

MATERIA MEDICA AND THERAPEUTICS, PHARMACY AND TOXICOLOGY, CHEMISTRY

ELDRIDGE C. PRICE, M.D., Prof. Materia Medica and Therapeutics
GEORGE T. SHOWER, M.D., Lecturer on Pharmacy and Toxicology
ALBERT M. REESE, A.B., Lecturer on Chemistry and Demonstrator of Chemistry

PRACTICE OF MEDICINE

CHARLES H. THOMAS, M.D., Prof. Clinical Medicine and Physical Diagnosis
ROBERT W. MIFFLIN, M.D., Prof. Pathology and Practice of Medicine, and Dermatology
O. EDWARD JANNEY, M.D., Prof. Diseases of Children
HENRY CHANDLEE, M.D., Prof. Nervous Diseases
LEWIS R. PALMER, M.D., Chief of Clinic, General Medicine, and of Out-patient Department
*A. S. ATKINSON, M.D., Chief of Clinic, Paedology
JOHN A. SHOWER, M.D., Chief of Clinic, Neurology and General Medicine

*Dr. Atkinson's name does not appear in the Faculty list, in the Commencement program of 1895, which does list the name of Z. B. Babbitt, M.D.

SURGERY

JAMES S. BARNARD, M.D., Prof. Operative and Orificial Surgery
T. L. MACDONALD, M.D., Prof. Principles of Surgery
O. EDWARD JANNEY, M.D., Prof. Orthopedic Surgery
CHARLES LESLIE RUMSEY, A.M., M.D., Demonstrator of Surgery
BARTUS TREW, M.D., Assistant Demonstrator of Surgery
MARSHALL G. SMITH, M.D., Chief of Clinic, Surgery
J. ARTHUR CLEMENT, M.D., Chief of Clinic, Surgery

GYNECOLOGY, OBSTETRICS

N. W. KNEASS, M.D., Prof. Gynecology
J. B. GREGG CUSTIS, M.D., Prof. Practice of Obstetrics
HENRY CHANDLEE, M.D., Prof. Principles of Obstetrics
LEWIS R. PALMER, M.D., Demonstrator of Obstetrics
BARTUS TREW, M.D., Chief of Clinic, Gynecology
W. M. PANEBAKER, A.B., M.D., Chief of Clinic, Gynecology

INSTITUTES AND HYGIENE, MEDICAL JURISPRUDENCE

ELIAS C. PRICE, M.D., Prof. Institutes and Hygiene
CHARLES E. HILL, A.M., Lecturer on Medical Jurisprudence

LARYNGOLOGY, RHINOLOGY, OPHTHALMOLOGY, OTOLOGY

ELDRIDGE C. PRICE, M.D., Clinical Prof. Laryngology and Rhinology
WM. R. KING, M.D., Associate Prof. Ophthalmology and Otology
CHARLES LESLIE RUMSEY, A.M., M.D., Clinical Lecturer on Ophthalmology and Otology
W. DULANY THOMAS, M.D., Lecturer on Laryngology and Rhinology
CLARENCE NICHOLS, M.D., Demonstrator of Ophthalmology and Otology

SESSION OF 1896-97

PROFESSORS

ELIAS C. PRICE, M.D., Professor Institutes and Hygiene
CHARLES H. THOMAS, M.D., Professor Clinical Medicine and Physical Diagnosis
ELDRIDGE C. PRICE, M.D., Professor Materia Medica and Therapeutics
ROBERT W. MIFFLIN, M.D., Professor Pathology and
Practice of Medicine, Dermatology
J. B. GREGG CUSTIS, M.D., Professor Practice of Obstetrics
O. EDWARD JANNEY, Ph.G., M.D., Professo Diseases of
Children and Orthopedic Surgery
JAMES S. BARNARD, M.D., Professor Operative Gynecology and Orificial Surgery
HENRY CHANDLEE, M.D., Professor Principles of Obstetrics,
Neurology and Mental Diseases
E. H. CONDON, M.D., Professor of Anatomy
T. L. MACDONALD, M.D., Professor Principles of Surgery
WILLIAM R. KING, M.D., Professor Ophthalmology and Otology
GEORGE T. SHOWER, M.D., Professor Physiology, Pharmacy
CHARLES LESLIE RUMSEY, A.M., M.D., Professor Clinical
Ophthalmology and Otology, Pathology
E. Z. COLE, M.D., Professor Clinical and Operative Surgery
ZENO B. BABBITT, M.D., Associate Professor Medical Diseases of Women

LECTURERS, DEMONSTRATORS AND ASSISTANTS

CHAS. E. HILL, A.M., Lecturer on Medical Jurisprudence
W. DULANY THOMAS, M.D., Lecturer on Rhinology and Laryngology
MARSHALL G. SMITH, M.D., Lecturer on
Surgical Anatomy, Demonstrator of Anatomy
ALBERT M. REESE, A.B., Lecturer on
Chemistry, Demonstrator of Chemistry
BARTUS TREW, M.D., Demonstrator of Pedology,
Assistant Demonstrator of Pathology
CLARENCE NICHOLS, M.D., Demonstrator of Ophthalmology and Otology
LEWIS R. PALMER, M.D., Demonstrator of Obstetrics, Clinical Medicine
J. ARTHUR CLEMENT, M.D., Lecturer on Hygiene, Demonstrator of Surgery
W. M. PANNEBAKER, A.M., M.D., Demonstrator of Histology,
Assistant Demonstrator of Gynecology
J. WARD WISNER, M.D., Demonstrator of Gynecology,
Assistant Demonstrator of Anatomy
B. C. CATLIN, M.D., Assistant Demonstrator of Histology,
Chief of Clinic, Ophthalmology and Otology
DONNA A. WALDRAN, M.D., Chief of Clinic, Pedology
EDMUND L. YOUREX, M.D., Chief of Clinic, General Medicine
J. L. HOOPER, M.D., Chief of Clinic, Dermatology
JULIA V. DOWNS, M.D., Chief of Clinic, General Medicine

SESSION OF 1899-1900

INSTITUTES, SANITARY SCIENCE, MEDICAL JURISPRUDENCE

J. B. GREGG CUSTIS, M.D., Professor Institutes of Homoepathic Medicine
C. E. HILL, A.M., Lecturer on Medical Jurisprudence
W. C. COMSTOCK, M.D., Lecturer on Sanitary Science

MATERIA MEDICA AND THERAPEUTICS, PHARMACY, TOXICOLOGY

GEORGE T. SHOWER, A.M., M.D., Professor Materia Medica and Therapeutics
EDMUND L. YOUREX, M.D., Lecturer on Pharmacy and Toxicology

PRACTICE OF MEDICINE, PAEDIATRICS, PHYSICAL DIAGNOSIS, NEUROLOGY, DERMATOLOGY

OLIVER EDWARD JANNEY, M.D., Professor Practice of Medicine

E. J. EVANS, M.D., Professor Clinical Medicine and Physical Diagnosis
LEWIS R. PALMER, M.D., Associate Professor Diseases of Heart and Lungs
M. E. DOUGLASS, M.D., Lecturer on Dermatology and Neurology
MARTHA C. BURRITT, M.D., Lecturer on Diseases of Children

OBSTETRICS

JOHN W. DEHOFF, M.D., Associate Professor of Obstetrics
JOHN A. SHOWER, M.D., Associate Professor of Obstetrics

GYNECOLOGY

JAMES S. BARNARD, M.D., Professor Gynecology
BARTUS TREW, M.D., Associate Professor Medical Diseases of Women
WILLIAM M. PANNEBAKER, A.M., M.D., Demonstrator of Gynecology

OPHTHALMOLOGY AND OTOLOGY, RHINOLOGY AND LARYNGOLOGY

WILLIAM R. KING, M.D., Professor Ophthalmology and Otology
CHARLES LESLIE RUMSEY, A.M., M.D., Professor
Clinical Ophthalmology and Otology
W. DULANY THOMAS, M.D., Associate Professor Rhinology and Laryngology
CLARENCE NICHOLS, M.D., Demonstrator of Eye and Ear

ANATOMY

EDWARD H. CONDON, M.D., Professor of Anatomy
CLARENCE NICHOLS, M.D., Lecturer on Anatomy
M. ALVA FAIR, M.D., Lecturer and Demonstrator of Anatomy
GARA WAREHEIM, M.D., Demonstrator of Anatomy

PHYSIOLOGY, CHEMISTRY

WILLIAM M. PANNEBAKER, A.M., M.D., Associate Professor Physiology
HAROLD J. TURNER, Ph.D., (J.H.U.), Associate Professor Chemistry
J. A. RIGGAN, A.B., Demonstrator of Chemistry

PATHOLOGY, HISTOLOGY, BACTERIOLOGY

CHARLES LESLIE RUMSEY, A.M., M.D., Professor Pathology and Bacteriology
WILLIAM M. PANNEBAKER, A.M., M.D., Lecturer on Histology
BARTUS TREW, M.D., Demonstrator of Pathology
GEORGE E. HOUCK, M.D., Demonstrator of Histology

SURGERY

T. L. MACDONALD, M.D., Professor Principles and Practice of Surgery
HENRY CHANDLEE, M.D., Professor Clinical and Operative Surgery
BARRETT C. CATLIN, M.D., Lecturer on Minor Surgery

BIOLOGY, EMBRYOLOGY

W. MC E. KNOWER, Ph.D., Lecturer on Biology and Embryology

SESSION OF 1900-01

PROFESSORS

J. B. GREGG CUSTIS, M.D. .... Institutes
O. EDWARD JANNEY, M.D. .... Practice of Medicine
GEORGE T. SHOWER, A.M., M.D. .... Materia Medica and Physiology
WILLIAM R. KING, M.D. .... Ophthalmology and Otology
JAMES S. BARNARD, M.D. .... Gynecology
HENRY CHANDLEE, M.D. .... Clinical and Operative Surgery
EDWARD H. CONDON, M.D. .... Anatomy
T. L. MACDONALD, M.D. .... Principles of Surgery

C. L. RUMSEY, A.M., M.D. ....Clin. Ophthalmol., Otol., Pathology
HENRY J. EVANS, M.D. ....Clinical Medicine and Diagnosis
JOHN W. DEHOFF, M.D. ....Obstetrics

ASSOCIATE PROFESSORS

LEWIS R. PALMER, M.D. ....Heart and Lungs
WM. DULANY THOMAS, M.D. ....Rhinology and Laryngology
HAROLD J. TURNER, Ph.D., (J.H.U.) ....Chemistry
BARTUS TREW, M.D. ....Medical Diseases of Women
WM. M. PANNEBAKER, A.M., M.D. ....Biology and Histology
M. E. DOUGLASS, M.D. ....Materia Medica, Neurology, Dermatology
JOHN A. SHOWER, M.D. ....Obstetrics

LECTURERS AND DEMONSTRATORS

CLARENCE NICHOLS, M.D. ....Eye and Ear
BARRETT C. CATLIN, M.D. ....Chief of Clinics
EDMUND L. YOUREX, M.D. ....Pharmacy, Toxicology, Obstetrics
MARTHA C. BURRITT, M.D. ....Pediatrics
M. ALVA FAIR, M.D. ....Anatomy
W. T. WILLEY, M.D. ....Minor Surgery
ROBERT F. LEACH, JR., Esq. ....Medical Jurisprudence
GEO. E. HOUCK, M.D. ....Genito-Urinary Diseases
HARPER PEDDICORD, M.D. ....Pathology

ADDITIONAL LECTURES

Special lectures will be delivered during the term by DR. ALFRED WANSTALL on Blood Analysis and Diseases of the Blood.

DR. IRVING MILLER will deliver a series of clinical lectures on Gynecology.

BOARD OF DIRECTORS

President – LEVI Z. CONDON
Vice-President – O. EDWARD JANNEY
Secretary – GEORGE T. SHOWER
Treasurer – GUSTAVUS A. DOBLER

WM. R. KING
E. H. CONDON
*F. C. PEARRE
*O. E. JANNEY
*LEVI Z. CONDON
JAMES CLEMENT

*GUSTAVUS A. DOBLER
J. B. GREGG CUSTIS
*ROBERT W. MIFFLIN
J. S. BARNARD
*GOERGE T. SHOWER
*HENRY CHANDLEE

OFFICERS OF THE COLLEGE

Executive Committee –
GEORGE T. SHOWER, A.M., M.D., Dean
CHARLES LESLIE RUMSEY, A.M., M.D., Registrar
O. EDWARD JANNEY, M.D.

Janitor – JOHN YENT, College

*Member of the Board of Regents

SESSION OF 1901-02

PROFESSORS

Institutes
J. B. GREGG CUSTIS, M.D.
Practice of Medicine
O. EDWARD JANNEY, M.D.

Materia Medica and Therapeutics
GEO. T. SHOWER, A.M., M.D.
Ophthalmology and Otology
WILLIAM R. KING, M.D. (Emeritus)

Clinical and Operative Surgery
HENRY CHANDLEE, M.D.
Anatomy
EDWARD H. CONDON, M.D.
Principles of Surgery
T. L. MACDONALD, M.D.
Ophthalmol., Otol., and Gen. Patho.
C. L. RUMSEY, A.M., M.D.
Clinical Medicine and Diagnosis
HENRY J. EVANS, M.D.

Obstetrics
JOHN W. DEHOFF, M.D.
Rhinology and Laryngology
WM. DULANY THOMAS, M.D.
Gynecology
BARTUS TREW, M.D.
Diseases of the Chest
LEWIS R. PALMER, M.D.

ASSOCIATE PROFESSORS

Chemistry
HAROLD J. TURNER, Ph.D.
Biology and Histology
WM. M. PANNEBAKER, A.M., M.D.
Physiology, Materia Medica, Neurology
M. E. DOUGLASS, M.D.

LECTURERS AND DEMONSTRATORS

Ophthalmology and Otology
CLARENCE NICHOLS, M.D.
Chief of Clinics
BARRETT C. CATLIN, M.D.
Practical Obstetrics
EDMUND L. YOUREX, M.D.
Pediatrics
MARTHA C. BURRITT, M.D.
Anatomy
M. ALVAH FAIR, M.D.
Ophthalmology and Otology
W. C. COMSTOCK, M.D.
Minor Surgery
W. T. WILLEY, M.D.
Medical Jurisprudence
ROBERT F. LEACH, JR., Esq.
Genito-Urinary Diseases
GEO. E. HOUCK, M.D.
Sanitary Science
ARTHUR W. H. SEIPLE, M.D.
Pharmacy and Toxicology
ROSCOE L. COFFIN

Chemistry
ALBERT M. REESE, Ph.D.
Dermatology
J. L. HOOPER, M.D.
Anatomy
M. B. BONTA, A.B.
Physiology
MARY MEAD DEAN, M.D.
Physiology
EMILY F. TYDEMAN, M.D.
Pathology and Bacteriology
H. MC K. STEVENSON, M.D.
Medical Terminology
F. C. FISHER, A.B.
Biology and Embryology
ENGLISH EYSTER, A.B.
Surgery
HARPER PEDDICORD, M.D.
Histology
F. D. MC CARRIAR, M.D.

SPECIAL LECTURES

DR. ALFRED WANSTALL will repeat his course of lectures on Blood Analysis and Diseases of the Blood.

PROF. J. S. BARNARD will deliver a series of clinical lectures on Gynecology.

SESSION OF 1902-03

PROFESSORS

Institutes
J. B. GREGG CUSTIS, M.D.
Prac. of Medicine, Clin. Pediatrics
O. EDWARD JANNEY, M.D.
Materia Medica and Therapeutics
GEO. T. SHOWER, A.M., M.D.
Ophthalmology and Otology
WILLIAM R. KING, M.D. (Emeritus)

Clinical and Operative Surgery
HENRY CHANDLEE, M.D.
Anatomy
EDWARD H. CONDON, M.D.
Ophthalmol., Otolo., and Gen. Pathol.
C. L. RUMSEY, A.M., M.D.
Obstetrics
JOHN W. DEHOFF, M.D.
Rhinology and Laryngology
WM. DULANY THOMAS, M.D.

Gynecology
BARTUS TREW, M.D.

Diseases of the Chest
LEWIS R. PALMER, M.D.

ASSOCIATE PROFESSORS

Chemistry
HAROLD J. TURNER, Ph.D. (J.H.U.)
Biology and Histology
WM. M. PANNEBAKER, A.M., M.D.

Ophthalmology and Otology
W. C. COMSTOCK, M.D.
Surgery
J. OLIVER HENDRIX, M.D.

ASSOCIATES

Pediatrics
MARTHA C. BURRITT, M.D.
Genito-Urinary Diseases, Urinary Anal.
GEO. E. HOUCK, M.D.
Dermatology
J. L. HOOPER, M.D.

Physiology
MARY MEAD DEAN, M.D.
Pathology and Bacteriology
HY. MC K. STEVENSON, M.D.

LECTURERS AND DEMONSTRATORS

Anatomy
BARRETT C. CATLIN, M.D.
Anatomy
M. ALVAH FAIR, M.D.
Medical Jurisprudence
ROBERT F. LEACH, JR., Esq.
Pharmacy
ROSCOE L. COFFIN
Medical Terminology
F. C. FISHER, A.B.
Normal Histology
F. D. MC CARRIAR, M.D.
Physiology
CHARLES E. DENNIS, M.D.

Anatomy
WINFRED WILSON, A.B.
Embryology
D. BOWMAN HOOD, M.D.
Obstetrics
FRANK M. HAMBLIN, M.D.
Pathological Histology
GEO. L. EWALT, M.D.
Surgery
GEO. I. YOUNG, M.D.
Anatomy
HY. HOBART KEECH, M.D.

SPECIAL LECTURER

DR. ALFRED WANSTALL will devote the full term to a course of lectures on Blood Analysis, Diseases of the Blood, and Diseases of the Alimentary Tract.

HOSPITAL STAFF

The authorities of the Maryland Homoeopathic Hospital have placed all the patients in the free wards of the Hospital under the charge of the Faculty of this College, who will hereafter give the necessary medical and surgical care to this class of patients.

The pay wards and private rooms will be, as heretofore, open to the patients of all reputable physicians.

DISPENSARY STAFF

Committee in Charge
PROF. WM. DULANY THOMAS
PROF. BARTUS TREW
ASSOCIATE PROF. W. C. COMSTOCK
Pharmacist
DR. GEO. I. YOUNG
Eye and Ear
PROF. C. L. RUMSEY
ASSOCIATE PROF. W. C. COMSTOCK
DR. BARRETT C. CATLIN
Surgery
PROF. HENRY CHANDLEE
ASSOCIATE PROF. J. O. HENDRIX
Gynecology
PROF. BARTUS TREW
ASSOCIATE PROF. WM. M. PANNEBAKER

DR. W. T. WILLEY
DR. EMILY F. TYDEMAN
DR. FLORENCE L. A. EVANS
Children's Diseases
PROF. O. E. JANNEY
DR. MARY MEAD DEAN
DR. EMILY F. TYDEMAN
DR. FLORENCE L. A. EVANS
Nose and Throat
PROF. WM. DULANY THOMAS
DR. EMILY F. TYDEMAN
DR. FRANKLIN H. ERB
Dermatology
DR. JAMES L. HOOPER

Neurology
DR. JOHN A. EVANS
DR. EMILY F. TYDEMAN
General Medicine
PROF. GEO. T. SHOWER
DR. H. MC K. STEVENSON
DR. OLIVER N. DUNVALL
DR. HENRY HOBART KEECH
DR. GEORGE L. EWALT
Genito-Urinary Diseases
DR. GEO. E. HOUCK

SESSION OF 1903-04

Same as that of 1902-03, with the following exceptions:

Drs. Trew, Turner and Hendrix were no longer among the professors, nor were Drs. Fair, McCarriar, Dennis, and Hood among the lecturers and demonstrators. F. M. Hamblin, M.D. was an associate in obstetrics. Below are given the names of lecturers, demonstrators and dispensary staff:

LECTURERS AND DEMONSTRATORS

Obstetrics
BARRETT C. CATLIN, M.D.
Medical Jurisprudence
ROBERT F. LEACH, JR., Esq.
Pharmacy
ROSCOE L. COFFIN
Medical Terminology
F. C. FISHER, A.B.
Anatomy and Embryology
WINFRED WILSON, A.B.
Pathological Histology
GEO. L. EWALT, M.D.
Surgery
GEO. I. YOUNG, M.D.
Anatomy
HY. HOBART KEECH, M.D.
Surgery
H. OTTO SOMMER, M.D.
Chemistry
CHARLES G. CARROLL, M.D.
Toxicology
HENRY RUSSELL, M.D.
Pathological Histology
EDWARD O. MURRAY, M.D.

DISPENSARY STAFF

Committee in Charge
PROF. WM. DULANY THOMAS
ASSOCIATE PROF. W. C. COMSTOCK
ASSOCIATE GEORGE E. HOUCK
Pharmacist
DR. GEORGE I. YOUNG
Eye and Ear
PROF. CHARLES LESLIE RUMSEY
ASSOCIATE PROF. W. C. COMSTOCK
DR. BARRETT C. CATLIN
Surgery
PROF. HENRY CHANDLEE
PROF. EDWARD H. CONDON
DR. GEORGE I. YOUNG
DR. JAMES W. URIE
Gynecology
ASSOCIATE PROF. WM. M. PANNEBAKER
DR. EMILY F. TYDEMAN
DR. FLORENCE L. A. EVANS
Children's Diseases
PROF. O. EDWARD JANNEY
ASSOCIATE MARY MEAD DEAN
DR. EMILY F. TYDEMAN
DR. FLORENCE L. A. EVANS
Nose and Throat
PROF. WM. DULANY THOMAS
DR. HENRY RUSSELL
DR. FRANKLIN H. ERB
Dermatology
ASSOCIATE JAMES L. HOOPER
Neurology
DR. JOHN A. EVANS
General Medicine
PROF. GEORGE T. SHOWER
ASSOCIATE H. MC K. STEVENSON
DR. OLIVER N. DUVALL
DR. HENRY HOBART KEECH
DR. HENRY RUSSELL
Genito-Urinary Diseases
ASSOCIATE GEORGE E. HOUCK
DR. JAMES W. URIE

SESSION OF 1904-05

PROFESSORS

Practice of Medicine, Clin. Pediatrics
O. EDWARD JANNEY, M.D.
Materia Medica and Therapeutics
GEO. T. SHOWER, A.M., M.D.
Ophthalmology and Otology
WILLIAM R. KING, M.D. (Emeritus)
Clinical, Operative Surgery and Gynecology
HENRY CHANDLEE, M.D.
Anatomy
EDWARD H. CONDON, M.D.
Therapeutic Philosophy
ELDRIDGE C. PRICE, M.D.

Ophthalmology, Otology and Surgery
C. L. RUMSEY, A.M., M.D.
Obstetrics
JOHN W. DEHOFF, M.D.

Rhinology and Laryngology
WM. DULANY THOMAS, M.D.
Diseases of the Chest
LEWIS R. PALMER, M.D.

ASSOCIATE PROFESSORS

Medical Diseases of Women and Histology
WM. M. PANNEBAKER, A.M., M.D.
Ophthalmology and Otology
W. C. COMSTOCK, M.D.
Materia Medica and Institutes
M. E. DOUGLASS, M.D.
Pediatrics
M. C. BURRITT, M.D.
Genito-Urinary Diseases
G. E. HOUCK, M.D.

Dermatology
J. L. HOOPER, M.D.
Physiology
M. M. DEAN, M.D.
Medical Diagnosis and Pathology
H. M. STEVENSON, M.D.
Obstetrics
F. M. HAMBLIN, M.D.

ASSOCIATES

Obstetrics
BARRETT C. CATLIN, M.D.

Rectal Surgery
GEO I. YOUNG, M.D.

LECTURERS AND DEMONSTRATORS

Medical Jurisprudence
ROBERT F. LEACH, JR., Esq.
Pharmacy
ROSCOE L. COFFIN
Medical Terminology
F. C. FISHER, A.B.
Anatomy
HY. HOBART KEECH, M.D.
Toxicology
HENRY RUSSELL, M.D.
Pathological Histology
EDWARD O. MURRAY, M.D.
Preventive Medicine
DAVID C. STULTZ, M.D.
Anatomy and Embryology
J. WARD WISNER, M.D.

Surgery
W. T. WILLEY, M.D.
Surgery
H. J. WALTON, M.D.
Histology
H. H. FOX, M.D.
Anatomy
F. E. HESSER, M.D.
Medical Diagnosis
M. E. SHAMER, M.D.
Materia Medica
C. L. THUDICHUM, M.D.
Chemistry
BENJAMIN KLEIN, Phar. D.

DISPENSARY STAFF

Committee in Charge
PROF. WM. DULANY THOMAS
ASSOCIATE PROF. GEO. E. HOUCK
ASSOCIATE PROF. W. C. COMSTOCK
ASSOCIATE PROF. H. M. STEVENSON
Pharmacist
DR. HENRY RUSSELL
Eye and Ear
In Charge
PROF. CHAS. L. RUMSEY
ASSOCIATE PROF. W. C. COMSTOCK
Chief
ASSOCIATE B. C. CATLIN, M.D.
Children
ASSOC. PROF. M. C. BURRITT, In Charge
ASSOCIATE PROF. M. M. DEAN, Chief
ASSOCIATE PROF. F. M. HAMBLIN
DR. EMILY F. TYDEMAN
General Medicine
ASSOC. PROF. H. M. STEVENSON, In Charge
DR. O. N. DUVALL, Chief
DR. E. O. MURRAY

DR. M. E. SHAMER
Genito-Urinary
ASSOC. PROF. GEO. E. HOUCK, In Charge
Skin
ASSOC. PROF. JAS. L. HOOPER, In Charge
Nervous and Mental Diseases
DR. JOHN A. EVANS, In Charge
DR. WM. C. BODE, Chief
Nose and Throat
PROF. WM. DULANY THOMAS, In Charge
DR. F. H. ERB, Chief
DR. WM. C. BODE
Gynecology
PROF. HENRY CHANDLEE, In Charge
ASSOC. PROF. WM. M. PANNEBAKER, Chief
DR. EMILY F. TYDEMAN
DR. J. W. WISNER
DR. M. E. SHAMER
DR. F. A. EVANS
ASSOCIATE PROF. F. M. HAMBLIN
DR. M. L. WASHBURN

Surgery
In Charge
PROF. HENRY CHANDLEE
PROF. C. L. RUMSEY
Chiefs
ASSOCIATE PROF. JAS. L. HOOPER
DR. W. T. WILLEY
DR. JAS W. URIE
DR. H. J. WALTON
Rectal Diseases
ASSOCIATE GEO. I. YOUNG, In Charge
PROF. E. H. CONDON, Chief

SESSION OF 1905-06

Same as that of 1904-05, with the following exceptions:

Drs. King (see below under special lecturer) and Condon left. Robert W. Mifflin, M.D., became professor of medicine and clinical medicine, and E. Z. Cole, M.D., became professor of surgery.

Among the associate professors, Drs. Douglas and Hamblin left; B. C. Catlin, M.D., (Obstetrics), and G. I. Young, M.D., (rectal surgery), (who had previously been associates), and F. A. Swartwout, M.D. (obstetrics), were added.

The changes in lecturers and demonstrators were as follows:

Drs. Coffin, Fisher, Keech and Fox left. Joseph S. Garrison, M.D. (materia medica), John A. Evans, M.D., (neurology), H. H. Stansbury, M.D., (surgical anatomy), N. V. Wright, M.D., (anatomy), and Henry B. Jones, M.D., (medical diagnosis) were added. William R. King, M.D., former holder of the chair in ophthalmology and otology, was special lecturer on those subjects.

DISPENSARY STAFF

Committee in Charge
PROF. WM. DULANY THOMAS
ASSOCIATE PROF. GEORGE E. HOUCK
ASSOCIATE PROF. JAS. L. HOOPER
ASSOCIATE PROF. H. M. STEVENSON
Pharmacist
DR. FRED E. HESSER
Eye and Ear
In Charge
PROF. CHAS. L. RUMSEY
ASSOCIATE PROF. W. C. COMSTOCK
ASSOC. PROF. B. C. CATLIN, Chief
Children
ASSOC. PROF. M. C. BURRITT, In Charge
ASSOCIATE PROF. M. M. DEAN, Chief
DR. F. A. EVANS
DR. EMILY F. TYDEMAN
DR. F. M. SEWARD
General Medicine
ASSOC. PROF. H. M. STEVENSON, In Charge
DR. O. N. DUVALL, Chief
Dr. E. O. MURRAY
DR. M. E. SHAMER
DR. HENRY G. JONES
Genito-Urinary
ASSOC. PROF. GEO. E. HOUCK, In Charge
Skin
ASSOC. PROF. JAS. L. HOOPER, In Charge
Nervous and Mental Diseases
DR. JOHN A. EVANS, In Charge
Nose and Throat
PROF. WM. DULANY THOMAS, In Charge
DR. WM. C. BODE
DR. HENRY RUSSELL
Gynecology
PROF. HENRY CHANDLEE, In Charge
ASSOC. PROF. WM. M. PANNEBAKER, Chief
DR. E. F. TYDEMAN
DR. J. W. WISNER
DR. F. A. EVANS
DR. M. E. SHAMER
Surgery
PROF. E. Z. COLE, In Charge
ASSOCIATE PROF. JAS. L. HOOPER
DR. H. H. STANSBURY
DR. J. W. WISNER
DR. H. J. WALTON

SESSION OF 1906-07

Dean
ELDRIDGE C. PRICE, M.D.
Professor of Therapeutic Philosophy and
Materia Medica

REGISTRAR

LEWIS R. PALMER, M.D.
Professor of Diseases of the Chest

GEO. T. SHOWER, A.M., M.D.
Professor of Materia Medica
and Therapeutics
JOHN W. DE HOFF, M.D.
Professor of Obstetrics
ROBERT W. MIFFLIN, M.D.
Professor of Practice of Medicine
C. L. RUMSEY, A.M., M.D.
Professor of Surgery and
Ophthalmology and Otology
E. Z. COLE, M.D.
Professor of Gynaecology
W. D. THOMAS, M.D.
Professor of Rhinology and Laryngology
H. J. EVANS, M.D.
Professor of Clinical Medicine
WM. M. PANNEBAKER, A.M., M.D.
Associate Professor of Medical
Diseases of Women and Histology
M. C. BURRITT, M.D.
Associate Professor of Pediatrics
G. E. HOUCK, M.D.
Associate Professor of
Genito-Urinary Diseases
M. M. DEAN, M.D.
Associate Professor of Physiology
H. M. STEVENSON, M.D.
Associate Professor of Medical Diagnosis
B. C. CATLIN, M.D.
Associate Professor of Clinical Obstetrics
G. I. YOUNG, M.D.
Associate Professor of Rectal Surgery
F. A. SWARTWOUT, M.D.
Associate Professor of Obstetrics
F. E. HESSER, M.D.
Associate Professor of Anatomy
J. L. HOOPER, M.D.
Associate Professor of Dermatology

JOHN A. EVANS, M.D.
Associate Professor of Physiology
and Lecturer on Neurology
WILBUR M. PHELPS, M.D.
Associate Professor of Chemistry
JOSEPH S. GARRISON, M.D.
Lecturer on Obstetrics
HENRY RUSSELL, M.D.
Lecturer on Toxicology
EDWARD O. MURRAY, M.D.
Lecturer on Pathology and Bacteriology
DAVID C. STULTZ, M.D.
Lecturer on Preventive Medicine
J. WARD WISNER, M.D.
Lecturer on Surgery
HENRY C. JONES, M.D.
Lecturer on Medical Diagnosis
G. H. WRIGHT, M.D.
Lecturer on Neurology
CHAS. WISNER, A.B.
Lecturer on Medical Jurisprudence
M. BOWMAN HOOD, M.D.
Lecturer on Minor Surgery
and Life Insurance
AUSTIN F. ROBINSON, M.D.
Lecturer on Rhinology and Laryngology
F. D. MC CARRIAR, M.D.
Lecturer on Medical Terminology
H. WELLS WOODWARD, M.D.
Lecturer on Ophthalmology and Otology
GEARY A. LONG, M.D.
Lecturer on Electro-Therapeutics
GEORGE L. WETZEL, M.D.
Demonstrator of Anatomy
ROSCOE L. COFFIN
Lecturer on Pharmacy
W. E. RILEY
Demonstrator of Chemistry

DISPENSARY STAFF

Committee in Charge
ASSOCIATE PROF. F. E. HESSER
PROF. W. D. THOMAS
ASSOCIATE PROF. GEO. E. HOUCK
Pharmacist
DR. F. E. HESSER
Eye and Ear
PROF. C. L. RUMSEY, In Charge
Children
ASSOC. PROF. M. M. DEAN, In Charge
DR. OLLIE J. PRESCOTT
General Medicine
DR. O. N. DUVALL, Chief
DR. E. O. MURRAY
DR. JOS. S. GARRISON
DR. HENRY RUSSELL
Genito-Urinary
ASSOC. PROF. G. E. HOUCK, In Charge
DR. S. B. JACOBS

Skin
ASSOC. PROF. J. L. HOOPER, In Charge
DR. S. B. JACOBS
Nervous and Mental Diseases
DR. J. A. EVANS, In Charge
Nose and Throat
PROF. W. D. THOMAS, In Charge
DR. HENRY RUSSELL
DR. AUSTIN F. ROBINSON
Gynecology
PROF. E. Z. COLE, In Charge
ASSOCIATE PROF. W. M. PANNEBAKER
DR. AMY L. PLUM
Surgery
PROF. C. L. RUMSEY, In Charge
ASSOCIATE PROF. G. I. YOUNG, Chief
DR. M. BOWMAN HOOD
Dentistry
WM. H. RICHARDSON, D.D.S.
C. E. CHEW, D.D.S.

SESSION OF 1907-08

Same as that of 1906-07, with the following exceptions:

Drs. H. J. Evans, B. C. Catlin, J. L. Hooper, Geary A. Long, George L. Wetzel, and Mr. W. E. Riley were no longer on the Faculty. Dr. W. C. Comstock returned, as professor of ophthalmology and otology; C. L. Thudicum, M.D., was lecturer on electro-therapeutics; J. S. H. Potter, M.D., lecturer on embryology and demonstrator of obstetrics, and H. V. Deming, D.O., M.D., lecturer on osteology.

Other new members of the teaching staff were as follows:

FACULTY

J. W. SCHLIEDER, M.D.
Demonstrator of Anatomy
A. H. FRIEDMAN, M.D.
Lecturer on Physiological Materia Medica
J. P. SHARP, M.D.
Lecturer on Practice of Medicine
ALBION K. PARRIS HARVEY, M.D.
Lecturer on Clinical Medicine
C. L. MOORE, B.S., M.D.
Lecturer on Dermatology
F. V. BEITLER, M.D.
Demonstrator of Pathology
SHEPHERD DRAIN, Ph.G., M.D.
Lecturer on Older School Pharmacy
JOHN I. KUHN, M.D.
Lecturer on History of Medicine
E. J. COOK, M.D.
Demonstrator of Obstetrics

E. H. BITNER, M.D.
Lecturer on Medical Terminology
G. R. JONES, M.D.
Lecturer on Toxicology
M. B. WESSON, B.S.
Demonstrator of Anatomy
CHARLES L. LEY, M.D.
Lecturer on Rectal Surgery, and
Quaesitor on Surgery
H. C. HOUCK, M.D.
Lecturer and Demonstrator of Histology
HERMAN N. FRENTZ, Phar. D.
Demonstrator of Homoeopathic
Pharmacy, and Chemistry
CLAUDE D. HICKMAN, Ph.G.
Demonstrator of Older School Pharmacy
W. G. DE HOFF, M.D.
Instructor in Physical Culture.

DISPENSARY STAFF

Committee in Charge
DR. O. N. DUVALL
DR. HENRY RUSSELL
DR. M. M. DEAN
Pharmacist
DR. L. E. SHIPLEY
Eye and Ear
PROF. C. L. RUMSEY, In Charge
DR. L. E. SHIPLEY
Children
DR. M. M. DEAN, In Charge
DR. OLLIE J. PRESCOTT
General Medicine
DR. O. N. DUVALL, In Charge
DR. HENRY RUSSELL
Skin
DR. C. L. MOORE, In Charge
Nervous and Mental Diseases
DR. J. A. EVANS, In Charge

Nose and Throat
PROF. W. D. THOMAS, In Charge
DR. W. D. MC CARRIAR
DR. HENRY RUSSELL
Surgery
PROF. C. L. RUMSEY, In Charge
DR. SHEPHERD DRAIN
DR. W. M. HAMMETT
Diseases of Women
PROF. E. Z. COLE, In Charge
DR. W. M. PANNEBAKER
DR. OLLIE J. PRESCOTT
DR. A. H. FRIEDMANN
Dentistry
J. N. BAGWELL, D.D.S.
Genito-Urinary
DR. G. E. HOUCK, In Charge

SESSION OF 1908-09

Dean
ELDRIDGE C. PRICE, M.D.
Professor of Therapeutic Philosophy and Materia Medica

REGISTRAR

LEWIS R. PALMER, M.D.
Professor of Physical Diagnosis

GEORGE T. SHOWER, A.M., M.D.
Prof. of Materia Medica and Therapeutics
JOHN W. DE HOFF, M.D.
Prof. of Obstetrics
ROBERT W. MIFFLIN, M.D.
Prof. of Practice of Medicine
C. L. RUMSEY, A.M., M.D.
Prof. of Surgery and Clinical
Ophthalmology and Otology
E. Z. COLE, M.D.
Prof. of Gynecology
W. D. THOMAS, M.D.
Prof. of Rhinology and Laryngology
W. M. PANNEBAKER, A.M., M.D.
Prof. of Medical Diseases of
Women and Histology
M. M. DEAN, M.D.
Prof. of Physiology
F. E. HESSER, M.D.
Prof. of Anatomy
WILBUR M. PHELPS, M.D.
Prof. of Chemistry
M. C. BURRITT, M.D.
Associate Prof. of Pediatrics
G. E. HOUCK, M.D.
Associate Prof. of Genito-Urinary Diseases
G. I. YOUNG, M.D.
Associate Prof. of Surgery
F. A. SWARTWOUT, M.D.
Associate Professor of Obstetrics
JOHN A. EVANS, M.D.
Associate Prof. of Physiology and
Lecturer on Neurology
HENRY RUSSELL, M.D.
Associate Prof. of Materia Medica
EDWARD O. MURRAY, M.D.
Associate Professor of Pathology
and Bacteriology
DAVID M. STULTZ, M.D.
Associate Professor of Sanitation
and Dietetics
JOSEPH S. GARRISON, M.D.
Lecturer on Obstetrics
J. WARD WISNER, M.D.
Lecturer on Gynecology
G. H. WRIGHT, M.D.
Lecturer on Neurology
W. M. LEWIS, M.D.
Lecturer on Clinical Diagnosis
CHARLES W. WISNER, JR., A.B., LL.B.
Lecturer on Medical Jurisprudence

E. J. COOK, M.D.
Lecturer on Descriptive Pathology
H. WELLS WOODWARD, M.D.
Lecturer on Ophthalmology and Otology
C. L. THUDICUM, M.D.
Lecturer on Electro-Therapeutics
J. S. H. POTTER, M.D.
Lecturer on Embryology and
Demonstrator of Obstetrics
B. P. HERZOG, M.D.
Demonstrator of Anatomy
ALBION K. PARRIS HARVEY, M.D.
Lecturer on Clinical Medicine
SHEPHERD DRAIN, Ph.G., M.D.
Lecturer on Older School Pharmacy
JOHN I. KUHN, M.D.
Lecturer on History of Medicine
J. CHARLES BECK, M.D.
Lecturer on Toxicology
H. H. STANSBURY, M.D.
Lecturer on Surgery
F. WILLIAMS, M.D.
Lecturer on Homoeopathic Pharmacy
T. W. KOLDEWEY, M.D.
Lecturer on Osteology
H. P. HADDOCK, M.D.
Lecturer on Physiological Materia Medica
W. M. HAMMETT, M.D.
Lecturer on Surgery
F. D. MC CARRIAR, M.D.
Lecturer on Rhinology and Laryngology
J. K. M. PERRINE, M.D.
Lecturer on Ophthalmology and Otology
W. T. SEABURY, M.D.
Lecturer on Dermatology
P. B. TOWLER, M.D.
Demonstrator of Clinical Diagnosis
C. C. PARRISH, M.D.
Demonstrator of Physiology
G. F. HARTZELL, M.D.
Demonstrator of Pathology
E. R. MAC DONALD, M.D.
Demonstrator of Bacteriology
CARLETON BATES, M.D.
Demonstrator of Histology
W. F. DONNELLY, M.D.
Lecturer on Medical Terminology
W. J. MARTIN, M.D.
Demonstrator of Biology
J. E. CUMMINS
Demonstrator of Chemistry

DISPENSARY STAFF

Committee in Charge
DR . O. N. DUVALL
DR. HENRY RUSSELL
DR. M. M. DEAN
Pharmacist
DR. L. E. SHIPLEY
Eye and Ear
DR. J. K. M. PERRINE, In Charge
DR. L. E. SHIPLEY

Children
DR. M. M. DEAN, In Charge
Dr. E. R. MAC DONALD
DR. T. I. KEALY
General Medicine
DR. ALBION K. PARRIS HARVEY, In Charge
DR. HENRY RUSSELL
DR. CARLETON BATES

Genito-Urinary
DR. G. E. HOUCK, In Charge
DR. C. C. PARRISH
Mental and Nervous Diseases
DR. J. A. EVANS, In Charge
Nose and Throat
DR. W. D. THOMAS, In Charge
DR. HENRY RUSSELL
DR. W. J. F. MARTIN
Surgery
DR. C. L. RUMSEY, In Charge
DR. W. M. HAMMETT
DR. W. F. DONNELLY
Gynecology
DR. E. Z. COLE, In Charge
DR. W. M. PANNEBAKER
DR. T. W. KOLDEWEY
Dermatology
DR. W. T. SEABURY, In Charge
Dentistry
J. N. BAGWELL, D.D.S.

SESSION OF 1909-10

FACULTY

Dean
ELDRIDGE C. PRICE, M.D.
Professor of Therapeutic Philosophy and Materia Medica

REGISTRAR

LEWIS R. PALMER, M.D.
Professor of Physical Diagnosis

JOHN W. DE HOFF, M.D.
Professor of Obstetrics
ROBERT W. MIFFLIN, M.D.
Professor of Practice of Medicine
C. L. RUMSEY, A.M., M.D.
Professor of Surgery and Clinical Ophthalmology and Otology
W. D. THOMAS, M.D.
Professor of Rhinology and Laryngology
W. M. PANNEBAKER, A.M., M.D.
Professor of Medical Diseases of Women and Histology
M. M. DEAN, M.D.
Professor of Pediatrics
F. E. HESSER, M.D.
Professor of Anatomy
WILBUR M. PHELPS, M.D.
Professor of Chemistry
GEO. H. EVERHART, M.D.
Professor of Electro-Therapeutics
B. P. HERZOG, M.D.
Professor of Pathology
M. C. BURRITT, M.D.
Associate Professor of Pediatrics
G. E. HOUCK, M.D.
Associate Professor of Genito-Urinary Diseases
G. I. YOUNG, M.D.
Associate Professor of Surgery
F. A. SWARTWOUT, M.D.
Associate Professor of Obstetrics
JOHN A. EVANS, M.D.
Associate Professor of Physiology and Lecturer on Neurology
HENRY RUSSELL, M.D.
Associate Professor of Materia Medica
DAVID M. STULTZ, M.D.
Associate Professor of Sanitation and Dietetics
ALBION K. PARRIS HARVEY, M.D.
Associate Professor of Clinical Medicine
C. L. THUDICUM, M.D.
Associate Professor of Obstetrics
B. C. CATLIN, M.D.
Associate Professor of Obstetrics
H. H. KEECH, M.D.
Associate Professor of Practice of Medicine
WILBUR F. SKILLMAN, M.D.
Associate Professor of Physiology and Stomach Diseases
J. WARD WISNER, M.D.
Lecturer on Gynecology
G. H. WRIGHT, M.D.
Lecturer on Psychiatry
CHARLES W. WISNER, JR., A.B., LL.B.
Lecturer on Medical Jurisprudence
M. BOWMAN HOOD, M.D.
Lecturer on Surgery
SHEPHERD DRAIN, M.D.
Lecturer on Older School Pharmacy
FRANK J. KENNY, Ph.G.
Lecturer on Toxicology
H. H. STANSBURY, M.D.
Lecturer on Surgery
EUGENE LEE CRUTCHFIELD, M.D., F.S., Sc.
Lecturer on Medical Terminology and History of Medicine
F. D. MC CARRIAR, M.D.
Lecturer on Rhinology and Laryngology
J. O. HENDRIX, M.D.
Lecturer on Gynecology
W. M. HAMMETT, M.D.
Lecturer on Surgery
W. T. SEABURY, M.D.
Lecturer on Dermatology
P. B. TOWLER, M.D.
Lecturer on Clinical Diagnosis
T. W. KOLDEWEY, M.D.
Lecturer on Osteology
F. L. BARKDOLL, M.D.
Lecturer on Genito-Urinary Diseases

DOUGLAS W. SIBBOLD, M.D.
Lecturer on Ophthalmology and Otology
C. A. SCHAEFER, M.D.
Lecturer on Homoeopathic Pharmacy
F. J. WEBER, M.D.
Lecturer on Physiological Materia Medica
C. C. MC CARTHY, M.D.
Demonstrator of Histology
J. A. MULLIGAN, M.D.
Demonstrator of Anatomy

F. S. BOOTAY, M.D.
Demonstrator of Clinical Diagnosis
R. L. KEYSER, M.D.
Demonstrator of Bacteriology
and Pathology
J. E. CUMMINS
Demonstrator of Chemistry

III (B) ALPHABETIZED LIST OF MEMBERS

OF THE FACULTY

(For Faculty grouped by year, see previous pages.)

The names of the members of the Hospital Staff do not appear in this alphabetical list.

Atkinson, A. S., M.D.
Babbitt, Zeno B., M.D.
Barkdoll, F. L., M.D.
Barnard, James S., M.D.
Bates, Carleton, M.D.
Beck, J. Charles, M.D.
Beitler, F. V., M.D.
Bitner, E. H., M.D.
Bonta, M.B., A.B.
Bootay, F.S., M.D.
Bright, James W., (H.), Ph.D.
Burritt, Martha C., M.D.
Carroll, Charles G., M.D.
Catlin, Barrett C., M.D.
Chandlee, Henry, M.D.
Clement, J. Arthur, M.D.
Coffin, Roscoe L.
Cole, E. Z., M.D.
Comstock, W. C., M.D.
Condon, Edward H., M.D.
Cook, E. J., M.D.
Crutchfield, Eugene Lee, M.D., F.S.Sc.
Cummins, J. E.
Custis, J. B. Gregg, M.D.
Dean, Mary Mead, M.D.
De Ford, Paul, M.D.
De Hoff, John W., M.D.
De Hoff, W. G., M.D.
Deming, H. V., D.O., M.D.
Dennis, Charles E., M.D.
Donnelly, W. F., M.D.
Douglass, M.E., M.D.
Downs, Julia V., M.D.
Drain, Shepherd, Ph.G., M.D.
Drane, Frank C., M.D.
Duvall, Oliver N., M.D.
Erb, Franklin H., M.D.
Evans, E. J., M.D.
Evans, Florence L. A., M.D.
Evans, Henry J., M.D.
Evans, John A., M.D.
Everhart, George H., M.D.
Ewalt, George L., M.D.
Eyster, English, A.B.
Fair, M. Alvah, M.D.
Fisher, F. C., A.B.
Fox, H. H., M.D.
Frentz, Herman N., Phar. D.
Friedman, A. H., M.D.
Garey, Henry F., M.D.
Garrison, Joseph S., M.D.
Haddock, H. P., M.D.
Hamblin, Frank M., M.D.
Hammett, W. M., M.D.
Hartzell, G. F., M.D.
Harvey, Albion K. Parris, M.D.
Heermann, V. Z., M.D.
Hendrix, J. O., M.D.
Herzog, B. P., M.D.
Hesser, F. E., M.D.
Hickman, Claude D., Ph.G.
Hill, Charles E., A. M.
Holbrook, E. H., M.D.
Hood, John, M.D.
Hood, M. (D.) Bowman, M. D.
Hooper, J. L., M.D.
Houck, George E., M.D.
Houck, H. C., M.D.
Janney, O. Edward, M.D.
Johnson, Philip T., M.D.
Jones, G. R., M.D.
Jones, Henry C. (B.), M.D.
Keech, Henry Hobart, M.D.
Kenny, Frank J., Ph.G.
Keyser, R. L., M.D.
King, William R., M.D.
Klein, Benjamin, Phar. D.
Kneass, Nicholas W., M.D.
Kneass, R. K., M.D.
Knower, W. McE., Ph.D.
Koldewey, T. W., M. D.
Kuhn, John I., M.D.
Leach, Robert F., Jr., Esq.
Lewis, W. M., M.D.
Ley, Charles L., M.D.
Lindley, Havard, M.D.
Long, Geary A., M.D.
Mac Donald, E. R., M.D.
Mac Donald, Thomas L., M.D.
Martin, W. J., M.D.
Mc Carriar, F. D., M.D.
Mc Carthy, C. C., M.D.
Mifflin, Robert W., M.D.
Miller, Irving, M.D.

Moore, C. L., M.D.
Mulligan, J. A., M.D.
Murray, Edward O., M.D.
Nichols, Clarence, M.D.
Palmer, A. G., Ph.D.
Palmer, Lewis R., M.D.
Pannebaker, William M., M.D.
Parrish, C. C., M.D.
Peddicord, Harper, M.D.
Perrine, J. K. M., M.D.
Phelps, Wilbur M., M. D.
Potter, J. S. H., M.D.
Price, Eldridge C., M.D.
Price, Elias C., M.D.
Reese, Albert M., Ph.D.
Riggan, J. A., A.B.
Riley, W. E.
Roberts, C. Wesley, M.D.
Robinson, Austin F., M.D.
Rumsey, Charles Leslie, A.M., M.D.
Russell, Henry, M.D.
Schaefer, C. A., M. D.
Schlieder, J. W., M.D.
Seabury, W. T., M.D.
Seiple, Arthur W. H., M.D.
Shamer, M. E., M.D.
Sharp, J. P., M.D.
Shower, George T., A.M., M.D.
Shower, John A., M.D.
Sibbold, Douglas W., M.D.
Skillman, Wilbur F., M.D.
Smith, Marshall G., M.D.
Sommer, H. Otto, M.D.
Stansbury, H. H., M.D.
Stevenson, Henry McK., M.D.
Stultz, David M. (C.), M.D.
Swartwout, F. A., M.D.
Thomas, Charles H., M.D.
Thomas, William Dulan(e)y, M.D.
Thudicum, C. L., M.D.
Towler, P. B., M.D.
Trew, Bartus, M.D.
Turner, Harold J., Ph.D.
Tydeman, Emily F., M.D.
Urie, James W., M.D.
Waldran, Donna A., M.D.
Walton, H. J., M.D.
Wanstall, Alfred, M.D.
Wareheim, Garaphelia B., M.D.
Webber, F. J., M.D.
Wesson, M. B., B.S.
Wetzel, George L., M.D.
Willey, W. T., M.D.
Williams, F., M.D.
Wilson, Winfred, A.B.
Wisner, Charles W. Jr., A.B., LL.B.
Wisner, J. Ward, M.D.
Woodward, H. Wells, M.D.
Wright, G. H., M.D.
Wright, N. V., M.D.
Young, George I., M.D.
Yourex, Edmund I., M.D.

IV. TEXT BOOKS USED

1891

"Students often ask for advice concerning the books they should study preparatory to attending lectures, and also what they should read on the principles of homoeopathy. Again, a student writes that he has not decided whether to pursue the study of medicine under the homoeopathic or allopathic system, and asks for literature bearing on the relative merits of the two schools of medicine. It is reasonable that a student should be informed on these points and know why one system is to be preferred above another. The principles of homoeopathy should be understood by him, and by preparatory reading he should fit himself for the college lecture course. We would, therefore, suggest the following books on the principles of homoeopathy to be read during the year preceding attendance at college.

"Fifty Reasons for being a Homoeopath," by J. C. Burnett, M.D. .... Price $ .75
"Ecce Medicus," by J. C. Burnett, M.D. 1.00
"Homoeopathic Tracts," by Wm. Sharp, M.D. .... .60
"The Grounds of a Homoeopathic Faith," by S. A. Jones, M.D. .... .25
"History of Homoeopathy," by Wm. Ameke, M.D. 2.25
"Hughes' Pharmacodynamics," 6.60

On general medicine the student should prepare himself by reading anatomy, physiology, chemistry and the history of medicine, selecting his books from the following list, which contains the textbooks he will need most in pursuing his medical studies."

INSTITUTE OF MEDICINE – Hindu Medicine, Dr. Wise; Francis Adams' Works of Hippocrates; Macdonald's Historical Sketch of Medicine; Russell's History and Heroes of Medicine; Dudgeon's Lectures on Homoeopathy, Hahnemann's Organon; Dakes' Therapeutic Methods; Ameke's History of Homoeopathy.

GYNAECOLOGY – Minton's Uterine Therapeutics; Thomas, Emmett, or Hart and Barber's Diseases of Women.

CHEMISTRY – Fowne's, Lloyd's or Attfield's Chemistry; Bowman's Medical Chemistry.

BIOLOGY, HISTOLOGY, HYGIENE – MacGinley's or Sedgwick and Wilson's General Biology; Nicholson's Introduction to the Study of Biology; Tyson's Practical Histology; Klein's Elements of Histology; Stirling's Textbook of Practical Histology; Wilson's of Rohr's Textbook of Hygiene.
PHYSICAL DIAGNOSIS – Da Costa's Physical Diagnosis.
MATERIA MEDICA AND THERAPEUTICS – Hughes' and Dake's Cyclopaedia of Drug Pathogenesy; Farrington's Clinical Materia Medica; Allen's Handbook of Materia Medica; Lilienthal's Therapeutics; Woods' Materia Medica.
PATHOLOGY AND PRACTICE – Arndt's System of Medicine; Hughes' Pharmacodynamics; Thomas' Morbid Anatomy; Flint's Practice.
OPHTHALMOLOGY AND OTOLOGY – Allen and Norton, Angell, Juler or Berry on the Eye; Stirling, Winslow or Politzer on the Ear; Houghton's Clinical Otology.
PAEDOLOGY AND ORTHOPAEDIC SURGERY – Guernsey's Obstetrics and Disorders of Children; J. Lewis Smith's Diseases of Infancy and Childhood.
SURGERY – Helmuth, Holmes, Gross, Erichseu or Roberts' System of Surgery; Smith's Operative Surgery; Gilchrist's Surgical Therapeutics; Ranney's Surgical Diagnosis.
PHYSIOLOGY – Foster, Dalton, Flint, Landois and Stirling; Martin's Human Body, Foster and Langley's Practical Physiology.
ANATOMY – Gray, Leidy, Weisse.
OBSTETRICS – Leavitt, Lusk, Guernsey, Playfair, Parvin, Gallabin; Stewart's Obstetric Synopsis.

1892

Same as in 1891, with the following exceptions:
INSTITUTES OF MEDICINE: Ameke abandoned.
GYNECOLOGY: Hart, Barber abandoned.
CHEMISTRY: *Remsen,* Simon, Attfield, *Tyson's Urinary Analysis, J. C. Draper's Practical Course in Medical Chemistry* were used. Fownes, Lloyd, Bowman abandoned.
HYGIENE AND SANITARY SCIENCE: *Rohe's Textbook of Hygiene.*
PHYSICAL DIAGNOSIS: *Loomis,* Da Costa.
MATERIA MEDICA AND THERAPEUTICS: *Cowperthwaite's Textbook of Materia Medica* (edition of 1891), Boericke and Tafel's Pharmacopoeia, U. S. Dispensatory, Mann's Manual of Prescription Writing were added. Lilienthal's Therapeutics abandoned.
PATHOLOGY AND PRACTICE OF MEDICINE: *Rau's Pathology and Therapeutica Hints,* Osler's Practice, Dickinson's Principles and Practice of Medicine, Pepper's or Reynold's System of Medicine were added. Hughes abandoned.
EYE AND EAR: Nettleship added. Berry, Juler, Stirling, Politzer abandoned.
PAEDOLOGY AND ORTHOPEDIC SURGERY: *Sayre's Orthopedic Surgery,* Barnwell's Plaster Jackets added.
SURGERY: Wyeth, Bryant, added.
PHYSIOLOGY: Yoe, Shaeffer's Physiology added.
OBSTETRICS: Gallabin added.
DICTIONARIES: Dunglison, Thomas, Keating, Gatchell.

1894

It is suggested that the following books on the principles of homoeopathy be read during the year preceding attendance at college.

"Fifty Reasons for being a Homoeopath," by
J. C. Burnett, M.D. .... Price $ .90
"What is Homoeopathy?" by
Wm. H. Holcombe, M.D. .... .15
"Homoeopathic Tracts," by Wm. Sharp, M.D. .... .60
"The Grounds of a Homoeopath's Faith," by
S. A. Jones, M.D. .... .30
"The Knowledge of the Physician," by
Richard Hughes, M.D. 1.80
"The History of Homoeopathy," by
Wm. Ameke, M.D. 2.80

Those whose titles are printed in italics, have been carefully selected as textbooks for the use of the student; the other are books of reference, or for collateral reading.

INSTITUTES OF MEDICINE – *Hahnemann's Organon; Dudgeon's Lectures on Homoeopathy;* Dake's Therapeutic Methods; Macdonald's Historical Sketch of Medicine; Russell's History and Heroes of Medicine; Francis Adams' Works of Hippocrates; Hindoo Medicine, Dr. Wise.

GYNAECOLOGY – *Cowperthwaite's Diseases of Women; Minton's Uterine Therapeutics; A Textbook of Gynecology*, Wood; Thomas, last edition by Munde; Emmett; American Textbook of Gynecology.
CHEMISTRY – *Simon's Manual of Chemistry*, 4th Ed. Remsen's Chemistry; Elements of Inorganic Chemistry, Shepard; *Tyson's Course in Medical Chemistry.*
HYGIENE AND SANITARY SCIENCE – *Rhoe's Textbook of Hygiene;* Billings on Ventilation and Heating.
PHYSICAL DIAGNOSIS – *Loomis*, Da Costa.
MATERIA MEDICA AND THERAPEUTICS – *A Pathogenetic Materia Medica (B. & T.); Cowperthwaite's Textbook of Materia Medica (edition of 1891); Farrington's Clinical Materia Medica;* Hughes and Dake's Cyclopaedia of Drug Pathogenesey; Allen's Encyclopaedia of Materia Medica; Boericke and Tafel's Pharmacopaeia; U. S. Dispensatory; G. B. Wood's Materia Medica; Mann's Manual of Prescription Writing.
PATHOLOGY AND PRACTICE OF MEDICINE – *Raue's Pathology and Therapeutic Hints; Arndt's System of Medicine;* Osler's Practice; Reynold's System of Medicine; American Textbook of Medicine (Pepper); Thomas' Morbid Anatomy; Green's Pathology.
EYE AND EAR – *Norton, (last edition);* Nettleship on the Eye; Angell; *Winslow on the Ear;* Houghton's Clinical Otology.
PAEDOLOGY AND ORTHOPEDIC SURGERY – *Guernsey's Obstetrics and Disorders of Children;* American Textbook, Diseases of Children, (Starr); *Sayre's Orthopedic Surgery;* Barnwell's Plaster Jackets.
SURGERY – *Helmuth's Surgery;* Robert's Modern Surgery; American Textbook of Surgery, (White & Keen); Moullin's Treatise on Surgery; Senn's Principles of Surgery; Wyeth's Operative Surgery; *Gilchrist's Surgical Therapeutics;* (Homoepathic Textbook of Surgery, in press).
PHYSIOLOGY – *Foster, Yoe,* Dalton, Flint, Landois and Sterling; *Martin's Human Body;* Foster & Langley's Practical Physiology; *Schaefer's Histology.*
NEUROLOGY – *Hirt's Diseases of the Nervous System.*
ANATOMY – *Gray,* Leidy, Weisse.
OBSTETRICS – *American System of Obstetrics; Landis, How to Use the Forceps; Leavitt, Guernsey, Playfair.*
DICTIONARIES – *Dunglison's, Thomas'* or *Keating's Medical Dictionary;* also, *Gatchell's Pocket Dictionary.*

1895

Same as in 1894, with the following exceptions:
GYNECOLOGY: *Ludlam's Diseases of Women,* Keating and Cole added. Minton, Thomas abandoned.
PATHOLOGY AND PRACTICE OF MEDICINE: Goodno's Practice added. Reynold's System of Medicine abandoned.
EYE AND EAR: Nettleship abandoned. Fuch's Ophthalmology added.
PEDOLOGY AND ORTHOPEDIC SURGERY: Tooker's Diseases of Children, *Young's Orthopedic Surgery,* Rotch's Pediatrics added. Guernsey abandoned.
SURGERY: *Homoeopathic Textbook of Surgery* added.
PHYSIOLOGY: Flint abandoned.
NEUROLOGY: Dana, Textbook of Nervous Diseases added.
OBSTETRICS: Grandin and Jarman added.
DICTIONARIES: Foster's Medical Encyclopedia added.

1896:

Same as in 1895, with the following exceptions:
MATERIA MEDICA: Shoemaker's Materia Medica and Therapeutics added. Wood abandoned.
EYE AND EAR: *Schweinitz's Diseases of the Eye, Burnett's Eye, Ear and Throat* added.
PEDOLOGY AND ORTHOPEDIC SURGERY: Fisher's Diseases of Children was added. Tooker abandoned.
SURGERY: Helmuth abandoned.
PHYSIOLOGY: Piersol's Histology added. Schaeffer abandoned.

1899-1900

GYNECOLOGY – *Cowperthwaite's Diseases of Women; Ludlam's Diseases of Women; A Textbook of Gynecology, Wood;* Keating & Coe's Diseases of Women; Kelly's Operative Gynecology; American Textbook of Gynecology.
CHEMISTRY – *Simon's Manual of Chemistry; Tyson's Course in Medical Chemistry, 4th*

Ed.; Remsen's Chemistry; Elements of Inorganic Chemistry, Shepard; *Student's Manual,* Underhill.

SANITARY SCIENCE – *Rohe's Textbook of Hygiene;* Egbert's Hygiene Sanitation; Billings on Ventilation and Heating.

PHYSICAL DIAGNOSIS – *Loomis,* Da Costa.

MATERIA MEDICA AND THERAPEUTICS – *A Pathogenic Materia Medica (B. & T.); Cowperthwaite's Textbook of Materia Medica (last edition); Farrington's Clinical Materia Medica;* Hughes' and Dake's Cyclopaedia of Drug Pathogenesey: Allen's Encyclopaedia of Materia Medica; Boericke and Tafel's Pharmacopaeia; Homoeopathic Pharmacopaeia; U.S. Dispensatory; Shoemaker's Materia Medica and Therapeutics; Mann's Manual of Prescription Writing.

PRACTICE OF MEDICINE – *Arndt's Practice of Medicine, 1899 Ed.;* Goodno's Practice; Osler's Practice; American Textbook of Medicine (Pepper).

PATHOLOGY – Stengel's Pathology; McFarland's Pathogenic Bacteria; Green's Pathology; Abbott's Bacteriology.

EYE AND EAR – *Norton, (last edition); Fuch's Ophthalmology;* Bishop's Diseases of the Ear, Nose and Throat; MacBride's Diseases of the Eye; Oliver M. Morriss' Diseases of the Eye; Augell; *Burnett's Eye, Ear and Throat; Winslow on the Ear;* Houghton's Clinical Otology.

PEDIATRICS – American Textbook, Diseases of Children (Starr); Rotch's Pediatrics; Holt, Diseases of Childhood.

SURGERY – *Homoeopathic Textbook of Surgery; Moore's Orthopedic Surgery;* Senn's Principles of Surgery, (new edition); Roberts' Modern Surgery; American Textbook of Surgery, (White & Keen); Moullin's Treatise on Surgery; Wyeth's Operative Surgery (last edition).

PHYSIOLOGY – *Kirke, Foster;* Bigler's Syllabus of Physiology; Raymond's Manual; Dalton; *Martin's Human Body;* Foster & Langley's Practical Physiology; *Piersol's or Schaefer's Histology.*

NEUROLOGY – *Hirt's Diseases of the Nervous System;* Textbook of Nervous Diseases, Dana.

ANATOMY – *Gray,* Weisse, Pract. Anatomy, Morris.

OBSTETRICS – *American Textbook of Obstetrics; Leavitt; Guernsey; King;* Landis, How to use the Forceps; Playfair.

LATIN – *Elements of Latin* (Crothers & Bice).

DICTIONARIES – *Dunglison's, Lippincott's* or *Keating's Medical Dictionary; Gatchell's Pocket Dictionary;* Foster's Medical Encyclopedia.

NOSE AND THROAT – Diseases of the Nose and Throat, Ivins; Diseases of the Ear, Nose and Throat, Bishop.

1900

Same as in 1899, with the following exceptions:

CHEMISTRY: Remsen's Organic Chemistry added. Underhill's Student's Manual abandoned.

PRACTICE OF MEDICINE: Ander's Practice added. Osler, Pepper's American Textbook of Medicine abandoned.

PEDIATRICS: Fisher, Raue added. Holt abandoned.

TOXICOLOGY: Reese.

HISTOLOGY: Piersol or Shaefer.

NEUROLOGY: Textbook of Nervous Diseases, Elliot added. Dana abandoned.

NOSE AND THROAT: Quain added.

DERMATOLOGY: Douglass' Skin Diseases.

1901:

Same as in 1900, with the following exceptions:

PHYSICAL DIAGNOSIS: Corwin added.

NEUROLOGY: Talcott's Mental Diseases and Their Modern Treatment. Oppenheimer added.

MEDICAL TERMINOLOGY: Campbell's Language of Medicine; Elements of Latin (Crothers and Bice).

1902:

Same as in 1901, with the following exceptions:

GYNECOLOGY: Penrose's Diseases of Women added. Cowperthwaite, Ludlam, Keating and Cole and American Textbook abandoned.

PRACTICE OF MEDICINE: Getchell's Diseases of the Lungs added.

PATHOLOGY: Coplin's Pathology, and Lehmann's and Neumann's Bacteriology.

TOXICOLOGY: Herold's Legal Medicine added.
HISTOLOGY: Bohrn-Davidoff, Stohr added.

1903-1904:

Same as in 1902, with the following exceptions:
EYE AND EAR: DeSchweinitz added. Fuchs, MacBride, Morris, Angell, Burnett, Winslow abandoned.
ANATOMY: Weisse abandoned.
NOSE AND THROAT: Burnett, Ingalls and Newcomb added. Quain, Bishop abandoned.
DERMATOLOGY: Allen, Stellwagon added.

1905:

Same as in 1903 and 1904, with the following exceptions:
INSTITUTES OF HOMOEOPATHIC MEDICINE: Russell's History and Heroes of Medicine replace Grauvogl.
PATHOLOGY: Green abandoned.
SURGERY: The following were used: *Modern Surgery, Da Costa; Principles of Surgery, Nancrede;* The Practice of Surgery, Wharton and Curtis; Operative Surgery, Bickham; The American Textbook of Surgery; Homoeopathic Textbook of Surgery.
MEDICAL DIAGNOSIS: Boston.

1906:

THERAPEUTIC PHILOSOPHY: *Hahnemann's Organon; Price's Philosophy of Therapeutics; Dudgeon's Lectures on Homoeopathy; Park's Epitome of the History of Medicine; Tuke's Influence of the Mind upon the Body;* Russell's History and Heroes of Medicine; Dake's Therapeutic Methods; Bradford's Life and Letters of Hahnemann.
GYNECOLOGY: *A Textbook of Gynecology, Wood; Penrose's Diseases of Women;* Kelly's Operative Gynecology; Ashton's Textbook on the Practice of Gynecology; Dudley's Principles and Practice of Gynecology; Byford's Manual of Gynecology.
CHEMISTRY: Remsen's Introduction; Remsen's Organic Chemistry; Simon's Manual; Tyson's Medical Chemistry; Shepard's Elements of Inorganic Chemistry.
PRACTICE OF MEDICINE: *Arndt's Practice of Medicine;* Robert's Practice of Medicine; Goodno's Practice; Ander's Practice; Gatchell's Diseases of the Lungs.
PHYSICAL DIAGNOSIS: *Da Costa; Loomis;* Musser; Corwin.
MEDICAL DIAGNOSIS: Boston.
DERMATOLOGY: Allen; Douglass; Stellwagon.
NEUROLOGY: *Talcott's Mental Diseases and Their Modern Treatment;* Elliott; Oppenheim; Hurt; Church and Peterson's Nervous Diseases; Pott's Diseases of the Nervous System.
PEDIATRICS: *Fisher;* Raue; American Textbook of Diseases of Children (Starr); Rotch's Pediatrics.
PREVENTIVE MEDICINE: *Rohe's Textbook of Hygiene;* Egbert's Hygiene Sanitation; Billings on Ventilation and Heating.
ANATOMY: Gray; Morris' Practical Anatomy.
SURGERY: Da Costa's Modern Surgery; Stimson's Operative Surgery; Moore's Orthopedic Surgery.
MATERIA MEDICA; TOXICOLOGY: *Cowperthwaite's Textbook of Materia Medica (last edition); Farrington's Clinical Materia Medica; A Pathogenetic Materia Medica (B. & T.);* Hughes' and Dake's Cyclopaedia of Drug Pathogenesy; Allen's Encyclopaedia; Boericke and Tafel's Pharmacopoeia; Pharmacopoeia of the American Institute of Homoeopathy; U. S. Dispensatory; Shoemaker's Materia Medica and Therapeutics; Mann's Manual of Prescription Writing; Reese's Toxicology.
PATHOLOGY: Stengel's Pathology; McFarland's Pathology; Coplin's Pathology; McFarland's Pathogenic Bacteria; Abbott's Bacteriology; Lehman and Neuman's Bacteriology.
HISTOLOGY: *Schaefer's Histology (6th ed.);* Bohm, Davidhoff and Huber; Ferguson's Histology.
PHYSIOLOGY: *Kirke; Foster; Howell's Essentials of Physiology;* Bigler's Syllabus of Physiology; Raymond's Manual; Dalton; Foster and Langley's Practical Physiology.
EYE AND EAR: Norton's Ophthalmic Diseases and Therapeutics; Ball's Modern Ophthalmology; Refraction, by Copeland and Ibershoff; Diseases of the Ear, by Vehslage and Hallett; Bacon's Manual of Otology.
OBSTETRICS: *Leavitt; Guernsey; King; Hirst; American Textbook of Obstetrics;* Landis. How to Use Forceps; Playfair.

NOSE AND THROAT: *Diseases of the Nose and Throat, Irvin's;* Diseases of the Ear, Nose and Throat, Burnett, Ingalls and Newcomb.
JURISPRUDENCE: *Herold's Legal Medicine.*
MEDICAL TERMINOLOGY: *Campbell's Language of Medicine; Elements of Latin (Crothers and Brice);* Dictionaries: *Dunglison's or Keating's Medical Dictionary; Gatchell's Pocket Dictionary;* Billings' National Medical Dictionary, or Foster's Encyclopaedic Dictionary.

1907:
Same as in 1906, with the following exceptions:
ANATOMY: Cunningham; *Spalteholz's Atlas* were added.
PHYSIOLOGY: *Rockwood's Physiological Chemistry* added.
CHEMISTRY: *Barker's Textbook of Elementary Chemistry* and *Richter's Organic Chemistry* added. Remsen's Organic Chemistry, Tyson, Shepard abandoned.
HISTOLOGY: Marden's Manual added.
GYNECOLOGY: *Montgomery's Gynecology* and Hirst's Diseases of Women were added. Ashton was abandoned.
NOSE AND THROAT: Bishop was added. Burnett, Ingalls and Newcomb were abandoned.
EYE AND EAR: *Jackson's Diseases of the Eye* was added.
MEDICAL TERMINOLOGY: *Dorland's Illustrated Medical Dictionary* was added.

1908:
Same as in 1907, with the following exceptions:
BIOLOGY: Huxley and Martin added (to texts on Histology).
PRACTICE OF MEDICINE: Halbert's Practice of Medicine added.
CLINICAL DIAGNOSIS: Simon.
GYNECOLOGY: Byford abandoned.
NOSE AND THROAT: Gleason; Kyle added. Bishop abandoned.
ELECTRO-THERAPEUTICS: Gottschalk's Practical Electro-therapeutics.

V. LIST OF MATRICULATES AND GRADUATES OF THE SOUTHERN HOMOEOPATHIC MEDICAL COLLEGE – ATLANTIC MEDICAL COLLEGE

The letters M.D. indicate that the degree of Doctor of Medicine was conferred by this school in the year stated immediately following the degree. The absence of M.D. after a name means that available records show only that the person named was a matriculate in the year or years given. If the M.D. is enclosed in parentheses, i.e., (M.D.), neither the date nor the school which conferred the degree is evident from the available records alone. Any years stated after the first date following the M.D. mean that the holder of the degree spent that time, subsequent to receiving the degree, as a postgraduate. Parentheses around a letter or name indicate that the existing records show variations in spelling, and the possibility that two different persons might be involved cannot be ruled out with certainty.

Tha names of all of the graduates, up to and including the year 1909, have been found, as have the names of matriculates up to 1904, except those for the years 1892, 1896 and 1897. (Many of the names of matriculates for the missing years will, however, be among the names of the graduates, and will, of course, bear dates subsequent to the years of their enrolment.)

Announcements of this school are located at the National Library of Medicine, the Library of the New York Academy of Medicine, the Maryland State Library, and the Medical Center Library of the University of Michigan. The Enoch Pratt Free Library of Baltimore and the Library of the College of Physicians of Philadelphia also have a small number of these.

Arringdale, Annie M., M.D., '98
Pennsylvania
Dr. Cora B. Brewster
Atkins, E. C., '94
Virginia
Prof. H. Chandlee
Atkinson, A. S., (M.D.), '98
Maryland
At(t)well, Lewis P., M.D., '04
Maryland
Ayler, Amos E., M.D., '97
(Indiana), Maryland
Dr. G. F. Nickerson, Dr. C. E. Nichols
Bagwell, Garaphelia Wareheim, M.D., '94
Maryland
Dr. W. W. Wareheim

Bain, Samuel A., '91
New York
Dr. J. W. Barnes
Barkdoll, F. L., M.D., '02
Maryland, Pennsylvania
Barton, Clyde E., '93
Illinois
Prof. O. E. Janney
Bates, Carleton, M.D., '08
Maryland
Beale, Norman Leslie, M.D., '09
Delaware
Bealor, Benjamin Albert, (M.D.), M.D., '09
Pennsylvania
Beckley, G. H., '98
Maryland
Beristain, David, '95
Mexico
Government School
Birney, Edith S., '98
District of Columbia
Bitner, Ernest H., M.D., '07
West Virginia
Bode, William C., M.D., '04
Maryland
Bonner, Eugene M., '00
Maryland
Bootay, Frederick Starr, (M.D.), M.D., '09
Maryland
Bowers, H. A., '95
Maryland
Dr. J. Ward Wisner
Bowers, John D., '03
Maryland
Branson, Joseph H., M.D., '94
Washington, D.C., Virginia
Prof. O. E. Janney
Brosius, Mary Alice, (M.D.), M.D., '95
Washington, D. C.
Howard University
Buhrman, E. Ray, M.D., '97
Pennsylvania
Dr. G. Wareheim
Burck, Lewis A., M.D., '95
Maryland
Prof. H. Chandlee
Burke, F. A., '98
Virginia
Burke, Merritt, '02, '03
Delaware
Burritt, Martha C., M.D., '98
Washington, D. C.
Carr, Cornelius, '95
Maryland
Prof. J. S. Barnard
Catlin, Barrett C., M.D., '95
Maryland
Dr. H. L. Dodd
Chandor, J. F., '03
Pennsylvania
Clark, Patrick Joseph, M.D., '09
New Jersey
Clarke, William T., '01
Maryland
Clement, J. Arthur (James A.), M.D., '04
Maryland
Dr. R. K. Kneass
Coffin, Roscoe L., '03
Maryland
Cook, Edward J., M.D., '07
Maryland
Cook, Julius H., '03
Maryland
Cor(e)y, Waterman F., (M.D.), Honorary M.D., '9
Washington, D. C.
Howard University
Cox, L. H., M.D., '01
Delaware
Currinder, Alva B., M.D., '07
Delaware
Dally, Wendell, M.D., '06
Maryland, Pennsylvania
Darrell, Mary H., M.D., '94
Maryland
Dr. Flora A. Brewster
Dean, Mary Mead, M.D., '01
Maryland
De Ford, Paul F., (M.D.), M.D., '92
Maryland, California
University of Maryland
Dehoff, George William, M.D., '05
Maryland, Pennsylvania
Dehoff, John (W.E.), M.D., '97
Pennsylvania
Dr. J. W. Dehoff
Dei(ie)trich, John W., M.D., '04
Pennsylvania
Deming, Herbert V., M.D., '07
Maryland
Dickinson, Harrington Stanley, M.D., '08
Pennsylvania
Donnelly, William Frederick, M.D., '08
Pennsylvania
Douglass, F. E., '99
Maryland
Down(e)s, Julia V., M.D., '95
Maryland
Woman's Medical College
Drain, Shepherd, (M.D), M.D., '07
Maryland
Duttera, M. C., '01
Maryland
Duvall, Oliver N., M.D., '01
Maryland
Elgin, Eugene, M.D., '09
Maryland
Erb, Franklin H., M.D., '02
Maryland
Evans, Florence L. A., M.D., '02
Maryland
Everhart, George S., M.D., '97
Pennsylvania
Dr. O. T. Everhart
Everhart, Oliver S., M.D., '97
Pennsylvania
Dr. O. T. Everhart
Ewalt, G. L., (M.D.), '00
Maryland

Fair, M. Alvah, M.D., '95
Maryland
Dr. H. W. Fair
Fair, Horace L., M.D., '94
Maryland, Pennsylvania
Dr. H. W. Fair
Ferguson, Clara M., M.D., '99
Delaware
Fields, Reuben H., M.D., '97
Oregon, Pennsylvania
Southern College
Flanigan, W. S., '99
Maryland
Fleagle, Roberta A., M.D., '01
Pennsylvania
Flentje, Amelia V., M.D., '95
Maryland
Dr. Marshall G. Smith
Forrest, F. B., M.D., '04
Pennsylvania
Fox, Henry H., M.D., '04
Maryland
Frederick, Clinton, (M.D.), M.D., '95
Delaware
University of Maryland
Freeland, John C., M.D., '01
Kentucky, Pennsylvania
Garcia-Ubarri, Angel Manuel, M.D., '09
San Juan, Puerto Rico
Garey, H. F., (M.D.), Honorary M.D., '92
Maryland
Goodman, James M., '98, '99
Maryland
Goodson, Catherine (S.M.), M.D., '02
Maryland
Gorman, W. Edward, M.D., '09
Maryland
Grimmel, H. C., '98
Maryland
Haddock, Horace P., M.D., '08
Maryland
Hamilton, Joseph, M.D., '09
Maryland
Hammett, Walter Mitchell, M.D., '08
Maryland
Hammond, D. A., '98
Maryland
Hammond, Milton, (M.D.), Honorary M.D., '92
Maryland
University of Maryland
Hammond, William Nelson, M.D., '96
Pennsylvania
Dr. R. Hammond
Han(d)by, Charles M., M.D., '02
Delaware, Maryland
Harmount, William Card, M.D., '09
Pennsylvania
Hartzell, G. Frederick, M.D., '08
Maryland
Hendrix, John O., M.D., '94
Maryland
Dr. H. W. Fair
Henry, Emory M., M.D., '92
West Virginia
N. Y. Hom. Col.
Hesser, Frederick E., M.D., '04
Maryland, Pennsylvania
Hicks, Frederick W., M.D., '07
New York
Hodges, Wyllys R., M.D., '00
Vermont
Holbrook, E. H., (M.D.), Honorary M.D., '92
Maryland
University of Maryland
Holland, Charles A., M.D., '04
Maryland, Delaware
Holloway, Don B. (M.), '95-'98
Washington, D. C.
Dr. R. Kingsman
Hood, D. Bowman, (M.D.), '01
Maryland
Hood, John, (M.D.), Honorary M.D., '92
Maryland
(University of?) Michigan
Hooper, James L., M.D., '94
Maryland
Dr. W. D. Thomas
Hopkins, H. Clayton, '91
Maryland
Dr. N. W. Kneass
Houlton, Samuel S., M.D., '95
Maryland
Prof. E. H. Condon
Hurtt, Harry, (M.D.), '95
Maryland
University of Maryland
Ingram, Marie Letitia, M.D., '07
Maryland, Kentucky
Inslee, J. Pennoyer, M.D., '08
New York
German Hospital of Brooklyn, N. Y.
Irwin, Rachel G., M.D., '07
Maryland
Jackson, H. E., '95
Maryland
Prof. H. Chandlee
Jackson, John Paul, M.D., '95
Virginia
Dr. N. Jackson
Jacobs, Silas B., M.D., '05
Maryland
Jennings, J. L., M.D., '00
Virginia
Johnson, F. E., '98
Virginia
Johnson, W. H., (M.D.), M.D., '92
Maryland
University of Maryland
Jones, George R., M.D., '07
Maryland
Jones, Henry G., M.D., '05
Maryland
Jump, Clarence K., (M.D.), M.D., '92
Maryland
University of Maryland
Kaiser, A. Jerome, M.D., '09
Connecticut
Kealy, Thomas Ignatius, M.D., '08
Pennsylvania
Keech, Henry H., M.D., '02
Maryland

Kenney, George W., M.D., '09
West Virginia
Keppel, F. D., M.D., '97
New York
Keyser, Robert Lee, M.D., '09
Maryland
Knickman, Walter Edward, (M.D.), M.D., '09
Maryland
Koldewey, Theodore William, (M.D.), M.D.,'08
Maryland
Koons, Henry E., M.D., '97
Virginia
Krych, Felix J., M.D., '09
Pennsylvania
Kuhn, John I., M.D., '07
Maryland
Leigh, Chester A., M.D., '04
New Jersey
Lekites, Lillian Rue, M.D., '08
Delaware
Levinson, Amelia, (M.D.), '94
California
Cooper Medical College
Lewis, George C., M.D., '01
Maryland, Washington, D.C.
Link, Annie K., '93
Maryland
Southern College
Linthicum, Edgar S., M.D., '05
Maryland
Long, Geary A., M.D., '99
Maryland
Dr. C. W. Weaver
Lothrop, Edwin (L.), (S.), (M.D.), M.D., '94
Washington, D. C.
Dr. Richard Kingsman
Lovell, Earl, '01
Maryland
Lucas, William Chisolm, M.D., '08
Colorado
MacDonald, Ernest Rayburn, M.D., '08
Maryland
MacNair, I. Foreman, M.D., '09
Pennsylvania
Marchant, Annie W., M.D., '99
Maryland
Markland, Alex. F., '91, '93, '94, '95
Maryland
Prof. F. C. Drane, Southern College
Martin, William John Francis, M.D., '08
Pennsylvania
Massinger, O. L., (M.D.), M.D., '97
Pennsylvania, Connecticut
Jefferson Medical College
Maucher, Rose, M.D., '05
Pennsylvania
McCallum, Malcolm J., (M.D.), M.D., '02
Pennsylvania
McCarriar, Francis D., M.D., '00
Maryland
McCarthy, Charles Carmoran, M.D., '08
Maryland (St. Luke's Hospital)
McConnel, Irwin H., M.D., '04
Washington, D. C.
McLaughlin, John Henry, M.D., '09
Connecticut
Meixsell, Charles Edward, M.D., '09
Pennsylvania
Merritt, Newton, '95
Maryland
Prof. C. H. Thomas
Meyers, Don M., M.D., '99
Pennsylvania
Southern College
Miller, Benneville, (Benjamin), F., M.D., '99
Pennsylvania
Mulligan, James Aloysius, M.D., '09
Maryland
Murray, E. Oliver, M.D., '03
Maryland
Pan(n)ebaker, William M., (A.B.), M.D., '94
Maryland
Dr. J. H. Sherman
Parrish, Clifford C., (M.D.), M.D., '08
Maryland
Peddicord, Harper, M.D., '99
Maryland
Dr. M. Hammond
Perkins, Roscoe L., '03
Massachusetts
Pfeiffer, Harry S., M.D., '99
Connecticut, Maryland
Dr. J. H. Sherman
Pfoutz, D. G., '98
Maryland
Plumb, Amy E., M.D., '98
Maryland
Powers, Lelia H., M.D., '99
Maryland
Prescott, Ollie J., M.D., '06
Price, Elias C., (M.D.), M.D. Honorary, '92
Maryland
Quinn, Ella X., '01
Maryland
Reeside, Armor, '94
Maryland
Dr. S. Armor
Reiley, William Edgar, M.D., '07
New York Post-Graduate Medical College
Reill(e)y, William F., M.D., '95
Ohio, Maryland
Dr. H. F. Garey
Rhea, Charles, '98, '99
Pennsylvania
Robbins, J. Ansel, (M.D.), M.D., '96
Washington, D. C.
Georgetown University
Robertson, H. Miller, M.D., '97
Pennsylvania, California
Dr. F. B. Dake
Robertson, Mary L., '95
Pennsylvania
Dr. F. B. Dake
Robinson, Austin F., M.D., '03
Maryland, Virginia
Roby, M. V., '95
Pennsylvania
Cincinnati Eclectic College
Roop, Susie A., '93, '94
Virginia
Dr. E. C. Williams

Roope, S. Abigail, M.D., '96
Virginia
Dr. E. C. Williams
Rowland, James Joseph, M.D., '09
Pennsylvania
Ruopp, Charles F., M.D., '08
New Jersey
Russell, Henry, M.D., '00
Maryland
Sanborn, Warren Bigelow, M.D., '09
Maine
Schaefer, Charles A., (M.D.), M.D., '09
Maryland
Seabury, William Thomas, M.D., '08
Maryland
Sefton, Martin F., '94, '95
West Virginia
Southern College
Seiple, Arthur H. W., M.D., '98
Kansas
Seward, Florence N., M.D., '05
Delaware
Shamer, Maurice E., M.D., '04
Maryland
Shipley, Lauretta E., M.D., '06
Maryland
Shorb, Marlin W., M.D., '06
Maryland
Shower, John A., M.D., '94
Pennsylvania, Maryland
Dr. G. T. Shower
Simmons, Oliver D., (M.D.), M.D., '09
Maryland
Smith, Annie M., M.D., '98
Pennsylvania
Smith, Charles H., M.D., '05
Pennsylvania College
Smith, Ira Mason, M.D., '08
Virginia
Smith, J. Almer, M.D., '09
Virginia
Smith, Marshall G., (M.D.), M.D., '92
Maryland
University of Maryland
Solakian, Esther K., M.D., '03
Massachusetts
Sommer(s), H. Otto, (Henry O.), M.D., '97
Washington, D. C.
Dr. J. B. G. Custis
Stadter, John Michael, M.D., '08
New Jersey
Stansbury, H. H., M.D., '96
Maryland
University of Maryland
Stearns, S. S., (M.D.), Honorary M.D., '92
Washington, D. C.
Georgetown University
Stevenson, H. H., (Henry McK.), M.D., '01
Maryland
Strayer, D. A., '98
Maryland
Stultz, Charles A., M.D., '93
Maryland
Stultz, David M., M.D., '95
Maryland
Dr. C. W. Weaver
Swartwout, Frank A., (M.D.), M.D., '94
Washington, D. C.
Dr. T. L. Macdonald
Swinney, Eva S., '98, '99
Delaware
Swinney, Grace E., '98, '99
Delaware
Swope, George C., M.D., '01
Pennsylvania
Taylor, Alfred H., M.D., '95
Washington
Dr. R. Kingsman
Teas, Nellie, M.D., '04
Delaware
Thomas, W. Dulan(e)y, (M.D.), M.D., '92
Maryland
University of Maryland
Thoms, Burton P., '93
Maryland
Prof. N. W. Kneass
Thudichum, Carl L., M.D., '04
Pennsylvania, Maryland
Towler, Philip Brook, M.D., '06
Maryland
Tydeman(n), Emily F., M.D., '01
South Carolina, Tennessee
South Carolina College
Van Dolsen, William Walling, M.D., '09
New Jersey
Van Nort, J. S., '98
New York
Vogel, Louis, M.D., '08
Maryland
Wage, Arnold E., M.D., '00
New York
Waldran, Donna A., M.D., '93
Maryland, Tennessee
Walton, Henry J., M.D., '02
Maryland
Washburn, Mrs. Mae D. (L.), M.D., '04
Pennsylvania, Maryland, Delaware
Washburn, Victor D., M.D., '05
Maryland, Delaware
Wareheim, Garaphelia, (see Bagwell)
Weant, John W., '93
Maryland
Dr. L. Kemp
Weber, Frederick J., M.D., '09
Maryland
Wessels, Asa L., M.D., '98
Maryland
Dr. M. G. Smith
Wetzel, George L., M.D., '06
Maryland, Pennsylvania
White, Rev. R. H., '00
Maryland
Wiley, Maurice G., M.D., '94
New Hampshire
Boston University
Willey, Waitman T., M.D., '98
Maryland
Williams, Frederick, M.D., '08
Maryland
Wisner, J. Ward, M.D., '95
Maryland
Prof. J. S. Barnard

Wright, Nathaniel V., (M.D.), M.D., '02
Maryland
Young, Carl W., M.D., '05
Pennsylvania

Young, George (I.,L.), M.D., '01
Maryland, New York
Zimmerman, Amelia V., M.D., '95
(See under Flentje)

FOOTNOTES TO CHAPTER FIVE

(1) William Harvey King: *History of Homoeopathy*, New York, 1905, Volume 2, pg. 146.

(2) The first meeting of the incorporators of the College was held in the home of Dr. Elias C. Price, a graduate of the University of Maryland (1848), who "after testing the old system five years, devoted a half century to the new" (op. cit., pp 148-149), becoming the pioneer in Baltimore County. He was elected a director and was professor of institutes of homoeopathic medicine.

(3) Op. cit., p. 166

ACKNOWLEDGMENTS

I am most deeply grateful to Miss Marion B. Savin and Mr. Kenneth V. Hahn, for a great deal of patient assistance, in connection with this school, and to Mrs. Thomas E. Crowther, for her help in the typing of the manuscript of this chapter. I also cheerfully acknowledge the very warm cooperation of Mr. Charles Roos, of the National Library of Medicine, Miss Gertrude L. Annan, of the Library of the New York Academy of Medicine, Miss Ruth D. Burton, of the Maryland State Library, and Miss Ruth L. Floyd, of the Medical Center Library, University of Michigan. Very kind assistance was also rendered by Miss Alice Hester Rich, of the Maryland Historical Society, Mr. P. W. Filby, of the Peabody Institute Library, Miss Elizabeth C. Litsinger, of the Enoch Pratt Free Library, and Dr. Robert P. Multhauf, of the Smithsonian Institution.

BIBLIOGRAPHY

1. Annual Announcements of the Southern Homoeopathic Medical College for the years 1891 to 1896, inclusive (except that for 1892), and for 1899 to 1906, inclusive; also those of the Atlantic Medical College for the years 1907-1909, inclusive.
2. William Harvey King: *History of Homoeopathy*, New York, 1905, (two volumes).
3. Thomas Lindsley Bradford: *Homoeopathic Bibliography of the United States from the Year 1825 to the Year 1891, Inclusive,* Philadelphia, 1892, p. 469.

ALSO:
Hahnemann Monthly, Volume 25, numbers 6, 9, 11; Volume 26, number 9.
The Medical Visitor, Volume 6, p. 213; Volume 7, p. 277, p. 368.
Medical Advance, Volume 25, p. 398.
The North American Journal of Homoeopathy, Volume 38, p. 414.
The American Homoeopathist, Volume 16, p. 297; Volume 17, p. 76.
The Homoeopathic Advocate and Guide to Health, Volume 3.
The Baltimore American, Sunday, August 16, 1891.

APPENDICES*

***Appendices A, B-1 and B-2 were very kindly supplied by Dr. Margaret B. Ballard, of Union, West Virginia, who also provided much of the material upon which Appendices C and D are based.**

APPENDIX A*

THE MEDICAL AND SURGICAL SCHOOL OF CHRIST'S INSTITUTION OF BALTIMORE CITY

Know all men by these Presents, That we George W. Kennard, William M. West, John F. Brown, James E. Smith, William M. A. Cole and Thomas H. Brown all being residents of Baltimore City being citizens of the United States and a majority of whom are citizens of the State of Maryland do hereby certify that we do under and by virtue of the General Laws of this State authorizing the formation of corporations hereby form a corporation under the name of "The Medical and Surgical School of Christ's Institutions of Baltimore City."

2. We do further certify that the said corporation so formed is a corporation for the creation and maintenance of a medical surgical and general educational college and therein to teach the science and art of medicine and surgery and the treatment of diseases of all kinds to confer degrees upon all persons who may become proficient under the tuition of said corporation and who may be morally worthy to practice the medical and surgical profession or and *any* special branch of the healing art and generally for all the objects and purposes for which medical and surgical colleges are founded and designed that the term of existence of said corporation is limited to forty years and that the said corporation is formed upon (the) articles, conditions and provisions herein expressed and subject in all particulars to the limitations relating to corporations which are contained in the General Laws of this State.

3. We do further certify that the operations of the said corporation are to be carried on in the State of Maryland and that the principal office of the corporation will be located in Baltimore City.

4. We do further certify that the said corporation has no capital stock.

5. We do further certify that the said corporation will be managed by six Trustees and that George W. Kennard, William M. West, John F. Brown, James E. Smith, William M. A. Cole and Thomas H. Brown are the names of the Trustees who will manage the concerns of the said corporation for the first year.

In witness whereof we have hereunto set our hands and seals this 14th day of May in the year nineteen hundred.

Witness:
William B. Hammond

William B. Hammond

George W. Kennard
William M. West
his
John F. x Brown
mark
James E. Smith
William M. A. Cole
Thomas H. Brown

(William B. Hammond, Justice of the Peace signs as witness on the 14th day of May 1900.)

(Henry D. Harlan, a Judge of the Supreme Bench of Baltimore City examined the records and found them in order.)

Recorded on May 14th, 1900 at 11:30 Oclk A.M., Robt. Ogle, Clerk.

from: Records of the Superior Court of Baltimore City Liber 38, Folio 570.

*The American Medical Directory refers to this school as "The Medico-Chirurgical and Theological College of Christ's Institution". (20th Edition, (1958) p. 39.)

"THE MEDICAL AND SURGICAL SCHOOL OF CHRIST'S INSTITUTION OF BALTIMORE CITY"

Amendment to Charter

George Kennard of Baltimore City
Thomas H. Brown of Anne Arundel County
James E. Smith of Baltimore City
August Monath of Baltimore City
William H. Fax of Baltimore City
Abraham Hill of Baltimore City

comprising the Board of Trustees, Certify at a meeting held on 25th May 1906, agreed to an amendment to the charter of the above institution – second paragraph to read

"We do further certify that the said corporation so formed is a corporation for the creation and maintenance of an Academic and Collegiate Theological Law and Medical School and Hospital and also for the purpose of teaching any academic or collegiate course science or art which the Trustees of said corporation may deem advisable and to confer degrees upon those who may become proficient in the schools of the said corporation that the term of existence of said corporation is limited to forty years and that the said corporation is formed upon the articles, conditions and provisions .... etc. .... contained in the General Laws of this State."

Judge Henry D. Harlan

Recorded June 16, 1905 (1906) at 10:10 O'clk A.M.

Robert Ogle, Clerk

from: Records of the Superior Court of Baltimore City.
R. O. Liber 46 folio 59.

APPENDIX B-1

"THE EASTERN UNIVERSITY SCHOOL OF MEDICINE OF THE CITY OF BALTIMORE, INC."

This is to certify that the Subscribers Frank J. Kenney residing in the City of Baltimore Lauren L. Dorman residing in the City of Baltimore and William M. White residing in the City of Baltimore all of whom are citizens of the State of Maryland all being of full legal age, do hereby certify that we do under and by the virtue of the General Laws of this State, authorizing the formation of corporations, associate ourselves with the purpose of forming a corporation:

1. The name of the corporation is
"The Eastern University School of Medicine of the City of Baltimore, Incorporated".

2. We do further Certify That the purpose for which said corporation is formed and the business or objects to be carried on are General instruction in medicine and Surgery, as well as instruction in Eclectic medicine, and that the said corporation formed upon the articles, conditions, and provisions herein expressed and subject in all particulars to the limitations relating to corporations which are contained in the General Laws of this State.

3. We do further Certify that the principal office of said corporation will be located in Baltimore City.

4. We do further Certify That the aggregate of the capital stock of the said corporation is five thousand ($5,000) dollars and that the said capital is divided into one hundred shares of the par value of fifty ($50.00) dollars each.

5. We do further Certify that the said corporation will be managed by a Board of three Directors and that Frank J. Kenney, Lauren L. Dorman and William M. White all of whom

are citizens of the State of Maryland, and actually reside therein are the names of those who shall act as Directors of the said corporation for the first year, or until their successors are duly chosen and qualify. In witness Whereof, we have hereunto set our hands this 29th day of October in the year nineteen hundred and twelve.

Witness:
Peter Sahm

Frank J. Kenney
Lauren L. Dorman
William M. White

State of Maryland, City of Baltimore to wit:

Before the subscriber a Justice of the Peace of the State of Maryland in and for the City of Baltimore personally appeared on this 29th day of October 1912, Frank J. Kenney, Lauren L. Dorman and William M. White and did severally acknowledge the foregoing certificate to be their act.

Peter Sahm, J. P.

State of Maryland, Baltimore City Sct:

I, Stephen C. Little, Clerk of the Superior Court of Baltimore City do hereby certify that Peter Sahm Esquire, before whom the annexed acknowledgement was made and who has thereto subscribed his name was at the time of so doing a Justice of the Peace of the State of Maryland in and for the City of Baltimore duly commissioned and sworn and authorized by law to administer oaths and take acknowledgements, or proof of Deeds to be recorded therein.

In Testimony whereof I hereunto set my hand and affix the seal of the Superior Court of Baltimore City this 29th day of October A.D. 1912.

Stephen C. Little Clerk of the Superior Court of Baltimore City.

I, James M. Ambler one of the Judges of the Supreme Bench of Baltimore City do hereby certify that the foregoing certificate has been submitted to me for examination and I do further certify that the said certificate is executed in conformity with the law.

James M. Ambler

Filed for record in office of State Tax Commissioner October 31, 1912 at 9:00 O.clock A.M. same day recorded in Liber B.S. No. 5 folio 438 one of the Charter Records of the State Tax Commissioner's office and examined.

Buchanan Schley
State Tax Commissioner

Received for Record Nov. 1, 1912 at 9 O'clk A.M. same day recorded and Exd per Stephen C. Little, Clk.

Papers delivered to F. J. Kenney, who signed for same, on Nov. 18, 1912. Paid $1.50 for recording.

from: Records of the Superior Court of Baltimore City, S.C.L.
Liber 58 folio 407, Item 198.

APPENDIX B-2

"MARYLAND COLLEGE OF ECLECTIC MEDICINE AND SURGERY INC."

This is to certify that the subscribers John M. Kerr residing in Baltimore City, P. August Grill residing in Baltimore county and John J. McLarney residing in Baltimore City, two of whom are citizens of the State of Maryland all being of full legal age, do hereby certify that we do under and by virtue of the General Laws of this State authorizing the formation of corporations associate ourselves with the purpose of forming a corporation.

1. The name of the corporation is "Maryland College of Eclectic Medicine and Surgery, Inc."

2. We do further certify that the purpose for which said corporation is formed and the business or objects to be carried on and promoted by it are to build construct, buy, lease or otherwise acquire, equip, maintain and conduct a College for the purpose of giving instruction and courses in study in medicine and surgery in all their branches and in connection with the foregoing to maintain clinics, dispensaries, and hospitals: also to confer upon those who have pursued such courses of instruction therein as entitle them to the same the usual degrees, and that the said corporation is formed upon the articles, conditions and provisions herein expressed and subject in all particulars to the limitations relating to corporations which are contained in the General Laws of this State.

3. We do further certify that the principal office of said corporation will be located in Baltimore City.

4. We do further certify that the aggregate of the capital stock of the said corporation is Ten thousand dollars ($10,000) and that the said capital is divided into one hundred shares of the par value of One hundred dollars ($100) each.

5. We do further certify that the said corporation will be managed by a board of three directors and that John M. Kerr, P. August Grill and John J. McLarney, two of whom are citizens of the State of Maryland and actually reside therein are the names of those shall act as Directors of the said corporation for the first year or until their successors are duly chosen and qualified. In witness whereof, we have hereunto set our hands this seventh day of February 1913.

Witness:
Mary M. McGraw

John M. Kerr
P. August Grill
John J. McLarney

7th February 1913

(Charles W. Henisler, one of the judges of the Supreme Bench of Baltimore City examined the records and found them in order.) Filed for record in office of State Tax Commissioner, Feb. 10th, 1913 at 1:30 O'clk P.M. same day recorded in Liber B.S. No. 6 folio 130 one of the charter records of the State Tax Commissioner's office and examined.

Buchanan Schley, State Tax Commissioner

Received for record February 12, 1913 at 9 O'clk A.M. same day recorded and exd.

Stephen C. Little, clerk

from: Records of Superior Court of Baltimore City, S.C.L.
Liber 59 folio 274.

APPENDIX C

From the Records of the Superior Court of Baltimore, (Charter Record, Liber 21, Folio 490-93) we learn that Harvey Leonides Byrd, M.D., Benjamin Franklin Leonard, M.D., Henry Froeling, M.D., Henry Wheaton Clapp, M.D., Leonard Robert Coates, M.D., William Robert Monroe, M.D. and Adolph G. Hoen, M.D., as directors of the Baltimore Medical College of Baltimore City, filed notice on September 13, 1881, that they had formed a corporation to be known under that name. In doing so they declared their belief in the Christian religion, as well as their intention of filling any future vacancies on the board of directors by vote of the remaining members, every person elected or appointed as a director, professor, or teacher in said College, having "before acting as such (to) declare his belief in the Christian religion and his intention faithfully to discharge the duties of director, teacher or professor . . . to the best of his ability and . . . subscribe his name to such declarations in a book to be kept for that purpose by the Dean . . . In testimony of this they declared their belief in the Christian religion and affixed their signatures". (An Act of the General Assembly, 1882, recognized the College.)

APPENDIX D

In the Circuit Court records of Baltimore City 24A, folio 248, 1884, we find that on November 18, 1884, the Baltimore Medical College, plaintiff in a suit, declares that three vacancies on the Board of Directors having occurred, these were filled, "according to the corporation papers, on December 29, 1883, after due notice, etc.," and that the "majority of the elected members" had "been conducting affairs of the College at 25-27 Linden Ave." Two members of the board of directors

> "becoming disaffected and dissatisfied with their associates, attempted to elect 2 other directors, for what purpose and under what authority your orator does not know, declared all the professorial chairs in the College vacant, filled them with other medical gentlemen, declared the office of Dean of the Faculty vacant, when no such vacancy existed, and filled it with a medical gentleman whom your orator does not know, but is informed his name is Zephaniah K. Wiley, and proceeded without sanction of law or authority to carry on a Medical College under the name of the Baltimore Medical College the corporate name of your orator as is shown by a catalogue of said college filed herewith and marked complainants exhibit No. 2."

The complaint further recites

> "That the 2 disaffected Directors, Dr. Harvey L. Byrd and Geo. E. Nelson, and the two gentlemen whom said H. L. Byrd and Geo. E. Nelson attempted to elect as Directors, viz; Robt. H. Carr and Rev. Julius H. Sams and the gentlemen who were declared professors, when no vacancies existed viz: Hampson H. Biedler, Jos. S. Lawrence, J. Janney Coffroth, John D. Blake, Jas. G. Linthicum, Geo. P. Yost, Alfred Whitehead, Louis M. Eastman, G. Granville Rusk, Geo. C. Shannon, Zephaniah K. Wiley whom they call Dean have usurped your orator's rights and are exercising the powers, privileges, prerogatives, and franchises which belong to your orator without shadow of authority are using your orator's name to attract students and to obtain other advantages which belong to your orator as an incorporated body incorporated for the purpose of disseminating a knowledge of the science and art of medicine and are doing your orator irreparable damage for which the Courts of Law afford no adequate remedy and besides are acting as a school of medicine without authority of law.
>
> "That the said Harvey L. Byrd, Geo. E. Nelson, Zeph. K. Wiley, J. Janney Coffroth and the gentlemen who are associated with them are vexing your orator with unbearable replevin suits before Justices of the Peace of this city brought for the purpose of possessing themselves of the property of your orator, and as to a part of which they are now in actual possession compelling your orator at great expense and trouble to defend these suits which it has done successfully in every instance, and are threatening other suits of a similar character against your orator.
>
> "Now, your orator shows that it is remediless at law to obtain relief against the unlawful acts of the said defendants, as well as to prevent the said suits

which are threatened and to get possession of the property which has been taken from it unlawfully by the defendants and therefore invokes the restraining power of this Court for its relief in the premises, and prays that a writ of injunction may issue directed to the defendants, Harvey L. Byrd, Geo. E. Nelson, Robt. H. Carr, Julius J. Sams, Zeph. K. Wiley, J. Janney Coffroth, Hampson H. Biedler, John D. Blake, Jas. G. Linthicum, Jos. S. Lawrence, Geo. P. Yost, Alfred Whitehead, Louis M. Eastman, G. Granville Rusk, Geo. C. Shannon, prohibiting them or any of them

1. From using the name of your orator
2. From carrying on a School of Medicine under the false pretence that it is conducted under the corporate power and authority of your orator
3. From usurping any of the rights, powers, and privileges of your orator
4. From the further prosecution of their law suits
5. From bringing other law suits to vex your orator in the premises
6. That they be compelled to surrender to your orator all the property they have taken under their pretended right in the said replevin suits
7. Compelling them to do or refrain from doing in all matters what they are bound by law to do or not to do towards your orator
8. And your orator prays for all other relief in the premises to which it may be entitled

"To the end therefore that the defendants may answer the said Bill your orator prays that a subpoena may issue to each and every of the said defendants, (names listed as before), commanding them and each of them to appear and under the rules of this Court answer the said Bill, and that in the meantime an injunction issue in the terms as above set forth against the defendants.

And as in duty bound etc.,

W. R. Monroe, M.D.
R. H. P. Ellis
Directors

John H. Findlay
David L. Brinton
Solicitors for the Complainant

sworn 17 Nov. 1884 before a Justice of the Peace (name is illegible)

The defendants denied that an election was held, that Dr. Monroe and Dr. Dougherty merely had an informal meeting, and that the proxies were illegal. Also illegal said the defendants was the election of G. Granville Rusk, R. H. P. Ellis, and Charles G. Hill.

(The requested injunction against Dr. Byrd et al was granted by George William Brown, Chief Judge of the Supreme Bench of Baltimore City.

The final act is recorded in the Baltimore Superior Court Records, Charter Record, Liber 23, folio 529-31 (December 13, 1884). James G. Linthicum, Zephaniah K. Wiley, Hampson H. Biedler, Hamilton Janney Coffroth and John D. Blake formed a new corporation, under the name of the Baltimore University of Baltimore City, for creating and maintaining a medical school and hospital and the teaching of any science or art which the directors may deem advisable. There was no capital stock. The persons named above, plus George E. Nelson and Robert H. Carr were to be directors during the first year.

(Dr. Harvey L. Byrd was, by date of this Act, already deceased, having passed away on November 29, 1884.)

APPENDIX E

(From *The Medical Gleaner*, January, 1906, pages 13 and 14)

ALUMNI NOTES

Fred. Clarke Jewett, M.D.

Things are looking better for the old school and at last it looks as if the board of directors mean [sic!] business. The following letter from Dr. Theodore Cooke, Jr. secretary of the board of directors of the Baltimore University, has been received by Dr. J. Mac Donald, Jr., secretary of the Baltimore Alumni Association:

J. Mac Donald, Jr., M.D.
Secretary of The Baltimore University
Alumni Association

Dear Doctor:

The board of directors of the Baltimore University has requested me to write you regarding a situation that is critical and which will mean a greater and better college or the failure of the Baltimore University, with all of its disagreeable consequences.

As you know, our University has steadily lost ground and it now has arrived at a stage of its existence where a new college building and hospital are necessary to permit us to properly teach medicine and at the same time draw about us men of a calibre as professors and teachers who will be an honor to your alma mater and make your diploma the more prized.

As above mentioned, one or two things are absolutely essential, either close the college or build new buildings. We, of course do not want to close our University as it will mean much to our graduates in practice, so have decided to submit a plan to the Alumni Association whereby we can place The Baltimore University on a teaching basis, comparing favorably with the best colleges in America.

The board has secured an option on a piece of ground on Maryland Avenue, which is in the most desirable section of Baltimore for a medical college. The board is willing to raise among its members, $10,000 to go toward a new building, etc. provided the Alumni will raise an equal amount. With this sum in hand sufficient additional capital can be raised to properly erect such buildings as are necessary.

We would suggest that the money raised by the alumni be used for endowing a chair to be known as the Baltimore University Alumni Pathological Chair, which chair could be at any time transferred to any other college, should the stockholders determine to discontinue the Baltimore University.

We would further suggest that the money contributed be deposited with a committee, consisting of the officers of the Alumni Association, who would place it in a trust company in such a manner that it can only be drawn for the purpose intended and then only after the board has raised and invested its $10,000 for the purchase of the necessary ground or for construction work. We would provide for the election of an alumnus designated by the Alumni Association, as a member of the board of directors of the Baltimore University, so that the alumni will have a voice in the management of the University. We make this appeal to the alumni for assistance, as it is imperative that something should be done, and done quickly, if we are to save our school. We trust you will place this matter before each and every graduate, as we feel that outside of his natural pride in wanting to see his college the first in the land, he also realizes what it will mean if we have to close the school, which we will be compelled to do unless we all work together at the time for new buildings.

Yours very truly,

Theodore Cooke, Jr., Secretary

92 William St., New York

Dr. Theodore Cooke, Jr.
Baltimore, Md.

My dear Doctor:-

Your letter received and I enclose you herewith a copy of the letter I will send to every graduate of our school whose name I have on our list.

To The Graduates of the Baltimore University School of Maryland.

My dear Doctor--I beg to hand you herewith a letter received from the Dean of the Baltimore University School of Maryland, your college which explains itself.

I have kept fairly well in touch with our college affairs the last few years and have realized for some time that to place our school on a basis to teach medicine in accordance with advanced requirements, and furthermore save our college, some change was necessary along lines presented in the Dean's letter.

This is a chance to help each other, and the plan proposed appeals to me as a most feasible one and I am sure will be carried out along the lines laid down, provided we give it our hearty support.

Although my time is more than occupoed as managing editor of the American Journal of Surgery, and as secretary and treasurer of the American Medical Editors' Association, I am willing to lay aside personal interests for the benefit of the school and support our Alma Mater, not only in a financial way, but give this effort as much of my time as may be required.

Now, Doctor, will you help us?

We should not allow our school to go out of existence, when a little support from each graduate now will save it. Twenty-five dollars from each graduate is all that will be necessary to accomplish our part, and surely this you can afford for such an important mission. I can assure you that if you will contribute to this just cause, which means so much to every one of us, your money will be used solely for the purpose intended, and then only when the faculty have carried out the plan as proposed.

As secretary of our Alumni Association I appeal to you for your support, not only in a financial way, but for your hearty co-operation in an effort to make our college an institution that will be an honor and pride to us. This is the first request ever asked for support for our college, so let us put our shoulder to the wheel for a common cause.

Trusting to hear from you at the earliest possible moment, I am

Very truly yours,

J. Mac Donald, Jr., M.D., Secretary

APPENDIX F-1

(From *Medical Education in the United States and Canada,* Abraham Flexner, New York, 1910, page 237)

LABORATORY FACILITIES: Small laboratories, scrupulously well kept, show a desire to do the best possible with meager resources. Pathology, bacteriology, embryology, chemistry and anatomy are thus taught.

CLINICAL FACILITIES: These are quite insufficient: across the street from the school is a hospital with 17 beds; supplementary material is obtained at several institutions through staff connections.

A suite of rooms in the College building is devoted to dispensary purposes. There is a fair attendance . . .

APPENDIX F-2

(From *Rhode Island State Board of Health, Report for 1895,* Volume 18, page 14)

. . . the Woman's Medical College of Baltimore . . . to be rated as colleges not in good standing, in the opinion of the Board for the years 1892, 1893, 1894. This ruling was made upon the information received from the Illinois Board that these colleges had not advanced the requirements for graduation to a three years graded course, in conformity with the action taken by all other colleges in good standing. This ruling shall not apply to any reputable college issuing diplomas of dates 1891 and prior thereto, nor will a three years course be required before 1892.